MICROWAVE MEASUREMENTS

INTERNATIONAL SERIES IN PURE AND APPLIED PHYSICS
LEONARD I. SCHIFF, CONSULTING EDITOR

The late F. K. Richtmyer was Consulting Editor of the series from its inception in 1929 to his death in 1939. Lee A. DuBridge was Consulting Editor from 1939 to 1946; and G. P. Harnwell from 1947 to 1954.

William Webster Hansen, 1909–1949. (*Photograph by B. Stewart.*)

Microwave Measurements

EDWARD L. GINZTON

Professor of Applied Physics and Electrical Engineering
Director of Microwave Laboratory,
W. W. Hansen Laboratories of Physics
Stanford University

McGRAW-HILL BOOK COMPANY, INC.

NEW YORK   TORONTO   LONDON

1957

MICROWAVE MEASUREMENTS

Library of Congress Catalog Card Number 56-13393

v

23270

THE MAPLE PRESS COMPANY, YORK, PA.

PREFACE

The need for a basic microwave-measurement reference book became obvious many years ago when, during the war, the accelerated research and development program created by the radar effort helped to establish a host of novel techniques for the measurement of important electrical quantities. Shortly after the war these technical advances were described in numerous journals and books which reported both the problems and the solutions in considerable detail. A student entering the microwave field today finds a mass of technical information in the literature; this makes it difficult for him to distill the essence of the subject without becoming involved with details of the particular problems which were responsible for the development of the subject but which today seem specialized and restricted.

The plans for this book, as a text and reference, to be written in collaboration with Dr. W. W. Hansen were altered by his untimely death. This, together with the delay in publication, has considerably changed the scope and emphasis in the book. Actually, this delay and the use of the material in classes have contributed to a selection of topics believed to be basic to all microwave measurements and have deemphasized many of the specialized techniques which were at one time prevalent owing to the dominating role of radar applications. Furthermore, it is now possible to discuss several topics which were either unknown or incompletely understood 10 years ago.

Although written as a basic text for a first year's graduate course in microwave measurements, this book should prove a useful reference for those who have more than a routine interest in microwave-measurement problems. Thus, there is no attempt to catalogue all possible techniques or to present in handbook form the characteristics of microwave components. Various laboratory instruments are discussed, but only to the extent necessary to enable the reader to use them without risking difficulties due to an incomplete understanding of their characteristics or functions.

In short, this book is concerned with the basic forms of electrical measurements encountered in the microwave region of the electromagnetic spectrum. The topics discussed provide a background for all

vii

common microwave measurements as well as for more specialized applications. A discussion of some important topics has been omitted in order to allow a more complete treatment of material regarded as fundamental. For example, this book is not concerned with the following types of measurements: transmitter and receiver characteristics; antennas; propagation; measurement of physical properties of materials; applications of microwaves to spectroscopy, paramagnetic resonance, etc. Each of these highly specialized topics requires individual treatment, both in theory and in experiment, and is to be found in other sources.

The reader is undoubtedly aware of the principal sources of detailed microwave information: the Radiation Laboratory Series, "Very High Frequency Techniques," "Radar Systems and Components," which contain summaries of the work performed during World War II at the Massachusetts Institute of Technology Radiation Laboratory, the Radio Research Laboratory of Harvard University, and the Bell Telephone Laboratories, respectively. The lecture notes of Dr. W. W. Hansen, presented as a lecture series at Massachusetts Institute of Technology (1941–1944), contain a wealth of information, much of it now available in other sources, but unique for the illuminating mathematical and theoretical approach characteristic of his methods of analysis. It is anticipated that this valuable material will soon be available in published form. Although numerous references to these and other sources of information are to be found throughout this book, no attempt is made to provide a complete guide to the literature, principally because of its extent. The references given refer to the more important journal articles, which will be found useful as an introduction to the original developments. Undoubtedly, many omissions of important contributions have occurred; because of the extent of the field, it is virtually impossible for one person to be completely aware of the work of the numerous laboratories and establishments, especially in foreign countries.

Perhaps it is appropriate to say a few words about the definition of the word *microwave*. It is possible to separate the electromagnetic spectrum into two parts, which differ from each other in the process of generating and detecting radiation. The first region extends from the shortest radiation through the X rays, into the visible radiation, into the infrared, and finally into the far-infrared region. All presently known methods of generating radiation involve transitions between the energy states of the various particles; thus, the discrete radiation frequency is determined by the quantum theory. Similarly, the detection of radiation by photoelectrical or photochemical processes is also based upon quantum effects. In the second region, commonly called the *radio region*, the generation of electromagnetic radiation is associated with the electrical phenomenon which occurs in conductors. Here, the frequency radiation can be controlled by the size and shape of the electrical circuits and can be detected by transforming the radio-frequency energy into some form of mechanical motion utilizing electromechanical phenomena. The short-wavelength region of the radio spectrum adjacent to the far infrared is commonly identified by the word *microwave*.[1]

It is also convenient to define the term *microwave* as that portion of the electromagnetic spectrum at which it is possible to make the laboratory equipment approximately equal in size to the operating wavelength. When this condition can be met, certain laboratory measurement techniques become practical regardless of the actual operating frequency. As the wavelength increases, microwave techniques are applicable indefinitely, although there are practical limitations which are related to the size of the equipment.

Within the broad qualitative limits of these definitions, the actual boundaries of the microwave spectrum are arbitrary.

At present, the shortest practical wavelengths are in the vicinity of 2 or 3 mm because of the difficulties in generating and detecting the radiation. Below these wavelengths the microwave laboratory equipment becomes too small to be practical, and it usually becomes desirable to adopt optical measurement techniques instead. The long-wavelength end of the microwave region is vague and, in reality, is established by the degree of refinement to which the ordinary low-frequency components, vacuum tubes, and measurement techniques can be pushed successfully. In applications requiring substantial power, waveguide components are sometimes used at wavelengths as long as 100 cm.

Since any laboratory study of the microwave phenomena requires an adequate knowledge of electromagnetic theory and practice, it is presumed that the reader possesses an understanding equivalent to that found in "Fields and Waves in Modern Radio," by S. Ramo and J. R. Whinnery. However, for the sake of completeness and because of their intrinsic importance, the elements of the theory needed to describe the behavior of electromagnetic waves in bounded regions and to justify the generalized impedance concept are presented in some detail. Although the development of the generalized transmission-line theory is beyond the purpose of this book, it was felt that a partial presentation was essential to enable the reader to connect the observations and interpretations of the standing-wave phenomenon in microwave transmission lines with the ordinary transmission-line theory. The reader must realize that the ordinary concepts of voltage, current, and impedance lose their conventional meaning when the operating wavelength is approximately equal to the dimensions of the laboratory system. Thus, the behavior of propa-

[1] C. G. Montgomery (ed.), "Techniques of Microwave Measurements," p. 1, McGraw-Hill Book Company, Inc., New York, 1947.

gating electromagnetic waves must be analyzed in terms of the electric and magnetic field quantities directly. Despite this complication, it has been possible to derive basic definitions of the *normalized voltage, normalized current*, and impedance which are as useful in the general case as their counterparts are at the lower radio frequencies. Microwave circuit theory, in analogy to the conventional circuit theory, has been equally helpful in arriving at methods of analysis, in the intuitive interpretation of the behavior of microwave systems, and in permitting a systematic approach to the problems of design and testing. These topics have been developed sufficiently in this text to make the application of the impedance concept, transmission-line theory, and the equivalent-circuit approach plausible and logical. A systematic and more detailed discussion of these topics is available in the published literature, especially in "Principles of Microwave Circuits," by C. G. Montgomery, R. H. Dicke, and E. M. Purcell, and also in the forthcoming book "Microwave Theory," by E. T. Jaynes.

In principle, the behavior of a given microwave system is completely described by the solution of Maxwell's equations appropriate to the particular boundary condition. Formally, if the response to the excitation by a signal of a given frequency is to be determined, the distribution of the electric and magnetic fields throughout the system must be measured. However, as there is no simple, direct way to make these measurements at microwave frequencies, it is necessary to resort to indirect methods. The measurement of power flow in a system specifies the product of the electric and magnetic fields, while the measurement of the impedance determines their ratio. Thus, these two measurements indirectly describe the distribution of the electric and magnetic fields in the system and provide its complete description. This is, in fact, the approach to most of the microwave measurements. In practice, this process is somewhat complicated by the ambiguity in the meaning of impedance and requires the selection of the field quantities which happen to be significant in a given problem. The arbitrariness of the impedance concept leads to conceptual difficulties and yet simultaneously makes it convenient to use in many problems. The importance of understanding the impedance concept, its proper application in the numerous forms of measurement, and the many possible practical laboratory techniques naturally make this topic one of the principal subjects of this book.

In passing, it may be of interest to compare the measurements of the electrical quantities in the various parts of the electromagnetic spectrum. Beginning with the direct current and proceeding into the X-ray region, the electrical quantities and methods used to measure each are shown in Table 1, which illustrates how the measurement of the basic quantities evolves as the frequency is increased.

TABLE 1. MEASUREMENT OF BASIC QUANTITIES

Frequency range	Voltage V	Current I	Impedance Z	Power W	Frequency f	Wavelength λ
Direct current...	Voltmeter 1. Electrostatic 2. Moving coil	Ammeter	1. Wheatstone bridge 2. V/I	1. Wattmeter 2. VI 3. Calorimeter		
Audio frequencies to 50 kc	Voltmeter, rectifier-type	Thermocouple ammeter	1. Wheatstone bridge 2. V/I	1. Wattmeter 2. Calorimeter	Frequency meter (cycle counter)	Not measured
Low radio frequencies	Voltmeter, rectifier-type	Thermocouple ammeter	1. Wheatstone bridge 2. V/I	Calorimeter	Frequency meter (cycle counter)	Coil and condenser wavemeter
High radio frequencies	Not accurate	Thermocouple ammeter	1. Bridge 2. Standing-wave detector	Calorimeter load lamps	Frequency meter (cycle counter)	Interference phenomenon using Lecher wires
Microwave.....	Usually not significant	Usually not significant	1. Standing-wave detector 2. Bridges	1. Calorimeter 2. Bolometer	Frequency meter (cycle counter)	Interference phenomenon using resonant-cavity wavemeter
Light..........	Not significant	Not significant	Not significant	1. Radiation pressure 2. Photometry 3. Calorimeter	Not measured	Interference phenomenon using diffraction grating
X rays.........	Not significant	Not significant	Not significant	Calorimeter	Not measured	Interference phenomenon using crystals as diffraction grafting

The mathematical symbols, as used in this book, require a word of explanation and justification. Whenever feasible, the notation prevalent in the literature is retained; however, occasionally this means that a given symbol is used with different meanings in different sections. For example, the symbol β is used to denote the propagation constant in the transmission line, the coupling coefficient in the klystron gap, the sensitivity coefficient of a crystal rectifier, the current sensitivity of a bolometer, the coupling coefficient between the transmission line and the resonant cavity, and certain geometrical shape factors. Generally, this should not cause confusion because the symbols appear in the equations in a characteristic way and are further defined whenever necessary. Occasionally the discussion of a particular topic involves several phenomena, so that a given symbol may occur in a given section with two different meanings. It is hoped that this word of caution will be sufficient to make the reader aware of this difficulty. In general, the mks system of units is used in the discussion relating to the electromagnetic phenomena; however, the cgs practical system of units is employed where it is more natural.

An explanation of the use of extensive footnotes should also be made. In several places in the text statements are made without proof to provide a continuity of thought for those who may not wish to concern themselves with a more detailed discussion. However, to indicate the basis for the statements, mathematical steps, other justification, and in some cases historical remarks, footnotes are used frequently.

The author is very grateful for many years of work with the late Professor W. W. Hansen, first as a student and later as an associate. Dr. Hansen can be considered, more than any other single person, as the founder of the modern microwave field. His many contributions to the field (aside from his work in physics) include fundamental studies of the cavity resonator, participation in the development of the klystron tube, development of the microwave theory, contributions toward development of the Doppler radar, development of the theory of the linear electron accelerator, and the study of many other topics in microwave electronics.

In addition to the association with Dr. Hansen, the author's professional development has been greatly aided by his many years of work with Drs. Marvin Chodorow, Edwin T. Jaynes, and John R. Woodyard. Also, many former graduate students have contributed significantly to the development of the microwave-measurements course which the author teaches at Stanford University. Special mention should be made of the work of Drs. H. John Shaw, Irving J. Nalos, and Kenneth B. Mallory and Mr. John Jasberg, who have helped in many ways, specifically and in general, in developing the material in this book and in organizing and teaching the student laboratory. I also wish to thank my wife, Artemas A. Ginzton, for helping to revise the manuscript into a more readable form.

EDWARD L. GINZTON

CONTENTS

CHAPTER 1

GENERATION OF LABORATORY SIGNALS

1.1. Laboratory Sources of Microwave Power. The primary requirement in nearly every microwave measurement problem is a satisfactory
source of microwave power. The specific requirements, of course, will
depend upon the experiment to be performed. In general, the power
output must be reasonably high; in many applications, power level in the
vicinity of 1 watt is desirable. Usually, the frequency and power output
must be stable with time, but it should be possible to adjust both conveniently. It is also often necessary to provide some means to minimize
the effect of load variations on power output and frequency. Since
modulation of the output signal is frequently desired, the signal source
should be of a type that can be either frequency- or amplitude-modulated.

It is found that velocity-modulation tubes can be made to meet these
general requirements. Such tubes can be made in the form of oscillators,
amplifiers, and frequency multipliers, and they can act as mixers or converters. In general, they can be made to do most of the functions
expected from the conventional tubes at a lower radio frequency.

The most common type of velocity-modulation tube is the *klystron*.
Numerous models are available which cover nearly the entire microwave
region. The reflex klystron is the simplest, for it has a single cavity, is
easily adjustable, and is the most common source of power for laboratory
purposes. Many other types of klystrons are also available in the form
of amplifiers, frequency multipliers, etc., which satisfy many specific needs
in the laboratory.

Another device employing the velocity-modulation principle is the
traveling-wave tube. In its conventional form, the traveling-wave amplifier provides an unusually large bandwidth and is very useful in some
applications. A more recently developed form, called the *backward-wave
oscillator*, promises to be of substantial value in numerous applications
because it can be voltage-tuned over a wide wavelength range.

Velocity-modulation tubes are not the only useful sources of microwave power. Close-spaced triodes are available at the lower microwave
frequencies. In the frequency region where their operation is satisfactory, the triodes possess several advantages over velocity-modulation

tubes. However, for reasons which will be apparent later, they are not so flexible as klystrons for most laboratory purposes. Magnetrons can also be used, but nearly all of the readily available tubes have been developed for transmitting purposes, and are not usually suitable for low-power laboratory requirements.

For certain microwave receiver measurements, the laboratory signals can be generated by devices which produce random noise, rather than sinusoidal signals. An example is the fluorescent-lamp source which produces noise because of the gas discharge. Although generation of noise provides but microscopic power, it is generally sufficient for accurate determination of receiver sensitivity.

At the extreme high-frequency end of the microwave spectrum, vacuum-tube oscillators are not yet available. Many types of exploratory measurements, however, may be carried out by using frequency multipliers employing nonlinear elements, such as crystal rectifiers. Although electromagnetic waves can be generated by this process in the millimeter and submillimeter regions, the measurement techniques for these applications are not fully developed and are not properly within the scope of the present discussion.

For most of the common applications, klystron tubes are found to be the most convenient and readily available sources of power. The principle of operation of the klystron is simple and only a rudimentary theory is required for a general understanding of its behavior. In several of the subsequent sections, the general characteristics of the klystron will be discussed with emphasis on those features which play an important role in their use as a laboratory signal source. Because triodes, traveling-wave tubes, backward-wave oscillators, and other devices are useful in numerous applications, several sections will be devoted to their discussion, which should be sufficient to introduce the reader to their general characteristics.

Further sections in this chapter will be concerned with matters pertaining to the practical use of laboratory oscillators. These range from methods of isolating the power source from its load, methods of modulation, to techniques for frequency stabilization of oscillators, etc.

A complete discussion of these topics is beyond the scope and purpose of this book. Abundant literature exists on the various topics mentioned to which the reader is referred for further study. The material presented is limited to a general description of the apparatus and techniques useful in microwave measurements, together with simple theoretical discussion. Understanding these elementary principles is essential for successful laboratory use of the various tubes in microwave measurements.

In planning a particular experiment, the specific requirements of the problem should be carefully considered when selecting the appropriate type of laboratory source. The questions of power level, frequency tuning range, type of modulation, and frequency stability are but examples of the interacting questions which must be considered. Careless choice in equipment may lead to unnecessary expense, either in the signal source itself, or in other auxiliary apparatus. A good knowledge of the relative merits of the various devices, their limitations, and availability is important to anyone seriously concerned with laboratory problems.

1.2. General Characteristics of Klystrons. The two principal features which distinguish the klystron from the lower-frequency tubes are: the use of cavity resonators as the resonant circuits and derivation of radio-frequency currents from direct currents by means of velocity modulation and resultant bunching. In the conventional triode-type tubes, the radio-frequency currents are obtained by direct action of the control grid which produces density modulation. The klystron tube is generally intended to operate at frequencies beyond those at which the control-grid action is possible. The process of converting the direct-current stream into time-varying density-modulated current is more complicated. In a klystron there are three separate regions of interest. In a cathode-anode region, the electrons are emitted under the influence of direct-current potentials. All of the electrons leave this region with a velocity which corresponds to the energy gained in passing through the cathode-anode potential, i.e., the accelerating potential, commonly referred to as the *beam voltage*. Electrons then pass into the second region called the *r-f interaction space* (or *gap*) where they are subjected to r-f potentials. The latter are usually small compared to the initial d-c accelerating potential, and the resultant variation in the velocity of electrons is not very large. Upon emerging from this region, there is still no evidence of density modulation. The electrons then enter the third region where there are no r-f potentials, but in which there may be present d-c potentials. In this space, usually called the *drift* or *bunching space*, the bunching action takes place as a consequence of the initial velocity variation. This process results in grouping of the electrons into bunches in space and creates the density modulation, corresponding to that produced directly by the control-grid action of the triode.

The klystron-type tubes can operate at higher frequencies than the triodes for the following reason: In passing through the r-f gap of the klystron tube, the electrons travel at a high velocity corresponding to the accelerating potential of the anode. In the grid-control region of the triode, the velocities are much lower. In both cases, the transit time of an electron through the interaction region should be appreciably less than the period of a single cycle of oscillation frequency. Because the electrons are traveling faster in the klystron, the interaction region can be longer than in the triode. In practice, it turns out that the klystron gap (for a given frequency) can be about 10 times greater than that of a triode. This means that the klystron may be expected to have an upper frequency limit about 10 times that of a triode.

The bunched-electron beam, being density-modulated, can be utilized in the same way as in the conventional triodes. In passing through an output resonant cavity, interaction takes place between the density-modulated current and the gap in a fashion similar to the operation of the grid-anode region of a triode and its resonant circuit. The power output is derived by slowing down the electron stream, and is equal to the difference in kinetic energy of the electrons averaged before and after passing the interaction gap. The power consumed at the input gap, required to produce the initial velocity variation, is generally small, making it possible to obtain substantial power gain in a single stage of amplification.

These principles have been applied in a variety of ways differing from each other in the number of resonant cavities, location of accelerating or retarding potentials, and in the purpose of application.[1] The most useful structure for laboratory application is illustrated in Fig. 1.1.

Figure 1.1*a* shows schematically a conventional *two-cavity klystron amplifier*. Historically, it is the oldest form of velocity-variation device; it is also the simplest from the viewpoint of theory, design, and general understanding of behavior of the velocity-modulation tube. Having two cavities which need to be adjusted to resonance makes this type of klystron more difficult to use than the single-cavity reflex klystron shown in Fig. 1.1*e*. The power gain and efficiency of the two-cavity klystron are not so high as those of a similar tube having three or more cavities along its beam. As a result, the two-cavity klystron is not so useful as some other members of the klystron family. The same remarks apply to the *two-cavity oscillator* shown in Fig. 1.1*b*. In order to adjust a two-cavity klystron oscillator to a predetermined frequency, the two cavities as well as the beam voltage must be set to the proper values. Making these three-variable adjustments is tedious and requires a carefully considered systematic procedure. The efficiency of the two-cavity klystron in either the amplifier or oscillator form may reach 40 per cent, and its power output can be very high by signal-source standards.

Several resonant cavities can be used along a single electron beam.

[1] The reader is referred to the abundant literature on this subject. See, for example, R. R. Warnecke, M. Chodorow, P. R. Guenard, and E. L. Ginzton, chapter on Velocity Modulated Tubes, in L. Marton (ed.), "Advances in Electronics," vol. 3, Academic Press, Inc., New York, 1951; the most complete account of this subject will be found in R. R. Warnecke and P. R. Guenard, "Les Tubes électroniques a commande par modulation de vitesse," Gauthier-Villars & Cie, Paris, 1951. The last reference contains an extensive bibliography.

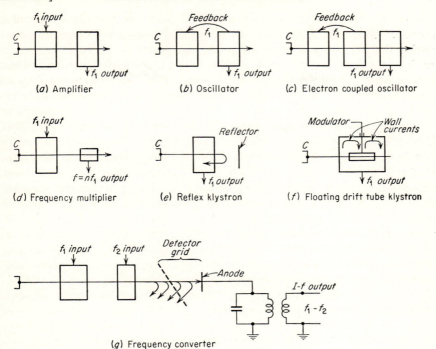

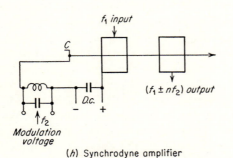

(h) Synchrodyne amplifier

FIG. 1.1. Symbolic representation of various forms of klystron tubes. Motion of electrons is indicated by an arrow originating at the cathode C. The resonant cavities are indicated by rectangles whose resonant frequencies are denoted by the symbol f; subscripts indicate harmonics or other frequencies.

For example, if three cavities are used, the first can be used as an input cavity and the third as the output. In this case, the device can be regarded as a two-stage amplifier, resulting in very high power gains. Fig. 1.1c shows another way to use a three-cavity structure. The first two cavities are connected together, forming a two-cavity oscillator. The output, however, is taken from the third cavity, rather than from the second. Thus, the load connected to the tube has no direct way of influencing the frequency of oscillation since the power delivered to the third cavity by a bunched stream is produced in an isolated structure. This arrangement may be called an *electron-coupled oscillator*, and is useful in applications where the frequency of oscillation must be independent of load adjustments.

For some applications, frequency multipliers may be required. The harmonic content of a bunched beam in a klystron happens to be high. If a frequency f_1 is used to produce velocity modulation at the first gap of a multicavity klystron, a desired nth harmonic may be selected by providing a cavity tuned to that frequency. The simplest structure of this kind is shown in Fig. 1.1d. This is the most common type of *frequency multiplier*, although other forms with more cavities can also be used. Relative strength of the various harmonics is shown in Table 1.1 which indicates that high-order frequency multiplication is practical. The values shown in the table are computed from first-order theory and cannot be expected to be accurate. Since klystrons utilize cavities with high Q values, it is possible to select a particular harmonic without appreciable output at other frequencies.

TABLE 1.1. MAXIMUM AMPLITUDES OF THE nTH HARMONIC OF THE FUNDAMENTAL AT THE OUTPUT GAP OF A TWO-CAVITY KLYSTRON FREQUENCY MULTIPLIER (IN PER CENT OF FUNDAMENTAL COMPONENT)*

Harmonic	Per cent fundamental
1	100
2	83
3	75
5	64
10	52
15	47
20	42

* The values for Table 1.1 are computed from Eq. (1.5) at the optimum value of bunching parameter in each case. See also Fig. 1.5.

The most generally useful type of an oscillator for laboratory purposes is the *reflex* klystron shown in Fig. 1.1e. A single resonant cavity is used simultaneously to provide the necessary velocity variation and to convert the resultant bunched r-f current into output power. The bunching process takes place under the influence of retarding d-c fields in the so-called reflection region. Because of its general usefulness, the principle of operation of the reflex klystron will be considered in some detail in

Sec. 1.6. The reflex klystron is preferred in many applications because of its relative simplicity; only two adjustments need to be made to produce oscillations at the desired frequency: the tuning of the resonant cavity and adjustment of the reflector voltage. The frequency of the reflex klystron will change with reflector voltage; in the neighborhood of maximum output, this relation is linear. This feature makes it possible to provide linear frequency modulation. It also means that the applied potentials need to be sufficiently constant to avoid undesirable frequency modulation. The latter difficulty is, in fact, generic with all microwave oscillator systems because the transit time in all known cases is dependent upon applied potentials.

Unfortunately, most reflex klystrons available for laboratory applications leave much to be desired because usually they have been designed for other applications, such as radar local oscillator service, relay link transmitters, etc. Despite many efforts to adapt them to laboratory service, most of these tubes and cavity combinations are relatively complicated and expensive. The greatest difficulties arise in providing tuning over a wide band. For relatively narrowband applications, many types of reflex klystrons exist and are generally satisfactory.

Another single-cavity klystron arrangement is shown in Fig. 1.1f. This arrangement resembles a two-cavity klystron in which the fields in the two cavities are equal and in time phase. Under these circumstances, the currents flowing in the common wall between the two cavities are equal and opposite in direction. Hence, the wall may be left out entirely without disturbing the cavity fields. This results in a single cavity which can be tuned with the same relative ease as the reflex klystron. The frequency of oscillation depends upon the beam voltage in the same way as it depends upon the reflector voltage in the reflex klystron. Frequency modulation can be obtained just as easily in the two cases. Structures of this type are known as *floating-drift* tube klystrons, or as *Heil* tubes. The *floating-drift* tube klystron has the efficiency and power output corresponding to the two-cavity klystron, the convenience of tuning and simplicity of frequency modulation of the reflex klystron, and nearly complete freedom from hysteresis, which is often present in the reflex klystron. However, despite these important advantages, the floating-drift tube klystron is not as yet commercially available.

Klystrons can also be used as detectors or frequency converters. This can be accomplished in a manner illustrated schematically in Fig. 1.1g, which shows two resonant cavities spaced along the electron beam. Beyond the last cavity resonator, a detector element is provided in the form of a grid and an anode plate. The grid is electrically connected to the cathode through a suitable d-c bias supply. The cathode, grid, and plate elements form a structure in which the plate current depends upon grid-bias voltage much as it does in an ordinary triode. If the grid is biased to cutoff, the electron current will reach the anode plate only if the r-f voltages in the cavities accelerate the electrons above the d-c value. If frequencies f_1 and f_2 are introduced into the cavities as shown, the nonlinear action of the detector will result in mixing action. The difference, or i-f frequency, $f_1 - f_2$, can be obtained by passing the detected current through a suitable resonant circuit. Klystrons equipped with detector circuits of this type are convenient in the laboratory for mixing signals, but generally suffer because of excessive noise.

In some applications, it is convenient to shift the signal frequency f_1 by a small amount. This is desired, for example: in the additive-frequency method of measuring frequencies; in cases where very high amplification at a single frequency is difficult because of regeneration; or, if two signals (a transmitter and a local oscillator) need to be generated at an accurately determined frequency interval. The shift in frequency may be accomplished by using a two- or three-cavity klystron (or a traveling-wave tube) as a phase-modulated amplifier in the manner indicated in Fig. 1.1h. Microwave frequency f_1 produces velocity modulation at the first gap and would normally appear as an amplified signal at the second cavity. If the beam voltage is modulated at some moderately high radio frequency f_2, sidebands are produced due to phase modulation. (This happens because the time of arrival of bunches is shifted in phase at the rate corresponding to f_2.) Sidebands are produced in the usual manner, displaced from the carrier f_1 by multiples of f_2. Any one of the sidebands may be selected by the last cavity and further filtered, if required, by external cavity filters. The output frequency is then $f_1 \pm nf_2$. This method of shifting the carrier frequency is commonly known as the *synchrodyne system* and amplifiers used in this manner are called *synchrodyne* amplifiers.[1]

Amplitude modulation of klystron amplifiers is best accomplished by modulating the beam current with the aid of control grids adjacent to the cathode. Amplitude modulation of klystron oscillators can be accomplished in the same way, but is difficult to achieve without simultaneously introducing frequency modulation. This effect is due to the fact that the presence of an electron beam in a cavity changes its resonant frequency in proportion to the magnitude of the d-c current. Under special circumstances, variation in frequency due to changes in current can be canceled by simultaneous modulation of the beam voltage in proper phase relationship. However, very few of the available klystrons have control grids because these are not needed for the usual system applications.

---

[1] The performance of the synchrodyne amplifier can be considerably improved if the modulating voltage f_2 is replaced by a saw-tooth waveform. This results in a higher gain and fewer unwanted sidebands.

1.3. Methods of Tuning of Klystrons.   Most klystron oscillators can be tuned over a narrow range by merely changing the operating potentials.   Such tuning is usually referred to as *electronic* tuning, because no mechanical motion of tube parts is involved.   The amount of electronic tuning obtainable with a given tube type depends upon its original design, and is relatively unaffected by loading of the cavity resonators.   The extent of available electronic tuning depends upon various factors which will be discussed later.   Some klystrons are electronically tunable over a bandwidth of about 3 per cent; usually, however, the tuning range is appreciably smaller.

Larger tuning range can be provided by means of *mechanical* tuning, which is accomplished by changing cavity dimensions.   For efficient interaction between an electron beam and the r-f field in a gap, the transit time of electrons through the gap must be less than one-half cycle. In practice, this implies that the cavities suitable for klystron applications must be built in reentrant form.   The electric and magnetic fields in reentrant cavities are markedly localized so that the cavities resemble lumped capacity and inductance circuits to a fair degree of accuracy. By analogy to ordinary tuned circuits, three methods of tuning are possible; either the capacity, the inductance, or both simultaneously can be varied.   These methods can be applied to the klystron cavity directly, as the gap region closely corresponds to the capacity of the LC circuit, and the reentrant loop of the cavity to the inductance.

The capacitance of the interaction gap can be varied by changing the spacing of the gap posts, as indicated in Fig. 1.2a.   Since the electrons are passing through the gap in vacuum, a flexible vacuum diaphragm must be used.   Mechanical motion of diaphragms is limited by the elastic limits of the material used.   In addition to the practical necessity of limiting excessive deformation of a diaphragm, the capacitive tuning cannot be used to provide large changes in frequency in a klystron tube. This can be understood with the aid of the following qualitative argument: In decreasing the spacing of the gap, it is found that the shunt resistance of a cavity decreases rapidly because of combined effects of increased capacity and excessive losses in the grid structure of the gap.[1] If the gap dimensions are increased beyond certain limits, the transit time of electrons increases in proportion, and the effective interaction or *coupling* between the gap and the beam becomes ineffective, as discussed in Sec. 1.4b.   Because of combined effects of this nature, it is impractical to change the gap spacing more than approximately 50 per cent, which

---

[1] The larger losses in a gridded gap are due to the comparatively high losses in the grid material.   The latter, being porous to the electrons, has a lower r-f conductivity than the solid walls of the cavity.   Smaller gap spacing results in larger circulating current in the grid material, and, hence, in higher loss.

limits the practical tuning range to about 25 per cent. In addition, at small gap spacings the tuning can become excessively critical and too easily affected by thermal drifts.

Appreciably greater tuning range can be provided by leaving the interaction gap dimensions at their optimum proportions and changing the inductance of the circuit. This can be done by changing the volume of the cavity in any of the several convenient ways. Two possible schemes are shown in Fig. 1.2b. The first of these shows a movable plug being placed so that its insertion into the cavity reduces the volume normally

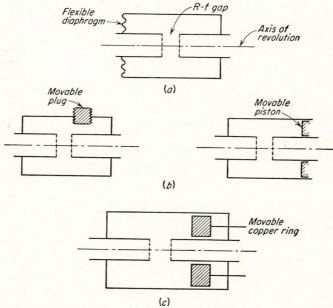

FIG. 1.2. Methods of tuning of reentrant klystron resonators. (a) Capacitive or gap tuning; (b) inductive or piston tuning; (c) inductive-capacitive tuning.

occupied by the magnetic field. A number of plugs can be used in this manner. The second method illustrated makes use of a movable piston at one end of the cavity to change its volume directly. In both of these methods, as well as in all related ones, the main practical problem pertains to extra losses which are introduced at the point of contact between the movable member and the cavity walls. Many effective methods have been devised to avoid physical contact between the tuning member and the cavity as, for example, by means of capacitive joints. However, a new set of problems is created because of extraneous resonances which may be excited in the complex circuit consisting of the cavity, the capacitive joint, and the space beyond. A variety of similar methods are known which differ only in the detail of introducing the plunger into the evacuated cavity and in the manner used to avoid or suppress unwanted resonances.

The third tuning method makes use of simultaneous changes in the capacity and inductance of the cavity. It is illustrated in Fig. 1.2*c*. A movable metallic ring is supported in the cavity by means of dielectric material or by metallic supports, which are (ideally) at right angles to the electric field. If the tuning ring is constructed of a good electrical conductor, the resultant cavity losses are not excessively altered. If the ring is placed in the middle of the inductive region of the cavity (roughly in the position shown) it will occupy the region of relatively weak electric and magnetic fields; thus its presence will not have a large effect upon the resonant frequency of the cavity. If the ring is moved closer to the r-f gap where the electric fields are strong, additional capacity is introduced from the gap to the outside cylinder. As the ring is moved toward the end of the cavity, the capacitive loading is decreased; simultaneously, the inductance is decreased because the volume occupied by strong magnetic fields is diminished. This simultaneous change in inductance and capacity permits a relatively large change in resonant frequency. The problems of unwanted resonances exist in this method as well, and tend to limit the useful range of the many possible variations.

By means of either the plunging or the capacity-inductance tuning, it is possible to obtain a two-to-one frequency range. Complicated mechanical devices required for this purpose can be attached to a klystron originally designed with provisions for *external tuning*. Such klystrons are constructed so that the terminals of interaction gaps extend beyond the vacuum envelope. Because of the mechanical complexity, the ensemble tends to be expensive. Certain klystrons are manufactured with integral cavities, i.e., with cavities as a part of the vacuum envelope. These are relatively inexpensive, but are nearly always tuned by capacitive methods, and consequently have a much narrower tuning range.[1]

The difference in cost between a wide-band commercial signal source arranged to provide large tuning range and an integral-cavity narrowband device can be as much as ten to one. Therefore, in selecting adequate laboratory apparatus, it is necessary to decide whether wide-band tuning is required. An additional consideration in the choice involves the power level; integral-cavity klystrons generally have much greater power output, although this is merely a matter of happenstance.

---

[1] Many modifications of the methods mentioned are possible. One commonly used is the coupled-cavity method. A klystron is built with an integral fixed-tuned cavity but with provision for strong coupling to an external cavity. The tuning of the latter permits convenient tuning of the ensemble.

1.4. Theory of Klystron Behavior. It is not possible to use a klystron in the laboratory proficiently without some understanding of the theory of its operation and the various predictable effects. Fortunately, only simplified theory is required to understand the gross effects of interest to most operators. The theoretical basis of the klystron behavior can be summarized by considering the essentials of the following topics:

a. Beam focusing. Typical klystrons use cylindrical beams which can be magnetically, electrostatically, or ion focused.

b. Gap interaction. The theory of interaction between an electron beam and radio-frequency gap fields predicts the amount of velocity variation produced by a given field and also the extent of *beam loading*. The latter term refers to exchange of energy between the cavity and the beam under small signal conditions. This theory also predicts the change in resonant frequency of a cavity due to the presence of the electron stream.

c. The theory of the bunching process for small signals predicts the dependence of radio-frequency current as a function of all variables. In its elementary form, this theory consists of two parts: the kinematics of electrons, neglecting space-charge repulsion; and the debunching theory which predicts for any given current-voltage combination the limits of variables over which the purely kinematic theory can be trusted.

d. The large-signal theory considers the details of exchange of energy at the output gap of the klystron.

e. The theory of complex bunching systems, such as three-cavity klystrons, shows what can be expected when the velocity variation is accomplished by radio-frequency fields, not localized at a single gap.

These topics will be considered briefly below. An interested reader is referred to extensive literature for further details.[1]

a. Beam Focusing. Electron beams used in most klystrons are cylindrical in shape, with the length of the beam being several times its diameter. The current density is generally very high. The main problem is the consideration of those factors which pertain to preservation of cylindrical flow of current in overcoming large internal space-charge repulsion forces.

---

[1] R. R. Warnecke et al., *op. cit.;* D. R. Hamilton, J. K. Knipp, and J. B. H. Kuper, "Klystrons and Microwave Triodes," Massachusetts Institute of Technology Radiation Laboratory Series, McGraw-Hill Book Company, Inc., New York, 1948; A. E. Harrison, "Klystron Tubes," McGraw-Hill Book Company, Inc., New York, 1947; A. H. W. Beck, "Velocity-modulated Thermionic Tubes," Cambridge University Press, Cambridge, England, 1948; W. W. Hansen, "Notes on Lectures" (given at Massachusetts Institute of Technology 1941 to 1944), McGraw-Hill Book Company, Inc., New York, in preparation; R. R. Warnecke and P. R. Guenard, *op. cit.;* J. R. Pierce and W. G. Shepherd, "Reflex Oscillators," *Bell System Tech. J.*, vol. 26, pp. 460–681, July, 1947 (the same material appears in "Radar Systems and Components," pp. 490–709, D. Van Nostrand Company, Inc., Princeton, N.J., 1949).

The problem of focusing electrons initially from the surface of a cathode is relatively simple. By choosing suitable focusing elements it is possible to cause electrons to flow toward a point of convergence. Once the electrons leave the cathode-anode region, they travel through an essentially field-free region. Internal space-charge forces make the beam slowly diverge, reach a point of minimum diameter, and proceed along divergent trajectories. In principle, the shape of the beam is symmetric about the point of minimum diameter. In many practical klystrons, the cavities are merely disposed along the electron beam with the diameter of the cavities and the drift tube fitting the shape of the beam.

In many klystron structures, the behavior of the beam is strongly affected by the presence of residual gas. Collisions between electrons and gas molecules produce positive ions. These tend to migrate toward the axis of the tube because of the negative potential created there by the presence of the electron stream. For most gas pressures, there are enough gas molecules present to provide sufficient ions to completely neutralize the negative space charge in the beam. If this were to happen, the electron stream, once parallel, would remain parallel indefinitely. This, indeed, can happen in klystrons which use grids at interaction gaps. These grids insure that the drift space becomes an "ion trap," confining the ions to the region of the electron stream. Sometimes, however, the grids are not used at all, or are so coarse that the cathode-anode potential can partially penetrate the drift-tube region. The ions can then migrate axially toward the cathode so rapidly that an insufficient number remain to produce complete neutralization. In many cases where ion trapping takes place, electron behavior is uncertain and is associated with unusual oscillations and noise.

In many tubes magnetic focusing is used to confine the flow of the electron stream. With proper design, electron beams can be confined to any desired length with nearly perfect transmission of current.

b. Gap Interaction. When an electron beam passes through a gap, such as is shown in Fig. 1.3, the r-f fields across the gap accelerate electrons on one half-cycle, and retard them on the other. If the transit time of electrons across the gap is very small compared to time of a half-cycle, and if the r-f voltage across the gap is small compared to the beam voltage, there will be no transfer of energy between the r-f fields and the beam. This happens because equal, but opposite, amounts of energy will be transferred on successive half-cycles. These idealized assumptions are not valid for the gaps ordinarily encountered. The exact exchange of energy and the extent of velocity modulation produced in the beam will depend upon the geometry of the gap, presence or absence of grids, the spacing between the latter, and beam velocity.

For small r-f voltages, all these effects have been analyzed and lead to the following general results.

The velocity modulation produced by an actual gap is smaller than it would be in an idealized gridded gap of zero width. The effective modulation can be computed by multiplying the actual r-f voltage by constant β, called the *beam-coupling coefficient*, which is computed from the geometry of the gap and the transit time of the electrons. For non-idealized gaps, the energy gained by the beam is not canceled by energy loss on the opposite half-cycles. As a result, there is an energy transfer

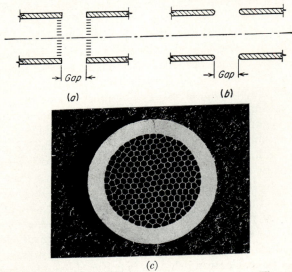

Fig. 1.3. Typical configurations of the r-f interaction gaps. The cross sections of gridded and gridless gaps are shown in (a) and (b), respectively; a photograph of a hexagonal "honeycomb" grid used in a 3-cm reflex klystron is shown in (c). (*The grid supplied by Varian Associates, Inc.*)

between the beam and the gap. This effect can be described by assigning a *beam-loading conductance* across the gap. This conductance, when multiplied by the square of rms voltage across the gap, gives the power lost (or gained) from the gap. The beam-loading conductance can also be obtained analytically. For a *plane-parallel gap with grids* these constants are given by the following formulas: The beam-coupling coefficient is

$$\beta = \frac{\sin (D/2)}{D/2} \tag{1.1}$$

and the beam-loading conductance is

$$\frac{G_b}{G_0} = \frac{\beta}{2}\left(\beta - \cos \frac{D}{2}\right) \tag{1.2}$$

where D = normalized gap distance, radians

    = $\omega d/u_0$

  d = gap separation, cm

  ω = angular frequency

  u_0 = velocity of electrons, cm/sec

  G_0 = d-c beam conductance = I_0/V_0

The quantities β and G_b/G_0 are shown plotted in Fig. 1.4.   For gridless gaps and for other gap geometries, the situation is more complicated. The beam-coupling coefficient and the beam-loading conductance depend upon the exact nature of the fields in the gap and upon the radius of the drift tube.

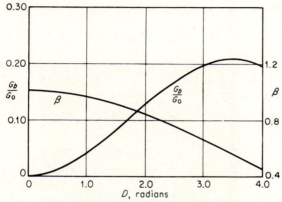

FIG. 1.4. Variation in beam-coupling coefficient and beam-loading conductance in a gridded interaction gap. D is the transit time of the electrons through the gap in radians.

Most klystrons suitable for laboratory service are low-voltage devices in which grids are used, and results of Fig. 1.4 will be applicable.   When the transit time through the gap is about a quarter-cycle, the coupling coefficient $\beta = 0.9$, and the beam conductance G_b is about $0.1G_0$.   The maximum value of beam loading occurs when the transit time is about a half-cycle.   At this point the cavity is loaded with a resistance equal to about 5 times the d-c resistance of the beam.   In cases other than gridded gaps the situation will be different in detail but the general expectations will not be materially changed.

The results described above are often referred to as *normal* beam loading.   The situation becomes considerably more complex if secondary electrons are created upon the opposing sides of the gap.   Secondary electrons can cause appreciably greater reduction of the cavity resistance than can be accounted for by the normal transit-time loading and can dominate the picture entirely; this is often the case with low-voltage gridded klystrons.

In addition to producing an equivalent conductance across the gap, the electron beam also changes the resonant frequency of the cavity. The magnitude of this effect can be ascribed by stating the equivalent *beam susceptance*. The susceptance effects can be due to either the primary or secondary electrons. The frequency change due to the presence of the beam susceptance is not, in general, very important because it can be compensated for by a slight readjustment of cavity tuning.

c. Bunching and Debunching. The r-f current can be predicted at any point along a velocity-modulated beam by means of the classical kinematic analysis of motion of electrons. The magnitude of the fundamental component of the r-f current measured at the second gap is given by

$$I_2 = 2I_0 J_1(x) \tag{1.3}$$

where I_2 is the current at the second gap, I_0 is the d-c current, $J_1(x)$ is the Bessel function of the first order of argument x. The *bunching parameter* x is given by

$$x = \pi N \frac{V_1}{V_0} \tag{1.4}$$

in which $N = (l/u_0)f$ is the transit time between the first and second gap measured in cycles of oscillation frequency, l is the bunching distance in centimeters, V_1 is the *effective* voltage causing velocity variation, and V_0 is the d-c beam voltage. The effective gap voltage is obtained by multiplying the voltage across the gap by the beam-coupling coefficient β, as discussed in Sec. 1.4b above. The nth-order harmonic component of the current can be calculated from the general expression

$$I_2 = 2I_0 J_n(nx) \tag{1.5}$$

Figure 1.5 shows the dependence of $J_n(x)$ upon x.

The value of the bunching parameter at which the fundamental component of current is maximum occurs at $x = 1.84$. The bunching voltage may be quite small but a sufficiently large transit time N will produce optimum bunching.

The kinematic analysis from which the above results are obtained neglects a number of factors. The most important of these are the following. First, in order to make the calculations simple, the analysis assumes that $\alpha_1 = V_1/V_2 \ll 1$. The consequence of this small-signal approximation is discussed in Sec. 1.4d and may or may not be important in practice. The second approximation involves the neglect of repulsion forces between electrons which tend to counteract the bunching process.

Evaluation of these space-charge forces is difficult but can be carried out in a hypothetical case of a beam of infinite cross section.[1] This calculation indicates that the r-f current in presence of space charge can be predicted by a Bessel function of argument x, but with the distance along the beam l replaced by a factor $\sin hl/h$ where h, the *debunching wave number*, is given by

$$h = \frac{1}{a}\left(\frac{60}{R_0\beta_0}\right)^{1/2} \tag{1.6}$$

where a is the radius of the beam, R_0 is its d-c impedance, and $\beta_0 = u_0/c$.

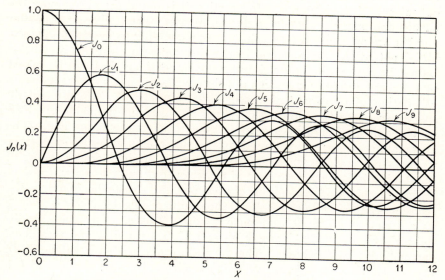

FIG. 1.5. Bessel functions $J_n(x)$ vs. x.   (*Courtesy of J. R. Woodyard.*)

Thus, in order to accomplish bunching with the minimum possible r-f voltage at the input gap, one would wish to use a long bunching distance. But if the distance is long enough to make hl approach π, the debunching forces become important and the current becomes small. The *optimum distance* is readily found when $hl = \pi/2$. Making the distance greater causes the bunching parameter to decrease.

When the beam is small compared to its length or is surrounded by metallic walls, the above remarks are not strictly valid. However, the more precise considerations do not change the nature of conclusions reached in the simpler case. Also, all present debunching theories are limited to the case of small signals, i.e., when $x < 1$. For this reason, the debunching theory is not used directly in calculating the values of

[1] Hansen, *op. cit.*

r-f currents, but only as a guide to specify the values of bunching distance which must not be exceeded.

d. Large-signal Theory. The factors described above determine the magnitude of the r-f current along the drift space. The bunching theory permits calculation of the current and determines the maximum bunching distance for a given current. The next step in analysis pertains to the extraction of r-f power from the bunched beam. For efficient operation, the kinetic energy of the beam must be extracted to the greatest possible extent. Ideally, the maximum efficiency would occur if all of the electrons in the beam could be brought to rest in passing through the output gap of the klystron. In practice, it is found that in passing the output gap many of the electrons are brought to rest whereas a smaller number are accelerated to a velocity corresponding to nearly double the initial potential. Such strong interaction between electrons and fields cannot be accounted for by simple analytic methods, but can be solved by graphical calculations which are simple in principle. This requires a calculation of electron trajectories for a number of electrons equally spaced over an oscillation cycle, taking into account the velocity which an electron may gain or lose in passing through the input gap. The average kinetic energy possessed by the electrons upon their emergence from the output gap, when compared with the original kinetic energy of the d-c beam, is then a measure of power output and efficiency. Calculations of this kind have been carried out and are to be found in the references cited. Figure 1.6 shows the results of calculations of efficiency as a function of input and output gap voltages.[1] In these graphs $\alpha_1 = V_1/V_0$, $\alpha_2 = V_2/V_0$ where V_1 and V_2 are the first and second r-f gap voltages, respectively. The curves are marked with values of D, the transit time of (average-velocity) electrons through the second gap expressed in radians.

The efficiency is a strong function of the input gap voltage for the following reason. The retarded electrons in the bunch will have an energy corresponding to $V_0 - V_1$. One would like to have the output gap voltage approach V_0, but this is now impossible as many electrons enter the gap with velocities as low as $V_0 - V_1$. These slow electrons will stop part way across the output gap, reverse their direction, and be ejected toward the cathode with a corresponding waste of output power. Thus, the greater V_1, the smaller V_2 must be.

It is now plain how the space-charge effects interact with large signal phenomena. In order to avoid serious debunching difficulties, the length of the beam is kept short as required by the condition $hl \leq \pi/2$. But short bunching distance (in order to obtain optimum bunching) requires that the input gap voltage V_1 be made large; this, as was just

[1] Original calculations of this type are due to E. Feenberg.

discussed, causes a loss in efficiency to the extent predictable from Fig. 1.6.   These considerations merely restrict the design of klystrons to a certain range of current densities.   When expressed in units of perveance,[1] it has been found that efficiencies in practical tubes may reach 40 to 50 per cent if perveance does not exceed 1 or 2.

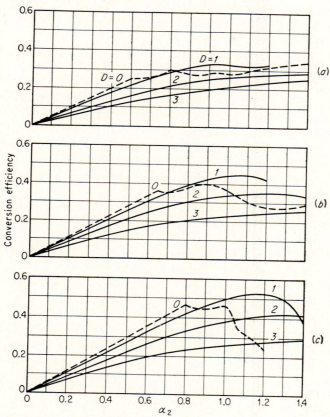

Fig. 1.6. Conversion efficiency of a klystron at large signals. α_1 and α_2 are normalized r-f gap voltages at the first and second gaps, respectively.   The curves are labeled with values of D, the d-c transit time of electrons through the output gap.   (a) $\alpha_1 = 0.6$; (b) $\alpha_1 = 0.4$; (c) $\alpha_1 = 0.2$.

e. *Complex Bunching Systems.*   The simple bunching theory, or the limiting values of the complete theory as described above, predicts the efficiency of the klystron to be 58 per cent.   This value cannot be

[1] Perveance is a unit which is related to the cathode-anode distance of the diode gun.   It is the constant of proportionality in the expression $I = kV^{3/2}$.   Its dimensions are of inverse length.   Perveance is said to be equal to unity for a cathode which emits 31.6 ma at 1,000 volts.

approached in practice because of finite transit-time effects and space-charge debunching. On the other hand, the idealized value of 58 per cent is not the maximum that can be obtained. This particular value is the consequence of the degree of bunching that can be attained with simple sinusoidal velocity modulation at the input gap. It can be easily shown that if the modulation voltage at the input gap could be made saw-tooth in shape, the efficiency under idealized conditions would approach 100 per cent.

It is difficult to develop voltages across a gap of a resonant cavity which would contain enough harmonics to be saw-tooth-shaped. However, the fact that efficiency can be improved by more complicated bunching voltages has led to the analysis of systems in which velocity variation takes place in a more complicated manner. For instance, a klystron using three cavities improves the efficiency considerably if both of the first two cavities produce significant amounts of velocity modulation. In this way it is possible to increase the idealized efficiency from 58 per cent to about 80 per cent. Other methods have been suggested but few as yet have been tried.

1.5. The Two-cavity Klystron. *a. General Remarks.* Although the two-cavity klystron is not the most useful type for general laboratory use for the reasons discussed in Sec. 1.2, it is still needed in various applications, either because of its larger power output, or because certain functions can be best accomplished by means of a multiple-cavity tube. It will be assumed that the reader understands the general theory of klystron operation and only topics of interest in laboratory applications will be discussed here.

The electron beam of a two-cavity klystron originates from a cathode, passes through the r-f interaction space and finally reaches the collector. In typical structures, the r-f section together with the collector forms a continuous metallic shell, and, with its coaxial or waveguide outputs, is electrically grounded for safety reasons. The cathode side of the power supply is at high voltage with respect to ground and the operator must be aware of the danger involved.

In some klystrons the collector is separated from the r-f interaction region, and a d-c meter can be inserted to indicate the value of the current which passes through the klystron. This permits determination of the fraction of the current lost in the r-f region due to poor focusing. It will also be generally observed that as the tube begins to oscillate the collector current changes; this effect can be utilized as an oscillation indicator. This latter change in current is due to the fact that bunching is invariably accompanied by transverse debunching which bulges the beam, and consequently affects the fraction of the beam lost to the walls of the drift tube.

The collector can be used as an oscillation indicator in another way.

Normally the collector is connected electrically to the body of the klystron and serves as the heat-dissipating element in the tube. However, if the collector is connected to the cathode instead, the electrons, upon emerging from the last r-f gap, will encounter a retarding field. In the region between the body and the collector, the electrons will come to rest just in front of the collector and will reverse their direction and proceed back to the body of the klystron. The returning beam will usually spread rapidly and only a small fraction of the beam will reenter the r-f gap region. Thus, the collector would not collect any electrons if there were no fields in the r-f gaps. But if r-f voltages are present in any of the klystron gaps, some of the electrons will be accelerated and will be able to reach the collector. A meter connected between the collector and the cathode will indicate the presence of oscillations.

The electrons reentering the klystron in the reverse direction are usually too few in number to cause any complications. But their presence makes the klystron resemble the reflex-klystron structure and, on occasion, can be troublesome.

It should be noted that in this connection of tube elements the body of the klystron will collect practically all of the current and dissipate nearly all of the heat. The maximum power input to the klystron will be determined by the ability of the klystron body to transfer the heat to the surrounding medium. If the collector is connected to the body, the heat is distributed between the body and the collector in proportion to the current division. With good focusing the collector will then dissipate most of the power.

b. Two-cavity Klystron Oscillator. Several conditions must be satisfied to convert a two-cavity klystron amplifier into an oscillator. To ensure oscillation, the following simultaneous adjustments must be made:

1. The two cavities must be tuned to the same frequency.

2. A sufficiently strong coupling must be provided between cavities.

3. The current passing through the klystron must exceed a certain value, called the *starting current*, which depends upon the load.

4. The proper beam voltage must be found.

These requirements will be briefly discussed below. The simplest way to satisfy them in the laboratory is the following: The coupling is provided between the cavities by any convenient method recommended by the manufacturer. The beam voltage is then applied, but in the a-c form (60 cycles, for example) instead of the d-c form. This insures that at some instant in time the applied voltage will have the right value. One of the cavities should be adjusted to a position which is believed to be in the middle of its tuning range. Tuning the second cavity from one extreme position to the other should result in oscillation if the current is high enough. The presence of oscillation can be detected by the method outlined above or by connecting a detector to the output terminals of

the klystron, making sure that the detector can handle the expected
power.   When oscillations have been detected both cavities can be tuned
simultaneously to the desired wavelength as indicated by a suitable wavemeter.   The a-c voltage can then be replaced by d-c voltage, and the
cavities be trimmed for maximum output and the precise wavelength
desired.   This procedure can be considerably simplified if each cavity is
pretuned to the desired frequency by means of a separate signal source.
It should be remembered that a klystron will oscillate at a number of
discrete voltages, or modes, as will
be discussed below.

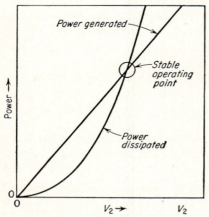

FIG. 1.7. Energy balance in a two-
cavity klystron oscillator.

*c. The Starting Current for Two-
cavity Klystron.*   To cause oscillations, the d-c current must be high
enough to generate sufficient power
to supply all losses, including the
useful output.   The dependence of
the starting current upon the various factors can be estimated as
follows: Let I_0 be the d-c current
that passes through the last r-f gap.
The magnitude of the r-f component of this current is given by
Eq. (1.3).   Let R be the shunt
impedance of the last cavity as seen
at its gap, taking into account all
sources of loss, i.e., Joule heating in the cavity walls, beam loading,
output, and any others that may be present.   The power output developed across this gap is equal to

$$P_{\text{out}} = \frac{V_2{}^2}{2R} \tag{1.7}$$

where V_2 is the voltage across the output gap.   This is a circuit condition, expressing the power in terms of circuit losses and the voltage
across R.   The power delivered to the cavity gap by the bunched beam
is $V_2 I_2/2$.   A stable operating condition exists when these quantities are
equal.   The two quantities are plotted against V_2 in Fig. 1.7.   If the
power generated is less than the power lost, oscillations cannot exist.
The limiting condition is obtained when the two curves are tangent at
the origin.   Thus,

$$\frac{1}{2} V_2 I_2 = \frac{1}{2} \frac{V_2{}^2}{R} \tag{1.8}$$

or

$$V_2 = 2 I_0 R J_1 \left(\pi N \frac{V_1}{V_0} \right) \tag{1.9}$$

If oscillations are small, the argument of the Bessel function is small, and power-series expansion of $J_1(x)$ can be used:

$$J_1(x) = \frac{x}{2} - \frac{x^2}{16} + \frac{x^4}{384} \tag{1.10}$$

or, as $x \to 0$,

$$J_1(x) = \frac{x}{2} \tag{1.11}$$

Assuming that the cavities are tightly coupled and are at resonance, $V_1 = V_2$, Eq. (1.9) becomes

$$I_0 = \frac{V_0}{\pi N R} = \frac{1}{\pi N} \frac{V_0}{R} \tag{1.12}$$

This value of the current is called the *starting current*. Oscillations cannot exist if the d-c current is smaller than this value. To insure stable operation in the laboratory, the operating current should be several times the starting current. Its value can be readily found experimentally for a given set of load conditions by temperature-limiting the cathode (or by using grid bias if it is available). Most of the uncertain points in the bunching theory are unimportant when oscillations are very weak, making an adequate determination of the value of starting current a relatively simple matter.

d. *The Operating Modes of an Oscillator.* Oscillation conditions also require that the phase conditions in the feedback path be correctly adjusted. The electrons can travel in the drift space for a number of cycles. The exact transit time depends upon both the distance l and voltage V_0; hence, there are several values of beam voltage at which the phase conditions are satisfied. The exact dependence of such *modes* will be found to be a function of the strength of coupling between the two cavities. This is due to the fact that the electric phase shift through a coupled circuit depends upon the coupling coefficient.

Figure 1.8 shows the equivalent circuit of the klystron. The hypothetical tube represents the amplifying action of the klystron, the two resonant circuits represent the cavity resonators, and the coupling is symbolic of many possible methods of transferring energy from one cavity to another. Oscillations can take place when the phase shift around the complete loop is equal to some multiple of 2π. In the klystron there are a number of effects that determine the phase shift. The important ones, measured in radians, are:

1. The delay due to the transit time of electrons from one gap to the other, τ_1

2. The length of the coupling line and the relative tuning of the two cavities, ϕ

There are other effects as well, such as dependence of phase angle upon the strength of oscillations; these and other higher-order effects will be mentioned in connection with anomalies of operation in Sec. 1.6h. If the klystron is to oscillate, the relation

$$\tau + \phi = 2\pi n - \frac{\pi}{2} = 2\pi \left(n - \frac{1}{4} \right) \tag{1.13}$$

must be satisfied in which n is an integer greater than 1.* In practice, n is often found to be between 1 and 10.

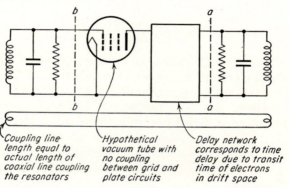

Coupling line length equal to actual length of coaxial line coupling the resonators

Hypothetical vacuum tube with no coupling between grid and plate circuits

Delay network corresponds to time delay due to transit time of electrons in drift space

FIG. 1.8. Equivalent circuit of the two-cavity klystron oscillator.

The dependence of phase shift upon the degree of coupling for this equivalent circuit is shown in Fig. 1.9 where both the relative output and phase shift are plotted as a function of frequency for two arbitrary degrees of coupling. When the coupling is weak, the amplitude and phase behave as shown by solid curves. If the coupling is higher than critical, there are two peaks in the amplitude response. Oscillations can exist only at or near the peaks of these amplitude curves. The phase shift is, of course, different at the two peaks requiring different values of transit time to satisfy the condition of Eq. (1.13). The separation of these peaks depends upon the strength of coupling; the manufacturer always adjusts the coupling to be very tight so that it will be strong enough under all possible conditions of loading. Under typical conditions, the separation of the peaks is very pronounced. Tuning of the cavities and adjustment of the feedback line can have pronounced effect on the relative amplitudes of the two peaks, as well as upon their separation.

* The fraction $\pi/2$ appears on the right-hand side of Eq. (1.13) because the bunch forms around the electron whose velocity is not changed by the buncher gap. At a later time the bunch passes through the output gap when the field there is maximum and retarding. Therefore, the bunched current can be said to be 90° out of phase with the buncher voltage that causes it. Similar phenomena occur in the reflex klystron and the traveling-wave tube. See Secs. 1.6d and 1.8, respectively.

If oscillations of the circuit in Fig. 1.8 are found at a given voltage or mode, then another corresponding mode can be found at a different voltage at which the transit time through the drift space of the klystron differs by n whole cycles. The transit time through the drift space of length l is equal to l/u_0 where u_0 is the velocity of unmodulated electrons. Measured in radians the transit time becomes

$$\tau = 2\pi \frac{l}{u_0} f = \frac{2\pi l}{\lambda} \frac{1}{\sqrt{V_0/250{,}000}} \tag{1.14}$$

in which V_0 is measured in volts. Eq. (1.13) thus becomes

$$\frac{500}{\sqrt{V_0}} = \frac{\lambda}{l}\left(n - \frac{1}{4} - \frac{\phi}{2\pi}\right) \tag{1.15}$$

This equation shows that if everything that controls the circuit phase conditions between the input and output gaps is left fixed (i.e., the value

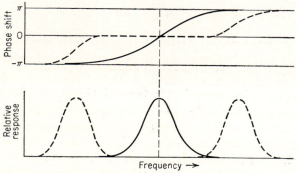

Fig. 1.9. Relative response and phase shift of a coupled circuit shown in Fig. 1.8 between points a-a and b-b (with the amplifier removed).

of ϕ remains constant) and the beam voltage alone is varied, then oscillation maxima will occur at discrete values of voltage which correspond to changes by integers in transit time n. If n is plotted as function of $500/\sqrt{V_0}$, a straight line should result with a slope equal to λ/l. Figure 1.10 shows a plot of output of a 10-cm two-cavity klystron oscillator, 3K21, as a function of voltage V_0. Each region of oscillation, corresponding to a certain value of n, consists of two humps. The two humps of a given pair correspond to the two response peaks of an overcoupled circuit as shown in Fig. 1.9. Since they have different values of ϕ, the output maxima occur at slightly different values of voltage. Starting from the right in Fig. 1.10, each pair of humps has a value of n which increases by integers of 1 progressively to the left. The left half of the sequential pairs has identical values of ϕ. The voltages corresponding to the two sets of ϕ are plotted in Fig. 1.11.

  e. Frequency Stability and Frequency Modulation. Most measurements in the microwave region require the frequency of the oscillator to be stable. There are two kinds of stability of interest, short-time and long-time. The short-time stability depends upon things that can vary rapidly, such as the applied potentials. The long-time stability depends upon the temperature variations of the tube. The latter, in themselves, can be caused by changes in potentials because of changes in heating. This can be especially serious if the changes in potentials change the distribution of current among the various tube parts. The principal reason

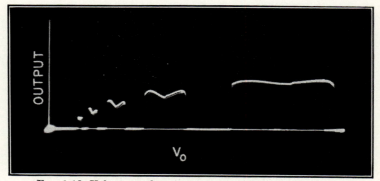

FIG. 1.10. Voltage modes of a two-cavity klystron oscillator.

for drift in frequency of a klystron over a long period, however, is due to the changes in the temperature of the surrounding medium. The actual change in frequency for a given change in temperature will depend upon the care in the design of the klystron, its cavities, and the tuning mechanism. Assuming that no crude mistakes have been made in the design and construction of the entire structure, satisfactory long-time stability can be obtained by sufficiently minimizing temperature fluctuations in the vicinity of the klystron. For most practical cases ordinary room conditions are satisfactory, but occasionally special arrangements are helpful, such as immersing the entire klystron into an oil bath.

  The short-time stability is of greater interest, because it determines the required stability of the applied voltages for a given case, and also because it is a measure of the ease with which the frequency can be modulated. The important question is the dependence of frequency upon the applied potential; in the two-cavity klystron this refers principally to the beam voltage.

  The purpose of the following material is to indicate approximately the expected variation of frequency with voltage and the dependence of *modulation* sensitivity upon parameters that are controllable in the laboratory. Some klystrons also have control grids which make it possible to change the current, leaving the voltage constant; in most klystrons, the current changes with applied voltage, as in a diode. The change in current at constant voltage also produces variations in frequency, but in a manner not easily predictable because of the susceptance effects due to

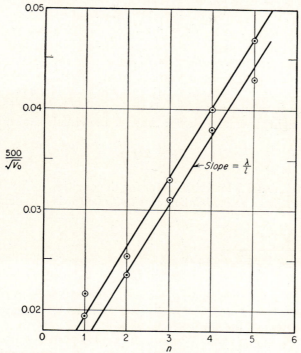

FIG. 1.11. Typical relation between the beam voltage V_0 and mode number n of a two-cavity klystron oscillator. The two curves correspond to different values of phase shift in the overcoupled circuit.

the secondary electrons. Variation of frequency with current is complicated and is best evaluated by experimental methods. Thus, the following analysis may not always predict the correct result, the principal deviations being due to the uncertain contributions of current modulation.

The phase conditions discussed in Sec. 1.5d must always be satisfied. If the voltage changes the transit time τ, the frequency of oscillation must change accordingly so that the resultant phase delay ϕ assumes a new value compensating for the changes in τ. From Eq. (1.13) it is plain that $d\tau = -d\phi$. This can be made more meaningful as follows: From Eq. (1.14)

$$\tau = \frac{2\pi l}{\lambda} \frac{1}{\sqrt{V_0/250{,}000}} \tag{1.16}$$

Differentiating,

$$d\tau = -\frac{1}{2}\tau\frac{dV_0}{V_0} \tag{1.17}$$

If τ is measured in cycles of oscillation frequency N, rather than in radians, $\tau = 2\pi N$, and

$$d\tau = -\pi N\frac{dV_0}{V_0} \tag{1.18a}$$

or

$$d\phi = \pi N\frac{dV_0}{V_0} \tag{1.18b}$$

It is now necessary to introduce the dependence of phase shift in the coupled circuits upon frequency. If the coupling between the two cavities is very tight, it can be shown that for the circuit shown in Fig. 1.8,

$$d\phi = 2Q\frac{df}{f} \tag{1.19}$$

where Q is the usual selectivity factor for the cavities. Combining these relations together, the *modulation sensitivity* factor is obtained:

$$\frac{df}{f} = \frac{\pi N}{2Q}\frac{dV_0}{V_0} \tag{1.20a}$$

or

$$\frac{df}{dV_0} = \frac{\pi Nf}{2QV_0} \tag{1.20b}$$

Although this relation is approximate and derived for a special type of coupling between the resonant cavities, more exact considerations do not change the result significantly.

Equation (1.20a) shows that for small changes in voltage the frequency changes linearly with voltage. The constant of proportionality depends upon operating conditions and can be changed. If, for instance, a stable source is required, the klystron should be operated at the highest possible voltage (making N small), and the highest possible Q (lightest loading of resonators). If one desires, on the other hand, to build a frequency-modulated source with a high modulation sensitivity, just the opposite would be done, using large N and low Q.

The filament current in the klystron can also change the frequency of oscillation. This is due to the magnetic field surrounding the filament which may cause current modulation. In some applications the filament must be operated from a d-c supply.

f. Amplitude Modulation of Klystron Oscillator. There is no simple way to produce linear amplitude modulation in a klystron oscillator. Even if some particular adjustment is found in which the output is approximately proportional to the input, serious frequency modulation will invariably result, as discussed in Sec. 1.5e. A complicated arrangement can be made to work as follows: The current can be grid modulated, resulting in amplitude modulation; accompanying this, there will be frequency modulation because of susceptance effect in the r-f gaps. The amount of such modulation can be determined experimentally. The frequency modulation can then be largely eliminated by simultaneous modulation of the beam voltage in the proper amount and phase. These adjustments are not easy to make and are critically dependent upon all operating conditions.

However, special types of modulation, such as square-wave or pulse, can be readily accomplished by inserting modulation voltage in series with the beam voltage. The modulating voltage should be adjusted so the tube is oscillating on one half-cycle but not the other. The proper biasing and modulating voltages can be obtained from a measurement of the mode characteristics of the type shown in Fig. 1.10. It should be noted that the square-wave modulation should be indeed square, because if the top is sloping, frequency modulation will take place. This will happen also if it takes an appreciable fraction of the modulating cycle for the voltage to change from the *off* to *on* position.

g. Klystron Amplifier. A klystron amplifier differs from the oscillator because its r-f driving power is obtained from a separate source. Many of the general characteristics of both are identical but there are some important differences. The klystron amplifier does not have operating modes and will amplify at any d-c voltage that happens to be convenient. The frequency of its output will be that of the source, and the applied voltages cannot vary the mean frequency of the carrier. If the applied beam voltage is made to change in magnitude with time, phase modulation will take place, since time of arrival (or phase) of the bunches at the second gap will be a function of the voltage.

Klystron amplifiers are used for various purposes. *Voltage* or *low-level* amplifiers are used to amplify weak signals to a higher level, and usually operate as linear devices. *Power* amplifiers are used to produce power and are usually operated at their maximum or saturation level. *Synchrodyne* amplifiers are used to change frequency, as discussed in Sec. 1.2. Currently available klystrons are not suitable for extremely low-level operations because of the relatively high inherent noise produced by shot effect. Nevertheless, there are applications in which the high gain of a klystron amplifier can be usefully exploited. For example, crystal-controlled microwave transmitters first generate the desired microwave frequency at a milliwatt level and then use klystron voltage amplifiers to bring the power level to the desired value. Only the last amplifier is driven to saturation.

A klystron amplifier may be used in the laboratory when (1) the power level of a given source is not high enough, (2) when it is desired to make the frequency of oscillation completely independent of load variations, and (3) when the frequency is to be shifted by synchrodyne method. If the first of these is the important consideration, the amplifier should be of the cascade type with three or more cavities, because of its high gain. If either of the last two applications happens to be important, either a simple klystron or a cascade amplifier can be used. In principle, a klystron amplifier isolates the load from the source because the output cavity of an amplifier receives its power from an electron beam which travels in one direction only so the load variations have no way of affecting the source directly. However, in some amplifiers secondary electrons from the collector return back through the klystron toward the cathode, making the above conclusion questionable.

The synchrodyne operation is useful in several different ways. Aside from its obvious application in merely shifting the frequency of the carrier by a predetermined value, it finds considerable use when changing the frequency of a microwave signal by small but precisely known amounts is desired. This may be of importance, for example, if tracing out the resonance curve of a very high Q circuit is required. If this is to be done, the beam voltage of the klystron amplifier can be modulated by an r-f voltage derived from a low-frequency standard signal generator. The second cavity of the klystron can then be tuned to the frequency of the first (or any other) sideband. Changing the frequency of the standard signal generator by known amounts will shift the frequency of the microwave signal by the same amount. The second cavity does not have to be retuned as long as frequency variations are not greater than its bandwidth.

h. Adjustment of Klystron Amplifiers. The klystron amplifier will operate properly if the following conditions are satisfied:

1. The cavities are tuned to proper frequencies.
2. The r-f voltage at the first gap is properly adjusted.

The tuning of the cavities is accomplished in the same way as it is done with the klystron oscillator. It should also be noted that there is no starting current for an amplifier. The power output of a klystron amplifier is given by $I_2{}^2R/2$, where I_2 is the r-f current in the bunched beam at the last gap. This equation is approximately correct as long as the gap voltage does not exceed the value $V_0 - V_1$, as discussed previously. The magnitude of the r-f current depends upon the bunching parameter as given in Eq. (1.3). For a given value of beam voltage, there will be a value of bunching voltage V_1 which will produce maximum current at the second gap, and, under the restrictions stated above, the maximum power. This happens when $x = 1.84$. Figures 1.12 and 1.13 show the typical dependence of output of a klystron amplifier upon the voltages V_1 and V_0. In the first of these, the beam voltage is constant and the r-f buncher voltage is varied. If it were not for second-order effects, this curve would be $[J_1(x)]^2$ vs. x^2.* Deviations from simple theory are of no special consequence in the laboratory. Figure 1.13 illus-

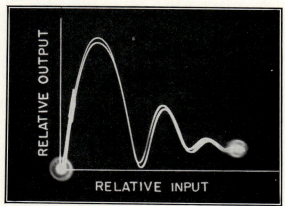

FIG. 1.12. Power output of a two-cavity klystron amplifier as a function of r-f drive power. The curve was obtained dynamically for 10-cm 3K21 klystron (the double trace should be disregarded).

trates the behavior of a klystron amplifier if V_1 is constant and the d-c beam voltage V_0 is varied. In this case, the resultant behavior is complicated by the fact that in the diode the d-c current varies as $V_0^{3/2}$. These curves, together with the simple theory, show how the operating potentials need to be adjusted for proper operation.

i. Modulation of Klystron Amplifiers. As contrasted with the oscillator, the average frequency of a klystron amplifier cannot be changed by modulation; but amplitude, phase, and pulse modulation can be accomplished.

If linearity is not important, amplitude modulation can be obtained by changing either the beam

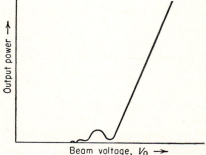

FIG. 1.13. Power output of a klystron amplifier as a function of beam voltage V_0 with constant drive power.

voltage or the current. If it is necessary to provide linear modulation, the d-c current should be varied. By rectifying the modulation envelope and returning the resultant modulation voltage by feedback

---

* Both quantities appear squared because curves shown were obtained with square-law response detectors.

methods into modulation circuits, it is possible to correct for various non-linearities. Pulse modulation can be produced by controlling either the voltage or the current.

Phase modulation can be obtained by varying the beam voltage as mentioned above. The transit time of electrons between the buncher and the catcher gaps determines the phase relationship between the two. If the voltage is changed, the phase changes will take place accordingly. If the voltage change is rapid, the phase modulation results in frequency modulation. The frequency deviation of the output will be proportional to the product of modulation voltage and modulation frequency, which is the familiar modulation index of phase modulation.

If F_m is the modulation frequency, and V_m is the modulation voltage placed in series with the beam voltage, the frequency deviation Δf may be found from the expression[1]

$$\Delta f = F_m V_m \left(\frac{\pi N \cos \omega_m t}{V_0} \right) \tag{1.21}$$

and the amplitude of the nth sideband is, from frequency-modulation theory,

$$A_n = J_n \left(\frac{\Delta f}{F_m} \right) \tag{1.22}$$

[1] This formula can be derived as follows, after the method presented by Harrison, op. cit. The transit time T of electrons from buncher gap to the catcher is $T = l/u_0$ where l is the drift-tube length and u_0 is the velocity of electrons at the first gap. Thus,

$$T = \frac{l}{\sqrt{\frac{2e}{m}} \, (V_0 + V_m \sin \omega_m t)} \tag{1.23}$$

Using binomial expansion, with $V_0 \gg V_m$, this becomes

$$T = T_0 - \frac{l}{2u_0} \frac{V_m}{V_0} \sin \omega_m t \tag{1.24}$$

where T_0 and u_0 are transit time and corresponding velocity of the unmodulated beam. Let τ be the phase angle of the bunched current at the catcher gap referred to the buncher gap, i.e., $\tau = \omega_1(t + T)$, where ω_1 is the angular frequency at the input gap. Hence,

$$\tau = \omega_1 t + \omega_1 T_0 - \frac{\omega_1 l}{2u_0} \frac{V_m}{V_0} \sin \omega_m t \tag{1.25}$$

But the output (angular) frequency ω_2 is merely $d\tau/dt$. Therefore,

$$\omega_2 = \omega_1 - \frac{\omega_1 \omega_m}{2u_0} l \frac{V_m}{V_0} \cos \omega_m t \tag{1.26}$$

Let $\Delta f = f_1 - f_2$,

$$\frac{\Delta f}{F_m} = \omega_1 \frac{l}{2u_0} \frac{V_m}{V_0} \cos \omega_m t \tag{1.27}$$

which leads to Eq. (1.21).

For example, the first sideband is maximum when $n = 1$, and $\Delta f/F_m = 1.84$. Hence, the peak modulation-frequency voltage, required to make the first sideband maximum, is

$$\frac{V_m}{V_0} = \frac{1.84}{\pi N} \tag{1.28}$$

In a typical case, N may be equal to 3, $V_0 = 2,500$. The required modulation voltage is then 500 volts peak. It is to be observed that the magnitude of the voltage required is independent of the frequency of the modulation voltage. The power required for modulation depends upon the dynamic impedance of the d-c beam at the operating point, and can be computed or measured when required.

1.6. The Reflex Klystron. *a. General Description.* A reflex klystron utilizes a single resonator for bunching and catching, and develops feed-

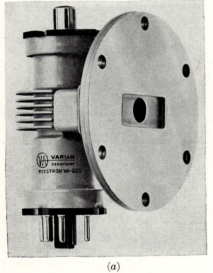

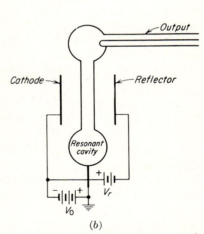

(a)   (b)

Fig. 1.14. (a) Photograph of a modern reflex klystron. (b) Basic power supply requirements for a reflex klystron. (*Photograph, courtesy of Varian Associates, Inc.*)

back by reflecting the electron beam so that it passes through the resonator a second time. The single resonant cavity makes it relatively easy to use and adjust. Principally for this reason, it is the most frequently used source of power in laboratory applications.

A photograph of a typical reflex tube is shown in Fig. 1.14a. The electrons are emitted from a cathode under the influence of the beam voltage V_0. A control grid is provided in some reflex klystrons, and determines the current for a given V_0. All of these elements are similar to the cathode structures of the multiresonant cavity klystron. The focused beam passes through the cavity into the retarding field between the reflector electrode and the resonant cavity. The reflector electrode is connected through a power supply to the cathode, the potential being so adjusted that the electrons are brought to rest, turned around, and passed through the cavity a second time. During the time the electrons spend in the reflection space, bunching occurs which is only slightly different from the bunching in the two-cavity klystron. Specific details of the bunching process and its consequences are described in the literature and will not be repeated here. It is assumed that the reader understands the first-order effects which govern the operation of the reflex klystron.

b. Operating Notes. Figure 1.14*b* shows the normal arrangement of operating potentials for a typical tube often used in the laboratory. Generally, when the power input to the klystron tube is below 10 watts, no special precautions are necessary. But when the power input is considerably in excess of 10 watts, the potentials should be applied in the following order: the filament power, the reflector voltage, the beam voltage, and then the grid voltage last. There are simple reasons for this order, and the user should understand them before attempting any changes. Under certain conditions it is possible to spoil the klystron if the order is reversed. If the power input exceeds a certain limit, forced air cooling is necessary, as recommended by the manufacturer.

The reflex klystron will oscillate when correct potentials are applied, provided that

1. The beam current is higher than the starting current. Stated differently, the loading due to the output circuits must not be too great. A way of adjusting the load at the tube terminals may have to be provided.

2. The reflector voltage V_r must be chosen so that the feedback conditions are satisfied.

3. The resonant cavity must be adjusted within the wavelength range as specified by the manufacturer.

The last of these points needs further discussion. If the reflex klystron is of the type in which the resonant frequency of the cavity is changed by changing the grid (gap) spacing, the klystron can fail to oscillate if the gap is either too narrow or too wide, as discussed in Sec. 1.3. With the cavity tuned to approximately the right wavelength, the proper potentials are applied. The reflector voltage is then varied; oscillations can be detected with the aid of the crystal detector connected to the tube, or by merely observing changes in the *beam* current. It will be found that the beam current changes in most tubes when the tube oscillates. Usually the oscillations result in the *increase* of total beam current.

c. Voltage or Operating Modes. For a given beam voltage, oscillations will be observed at several regions within the total range of the reflector voltage. Each region is known as the *reflector voltage mode*, and oscillation does not take place between such modes. Similar voltage modes occur when the beam voltage is varied for a given reflector voltage. The existence of these modes is due to the fact that the transit time in the reflection space is determined by the beam voltage and the reflector voltage. The transit time, in order to allow oscillations to exist, must satisfy the relation

$$fT_0 = n - \tfrac{1}{4} \tag{1.29}$$

where f is the frequency of oscillation, n is a positive integer greater than zero and T_0 is the transit time. This results from the requirement that

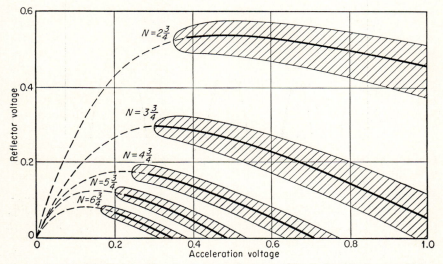

FIG. 1.15. Hypothetical family of voltage mode curves for a reflex klystron oscillator. Shaded areas indicate the region of oscillations. Solid curves show the combination of voltages required to produce maximum power output. Oscillations do not occur at low-beam voltages because of insufficient current.

the electrons must return to the cavity when the field there is retarding. If the klystron is tuned by changing the dimensions of the cavity, without readjusting the potentials, the electrons may return at a time when the cavity will not have a sufficiently strong r-f field to extract much energy from the passing bunch of electrons. Therefore, as tuning is varied, oscillations cannot exist continuously without readjusting the applied potentials.

In Fig. 1.15, the combination of potentials which allows the tube to oscillate at maximum strength is shown for a typical klystron. Figure 1.16 shows the variation of output as a function of reflector voltage for a given frequency and beam voltage. It is a vertical cross section of Fig.

1.15.   Figure 1.16 shows the variations of frequency with reflector voltage.   Further discussion of these points will be given below.

d. First-order Theory of the Reflex Klystron.   To understand the behavior of the reflex klystron as a laboratory oscillator, it is well to understand at least semiqualitatively the more important relationships between the various parameters which determine the operation of the

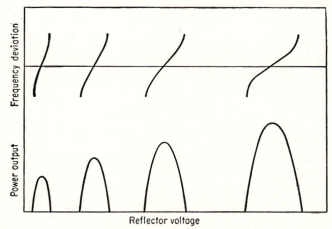

FIG. 1.16. Variation of power output and frequency with reflector voltage at a fixed beam voltage.

oscillator.   It is not necessary to be exact or to include all of the known effects in order to obtain a fairly complete picture of what happens inside the tube.   The analysis can be simplified if the following effects are neglected:

1. Space-charge effects, both of the d-c variety in the reflection space, and the debunching forces
2. Multiple-transit effects
3. Secondary electrons between the grids of the cavity
4. Large "signal" effects, i.e., effects which take place when r-f voltage across the gap is not small compared to V_0

Neglecting these factors may not be justified in practice, but an understanding of the simplified theory demonstrates some of the design problems encountered in building the tube, and allows one to make generalizations regarding possible applications in the laboratory.   The consequences of these approximations are sometimes important as, for example, in connection with *hysteresis*, which will be described in Sec. 1.6*h*.

From equations of motion of electrons in a retarding field, the equation relating the transit time T_0 (in seconds) to the electrode potentials and the reflector spacing S_0 may be found.   It is

$$T_0 = \frac{4S_0(mV_0/2e)^{\frac{1}{2}}}{V_0 + V_r} \qquad (1.30)$$

where m and e are the mass and charge of the electron, respectively.   A convenient and more physically significant quantity is the transit time measured in number of oscillation cycles N.   Then

$$N = fT_0 \qquad (1.31)$$

It is obvious that N cannot assume arbitrary values if the tube is to oscillate.   Consider the situation shown in Fig. 1.17.   Analysis of the

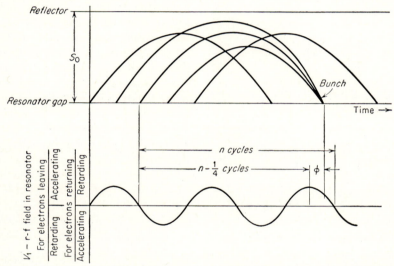

FIG. 1.17. Time-position diagram illustrating the bunching process in a reflex klystron.

bunching process shows that those electrons which pass through the cavity when the field is zero *and is changing from accelerating to retarding* become the center of the bunch.   If this bunch of electrons is to give up the maximum possible energy to the field in the cavity, it must return to the cavity when the field there is maximum, and is retarding with respect to the returning electrons.   This means that

$$N = n - \frac{1}{4} \qquad (1.32)$$

where N is the number of cycles of transit time and n is a positive integer greater than zero.   Thus, a reflex klystron can oscillate with a transit time of $\frac{3}{4}$, $1\frac{3}{4}$, $2\frac{3}{4}$, etc., cycles.   If the transit time is different from these values, the klystron can still oscillate, but at a smaller amplitude;

the range of transit times over which oscillations can take place will be discussed below.

A family of curves can be plotted from Eq. (1.30) which show how the reflector voltage has to be varied when the beam voltage is changed for a number of possible values of N, as shown in Fig. 1.15.

A kinematic analysis of the bunching process shows that the harmonic current content of the bunched beam is identical with the situation found in the two-resonant cavity klystron. The r-f current is given by

$$I_2 = I_0[1 + 2J_1(x) \sin (\omega t_2 - 2\pi N) + \cdot \cdot \cdot] \qquad (1.33)$$

The mechanism of oscillation can be understood by examining the interaction between the circuit and the bunched beam. Consider the

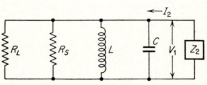

FIG. 1.18. Equivalent circuit of a reflex klystron oscillator.

equivalent circuit of the reflex klystron shown in Fig. 1.18. L, C, R_s represent the equivalent inductance, capacitance, and shunt resistance of the cavity; R_L is the load resistance due to the useful load. If the klystron is oscillating, then V_1 will exist across this equivalent circuit; and if V_1 exists across C, then the bunching theory predicts that r-f current I_2 will flow into the circuit. The ratio V_1/I_2 can be computed; this represents an equivalent impedance due to the bunching action of the klystron. Let it be called Z_2. By analyzing the nature of this fictitious impedance as a function of d-c voltages and currents, it is possible to predict the behavior of the equivalent circuit. This establishes a simple relationship between the various parameters in an oscillating klystron. The impedance Z_2 is often referred to as an *electronic impedance* because it relates to quantities which are determined by the electronic process. The combination of the electronic impedance in parallel with the *circuit* impedance, i.e., the resonant impedance of L, C, and R_s, determines the complete energy exchange between the cavity and the beam. Under steady-state conditions the electronic impedance must be equal in magnitude and opposite in sign to the circuit impedance.

The impedance Z_2 is a complex quantity, as can be seen from the fact that the transit time in the tube can assume any value. Referring to Fig. 1.17, the bunches arrive at an electrical angle ϕ with respect to the peak of the r-f (retarding) voltage. Hence,

$$Z_2 = - \frac{V_1}{2I_0J_1(x)(\cos \phi - j \sin \phi)} \qquad (1.34)$$

The real and imaginary parts of Z_2 expressed in the shunt form are plotted in Fig. 1.19 as a function of ϕ. For ϕ between $-\pi/2$ and $\pi/2$, the real shunt component of Z_2 is negative, since in this region the klystron is generating power as the bunches are being slowed down. In the shaded regions of Fig. 1.19 the real shunt component of Z_2 is positive; it corresponds to the phase angles at which the electron bunches are accelerated, thus showing that the tube cannot generate power. The klystron can oscillate if the power generated by the negative resistance is equal to (or greater than) the power lost. The values of ϕ for which $-Z_2$ (real) $< R_sR_L/(R_s + R_L)$ determine the region in which the klystron can oscillate.

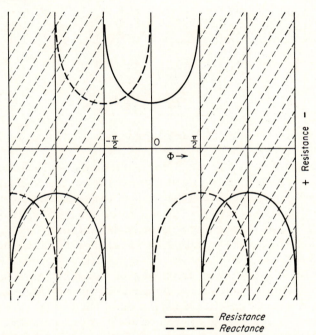

Resistance
Reactance

FIG. 1.19. Real and imaginary components of the electronic impedance Z_2 expressed in the shunt form.

The reactive part of Z_2 is also shown in Fig. 1.19. It shows that if $\phi = 0$, i.e., the electron bunch arrives in phase with the r-f voltage in the cavity, the oscillation will take place at the natural resonant frequency of the cavity. But at other values of ϕ, there will be a reactive component of Z_2, which will change the net capacity of the cavity and will shift the frequency of oscillation. The amount of this shift can be estimated by comparing the magnitude of the reactive component of Z_2 with the reactance of the cavity gap. (For approximate results, the value of C can be obtained from the parallel-plate capacitor formula, using the area and spacing of the r-f gap.)

Some immediate conclusions can be drawn from the above results in predicting the important characteristics of the reflex klystron. These are described in the next sections.

e. Starting Current. The minimum current at which a reflex klystron will oscillate for any given combination of other variables is known as the *starting current.* Of particular interest is the value of starting current at no load which can be found in the following manner. The minimum value of the negative resistance developed by the beam occurs when $\phi = 0$, being equal to $V_1/2I_0J_1(x)$. The oscillations can exist if the d-c current I_0 is adjusted to make this equal to the value of shunt resistance of the cavity R_s. The oscillations will be very weak, and, therefore, x will be very small. Under these conditions, from Eq. (1.10), $x \to 0$ and

$$J_1(x) = \frac{x}{2} \tag{1.35}$$

and

$$R_s = \frac{V_1}{2I_0J_1(x)} \tag{1.36}$$

or

$$(I_0)_{\text{starting}} = \frac{V_0}{R_s} \frac{1}{\pi N} \tag{1.37}$$

A typical set of operating conditions might be $V_0 = 300$ volts, $N = 4\frac{3}{4}$ cycles, $R_s = 100,000$. The starting current from Eq. (1.37) is 0.2 ma. If this tube is loaded so that 90 per cent of the generated power appears in the load and 10 per cent of it is lost in the resonant cavity, then $R_{sL} = 10,000$ and the starting current is about 2 ma. Stable operation requires that the actual operating current be several times this value, perhaps 10 ma.

f. Electrical Tuning. The frequency of the reflex klystron can be changed by causing the electron bunch to arrive at the gap when the field there is retarding, but not maximum. The frequency change can be estimated by comparing the values of the reactive part of the beam impedance with the reactance of the lumped capacity of the cavity. A simple calculation can be made for a particular situation when the angle of arrival ϕ is such that the negative resistance developed by the beam just supplies the necessary losses to maintain oscillations, i.e., when the strength of oscillations is approaching zero. This happens when the *loaded cavity impedance R_{sL}* equals the resistive component of Z_2, that is, if

$$R_{sL} = \frac{V_1}{2I_0J_1(x)\cos\phi} \tag{1.38}$$

When $V_1 \to 0$, $x \to 0$, and

$$R_{sL} = \frac{V_0}{I_0} \frac{1}{\pi N \cos\phi} \tag{1.39}$$

which means that the oscillations will just begin at

$$\phi = \cos^{-1} \frac{R_0}{\pi N R_{sL}} \tag{1.40}$$

The magnitude of the reactive component at this value of ϕ can be computed from the imaginary part of Z_2, which, under above assumptions, becomes $V_0/I_0\pi N \sin \phi$. This, when combined with the reactance of C, determines the new operating frequency. The total change in frequency from one end of the mode to the other is called *electrical tuning* (between zero-power points).

The dependence of frequency of oscillation upon the reflector voltage can be determined as follows. Equation (1.38) states that the negative resistance developed by the beam must assume a value equal to the loaded shunt resistance of the cavity. The phase angle ϕ is determined by the applied potentials. Thus, Eq. (1.38), expressing the principle of conservation of power, determines the value of $V_1/J_1(x)$. The beam susceptance is obtained from the imaginary part of Eq. (1.34). It is

$$\frac{2I_0J_1(x)}{V_1} \sin \phi = \frac{\sin \phi}{R_{sL} \cos \phi} \tag{1.41}$$

$$= \frac{\tan \phi}{R_{sL}} \tag{1.42}$$

This beam susceptance, when added to the circuit susceptance, must determine the frequency of oscillation. The summation of all susceptance terms is given by

$$-\frac{1}{\omega L} + \omega C + \frac{\tan \phi}{R_{sL}} = 0 \tag{1.43}$$

Rearranging terms, and making use of conventional approximations as used in the analysis of resonant circuits, this becomes,

$$\frac{\Delta f}{f} = \frac{1}{2Q_L} \tan \phi \tag{1.44}$$

where Q_L is the loaded Q of the cavity, and Δf is the frequency change from resonance. This equation makes it possible to predict the dependence of frequency upon the loaded Q of the cavity and the reflector voltage. The latter does not appear implicitly, but its relation to transit time ϕ can be evaluated with the aid of Eq. (1.30). It is necessary to remember that the range of phase angles over which oscillations can take place must be calculated separately using Eq. (1.40).

The variation of frequency and power output with reflector voltage is plotted in Fig. 1.20 for a typical situation for three values of load imped-

ance.   A number of interesting conclusions can be drawn from this
illustration.   The slope of the linear portion of the frequency curve is
inversely proportional to Q_L, as is expected from Eq. (1.44).   *Increasing
Q_L by decreasing the load does not decrease the electronic-tuning bandwidth;* higher Q_L increases the shunt resistance, causing the bunching

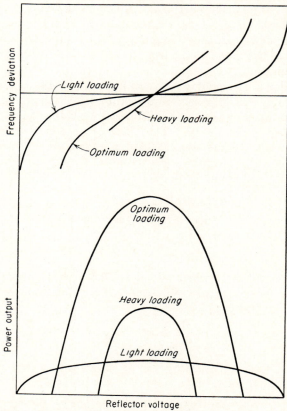

Fig. 1.20. Hypothetical curves showing the variation of output and frequency of a
reflex klystron oscillator with reflector voltage.   (*Adopted by permission from "Klystron Tubes," by A. E. Harrison.   Copyright, 1947.   McGraw-Hill Book Company, Inc.,
New York.*)

voltage to increase, and permits the phase angle to vary over a larger
range.   The bandwidth between zero-output points actually increases as
the loading is decreased; the bandwidth between half-power points is
decreased only slightly.   Decreased loading causes the amplitude characteristic to become more uniform over a large range of voltage, but the
frequency-deviation curve becomes nonlinear.

Some useful generalizations can now be made regarding the operation of the laboratory oscillator.   If one wishes the greatest stability, i.e., to make residual voltage changes perturb the frequency as little as possible, one should select conditions causing the reactance component developed by changes in ϕ to be as small as possible.   Examination of Eqs. (1.42) and (1.44) shows that this occurs when the added reactance is highest (smallest detuning effect).   This happens when the klystron is operated at high-beam voltage, smallest possible current, and short transit time, i.e., high reflector voltage.   On the other hand, if one desires to use the klystron as a frequency-modulated source with high modulation sensitivity, then just the inverse would be done.

  g. Power Output and Efficiency of a Reflex Klystron.   If the d-c current is increased above the starting current, the output will increase, but not in a simple way.   The average power P_2 delivered by the beam into the cavity is given by $\frac{1}{2}$ (peak cavity voltage $\times$ peak current), or

$$P_2 = \frac{1}{2}V_1[2I_0J_1(x)\cos\phi] = V_1I_0J_1(x)\cos\phi \qquad (1.45)$$

The generated power P_2 divides between the cavity and the useful load. The power delivered to the load is then

$$P_L = \frac{R_s}{R_L + R_s}P_2 \qquad (1.46)$$

$$= \frac{R_s}{R_L + R_s}V_1I_0J_1(x)\cos\phi \qquad (1.47)$$

$$= V_0I_0\frac{R_s}{R_s + R_L}\frac{\cos\phi}{\pi N}xJ_1(x) \qquad (1.48)$$

The efficiency η is defined as

$$\eta = \frac{P_L}{V_0I_0} \qquad (1.49)$$

or

$$\eta = \frac{R_s}{R_s + R_L}\frac{\cos\phi}{\pi N}xJ_1(x) \qquad (1.50)$$

The efficiency can be plotted as a universal curve shown in Fig. 1.21. The variation of efficiency (or output) as a function of any of the parameters can be obtained from this curve.   The abscissa in Fig. 1.21 is shown in two forms: in terms of the tube parameters, and also in terms of $x/2J_1(x)$.   The latter form is a quantity which is a measure of saturation effect in the klystron at high input levels.

  The maximum theoretical efficiency of a reflex klystron can be obtained from Fig. 1.21.   If the reflector voltage is adjusted for maximum output ($\phi = 0$), and most of the power is delivered to the load, then

$$\eta_{max} = \frac{1.25}{\pi N} \qquad (1.51)$$

This means that the efficiency should be inversely proportional to N; with $N = 1 + \frac{3}{4}$, efficiency reaches 23 per cent. Actually, there are many approximations in the above theory so that Eq. (1.51) is not valid for small values of N. In practice, efficiencies as high as 10 to 15 per cent have been observed, although the usual values are appreciably lower. Efficiency and output are found to vary approximately as $1/N$.

   h. Hysteresis. In some important respects, the behavior of the reflex klystron is found to differ markedly from the simple predictions of the first-order theory.[1] The most important of these from the laboratory viewpoint is found to occur when either the power output or the frequency is varied by means of electrode potentials. For example, the plots of reflector voltage modes may have a different appearance depending upon the direction in which the reflector voltage is changed in obtaining the given characteristic. The term *hysteresis* is often used to describe the observed anomalies, such as multiple dependence of output and frequency upon the applied voltages. Although hysteresis can occur with respect to any of the independent variables in a klystron (including variation in the load impedance) this section will be concerned with the most frequent types due to electronic phenomena.

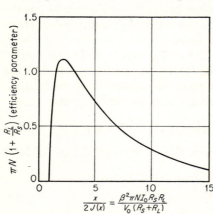

FIG. 1.21. Universal curve showing variation of efficiency of a reflex klystron as a function of operating parameters. *(Adopted by permission from "Klystron Tubes," by A. E. Harrison. Copyright, 1947. McGraw-Hill Book Company, Inc., New York.)*

   Hysteresis effects can sometimes be many and varied. They can be very pronounced, extending to the center of the operating mode, or even beyond, occurring several times in steps in one mode. Amplitude discontinuities can be accompanied by jumps in frequency. In extreme cases, the oscillator can become next to useless. In milder forms, hysteresis can occur near the side of the mode so that it may be of little or no concern to the user. At other times even minor perturbing effects can be of importance, as they can change the symmetrical appearance

   [1] Hamilton, *op. cit.*, pp. 384–440; J. R. Pierce and W. G. Shepherd, Reflex Oscillators, *Bell System Tech. J.*, vol. 26, pp. 460–681, July, 1947 (the same material appears in "Radar Systems and Components," pp. 490–709, D. Van Nostrand Company, Inc., Princeton, N.J., 1949); T. Moreno and R. L. Jepsen, Hysteresis in Klystron Oscillators, *Proc. IRE*, vol. 43, no. 3, March, 1955.

of a voltage mode, causing maximum power output to occur at a different voltage from that of the point of zero electrical tuning. This can be detrimental if the oscillator is to be used as a frequency-modulated source with linear frequency deviation.

Among the various electronic phenomena which can cause hysteresis are the following:

1. The dependence of the phase of bunched current upon r-f gap voltage. This phase shift is nearly always neglected in discussions based upon the first-order theory.

2. The variation of the magnitude of electronic impedance Z_2 with voltage in the low-order modes.

3. The presence of multiple-transit electrons, i.e., those electrons which can make more than one round trip between the cathode and the r-f gap. This effect causes contribution of r-f current to the gap that is not predictable by first-order theory.

4. Variation of the gap-coupling coefficient due to different distribution of electrons in oscillating and nonoscillating conditions.

The first of these can cause hysteresis in the following manner: The first-order bunching theory, as illustrated in Fig. 1.17, assumes that the time of arrival of bunches at the r-f gap is determined solely by the d-c transit-time conditions in the reflection space and is independent of the magnitude of the r-f gap voltage. This is not true in general, as the transit time of the bunch will be found to be affected by the strength of oscillations.[1] The first-order theory, neglecting the contribution to the phase shift due to this effect, predicts that the oscillations will stop at a value of reflector voltage at which the electronic resistance can no longer remain equal to the circuit resistance. The same condition must be satisfied in the large-signal case, except that the value of the reflector voltage at which this happens will be different because of the contribution of extra phase shift caused by the bunching process itself. If the voltage mode is approached from the nonoscillating direction, the extra phase shift will not be present and the klystron will begin to oscillate at

[1] This can be due to a number of effects. Second-order bunching theory (including higher-order terms in binomial expansion relating transit time of electrons and r-f voltage V_1) makes the prediction that the time of arrival of an electron bunch at the catching gap will depend upon the magnitude of the bunching voltage. The time of arrival of the bunch also depends upon the exact field distribution in the bunching space. For example, space-charge conditions in the reflection space will also affect the phase shift. This is principally due to the fact that the fast electrons are reflected in the region where space charge is small, while the slow electrons are reflected in regions of excessive space charge. This can be understood by examining the condition of space charge in the nonoscillating condition. Beyond the point of reflection, there is no space charge; the fast electrons in the oscillating condition penetrate into this region, tending to cause the effect mentioned.

the value of reflector voltage predicted by the small-signal theory.[1] The presence of phase shift will also make the mode appear asymmetrical with respect to the point of maximum power output. A typical reflector mode disturbed in this manner is shown in Fig. 1.23.

[1] The hysteresis phenomenon can be explained more completely as follows. Figure 1.22a shows the electronic impedance Z_2 as given by Eq. (1.34), plotted in the vector form. The magnitude of the electronic admittance is determined by the various factors shown in Eq. (1.34); however, according to the simple theory the phase angle is not affected by the magnitude of oscillations. As the reflector voltage is varied, the phase angle ϕ changes so that the tip of the electronic-admittance locus traces out

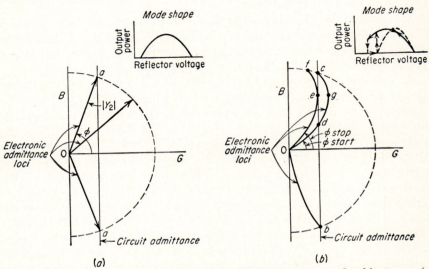

FIG. 1.22. Effect of phase shift on electronic admittance of a reflex klystron.   (a) Vector form of electronic admittance under idealized conditions; (b) curvature in electronic-admittance locus due to the presence of amplitude-sensitive phase shift causes hysteresis. (By permission from Hysteresis in Klystron Oscillators, by T. Moreno and R. L. Jepsen, Proc. IRE, vol. 34, no. 3, March, 1955.)

the dashed semicircle shown. The circuit admittance is represented in Fig. 1.22a by a vertical line. The klystron may oscillate between points a-a, i.e., when the magnitude of the electronic conductance exceeds the conductance of the circuit. Under the conditions shown in Fig. 1.22a, the mode shape is symmetrical, as shown in the inset.

According to the more complete theory, the phase angle of the electronic admittance depends upon the magnitude of oscillations. The resultant electronic-admittance loci will appear as shown in Fig. 1.22b. The loci are curved in a manner depending upon the cause of the phase shift, as mentioned above. Examination of Fig. 1.22b shows that rotation of the curved electronic-admittance locus in the clockwise and counterclockwise directions will produce different effects. Under nonoscillating conditions the admittance vector is located along the dashed circle at points f, c, b. Thus, clockwise rotation of point f will result in oscillation when it reaches position c. Strong

The second reason for mode asymmetry, closely related to the first, can exist in cases where very short transit time is used in the reflection space. In the small-signal theory, the electronic admittance is computed by taking the ratio of the r-f bunched current and the r-f voltage that causes it. The phase of the current is computed from the time of arrival of the middle of the bunch to the r-f gap. This calculation neglects the fact that the bunching parameter x also contains the transit time through the variable N. Thus, if the total transit time is short, the phase shift over the voltage mode can cause an appreciable fractional change in the transit time N, making the magnitude of the electronic impedance Z_2 vary with reflector voltage. This causes mode asymmetry in the manner discussed above. This effect is not generally important because very low values of N are not often used.

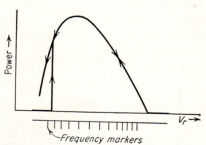

FIG. 1.23. Hysteresis effects in the reflex klystron caused by phase-shift phenomenon. Note characteristic discontinuity in output at one side of the mode only. The lower line shows evenly spaced frequency markers; the region of frequency linearity is displaced with respect to maximum power output. (*Adopted by permission from "Klystrons and Microwave Triodes," by D. R. Hamilton, J. K. Knipp, and J. B. H. Kuper. Copyright, 1948. McGraw-Hill Book Company, Inc., New York.*)

The third type of mode asymmetry and hysteresis is due to the presence of multiple-transit electrons. These pass through the r-f gap in the form of the desired r-f bunch, penetrate into the cathode region, and return to the cavity for another round trip. Some of the electrons can oscillate between the cathode and the reflector several times. It is plain that these electrons will contribute to the total r-f current at the gap, but in an unpredictable way, since they are subjected to very complicated bunching and defocusing forces. Even though the number of electrons participating in the multiple-transit process may be small, often a sufficient number remain to modify the simple first-order theory in a profound manner. Since the bunching time for the multiple-transit electrons may be quite large, only a moderate change in operating potentials

---

oscillations are caused immediately, and the admittance vector jumps from c to d. Under oscillating conditions, counterclockwise rotation of the impedance vector gradually shifts the admittance vector to some point such as g. Further rotation of point g to position e abruptly stops oscillations, returning the admittance vector to f. Thus, hysteresis with two discontinuities occurs only on *one* side of the mode. It can also be shown that an increase in the load conductance causes hysteresis discontinuities to be displaced toward the edge of the mode. The shape of the mode caused by the phase-shift type of hysteresis is indicated in the inset of Fig. 1.22b.

is required to produce complete reversal in phase of the r-f current contributed by the multiple-transit current. Thus, variation of the reflector voltage within a given mode can cause several reversals in phase in the multiple-transit current. As a result, the multiple-transit electrons can either reinforce or decrease the primary current at several points within a given mode. The appearance of a mode in the presence of multiple-transit electrons can become highly irregular, resulting in severe discontinuities in power output. An extreme case of hysteresis due to multiple transit is illustrated in Fig. 1.24. Two photographs of oscilloscope patterns are shown displaying the output of a reflex klystron as a

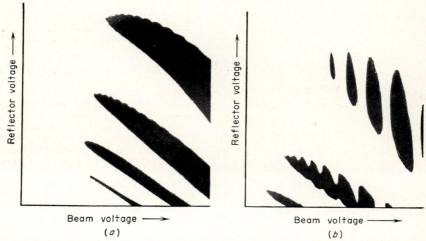

FIG. 1.24. Oscillographically obtained voltage-mode diagram showing multiple transit effects in a reflex klystron (cf. Fig. 1.15). Dark regions correspond to oscillating conditions. (a) Nearly ideal mode pattern, but note slight scalloping at the edge of the mode; (b) an extreme case of multiple-transit hysteresis in which oscillation is completely stopped within the upper mode.

function of the beam and reflector voltages. Figure 1.24a shows a nearly normal mode pattern. In Fig. 1.24b, multiple-transit electrons are found in sufficient number to completely break up the normal appearance of the modes; the effect is especially severe at the higher voltages.

Another cause for hysteresis may be due to the difference in magnitude of the electronic admittance under the oscillating and nonoscillating conditions. It is usually found that the presence of bunching causes transverse spreading of the beam, which can increase the beam coupling coefficient β. Alternatively, the spreading can decrease the space-charge density and, therefore, reduce the debunching effects. The reduction in space-charge density also can favorably affect the focusing of the returning beam. Any of these effects would tend to increase the magnitude of the r-f current at the gap and would permit the tube to oscillate over a wider range of phase angle than in the nonoscillating condition. This phenomenon may occur in two-cavity klystrons as well as in reflex tubes. A typical mode pattern illustrating this effect for a two-cavity klystron is shown in Fig. 1.25. It is characterized by discontinuities on both sides of the mode, and is aggravated by heavy loading (large load conductance).

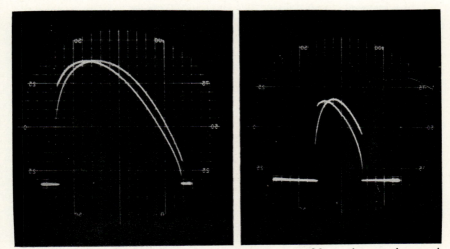

FIG. 1.25. Hysteresis effects in a two-cavity klystron caused by an increase in magnitude of electronic conductance under oscillating conditions. Curves show relative output as a function of beam voltage. (*Oscillographs, courtesy of Varian Associates, Inc.*)

The most serious type of hysteresis occurs because of multiple-transit electrons. Most modern tubes are constructed to minimize their presence. The remaining forms of hysteresis are further improved by operating with modes with large transit times, which result in small r-f signals and make the tube operation resemble more closely the first-order theory.

i. Long-line Effects.[1] In the preceding section a source of hysteresis was described which was caused by complicated electronic phenomena taking place inside the tube. Another source of hysteresis found to occur with reflex klystron oscillators is due to the variation of the load impedance with frequency. In some applications it may be necessary to supply power to a load which is highly resonant. In another common situation, a long transmission line may be present between the tube and an imperfectly terminated load. The apparent magnitude of the impedance as seen by the oscillator will be dependent not only upon the load but also upon the rate of change of impedance with frequency and will be strongly affected by the presence of long lines. Even when the combined

[1] Pierce and Shepherd, *op. cit.*, pp. 540–564.

effect of a mismatch and a long line is not serious enough to produce hysteresis effects, it can still seriously affect the frequency-deviation characteristic of the oscillator. While these problems are too complicated to discuss in greater detail, it should be pointed out that the best way to avoid them is to place the oscillator close to the load. If this is impossible, it is advisable to provide resistive padding or other forms of isolation between the oscillator and the long line as described in Sec. 1.10.

j. Mode Interference.[1] Special problems are encountered in designing resonant cavities for reflex klystron tubes for tuning over a wide frequency range. It is often found that in wide-range oscillators parasitic resonances occur which introduce drastic changes in power output, frequency, or both. Sources of difficulties are usually found to be due to the use of a short-circuiting plunger of the choke type; to resonances due to higher-order modes in the cavity proper; and to resonances in the tuning plunger itself.

These problems may be further aggravated if it is necessary to use a cavity in a higher-order mode. It is usually advantageous to use a resonant cavity in its lowest mode, corresponding to the fields expected in a quarter-wave resonant-line cavity. However, the mechanical limitations placed by the configuration of tube elements frequently require the operation of the cavity at a higher-order mode. For instance, in an external-cavity klystron, the highest frequency obtainable in the lowest mode results from placing a metallic envelope adjacent to the glass section that surrounds the r-f gap. If the tube is to be used at a higher frequency, it becomes necessary to use higher-order modes, such as the three-quarter wavelength cavity, to effectively place a short circuit within the glass envelope. Although this practice allows the use of the tube at higher frequencies, it simultaneously develops spurious resonances due to oscillations in the lowest mode. Under these conditions, a reflex klystron may operate at two or more frequencies. This effect, commonly referred to as *mode interference*, is shown for a typical case in Fig. 1.26a. This illustration shows the regions of oscillation encountered at various positions of the tuning plunger. The mode chart shown is, in effect, a superposition of mode charts for the several types of resonances which the resonator supports. For each particular field configuration in the cavity (occurring at a given frequency) there will be a number of reflector modes of the type previously discussed. Mode interference will result when the reflector modes of one frequency happen to coincide with a reflector mode or mode patterns of another frequency. In practice, mode interference is complicated by the fact that the loading of the resonator

---

[1] Terman and Pettit, *op. cit.*, pp. 526–529; A. Fong, New 7-11 Kmc Signal Generator Yields Valuable Design Hints, *Tele-Tech. and Electronic Industries*, p. 92, August, 1954; Yunker, Early, Hok, and Bridgeford, *op. cit.*, chap. 32.

at various frequencies is not equal, as the field distribution at the coupling system is different from mode to mode.   The use of choke-type shorting plungers also permits many other classes of resonance, further increasing the possible number of interfering modes.

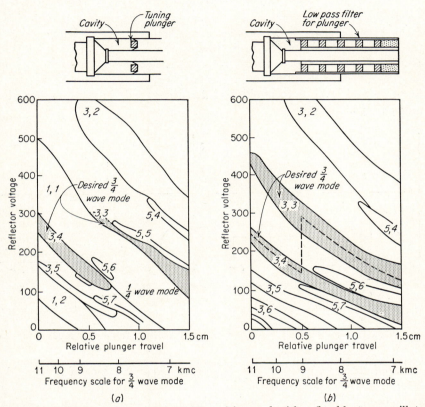

FIG. 1.26. Mode interference in coaxial cavities used with reflex klystron oscillator. The curves are identified by two numbers: the first is the number of quarter-wavelengths in the coaxial cavity; the second is the reflector mode number *n*.   (*a*) Using coaxial cavity reflector modes encountered with cavity tuned by shorting plunger; (*b*) mode pattern obtained with a specially designed plunger.   (*Courtesy of Hewlett-Packard Company.*)

Various techniques are used to minimize the disturbing effects of interfering modes.   One approach depends upon displacing undesired modes by placing disturbing objects into the cavity which are oriented to greatly affect the resonant frequency of undesired modes without appreciably changing the field pattern of the desired mode.   Another approach makes use of specially designed plungers which act as filters.   In one successful design shown in Fig. 1.26*b*, the plunger is constructed as a low-pass filter providing a mechanism for heavily loading the low-order modes. The desired three-quarter wavelength mode is designed to be above the cutoff frequency of the filter and is tuned by the plunger as if it were an ordinary shorting plate.[1]

In tuning the klystron over a wide frequency range, it is often necessary to track the reflector voltage as required by the mode characteristic of the tube. This is often done by providing a mechanically ganged system to move the cavity tuning mechanism and a potentiometer to provide proper reflector voltage. It is often found convenient to switch from one reflector mode to another, either to maintain the power output at the desired level or to avoid an interfering mode in some part of the tuning range.

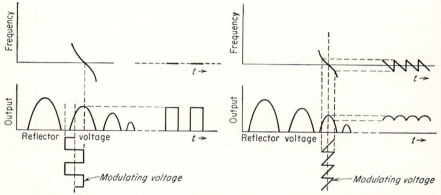

Fig. 1.27. Methods of applying square-wave and linear frequency modulation to reflex klystrons.

k. Modulation of the Reflex Klystron. Examination of the mode patterns of the reflex klystron shows that linear frequency modulation can be easily obtained by superimposing a modulating voltage on either the beam or the reflector electrodes. It is also possible to amplitude-modulate the klystron by controlling the current. However, for reasons mentioned in Sec. 1.5f, this results in significant frequency modulation. Special forms of amplitude modulation, such as square-wave, can be applied successfully in a manner described below.

In modulating the reflex klystron by superimposing the modulation voltage upon d-c reflector voltage, it is necessary to carefully select the d-c reflector voltage to prevent the reflector from becoming positive at any part of the modulation cycle. In using square-wave amplitude modulation the complete reflector mode diagram should be examined to assure that the modulation waveform will result in maximum power out-

[1] Fong, *op. cit.*

put on one-half of the modulation cycle, and zero output on the other. The off-part of the cycle can swing into an adjacent mode or part of the same mode, resulting in simultaneous oscillation at two or more frequencies. Undesirable frequency modulation can be minimized by keeping the waveshape as square as possible.

Frequency modulation can be obtained by superimposing the desired modulation signal upon the d-c reflector voltage when the latter is adjusted for maximum power output. The frequency swing is determined by the amplitude of the applied voltage. As discussed previously, frequency modulation is most linear in this region, unless hysteresis or other effects are prominent. In order to minimize amplitude modulation, it is necessary to limit the modulation voltage to a sufficiently small part of the mode characteristic. The proper adjustments for square-wave and frequency modulation are indicated in Fig. 1.27.

1.7. Microwave Triode Oscillators. *a. General Characteristics of Microwave Triode Circuits.* At the lower radio frequencies the triode oscillator is a versatile and highly successful source of power for laboratory applications. A number of circuit arrangements are known in which the frequency of oscillation is largely independent of voltage variations. Provisions can be made to isolate the oscillator circuit from the load by means of multielectrode tubes connected in electron-coupled circuits, or by the addition of subsequent amplifiers. Even though the number of tuned circuits may be larger than one, gang tuning is relatively simple and affords an opportunity to exploit the advantages of complex circuits without requiring multiple controls. Arrangements using master-oscillator power-amplifier circuits permit the use of amplitude modulation with little incidental frequency modulation. Requiring but a single low-voltage power supply, the triode laboratory sources tend to be simpler, cheaper, and lighter than other sources of r-f power.

Usual triode practice can be extended into the microwave region, although with the increasing frequency most of the advantages previously mentioned rapidly become more difficult to attain. Long before the high-frequency limit of a given tube is reached, the convenient lumped-circuit design becomes impractical because of the small size of the circuit elements and the excessive loss in them at the high frequencies. However, at frequencies as high as 1,000 Mc it is possible to use conventional triode tubes in resonant-line circuits. These may take the form of parallel lines, coaxial resonators, or modified forms of both. In using the conventional-type tubes, many practical problems are encountered due to the difficulties of connecting the circuits to the tube elements. At higher frequencies the connections begin to play an important part in the circuit performance and become the limiting factor in the usefulness of the tubes. Topological design problems generally preclude the use of gang-tuning controls, reducing the merit of the attractive circuit combinations which are so convenient at the lower frequencies.

Above approximately 1,000 Mc the use of conventional tubes becomes impractical due to the inductance of the lead-in wires. This problem has been resolved by designing triode structures specifically for cavity applications. In these designs, the tube elements are extended beyond the tube envelope by means of rigid, symmetrical, low-inductance supports. This permits the spacing of the tube elements to be made appreciably smaller. The resultant close-spaced triodes are superior to the ordi-

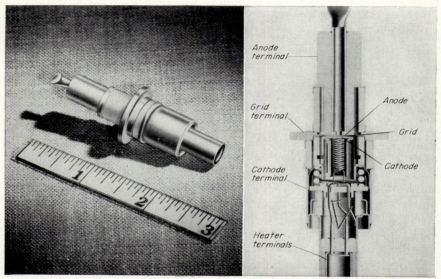

FIG. 1.28. Photograph and cross-sectional views of a pencil-type parallel-plane triode. (*Courtesy of General Electric Company.*)

nary triodes for high-frequency service. Because of their topological resemblance to some common geometric forms, these tubes are often called lighthouse, pencil-type, etc. Tubes of this type are available for operation above 4,000 Mc. An example of a modern pencil tube (GL-6442) is shown in Fig. 1.28.

Close-spaced triodes provide a method of extending the usefulness of triode arrangements into the microwave region. In the approximate frequency range of 1,000 to 4,000 Mc, the triode and klystron tubes are competitive, as there are practical advantages in each case. Triode tubes require lower voltages for operation, fewer power supplies, and generally result in better frequency stability. At the lower end of this frequency range, multiple tube circuits can easily be devised to take advantage of the master-oscillator power-amplifier combinations. However, at the higher end of this frequency region, wide-range tuning becomes more difficult to attain because of the necessity of readjusting the feedback with tuning.

Above approximately 4,000 Mc, the use of triode circuits becomes impractical, although experimental tubes have been built to operate at over twice this frequency.

b. Circuits for Microwave Triodes. The arrangement of circuit elements for microwave oscillators closely follows the usual practice. In Fig. 1.29a, the conventional tuned-plate connection is shown with a grounded cathode. For topological reasons which will become clearer below, it becomes necessary to modify this circuit by grounding the grid

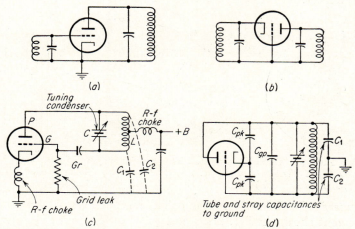

Fig. 1.29. Circuits suitable for use with microwave triode oscillators. (a) Basic grounded-cathode arrangement useful at low frequencies; (b) modified arrangement known as the grid-separation circuit; (c) example of the ungrounded-cathode circuit; (d) an equivalent circuit representing the actual circuit shown in (c). (*By permission from "Electronic Measurements," by F. E. Terman and J. M. Pettit. Copyright, 1952. McGraw-Hill Book Company, Inc., New York.*)

as shown in Fig. 1.29b. This arrangement is generally known as the *grounded grid*, or *grid-separation* circuit. As can be seen easily, the grounded-grid system permits each of the two resonant circuits to be constructed in the form of cavity resonators. In this arrangement there is no natural coupling between the cathode-grid and cathode-anode regions, except as provided by the electron stream and the small electromagnetic coupling through the grid wires. The separation of the two circuits is advantageous in amplifiers, but requires that external coupling be provided for an oscillator. In all known arrangements, the problem of providing feedback coupling is complicated and becomes one of the main problems in the design of a tunable oscillator.

The arrangement in Fig. 1.29c shows the ungrounded-cathode circuit which allows the use of a single resonant circuit. In this form, two r-f chokes are needed. If the impedance of these chokes is sufficiently high, the circuit may be represented by an equivalent circuit shown in Fig. 1.29d, easily recognized as a Colpitts arrangement. The single resonant tuning system needs only two connections between the tube and the resonant circuit. The tuning condenser may be of a split-stator type, thus avoiding moving contacts, and is particularly advantageous for use at the lower frequencies with conventional triode tubes. The usefulness of this circuit is limited to an upper limit of about 500 or 1,000 Mc because of the difficulty of maintaining sufficiently high impedance in the cathode circuit.[1]

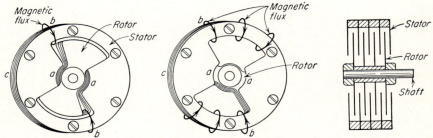

Fig. 1.30. Butterfly resonant circuit. (*By permission from "Electronic Measurements," by F. E. Terman and J. M. Pettit. Copyright, 1952. McGraw-Hill Book Company, Inc., New York.*)

c. Butterfly Oscillators.[2] A convenient resonant circuit for use in the arrangement shown in Fig. 1.29c and suitable for use in the frequency range of 100 to 1,000 Mc can be constructed in the manner shown in Fig. 1.30. It is a form of a parallel-line resonant circuit, tuned by simultaneous change of the inductance and capacity. If the rotor were completely removed, the arrangement would closely resemble the cross section of an ordinary klystron resonator. With the rotor plates located inside the stator, the capacity from post to post is greatly increased. In this position the inductance is at its maximum value. If the rotor is placed in the minimum capacity position, the inductance between the posts reaches its minimum value as the area of inductive loop is reduced by the metallic plates which restrict the volume available for the magnetic flux. This arrangement permits a large tuning range, about 5 to 1.

[1] For details of these circuit arrangements and further reference to the available literature, see F. E. Terman and J. M. Pettit, "Electronic Measurements," pp. 510–521, McGraw-Hill Book Company, Inc., New York, 1952.

[2] E. Karplus, The Butterfly Circuit, *General Radio Experimenter*, vol. 19, October, 1944; Terman and Pettit, *op. cit.*, p. 513. This reference also cites an extensive bibliography pertaining to butterfly oscillators.

Because of its distributed form, the losses are low and the circuit is useful up to 1,000 Mc. The butterfly circuit can be used in the ungrounded-cathode system shown in Fig. 1.29c by connecting the grid and plate terminals of the tube at points *a-a* as indicated in Fig. 1.30. Because of the limitation of the ungrounded-cathode system, the use of butterfly circuits is not feasible above 1,000 Mc.

d. Coaxial-line Oscillators.[1] Above 1,000 Mc microwave triode oscillators invariably employ close-spaced triodes in one of the many variations of the grid-separation circuit. The resonant circuits take the form

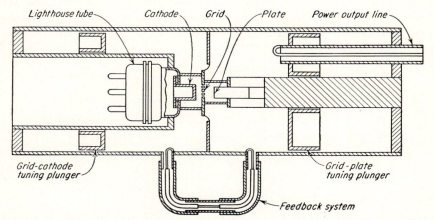

Fig. 1.31. Typical grid-separation circuit using the "end-to-end" design. (*Adopted by permission from Microwave Oscillators Using Disk-Seal Tubes, by A. M. Gurewitsch and J. R. Whinnery, Proc. IRE, vol. 35, no. 5, May, 1947.*)

of coaxial-type resonant cavities. By suitable arrangements, the circuit almost becomes an integral part of the tube. The design of the coaxial circuits must take into account the geometrical discontinuities formed by the junction of the circuit elements and the tube. The mechanical design of a suitable cavity must resolve the problem of making an adequate electrical contact to the tube elements without creating dangerous mechanical stresses. Cooling of the tube may present an additional problem because the tube structure is surrounded by closed metallic shells.

Three typical arrangements employing close-spaced disk-seal tubes in grid-separation circuit are shown in Figs. 1.31, 1.32, and 1.33. The first of these, representing the simplest geometrical design, is called the *end-*

---

[1] A. M. Gurewitsch and J. R. Whinnery, Microwave Oscillators Using Disk-seal Tubes, *Proc. IRE*, vol. 35, no. 5, pp. 462–473, May, 1947; Radio Research Laboratory, Harvard University, "Very High-frequency Techniques," chap. 15, McGraw-Hill Book Company, Inc., New York, 1947; chap. 7 in "Klystrons and Microwave Triodes," Massachusetts Institute of Technology Radiation Laboratory Series, McGraw-Hill Book Company, Inc., New York, 1948.

to-end design. It closely resembles the schematic diagram shown in Fig. 1.29*b*. The resonant circuits are provided by shorted sections of coaxial lines, forming resonant cavities. These are essentially λ/4 (or 3λ/4, etc.) resonant lines foreshortened by the presence of terminating tube capacities. The cavities can be tuned by any of the methods discussed in Sec. 1.3, although only the plunger tuning method is illustrated in the diagrams. The grid forms an effective shield between the cathode and the anode cavities, permitting this arrangement to be used either as an amplifier or an oscillator. In Fig. 1.31, the feedback line necessary to convert the amplifier into an oscillator is shown connecting two inductive loops; but many other forms of coupling can be devised also. The advantage of end-to-end design lies in its simplicity of construction and the

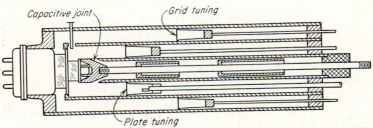

FIG. 1.32. Example of the "folded-back" oscillator. (*Adopted by permission from Microwave Oscillators Using Disk-Seal Tubes, by A. M. Gurewitsch and J. R. Whinnery, Proc. IRE, vol. 35, no. 5, May, 1947.*)

physical accessibility to both of the resonant cavities for coupling and tuning. Among its disadvantages are its greater length and the difficulty of ganging the tuning mechanisms. In the oscillator connection, the feedback path is easily provided for a narrowband operation, but may require additional tuning adjustments to maintain the proper feedback conditions in wide-range tuning applications.

The second arrangement, shown in Fig. 1.32, is called the *folded-back* oscillator. It represents a simple modification of the end-to-end arrangement by folding back one of the coaxial lines over the other. Feedback can be provided from one cavity into the other by a number of obvious ways involving loops, probes, or combination of both. Since both cavities can be tuned with plungers on the same side, the folded-back design makes it more convenient to provide single-control tuning. If a relatively small tuning range is desired, a fixed feedback system can be employed. The resultant structure is small, and can be easily arranged to operate with a single tuning control.[1] By providing independent

[1] Gang-tuning of the two cavities is not as simple as it may seem at first. The capacitive loading of the resonant lines is different on the two sides of the grid; and the characteristic impedance of the transmission lines is generally unequal. This causes the tuning curves of the two cavities to be somewhat different.

tuning for the two cavities and a suitable provision for readjustment of the feedback, wide-range tuning can be obtained.   The folded-back oscillator shown in Fig. 1.32, using a 2C40 tube, can be tuned over the range of 9 to 30 cm.

Another circuit arrangement, called the *reentrant* type, is shown in Fig. 1.33.   The cavity of the reentrant oscillator resembles the floating drift tube klystron shown in Fig. 1.1*f*, since the anode and cathode cavities are merged into one by leaving out a part of the partition between them.   This evolution can be understood readily by examining the structure of the folded-back oscillator and imagining that the grid cylinder is cut circumferentially.   If this cut were located at an electrical distance

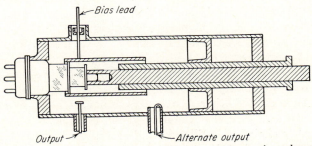

FIG. 1.33. An example of a "reentrant" oscillator.   The tuning plunger, adjusted for proper feedback, is locked to the tuning sleeve.   (*Adopted by permission from Microwave Oscillators Using Disk-Seal Tubes, by A. M. Gurewitsch and J. R. Whinnery, Proc. IRE, vol. 35, no. 5, May, 1947.*)

of half-wavelength from the tube, its presence would not matter as it would be located at a point of zero current.   By displacing the slot longitudinally, the axial flow of r-f current is interrupted and provides a method of coupling the two cavities.   The contact to the isolated grid cylinder to provide d-c connection must be made either at a zero r-f potential point, or by means of a high impedance r-f choke.   The frequency of oscillation of the reentrant oscillator depends principally upon the length of the grid cylinder; the position of the plunger is adjusted to provide proper feedback conditions.   Under certain circumstances, other modes in the cavity may be excited and the plunger position will also affect the oscillation frequency.

The reentrant oscillator is simple mechanically, is not critical to exact feedback adjustments, and can be made tunable by a single control over a considerable range of frequency.   Tuning can be done in several ways. The grid cylinder can be extended by means of telescopic tubing.   Alternatively, motion of the tuning sleeve inserted into the grid cylinder permits substantial tuning as shown in Fig. 1.33.

The tube elements can be supplied with proper potentials by insulating the various metallic parts from each other as necessary by means of bypass capacitors or resonant chokes. The design of these elements is well understood and does not present special problems. The output power can be obtained from coaxial cavities by methods previously discussed in connection with klystrons.

As mentioned previously, one of the particular advantages of triode circuits is the simplicity of constructing master-oscillator power-amplifier arrangements. Although no specific examples of such circuits were given, it can easily be seen that suitable combinations can be composed with the circuits shown. The principal problem encountered in connecting successive cavities in cascade is the problem of impedance matching. Over narrow bandwidth, this problem is simple, but becomes progressively more difficult with larger tuning requirements. The difficulties are especially severe at the higher frequencies.

1.8. Traveling-wave Tubes.[1] In numerous laboratory applications it is desirable to employ r-f amplification over bandwidths larger than can be obtained with klystrons and triodes because of their relatively high-Q circuits. Wide-band amplification is necessary for observation of rapidly varying phenomena or other signals containing a widely distributed frequency spectrum. It is also a matter of considerable convenience to be able to employ chains of oscillators and amplifiers without being forced to the tedious task of readjustment of a multitude of resonant cavities.

By means of the traveling-wave tube principle, it is frequently possible to obtain amplification over a wide frequency range, such as 2 to 1 or more. In its simplest form the traveling-wave tube (abbreviated TWT) consists of a long cylindrical electron beam passing through a microwave structure capable of propagating electromagnetic waves over the desired frequency band. The propagating structure must be designed to provide an axial electric field at the electron beam; the phase velocity of the traveling waves must be approximately equal to the electron velocity. Since at convenient voltages the velocity of electrons is in the neighborhood of one-tenth of the velocity of light, the propagating structure must be of an unusual type to provide propagation of electromagnetic waves at such slow velocities.

Figure 1.34 shows one common arrangement in which the propagating structure takes the form of a helix. It is found that electromagnetic waves can propagate along the wire of the helix essentially with the

[1] J. R. Pierce and L. M. Field, Traveling-wave Tubes, *Proc. IRE*, vol. 35, pp. 108–111, February, 1947; R. Kompfner, The Traveling-wave Tube as Amplifier at Microwaves, *Proc. IRE*, vol. 35, pp. 124–127, February, 1947; H. J. Reich, P. F. Ordung, H. L. Krauss, and J. G. Skalnik, "Microwave Theory and Techniques," chap. 15, D. Van Nostrand Company, Inc., Princeton, N.J., 1953; J. R. Pierce, "Traveling-wave Tubes," D. Van Nostrand Company, Inc., Princeton, N.J., 1950.

velocity of light, so that the forward progress of the waves along the helix is reduced in proportion to the pitch of the helix. Examination of the electric fields around the wire of the helix will show that this structure provides the necessary axial electric field in its central region. The axial electric field of the propagating waves permits interaction with the electrons causing velocity variation and bunching. The r-f power can be supplied to the helix at the gun end and an amplified signal can be removed at the far end. Since the waves and the electrons travel at nearly the same velocity, the electrons experience forces which persist for relatively long periods. Due to the extended interaction, it is possible to obtain relatively high amplification in spite of the low impedance of the nonresonant propagating structure. Because the propagating slow-wave structures are not resonant, it is possible to obtain amplifi-

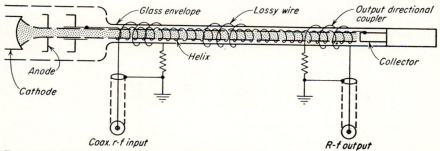

FIG. 1.34. Schematic drawing of the traveling-wave tube employing a wire helix. The input and output couplers shown represent counterwound helix directional couplers.

cation over a bandwidth much greater than is obtained in the klystron.

The principle of operation of the traveling-wave tube can be understood as follows:[1] Figure 1.35 shows an instantaneous distribution of the axial electric field of the traveling-wave at the beginning of the tube. The force on an electron due to positive E_z will be assumed to cause motion to the left, and a negative E_z will cause motion to the right. At the entrance to the helix, the electrons arrive from the accelerating gun region and may be assumed to be uniformly spaced over the r-f cycle. An electron which travels at the position B may be seen to experience no axial forces; however, electrons on both sides of this position experience forces as indicated in the diagram, causing the electrons to form a bunch about the position B. The electrons traveling at position A become the centers of the antibunch, i.e., the position of the minimum electron charge density. The bunching process described is continuous and differs in an important respect from the similar bunching action in

[1] The following explanation is based upon an internal memorandum prepared by D. Dunn, Stanford University, 1952.

the klystron. Because the bunching forces are constant, it can easily be demonstrated that the r-f current content in the bunch is proportional to the square of the bunching time, or to the square of the distance from the input end.[1] As the result of the bunching phenomenon, the electron

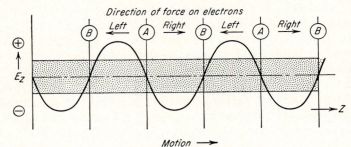

FIG. 1.35. Initial forces on the electrons in the traveling-wave tube.

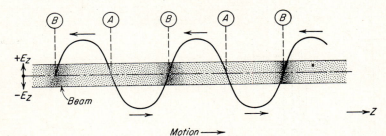

FIG. 1.36. Initial bunching in the traveling-wave tube.

stream charge density will be modified and will appear as shown in Fig. 1.36.

As soon as the electron stream exhibits concentration of space charge in bunches, an induced r-f current will appear in the propagating circuit. The action of the electron beam upon the circuit can be predicted by subdividing the electron stream into small axial elements and summing

---

[1] This physical picture is correct only as long as the degree of bunching is small. In terms of the bunching theory of the klystron, the limit of validity of these arguments ceases when the equivalent bunching parameter $x \geqq 1$. In the klystron, for small signals the r-f current is given by

$$I_2 = 2I_0 J_1(x)$$

and, for small x, by

$$I_2 = I_0 \pi N \frac{V_1}{V_0}$$

Thus, the current under this simplifying assumption is found to be proportional to N, or to the transit time from the gun end. In the TWT, the bunching forces are continuous; summation of current contributions from all points along the beam up to the point in question leads to the conclusion that r-f current is proportional to N^2.

the effect of each current increment in the circuit.   In doing this, it is possible to neglect reaction of the incremental current elements upon the circuit at all places except the immediate proximity of the current element, as indicated in Fig. 1.37.

Each infinitesimal current element induces two waves in the propagating circuit, as indicated in Fig. 1.37; one of these will propagate in the direction of the beam, and the second in the opposite direction.   If the electron and wave velocities are identical, the summation of the waves propagating in a forward direction in the circuit will result in a growing wave and only a negligibly small wave in the opposite direction. This is true because each induced wavelet is in time phase with the exciting current.

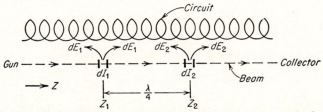

FIG. 1.37. Action of the incremental current elements upon the helix.

If the r-f current content of the beam were constant, the resultant wave induced in the circuit would increase linearly with distance because of continuous reinforcement of the wavelets (just as, for example, in a long-slot directional coupler, distributed amplifier, etc.).   However, because the inducing r-f current increases as N^2, the total induced field will be found to increase as N^3.   The presence of the rapidly growing wave causes further bunching in exactly the same manner as that caused initially by the *primary* wave introduced into the circuit.   The resultant *secondary* bunched current will increase as the fifth power of the distance, just as the initial wave caused the primary current to increase as the square of the distance.   The final wave may be obtained by summing the incremental series derived in the above manner.   The final wave is found to increase exponentially with distance.[1]

A more complete quantitative analysis of the behavior of the TWT can be obtained by taking into account the electron stream and considering its effect upon the propagation constants of the slow-wave structure.[2] It can be shown that the presence of interaction of the electron beam with the circuit causes the existence of four possible propagating waves. Two of these waves, forward and backward, are the ordinary propagating

[1] For further details of this analysis, see R. Kompfner, The Traveling-wave Tube, *Wireless Engineer*, vol. 24, pp. 255–266, 1947.

[2] Pierce, *op. cit.*, chaps. 1 and 2.

circuit waves and are unperturbed by the presence of the electron stream. The third wave is found to have a propagation constant with a negative real part and results in a *growing wave*. The fourth wave has a propagation constant with a positive real component and is called an *attenuated wave*. Excitation of the r-f structure at the input end causes the excitation of three of these waves. This results in an initial loss of power in launching the desired growing wave. Because of the exponential increase of the growing wave, the desired wave rapidly dominates the remaining waves. The characteristic behavior of the growing wave can be described by the expression

$$V = V_1 e^{2\pi NCx} \tag{1.52}$$

where V = magnitude of the propagating wave
V_1 = its initial value
N = the length of the TWT in guided wavelengths
C = the Pierce gain parameter given by $\left(\dfrac{1}{4}\dfrac{K}{R_0}\right)^{1/3}$
K = the slow-wave circuit impedance
$R_0 = V_0/I_0$
$x = \sqrt{3/2}$ for synchronous beam and wave velocities and with negligible space charge

The gain for the traveling-wave tube can be obtained by taking the logarithm of Eq. (1.52). If G is the gain in decibels,

$$G = A + BCN \tag{1.53}$$

where A is a negative constant representing the fact that only a part of the initial signal produces the desired growing wave, and $B = 54.5x$. Thus, the gain per guided wavelength is BC. For the conditions of synchronous velocity, negligible circuit losses, negligible space charge, Eq. (1.53) can be rewritten as

$$G = -9.54 + 47.3CN \tag{1.54}$$

Specially prepared design charts can be used to calculate the behavior of the traveling-wave tube under different operating conditions.[1]

In an actual operating tube, it is necessary to provide isolation between the input and output ends of the propagating structure in order to prevent possible oscillations, as indicated in Fig. 1.34. This is essential because any reflected power at the output terminal will propagate backwards in an unattenuated wave and provides a mechanism for feedback and possible oscillations. In general, at some frequency there will always

---

[1] For other conditions, such as nonsynchronous operation, effect of space charge, etc., the reader is referred to C. C. Cutler, The Calculation of Traveling-wave Tube Gain, *Proc. IRE*, vol. 39, pp. 914–917, August, 1951.

be sufficient feedback to create oscillations.   It is usual practice to introduce an r-f attenuator near the middle of the TWT so that the loss in
the backward direction is approximately equal to the gain in the forward
direction.   It is important that the loss be uniform over the passband
of the amplifier and that it be located in the central section of the tube.
Locating the attenuator too close to the input end prevents the required

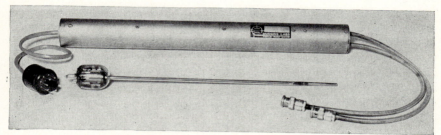

FIG. 1.38. A typical traveling-wave tube and a tube assembly encapsuled in a metallic
envelope.   (*Photograph, courtesy of Huggins Laboratories, Inc.*)

initial exponential growth of the wave.   Placing the attenuator too close
to the output limits the saturation power.

The most common slow-wave structure consists of the helix shown in
Fig. 1.34.   Several ways have been devised to launch the initial waves
and remove the signal from the helix.   These may consist of antennas,
coupling cavities, or directional couplers using overwound helices.   In
addition to the helix, many other types of slow-wave structures with

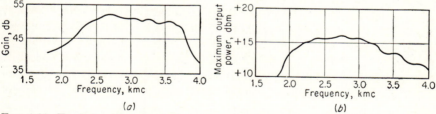

FIG. 1.39. Typical performance of a low-level traveling-wave tube.   (*a*) Small signal gain (−35-dbm input); (*b*) saturation power output.   (*Data for Hewlett-Packard
490A TWT amplifier.   Courtesy of Hewlett-Packard Company.*)

axial component of the electric field have been found adequate for
interaction with electron streams.   Some of these are described in the
literature.[1]

Figure 1.38 shows a photograph of a practical traveling-wave tube
assembly.   The tube is contained in a metallic envelope or a *capsule*
which may be inserted into a magnetic solenoid to provide the required d-c

[1] Pierce, *op. cit.*; L. M. Field, Some Slow-wave Structures for Traveling-wave Tubes,
Proc. IRE, vol. 37, no. 1, pp. 34–40, January, 1949.

magnetic field for focusing the electron beam.   Figure 1.39 shows gain and saturation power of a typical low-level amplifier.

1.9. Backward-wave Oscillator.[1]   A traveling-wave tube amplifier can be made to oscillate in a number of different ways.   If an external feedback path is provided, oscillations will exist at the frequency or frequencies at which the loop gain exceeds unity and at which the phase shift corresponds to a whole number of wavelengths around the complete loop.   In this arrangement the frequency of oscillation will be determined by the mechanical arrangement of parts and the frequency will not be greatly affected by the applied potentials.   In addition, oscillations are likely to exist in several possible modes at one time.   If a resonant cavity is inserted in the feedback loop, controlled oscillations can be caused to exist in one mode only and the frequency can be changed electronicly over a limited region since the phase shift through the traveling-wave tube depends upon the electron velocity.

Another possible method of tuning a traveling-wave tube oscillator is based upon the dispersive properties of the slow-wave structure.   For instance, if the helix circumference is much smaller than the wavelength of the propagating wave along the helix, the phase velocity of the propagating wave will vary rapidly with wavelength.   Under these conditions, the traveling-wave tube amplifier will work properly only if the electron velocity is adjusted for synchronism at each frequency.   Because of this strong dispersion, at a given beam voltage the bandwidth of the traveling-wave tube becomes restricted.   It is possible to make use of this phenomenon to provide an electronicly tunable amplifier whose mean frequency can be adjusted by controlling the beam voltage.   Nonresonant feedback in a dispersive amplifier can be used to cause oscillations; the frequency can be changed within a given mode by changing the voltage.   However, it is found that it is necessary to make the electrical length of the tube N very small in order to avoid frequency jumps between possible modes.   By making N sufficiently small, satisfactory operation can be

[1] R. Kompfner, Backward-wave Oscillator, *Bell Labs. Record*, vol. 31, pp. 281–285, August, 1953; R. Kompfner and N. T. Williams, Backward-wave Tubes, *Proc. IRE*, vol. 41, pp. 1602–1611, November, 1953; H. Heffner, Backward-wave Tubes, *Electronics*, vol. 26, no. 10, pp. 135–137, October, 1953; H. Heffner, Analysis of the Backward-wave Traveling-wave Tube, *Proc. IRE*, vol. 42, no. 6, pp. 930–937, June, 1954; D. A. Watkins and E. A. Ash, The Helix as a Backward-wave Structure, *J. Appl. Phys.*, vol. 25, no. 6, pp. 782–790, June, 1954; P. K. Tien, Bifilar Helix for Backward-wave Oscillators, *Proc. IRE*, vol. 42, no. 7, pp. 1137–1143, July, 1954; M. Muller, Traveling-wave Amplifiers and Backward-wave Oscillators, *Proc. IRE*, vol. 42, no. 11, pp. 1651–1658, November, 1954; R. W. Grow and D. A. Watkins, Backward-wave Oscillator Efficiency, *Proc. IRE*, vol. 43, no. 7, pp. 848–856, July, 1955; H. R. Johnson, Backward Wave Oscillators, *Proc. IRE*, vol. 43, no. 6, pp. 684–697, June, 1955; M. R. Currie and J. R. Whinnery, The Cascade Backward-wave Amplifier: A High-gain Voltage-tuned Filter for Microwaves, *Proc. IRE*, vol. 43, no. 11, pp. 1617–1631, November, 1955.

obtained, but the resultant performance is not distinctly better than that of the simpler reflex klystron.

The difficulties of providing the necessary feedback properly (so that the phase shift around the feedback loop can be kept constant and equal to a whole multiple of 2π at all frequencies) can be resolved by means of the modified traveling-wave tube principle commonly referred to as the *backward-wave interaction*. In this device, oscillations result from a process of continuous feedback along the circuit without additional external feedback provisions. The backward-wave tube is capable of acting either as an amplifier or as an oscillator. As an oscillator, the tube is capable of oscillating at any beam voltage and has no discrete modes as those in the reflex klystron. The backward-wave oscillator (abbreviated as BWO) can be used to tune over a large frequency range by merely adjusting

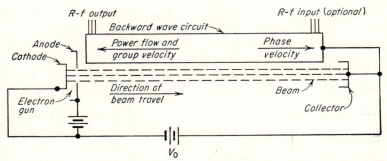

Fig. 1.40. Symbolic representation of the backward-wave oscillator or amplifier.

the beam voltage. When used as an amplifier, the device can be adjusted to provide a narrow bandwidth, the center frequency of which can be changed by varying the beam voltage.

The amplification process of the BWO is nearly identical to the traveling-wave tube, but with some important differences. The essential elements of the backward-wave oscillator are shown schematically in Fig. 1.40. An electron beam is accelerated to a desired velocity V_0 and is projected through a suitable slow-wave structure. However, the necessary practical circuit will be different from the conventional slow-wave circuit; it must possess an unusual property, having the phase and group velocities in the opposite directions.[1] As in the traveling-wave tube, the

[1] This unusual property of slow-wave structures is found to be a characteristic of any *periodically loaded* transmission line including the helix. Periodic disturbances of the natural fields of the transmission line can be analyzed with the aid of Fourier series; the Fourier *components* of the traveling waves propagate with different velocities. Some of these components or *space harmonics* possess the required characteristics for backward-wave interaction. For a more complete discussion of related problems, see J. C. Slater, "Microwave Electronics," chap. 8, D. Van Nostrand Company, Inc., Princeton, N.J., 1950.

electron velocity must be nearly identical to the phase velocity of the waves on the circuit; however, because of the negative group velocity, the signal power introduced at the collector end of the tube will appear amplified at the input end. With sufficient current, oscillations can be induced, even if the circuit is perfectly terminated at both ends.

The process of amplification of the BWO can be explained in the same manner as for the TWT. Suppose that an r-f signal is introduced at the r-f input terminals, as shown in Fig. 1.40, and that the electron velocity is adjusted to equal the phase velocity of the propagating slow wave. As a consequence of the steady forces acting upon the electrons under these conditions, the bunching action takes place just as in the traveling-wave tube, creating a bunched current in which the r-f content is proportional to the square of the distance the electrons travel from the gun end.

As in the traveling-wave tube, the action of the bunched current upon the circuit can be understood by considering the addition of induced

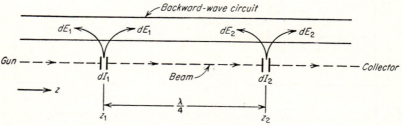

FIG. 1.41. Initial action of the bunched current in a backward-wave circuit.

wavelets in the circuit produced by incremental segments of current shown in Fig. 1.41. Consider, for example, the pair of current elements dI_1 and dI_2 which induce fields dE_1 and dE_2 as indicated. By considering the current elements spaced one-quarter wavelength apart, it is possible to show that the wavelets propagating in the direction of the electron stream will almost completely cancel. To understand this process, it is necessary to remember that the signal propagating from the input (at the collector) toward the output (at the cathode) has a positive group and a negative phase velocity. Thus, the wavelet dE_1 in propagating one-quarter wavelength toward the collector has decreased in phase by 90°. The current element dI_2 in moving from z_1 to z_2 had advanced in phase by 90° so that the relative phase between dE_1 and dE_2 becomes 180°, causing cancellation of the waves in the direction of motion of the electrons.

Similarly, the wavelets induced in the backward direction can be shown to be everywhere in phase and to add constructively. This happens because the phase advance experienced by the current element traveling in a forward direction is precisely canceled by the decrease phase along the circuit. Therefore, the induced wavelets traveling from the collector toward the gun end add in phase to produce a wave which increases with distance from the collector end. Remembering that the inducing current is proportional to N^2 (where N is the distance measured in cycles from the gun end of the tube) summation of the wavelets leads to the total induced field to be proportional to $1 - (N_z/N)^2$, where N_z is the distance from the gun end up to a point z along the tube.

The variation of the induced field along the length of the tube is shown in Fig. 1.42. This induced field is but the first of the infinite series which results from the continuous interaction between the electron

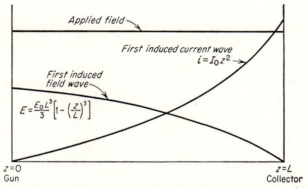

FIG. 1.42. Initial induced current and induced fields in the backward-wave tube.

stream and the waves. Each field obtained in this manner induces new current waves, and each new current wave induces its corresponding field. The total field is then obtained by summation, as in the case of TWT. The result of this summation leads to the conclusion that the total field increases from zero at the collector to the maximum value at the gun end. If the tube is sufficiently long, or the current large enough, the primary induced field wave can be larger than the applied wave at the gun end. The remaining induced fields and corresponding induced currents will become successively greater. The summation of the induced fields produces a divergent series which corresponds to instability, or oscillation.

An example of a structure capable of providing backward-wave interaction is shown in Fig. 1.43. Suppose two parallel metal plates are formed into a series of undulations. Transverse electromagnetic fields can propagate between the plates with the velocity of light. Because of the periodic undulations, the propagation of energy from left to right can be slowed down to any value. The electron stream can be made to pass through the structure through a series of holes, as shown.   Consider the situation shown in Fig. 1.43, in which the wavelength inside the structure is appreciably longer than the length of a single undulation.   Suppose that the velocity of the electrons is adjusted so that the transit time from A to B corresponds to the half-cycle of the propagating wave.   An electron which enters at A at the moment the field has just reversed in sign will travel from A to B, experiencing a force which will vary in magnitude with time, but of *constant direction*.   During the next half-cycle, the electrons will travel from B and C, in the region where there are no r-f fields.   Upon entering the next undulation at point C, the electron will again experience a force of constant direction, as it did at A. Thus, in passing through the undulations the electrons experience pulsating forces in time, but always in the same direction.   Since these forces

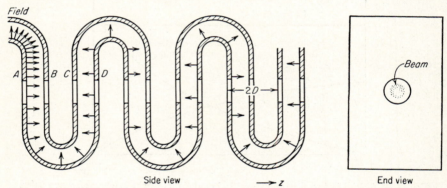

FIG. 1.43. Folded-parallel plate line suitable for use in a backward-wave tube.

are periodic in space, they can be analyzed by the Fourier series, resulting in an infinite series.   Each component of the series is known as the *space harmonic*.

Further analysis of the situation shown in Fig. 1.43 indicates that the forces upon the electrons can be produced in the same direction, regardless of the direction of propagation of fundamental wave through the structure.   This leads to the conclusion that the electron can interact with waves of either positive or negative group velocities; thus a structure such as that shown in Fig. 1.43 is suitable for supplying the waves required for backward-wave interaction.   A properly proportioned helix is satisfactory for the purpose also.

Analysis of Fig. 1.43 will also indicate that the phase velocity of a particular space harmonic will depend upon frequency.   Since the electron velocity must always be equal to phase velocity, this condition provides the mechanism of obtaining voltage tunable oscillations.   This may be shown as follows: In order to remain synchronous with the wave, the electrons must pass from A to C in one cycle. If the wavelength of the fundamental is assumed to be equal to the free-space wavelength, the shorter the wavelength the less time it will take for the fundamental wave to pass a given point. Thus the electrons must have a velocity inversely proportional to the free-space wavelength, or directly proportional to the frequency. This leads to the final conclusion that the frequency of a backward-wave oscillator is proportional to the square root of the voltage. A frequency coverage of 2 to 1 requires a change in beam voltage of 4 to 1. In many practical tubes, additional tube elements are

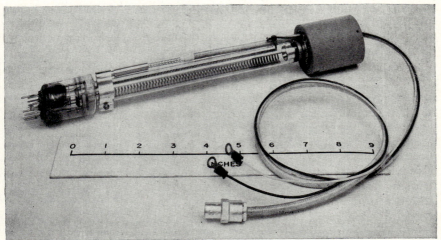

FIG. 1.44. Typical backward-wave oscillator using a helix circuit. It is suitable for 2- to 4-kMc use and requires a variation in the beam voltage of approximately 150 to 1,400 volts. Photograph of Sylvania type 6496 tube.

provided to control the beam current and prevent unusually large variations in beam power and output. A typical backward-wave tube is shown in Fig. 1.44.

1.10. Isolation of Laboratory Oscillators. From the standpoint of simplicity, a simple oscillator is the most convenient and useful source of microwave power. However, with the exception of the backward-wave oscillator, all oscillator systems are highly sensitive to load variations. When the oscillator is located at a considerable distance from the load, or when the load is highly resonant, the oscillator may become unstable or at times cease to oscillate when tuned over its normal frequency range. In numerous other applications, it is highly desirable to have the frequency of oscillation remain constant as various load adjustments are carried out. For these and other related reasons (cf. Sec. 1.6i), it is often necessary to provide some means of isolating the load from the oscillator.

Decoupling or isolation can be partially or completely accomplished by separating the load from the oscillator by the following devices:

a. Attenuator pad
b. Power amplifier
c. Ferrite isolator

These devices differ greatly in complexity and in the degree of isolation they provide. A brief description of each is given below.

a. Attenuating Pads. Variation in a load impedance at the terminals of an oscillator can be reduced by connecting an attenuator or a *pad* between the two. A traveling wave originating at the oscillator will return to the oscillator owing to a reflection at the load, traversing the attenuator twice. Thus, by providing a moderate loss in the forward direction, substantial isolation can be provided. The degree of decoupling can be measured by comparing the voltage standing-wave ratio (VSWR) r at the load with the observed standing-wave ratio r_m at the oscillator. If the pad provides an attenuation of αl nepers, the desired relation can be shown to be (cf. Eq. 5.28)

$$\frac{r_m}{r} = \frac{1 + 1/r \tanh \alpha l}{1 + r \tanh \alpha l} \tag{1.55}$$

This relation is plotted in Fig. 5.27. It will be observed that a 3-db pad reduces the load standing-wave ratio of 5 to 2; a 10-db pad reduces VSWR of 10 to 1.2.

The principal merit of an attenuating pad is the simplicity with which isolation can be provided. It is very wasteful of power and can be used only if the source provides more power than is needed.

b. Power Amplifiers. Insertion of a power amplifier between the source and the load provides an excellent means for isolation and simultaneously increases the power level. Possible arrangements can take the form of an electron-coupled oscillator shown in Fig. 1.1c, or a master-oscillator power amplifier. In the latter, the oscillator can be followed by a klystron, a triode, or a traveling-wave tube. The klystron amplifier provides more complete isolation than the other devices because of the absence of electrical coupling between the input and output circuits. In spite of the obvious advantages of the power-amplifier arrangement, in practice it is seldom used because of the inconvenience of the additional equipment. Perhaps the simplest and most satisfactory arrangement is an oscillator followed by an untuned wideband traveling-wave tube.

c. Ferrite Isolators.[1] A ferrite isolator is a unidirectional transmission device based upon the gyromagnetic nature of ferrite materials at micro-

---

[1] Ferrites are magnetic materials, but having resistivity typically 10^{12} times that of iron. As a result, microwave signals can easily penetrate through substantial thick-

wave frequencies.   The use of these nonreciprocal devices permits transmission of power in one direction and leads to many important classes of devices in which phase shift, attenuation, or field distribution in the cross section of the waveguide are nonreciprocal, i.e., different in the two directions of propagation.

Ferrite materials are electrical insulators which exhibit magnetic properties.   When a ferrite material is subjected simultaneously to d-c and r-f magnetic fields, the resultant magnetic flux is produced which has a component at right angles to the applied r-f magnetic intensity.   This

---

ness of ferrite without serious loss.   Thus, a propagating electromagnetic wave through the ferrite medium is able to encounter strong interaction with the spinning electrons which cause the magnetic properties of the material.   A classical picture of the behavior of ferrite material can be obtained by considering the unpaired electrons in ferrite as rotating charged tops.   Rotation of the electron causes it to have an angular momentum and a magnetic moment along the axis of rotation.   Placing of the ferrite material in a strong d-c magnetic field causes the axis of electron spin to line up with the applied field (as a compass needle in the earth's field).   Due to the gyroscopic forces, a displacement of the spin axis from this orientation causes it to precess about the direction of the d-c magnetic field at a frequency which is proportional to the magnitude of the d-c field.   (This frequency is called the gyromagnetic resonant frequency.)   Hence, application of a transverse r-f magnetic field will cause displacement of the spin axis and precession.   Furthermore, not only will magnetic flux be induced along the expected direction corresponding to the applied r-f magnetic intensity, but also a component at right angles will exist as well.   This phenomenon results in rotation of plane polarization of the incident r-f wave, as indicated in Figs. 1.45b and 1.45c, and is similar to the Faraday effect observed at optical frequencies discovered by Michael Faraday in 1845.   For further details pertaining to application of ferrite materials to microwave circuit elements, see C. L. Hogan, The Ferromagnetic Faraday Effect at Microwave Frequencies and Its Applications, *Bell System Tech. J.*, vol. 31, no. 1, p. 1, January, 1952; J. H. Rowen, Ferrites in Microwave Applications, *Bell System Tech. J.*, vol. 32, no. 6, p. 1358, November, 1953; A. G. Fox, S. E. Miller, and M. T. Weiss, Behavior and Applications of Ferrites in the Microwave Region, *Bell System Tech. J.*, vol. 34, no. 1, pp. 5–103, January, 1955; H. Suhl and L. R. Walker, Topics in Guided Wave Propagation through Gyromagnetic Media, *Bell System Tech. J.*, vol. 33, nos. 3, 4, and 5, pp. 579–660, 939–986, 1133–1194, May, July, and September, 1954; N. G. Sakiotis and H. N. Chait, Ferrites at Microwaves, *Proc. IRE*, vol. 41, no. 1, pp. 87–93, January, 1953; P. J. Allen, A Microwave Magnetometer, *Proc. IRE*, vol. 41, no. 1, pp. 100–104, January, 1953; P. H. Vartanian, J. L. Melchor, and W. P. Ayres, A Broadband Ferrite Microwave Isolator, *Trans. IRE*, vol. MTT-4, no. 1, pp. 8–13, January, 1956.

For a more detailed list of references concerning microwave Faraday effect and ferrite materials, see Hogan, *op. cit.*, and Fox, Miller, and Weiss, *op. cit.*   In addition, an interested reader will find a complete review of the subject in the October, 1956, issue of *Proc. IRE*, vol. 44, no. 10, which is devoted to the subject of ferrites   This issue presents: a comprehensive survey of the properties and applications of ferrites; the theory of ferromagnetism and paramagnetic resonance; general physical properties of ferrites and their measurement; and in addition, 15 papers concerning the theory and application of various microwave ferrite devices.

phenomenon can be utilized in a number of ways to provide nonreciprocal behavior of four-terminal microwave devices.

Several forms of ferrite isolators based upon gyromagnetic phenomena are shown in Figs. 1.45 to 1.48.   The first of these, making use of the Faraday effect, is explained below.   For more complete discussion of the other devices, the reader is referred to the literature cited.

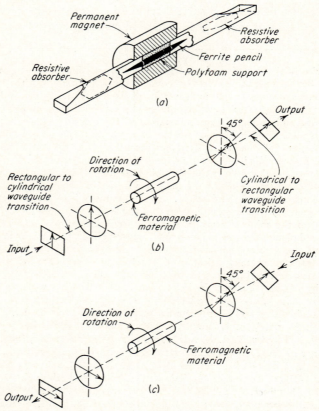

FIG. 1.45. Faraday rotation isolator.   (a) Schematic representation of the main elements; (b) transmission of energy through the isolator in the forward direction; (c) transmission in the reverse direction.

A schematic illustration of the Faraday rotation isolator is shown in Fig. 1.45a.   It consists of a TE_{11} circular waveguide with transitions to normal rectangular waveguides at both ends.   The central region of the isolator contains a pencil-shaped section of ferrite material, tapered at both ends (to minimize reflections).   A permanent magnet is placed outside of the waveguide to provide longitudinal magnetic field through the ferrite pencil. The presence of magnetized ferrite material causes the plane of polarization to rotate in the circular waveguide by an amount determined by the size of the ferrite pencil, its length, and the strength of the magnetic field. The direction of rotation of the plane of polarization due to the Faraday effect is determined only by the *direction* of the d-c magnetic field. In the isolator, the plane of polarization is made to shift by 45°. The behavior of the isolator can be understood with the aid of diagrams shown in Figs. 1.45*b* and 1.45*c*. The input energy enters the waveguide from the left side in TE_{10} mode and is transformed into a TE_{11} plane polarized wave in a circular guide. In passing through the ferrite material, the polarization is shifted *clockwise* by 45°. Upon being transformed back to a rectangular mode, the energy leaves the isolator through a rectangular waveguide which is oriented to correspond to the emerging polarization. Thus, the energy propagates through this device and suffers only a small attenuation in the ferrite material.

The propagation in the reverse direction, however, is impossible, as can be seen in Fig. 1.45*c*. The input energy arriving from the right side is transformed into a plane polarized wave in the circular waveguide as before and is rotated by 45° in the *clockwise* direction. This produces a plane of polarization which cannot propagate in the rectangular waveguide on the left-hand side. A resistive attenuator card placed parallel to the wide dimension of the input guide can be made to absorb this signal. Under idealized conditions, no propagation from right to left is possible. Practical isolators of this type having a forward loss of 0.8 db may provide upwards of 20 db of loss in the reverse direction. Two or more isolators can be added in cascade, if desired, resulting in increased insertion losses in both directions.

Faraday rotation exhibited by circular waveguides partially filled with ferrite materials represents but one possible way of providing nonreciprocalbehavior. Ferrite-loaded rectangular waveguides can also be made to show nonreciprocal characteristics. Phase and attenuation constants, as well as distribution of the magnetic and electric field, can be made different in the two directions of propagation. Examples of isolators making use of some of these phenomena are shown in Figs. 1.46 to 1.48.

Figure 1.46 shows a section of rectangular waveguide containing a sheet of ferrite material. The attenuation constant in the two directions of propagation is different, depending upon d-c magnetization and position of the ferrite strip. The d-c magnetic field is adjusted to equate the gyromagnetic resonance frequency to the r-f frequency. For this reason, the device is called the "resonance" isolator. Its performance vs. frequency is shown in Fig. 1.46. Figures 1.47 and 1.48 show two isolators based upon nonreciprocal displacement of transmitted fields. In both figures ferrite sheets, magnetized transversely, are placed along

narrow edges of the waveguide.   Propagation in the two directions results
in different distribution of the fields in the waveguide, as indicated schematically in Fig. 1.47a.   An isolator may be formed by placing a
resistance sheet on one side of the waveguide, as indicated in Fig. 1.47a,
causing appreciably greater loss in one direction of propagation than the
other.   In Fig. 1.48, the field displacement is utilized in a different way.
A slot is cut longitudinally in the waveguide along a line of maximum
electric field intensity for one direction of propagation.   As in the case
of a standing-wave detector, the presence of the slot does not disturb
the propagation.   In the reverse direction, however, the slot is located

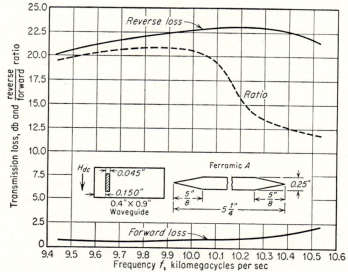

FIG. 1.46. Cross-sectional view and typical behavior of a resonance-type ferrite isolator.   (By permission from A. G. Fox, S. E. Miller, and M. T. Weiss, Behavior and
Applications of Ferrites in the Microwave Region, Bell System Tech. J., vol. 34, no. 1,
pp. 5–103, January, 1955.)

along a line of substantial transverse currents, causing appreciable leakage
of magnetic field into the slot.   Loading of the slot with lossy dielectric
material introduces substantial loss in the reverse direction.

Ferrite isolators are simpler and less expensive than power amplifiers.
They are most useful in applications where perfect isolation is not necessary, and where additional power amplification is not sufficiently important to compensate for the additional complexity and expense of the
amplifier stage.   Because of the characteristics of ferrite materials, ferrite
isolators are progressively more difficult to build at lower frequencies.

1.11. Variable Transmission Modulators.   Amplitude modulation of
radio-frequency signals can be produced by inserting a variable attenu-

ator between the r-f source and the load.   Devices of this type can be
used to produce amplitude modulation without disturbing the operating
potentials of the oscillator.   This permits the use of simpler power supplies in the oscillator circuits and avoids incidental frequency modulation

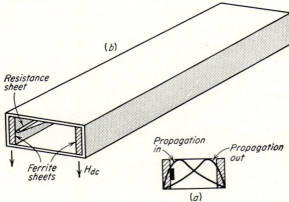

Fig. 1.47. Field-displacement isolator of the resistance type.   (a) Approximate field
distribution in the waveguide for the two directions of propagation; (b) suitable position for the resistance sheet attenuator.   (By permission from A. G. Fox, S. E. Miller,
and M. T. Weiss, Behavior and Applications of Ferrites in the Microwave Region, Bell
System Tech. J., vol. 34, no. 1, pp. 5–103, January, 1955.)

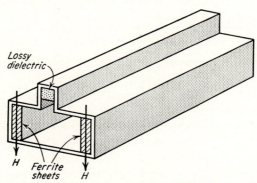

Fig. 1.48. Field-displacement isolator of the lossy-slot type.   (By permission from
A. G. Fox, S. E. Miller, and M. T. Weiss, Behavior and Applications of Ferrites in the
Microwave Region, Bell System Tech. J., vol. 34, no. 1, pp. 5–103, January, 1955.)

due to the variation of potentials.   This arrangement provides further
freedom in selection of modulation waveform.   It will be recalled that
in most microwave oscillators only special waveshapes may be used to
produce amplitude modulation; for example, sinusoidal amplitude modulation is generally impossible.   These restrictions on waveshape need not
apply to a modulator based upon the principle of variable transmission

provided that the device is arranged to present a constant impedance throughout the modulation cycle.

An ideal variable transmission modulator should present continuously variable attenuation, constant input and output impedances, and preferably should provide means to produce 100 per cent linear modulation. These requirements can be approximated closely by a number of devices, including the following:

1. Mechanically driven attenuators
2. Electrical absorption attenuators—crystal absorption attenuators, gas discharge attenuators, ferrite modulators
3. Miscellaneous electrical methods—electron streams in waveguides and cavities, Stark and Zeeman effect modulators, etc.

Some examples of these devices and their salient characteristics are described briefly below.

A variety of mechanically driven attenuators can be designed to provide variable attenuation.   An example of a convenient arrangement is

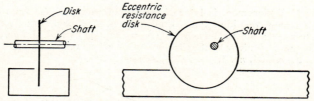

FIG. 1.49. Variable attenuator using a rotating resistive disk.

shown in Fig. 1.49.   A rotating disk of resistive material penetrates the waveguide through a longitudinal slot.   Rotation of the eccentric disk causes variable insertion of the resistive material into the waveguide. A sufficiently large disk radius permits gradual loading of the waveguide under all conditions of insertion and minimizes reflections.   The loss is negligible when the disk is removed and can be large at maximum insertion.[1]

Mechanical modulation methods are limited in usefulness to those applications where simple modulation waveform, low in frequency, is acceptable.   These restrictions can be removed by providing electrically controlled dissipation in the transmission line.   Many such devices are possible.   An example of a simple absorption modulator, employing crystal rectifiers, is shown in Fig. 1.50.   In this arrangement, two crystal rectifiers are placed across a coaxial line in series with suitably arranged bias and modulation voltages.   The rectifiers are connected to the coaxial

[1] R. H. Dicke, The Measurement of Thermal Radiation at Microwave Frequencies, Rev. Sci. Instr., vol. 17, no. 7, pp. 268–275, July, 1946.

line through a one-half wavelength transmission line so that the r-f voltages appear at the crystals 180° out of phase. The d-c bias and modulation voltages are connected to the crystals as indicated; because the modulation signal is applied to the crystals in opposite polarity, the modulation signal increases the impedance of one of the crystals while decreasing the impedance of the other. By careful control of bias and balancing voltages, it is possible to obtain 100 per cent modulation with good linearity.

Many other forms of microwave circuits employing similar principles are feasible. The arrangement shown in Fig. 1.50 is found useful up to about 2,300 Mc; above this frequency other balanced arrangements, such as magic-T bridges, are preferable. There are no special limitations on the usable frequency range of devices of this type.

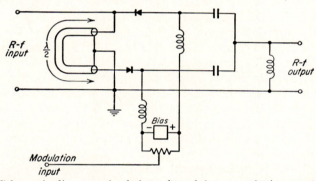

FIG. 1.50. Schematic diagram of a balanced modulator employing crystal rectifiers.

The balanced modulator discussed above does not have ideal constant input and output impedances, as these are found to vary with bias and modulation voltages. For best performance, it is necessary to isolate the modulator from the source by means of suitable attenuator pads or other isolators, as discussed in Sec. 1.10.

The power output from the crystal modulator is determined by the available power and the power-handling capacity of the crystal rectifiers. With present-day crystals, such as 1N21, the incident power upon a crystal should not exceed 100 mw. Corresponding output power under these conditions is usually less than 10 mw. This power limitation, together with undesirable variable input impedance, makes the crystal-balanced modulator less attractive than other possible arrangements.

Another form of variable attenuator can be provided by use of ferrite isolators. For example, if the magnetic field of the Faraday rotation isolator shown in Fig. 1.45a is supplied from an a-c source, the transmitted power will vary in proportion to the modulating voltage. As can be seen from Figs. 1.45b and 1.45c, this is due to the rotation of the plane of polarization of the emerging signal. Ferrite isolators are simple in construction and use and provide constant input and output impedances. Modulation rates, however, are limited by the fact that magnetic fields produced by the external magnet must permeate the metallic wall of the waveguide. This generally limits the modulation frequencies to low audio frequencies. Because of the characteristics of the ferrite materials, this method is limited to frequencies above about 3,000 Mc.

Ferrite phase shifters can also be used to produce single-sideband modulation. A ferrite device, similar in construction to the isolator shown in Fig. 1.45a, can be employed for the purpose. If the ferrite material is magnetized by means of a two-phase rotating field produced in a plane transverse to the direction of propagation, the circularly polarized wave emerging from the ferrite section will rotate at the rate of the modulating field and will cause the output frequency to be shifted by twice the rotation frequency of the magnetic field.[1] By means of such devices, it has been found possible to shift the incident signal by as much as 20 kc. This arrangement is particularly useful for providing two signals simultaneously, separated by the audio-modulation frequency; one of these can be used as a signal source and the other as a local oscillator in the detecting equipment. This arrangement is considerably simpler than the synchrodyne operation of velocity-modulated devices, as long as the needed frequency shift does not exceed the audio frequency mentioned.

Electrically controlled attenuation can be provided also by means of gas discharge initiated by modulating voltages or external electron streams. For example, a section of waveguide can be provided with a gas discharge tube in which ionization is created by means of an electron stream introduced into the discharge tube from a cathode external to the waveguide. Attenuation results due to absorption of the propagating signal in the ionized gas. Attenuation in a suitably constructed device can be controlled by varying the discharge current. Commercially available devices have been made in which the attenuation can be varied from 0 to 40 db. Modulation rates are limited by the discharge phenomena.[2]

Other miscellaneous methods for electrically controlling attenuation which will be useful under special circumstance have been devised. Electron streams passing through waveguides or cavities under the influ-

---

[1] See J. C. Cacheris and H. A. Dropkin, Compact Microwave Single-sideband Modulator Using Ferrites, *Trans. IRE*, vol. MTT-4, no. 3, pp. 152–155, July, 1956; J. C. Cacheris, Microwave Single Sideband Modulator Using Ferrites, *Proc. IRE*, vol. 42, no. 8, pp. 1242–1247, August, 1954.

[2] Devices of this type are manufactured by Roger White Electron Devices, Inc., Ramsey, N.J.

ence of d-c magnetic fields can be used to provide means for absorption of the r-f power.[1]

Still other natural phenomena can be employed to provide attenuation. Many gases are known which show strong resonant absorption at microwave frequencies due to molecular phenomena. This absorption, occurring at discreet frequencies, is often sufficient in magnitude to provide strong attenuation. The frequency at which prominent absorption occurs depends on the nature of the gas, but can be modified by exposing the gas molecules to strong electric or magnetic fields. Thus, a waveguide cell filled with a suitable gas, such as ammonia, will exhibit absorption at certain frequencies. Application of sufficiently strong electric field will shift the absorption frequency greatly, reducing or eliminating the loss. The d-c fields can be applied inside the waveguides by placing a septum plate perpendicularly to the electric field in the waveguide and supported by suitable dielectric insulators. Devices of this type, called *Stark effect modulators*, are commonly used in microwave spectroscopic experiments. Because microwave absorption occurs only at discreet frequencies, the method is not generally useful in ordinary laboratory applications.

1.12. Power Supplies for Laboratory Oscillators. *a. General Requirements.* Power-supply requirements for microwave oscillators and amplifiers depend upon the specific tube in question. Since both amplitude and frequency in most microwave devices are determined by transit-time effects, voltage-stability considerations form the primary criteria in the design of power supplies. Although design problems are not unduly critical, considerable care is sometimes necessary to avoid undesirable amplitude and frequency modulation.

Except for the triode, microwave tubes usually employ relatively high voltages and low currents. The resultant high-impedance power-supply circuits must be carefully designed to avoid numerous instabilities and electrical pickup. In certain klystrons, some electrodes can exhibit negative resistance characteristics due to secondary emission; excessively high impedance in the power supply can cause progressively increasing current and, in the extreme cases, can destroy the tube under seemingly safe conditions. As a result, design of power supplies must take into account these possibilities, in addition to the more obvious voltage, current, and stability requirements.

It is not inappropriate to warn the prospective user of velocity-modulation tubes that their operation entails the use of dangerously high potentials. High voltages can appear at various places along the tube structure besides the cathode terminal. To avoid accidents, it is always

---

[1] J. S. Donal and R. R. Bush, A Spiral-beam Method for the Amplitude Modulation of Magnetrons, *Proc. IRE*, vol. 37, no. 4, pp. 375–382, April, 1949.

wise to turn off electrical power before disconnecting cables or making other similar adjustments. Resonant cavities of a klystron tube form a part of the anode and are generally electrically grounded, since the output transmission lines, connected to the cavities, are nearly always directly accessible to the operator. This implies that the positive terminal of the power supply is grounded but this does not present any special safety hazard. However, in certain applications, potentials for the microwave tube are derived from other electronic circuits operated with grounded negative terminal. To make this possible, cavities must be insulated from their output transmission lines by means of suitable capacity joints and become at high voltage with respect to ground. Under these circumstances, additional protection is necessary to guard against possible accidents in adjustment of the klystron or its cavities. In particular, tuning of the klystron cavities must be accomplished by means of an insulated tool. These and many other similar precautions can be learned by study of instructions furnished by the manufacturer of the particular tube or apparatus.

b. Sources of Stable Voltage. Voltage-stability requirements for microwave tubes form the primary consideration in the design and choice of power supplies. An examination of formulas for modulation sensitivity for various oscillators shows that frequency deviation in the order of 1 Mc/volt is not unusual. Many practical circumstances require frequency stability of the order of 1 kc or less; this implies that power supplies must often be provided with voltage fluctuations of less than 1 mv. If the applied voltages are in the range of 500 volts, stability requirements correspond to a few parts in a million. Voltage stability of this magnitude, at least for short periods, can be obtained by paying careful attention to the various circuit problems.

It is convenient to subdivide the stability criteria into statements of long-time and short-time stability. The exact meaning of these terms cannot be stated without discussing the specific application, but becomes obvious in relation to particular problems. Generally, long-time stability refers to voltage (or frequency) stability when measured over periods of minutes, hours, or longer periods. Short-time stability refers to phenomena which occur due to the presence of random voltage fluctuations or other electrical pickup, such as 60-cycle hum. It often happens that in a given problem one type of stability is more important than the other. For example, in measurements of impedance at microwave frequencies, the frequency must remain constant during a period of a single measurement, such as a few seconds; stability over periods of minutes or hours is not important. In other applications, long-time stability is more important, for example, in the problems pertaining to frequency standardization of transmitters or in the study of highly resonant systems.

Perhaps the ultimate in voltage stability is obtained by the use of batteries which have extremely stable voltages provided they are new, the current is not excessive, and the wiring is properly arranged to avoid electrical pickup. With age, the voltage can either change slowly or contain random fluctuations. For general purpose applications, batteries are not suitable because of high operating cost, excessive weight, and bulk. Battery-type high-voltage supplies should be handled carefully since the danger to personnel is especially high because of low internal impedance.

In nearly all common applications, the power is furnished by means of ordinary rectifier-type power supplies followed by degenerative electronic voltage regulators. The power-supply design follows conventional practice and will not be discussed in detail. The degenerative electronic

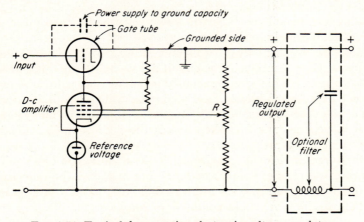

FIG. 1.51. Typical degenerative electronic voltage regulator.

regulator can take several forms, one of which is illustrated in Fig. 1.51. It consists of four main elements: a stable source of reference voltage; a voltage divider across the output; a d-c amplifier; and a series gate tube. A part of the output voltage is compared with the reference voltage, the difference being amplified by the d-c amplifier which controls the voltage drop across the gate tube. This arrangement may be regarded as a negative feedback system with a large feedback factor. Design of the voltage regulator circuit follows the accepted practice.

Two features of regulators require special mention. The output voltage cannot be more stable than the reference voltage; although batteries can be used for the purpose, the more common source is a voltage regulator tube of a gaseous-discharge type. Even if the current through the reference tube is constant, the voltage can still vary with ambient temperature, aging of the tube, and other uncontrollable factors. The long-time stability of the power supply will depend upon these characteristics of the reference voltage supply. The short-time stability of the regulator, even in the limit of infinite feedback ratio, is limited by the general configuration of the electronic regulator. It will be noted that the cathode of the gate tube is grounded; examination of typical power-supply circuits will show that capacity exists from positive side to ground. This results in the gate tube being shunted by this capacity, permitting power-supply ripple to appear in the output circuit. To avoid this situation, it is generally best to satisfy the required long-time and short-time stability by different means. The former can be adequately met by the use of the electronic voltage regulator, and the latter by the addition of suitable LC filters in the negative lead of the output circuit.

In using electronic regulators of the type shown, it is necessary to insure that the gate-tube voltage is always within design limits. Excessive voltage can spoil the tube while low voltages will cause the circuit to operate improperly. This means that output voltage from the regulator must be adjusted by a two-step process. With potentiometer R in Fig. 1.51, the potentials in the circuit are varied to provide the desired output voltage. This simultaneously changes the gate-tube voltage which will have to be kept at a nearly constant value by suitable readjustments of the voltage furnished by the power supply. In many practical designs, a voltmeter is furnished across the gate tube to indicate the proper range of operation.

Voltages required for electrodes other than the anode can be derived from power supplies of simpler design. For example, the reflector electrode of a reflex klystron does not draw any current, so that the required potentials can be provided in a number of simple ways. Despite the low current needed, it may still be necessary to keep the internal resistance of the power supplies at reasonably low values. In order to avoid electrical pickup in the high impedance leads, a condenser is generally placed across the reflector terminals at or near the klystron. The time constant of the circuit can become inconveniently large if the power-supply impedance is too high. Further, possible secondary emission from the reflector electrode can cause the klystron to become unstable and to draw the full current to the reflector. This can cause overheating and destroy the tube. In cases where high impedance in the reflector circuit is essential, it is good practice to provide a diode between the cathode and reflector connected in such a way that the latter is prevented from becoming positive with respect to the cathode.

An example of a circuit needed to provide operating potentials for a reflex klystron is shown in Fig. 1.52. This diagram also indicates possible means of introducing modulation voltages to the reflector electrode. Capacity C_2 represents the reflector electrode and wiring capacity to ground. Resistor R is chosen to make the time constant RC_2 appropriate to the high-frequency components of the modulation voltage. The coupling condensers C_1 permit the modulation circuits to remain at ground potential; these need to be large enough to provide negligibly low reactance at the lowest frequency component of the modulation voltage.

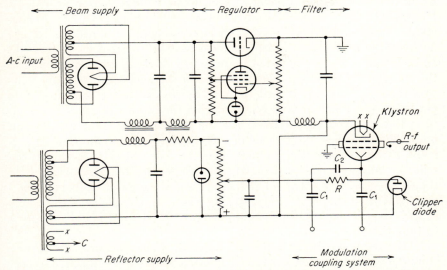

FIG. 1.52. Simplified circuit diagram showing an arrangement of power-supply components for a reflex klystron oscillator.

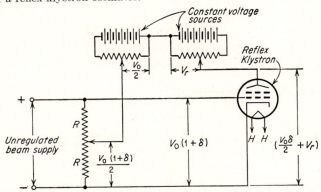

FIG. 1.53. Simplified circuit showing a method of using unregulated beam-voltage supply in a reflex klystron oscillator.

    c. Voltage-compensating Circuit for Reflex Klystrons. Frequency changes in the reflex klystron due to changes in applied potentials are caused by changes in the transit time of electrons in the reflection space. It is possible to make the transit time of electrons independent of the beam voltage by means of a compensating arrangement shown in Fig. 1.53. Examination of Eq. (1.30) shows that transit time through the reflection space can be kept constant if a change in the beam voltage is compensated by a proper change in reflector voltage.[1] The proper conditions for compensation may be accomplished as follows: The unregulated beam voltage supply shown in Fig. 1.53 is tapped at its midpoint by means of a voltage divider. A constant voltage source provides a bias voltage equal to one-half of the beam supply voltage; a normal constant voltage supply provides the reflector voltage V_r. Thus, the voltage between the reflector and cathode consists of the desired d-c voltage V_r and one-half of the unregulated beam supply fluctuations. According to the theory of the method, these changes in the anode and reflector voltages result in constant transit time. The simple theory presented does not hold when reflector voltage approaches the beam voltage. The compensation still can be obtained, but the proper adjustment will depend upon the magnitude of the reflector voltage and requires empirical adjustment of the compensating voltage. As the reflex klystron is tuned, the reflector voltage must be changed and this necessitates readjustment of the compensating voltage. For these reasons, the merit of this arrangement is limited to special circumstances where the simplicity of the power supply arrangement is of prime importance, or where it is not necessary to tune the klystron at all.

1.13. Frequency Stabilization of Laboratory Oscillators. Frequency stability of free-running oscillators is often found to be unsatisfactory. In a reflex klystron, for example, operating conditions can cause variations in frequency for two reasons: changes in natural resonant frequency of the cavity, and changes in applied potentials. The natural resonant frequency of a cavity can be altered by thermal expansion of its parts, by changes in humidity and air pressure, and by mechanical or acoustical vibration. Variations in load impedance, when referred to the r-f gap

---

[1] Equation (1.30) can be rewritten as

$$V_r = \sqrt{\frac{V_0}{K}} - V_0 \tag{1.56}$$

Differentiating this with respect to V_0, the slope is found to be

$$\frac{dV_r}{dV_0} = \frac{1}{2K^{1/2}} V_0^{-1/2} - 1 \tag{1.57}$$

For the region in Fig. 1.15 corresponding to $V_0 \gg V_r$, the slope dV_r/dV_0 can be determined by eliminating K from Eqs. (1.56) and (1.57). This leads to

$$\left. \frac{dV_r}{dV_0} \right|_{V_r \approx 0} = -\frac{1}{2} \tag{1.58}$$

or

$$dV_r = -\frac{dV_0}{2} \tag{1.59}$$

Equation (1.59), derived by elimination of K, states the relation between V_0 and V_r for the condition of constant transit time.

terminals, result in both resistive and reactive components and also cause frequency changes. Variations in applied potentials cause the frequency to change from the natural frequency by an amount Δf as given by Eq. (1.44), repeated below:

$$\Delta f = \frac{f}{2Q_L} \tan \phi \tag{1.44}$$

Frequency deviations due to these effects can be minimized by paying proper attention to the factors mentioned, or by employing external means of stabilization. Several methods can be resorted to for improving frequency stability. Among the most common are the following:

1. Eliminating or reducing the causes of instability
2. Use of electronic stabilization, i.e., application of negative feedback principle by converting frequency fluctuations into amplitude modulation with the aid of a stable reference cavity
3. Cavity stabilization, i.e., increase of the operating Q of the oscillator by means of a coupled external cavity

Although these methods can be applied to any microwave oscillator, the following discussion will be limited to the applications in the reflex klystron.

The degree of stabilization obtained by means of a given method is usually described by specifying a *stabilization factor S* as the ratio of frequency change without stabilization to the frequency change with stabilization. Usually a subscript is added to the symbol S to denote the particular quantity against which the frequency stabilization is effective.

In general, stabilization S against various causes of instability will differ in a manner depending upon the specific details of the stabilization process.

a. Stabilization of Operating Conditions. The first obvious method of improving the stability of an oscillator is to determine the cause of instability and to minimize its effect by appropriate corrective measures. If the applied potentials vary excessively with time due to the instability of the power supply, an appropriate use of voltage regulators, filters, or batteries, as discussed in Sec. 1.12, will be found helpful.

It may also be necessary to reduce the changes of cavity dimensions with temperature. Changes in temperature can be caused by either changes in the ambient temperature or by changes in power input to the tube. The effect of the two is not equivalent, as distribution of heat flow among the various tube and cavity parts is strongly affected by details of tube design. Klystrons designed for stable operation use materials selected to provide automatic temperature compensation in cavity dimensions for changes in power and for subsequent internal heat

redistribution.   Except in unusual cases, the user has no control over
stability characteristics of the tube itself against changes in power input.
Stabilization of voltage and current remains as the only practical expedient to maintain the tube dimensions at constant values.

Changes in ambient temperature will affect the frequency of oscillation
to a degree which is dependent upon the construction of the klystron
and the care taken in controlling the temperature compensation of important parts.   The effect of temperature changes can be minimized by
insulating the klystron from its environment or by placing the klystron
into suitable constant-temperature enclosures.   The latter can take the
form of temperature-controlled chambers with thermostatically regulated
air flow.   In the case of klystrons with integral cavities, it is sometimes
practical to place the entire tube in a bath of oil kept at a constant
temperature by water cooling.   Liquid cooling methods of this type also

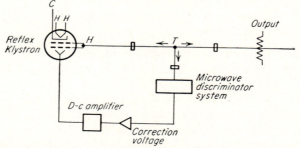

FIG. 1.54. Block diagram showing main components needed for an electronic frequency-
stabilization system.

help to eliminate the acoustical and mechanical vibrations often encountered with turbulent air cooling.

b. Electronic Stabilization.   There are many possible ways to electronicly stabilize a microwave oscillator.   Essential features of a typical system are shown in Fig. 1.54.   The oscillator is connected to its
output load, but a fraction of the power is diverted to a microwave
discriminator.   Although the latter can take any of a large number of
possible forms, the essential feature consists of an arrangement permitting the signal to be compared against a stable high-Q cavity producing a sensing signal dependent upon relative tuning of the oscillator
and the cavity.   The correction voltage obtained from the discriminator
can be applied to the klystron to force the oscillation frequency closer to
the resonant frequency of the reference cavity.

A microwave discriminator can be constructed in several ways.   A
conventional form of radio-frequency discriminator employing two resonant circuits, tuned slightly above and below the resonant frequency,
can easily be formed using resonant cavities connected in parallel to the

r-f source. Crystal detectors coupled to the two resonant cavities are connected in phase opposition.   The difference voltage derived from them makes the detected signal correspond closely to the usual discriminator characteristic.   While simple conceptually, this arrangement suffers somewhat in performance because the proper behavior of the circuit depends upon the stability of the two detectors.

Another method of detecting frequency displacement of r-f signal from its proper value is to rapidly sweep the cavity tuning about its mean frequency.   This can be done, for example, by mechanically modulating the cavity with an acoustical diaphragm.   Rectified output from the

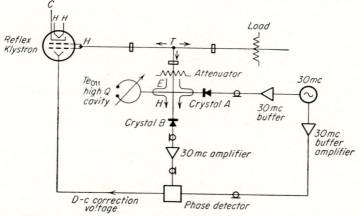

Fig. 1.55. Electronic frequency-stabilization system employing Pound microwave discriminator.

cavity is compared in a phase-detector circuit against modulation voltage; the d-c output from the phase detector provides a d-c correction voltage suitable for controlling the oscillator frequency.   Using but one crystal detector, this system avoids the difficulties with the two-cavity method.   However, it is only capable of correcting frequency changes when these are slow compared to the cavity-modulation frequency.

Many other forms of microwave discriminators can also be devised. An example of a highly developed electronic stabilization system is shown in Fig. 1.55, commonly referred to as a *Pound stabilizer*.[1]   In the form

---

[1] For further details, see R. V. Pound, Electronic Frequency Stabilization of Microwave Oscillators, *Rev. Sci. Instr.*, vol. 17, no. 11, pp. 490–505, November, 1946; also R. V. Pound, Frequency Stabilization of Electronically Tunable Microwave Oscillators, pp. 58–78 in C. G. Montgomery (ed.), "Technique of Microwave Measurements," McGraw-Hill Book Company, Inc., New York, 1947.   Improved version of this system is described by W. G. Tuller, W. C. Galloway, and F. P. Zaffarano, Recent Developments in Frequency Stabilization of Microwave Oscillators, *Massachusetts Institute of Technology Research Laboratory of Electronics Tech. Rept.* 53, Nov. 20, 1947.

shown, the principal amplification of the correction voltage occurs at 30 Mc, which is obtained as follows: The microwave signal from an oscillator divides in a T junction, permitting part of the available power to reach a magic-T junction which forms the microwave discriminator. The symmetrical arms of the magic-T junction are terminated by a high-Q reference cavity and a crystal rectifier labeled A, the latter being biased with 30-Mc voltage as indicated. The periodic variation of impedance of the crystal causes 30-Mc modulation of the r-f signal which reaches this arm. The signals arriving at crystal B consist of the signal reflected from the cavity and two sidebands resulting from the modulation of the carrier at crystal A. The output of crystal B can be shown to consist of a 30-Mc voltage whose phase depends upon the relative tuning of the cavity and the incoming r-f signal, with the magnitude of the voltage being proportional to the frequency deviation. The amplified 30-Mc signal voltage is compared with the 30-Mc reference voltage in a phase detector. The output of the latter corresponds closely to the familiar discriminator characteristic. With sufficient amplification of the 30-Mc signal, the phase detector will develop sufficient signal to be applied as a correction voltage to the klystron directly, eliminating the need for any d-c amplification.

By careful design of the apparatus, it is possible to obtain a short-time frequency stability in the order of one part in 10^8. Long-time stability is nearly completely determined by the characteristics of the reference cavity. By careful construction and temperature compensation, the stability of the latter can approach the performance of quartz-crystal systems. The adjustment of the Pound system is straightforward. The reference cavity is first tuned to the desired frequency, and the oscillator is merely tuned for maximum output. Small changes in frequency can be made by tuning the reference cavity alone.

c. Cavity Stabilization.[1] Examination of Eq. (1.20) or Eq. (1.44) will show that the frequency stability with respect to operating potentials may be improved by increasing Q_L. To a small extent, this can be accomplished by merely reducing the coupling between the klystron and its load. Greater improvement can be realized by coupling an external cavity with considerably higher Q than it is possible to obtain with the reentrant klystron resonator.

As shown in Sec. 9.1, the klystron resonator can be represented by an equivalent shunt resonant circuit at the detuned-short position. If an external cavity is connected to the klystron so that the detuned-short position of the klystron and the external cavity coincide, the two cavities can be considered to be in parallel. The effective Q of the system is

---

[1] G. B. Collins, "Microwave Magnetrons," p. 305, McGraw-Hill Book Company, Inc., New York, 1948.

determined by the parallel combination of the two circuits and is approximately equal to the arithmetic mean of the two Q values.

The necessary equipment can be arranged in two ways. The stabilizing cavity can be connected to the main transmission line by means of a T junction between the oscillator and the load. Alternatively, the stabilizing cavity can be placed between the load and the klystron. The second of the two permits greater stabilization against variations in load impedance at the cost of reduced power output and efficiency.

Figure 1.56 shows a photograph of a transmission-type stabilization cavity attached to an X-band klystron. Rigid cavity construction permits high degree of mechanical stability; unloaded Q of 150,000 produced by $TE_{0,1,17}$ mode results in a stabilization ratio of approximately 100 against changes in potentials. Operation of the stabilization cavity in this high-order mode necessarily greatly restricts the tuning range because of the presence of interfering modes. The transmission-type method provides stabilization factor S_L against load variation of the order of 1,000.*

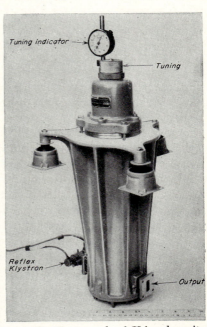

Fig. 1.56. Photograph of X-band cavity stabilizer for a reflex klystron. (*Courtesy of Varian Associates, Inc.*)

1.14. Standard Signal Generators. *a. Basic Requirements.* A standard signal generator is a laboratory oscillator equipped with suitable provisions for carefully controlling and monitoring the output power and frequency. They are used principally for determining sensitivity of receivers but also have numerous other laboratory applications. While they can also be used for more ordinary applications such as a source of r-f power for standing-wave detectors, bridges, etc., their low power output makes them less useful than the simpler laboratory oscillators previously described. Their relative complexity and high cost should preclude their use unless the application requires standard signals.

If used for testing of receivers, the signal generators can take one of two different forms. In the first, the r-f power is generated at some con-

* The example referred to is due to developments at Varian Associates. Private communication from M. Stitch and M. St. Clair.

venient low power level, perhaps in the range of tens of milliwatts, which is ideal for the purpose of power monitoring. With the aid of a variable r-f attenuator, the output is then reduced to the noise level of the receiver under test. Since the equivalent input noise power in a typical receiver can be as low as 10^{-15} watts, large attenuation is required which introduces various difficulties, as will be mentioned later. This arrangement, however, provides continuously variable signals over large power range which may be needed for such purposes as studying receivers with poor sensitivity, testing the performance of receivers with several stages of amplification, determining overload characteristics of a receiver as a function of input power, and other diverse and useful tasks.

The second method of generating standard signals consists of deriving known *noise* signals at a power level in the general vicinity of the inherent receiver noise. Many systems capable of generating random noise have been devised whose noise output can be predicted from the physical phenomenon involved. Careful comparison against signals from standard signal generators can be used to assure the accuracy of the calibration. The advantage of the noise-source method is its simplicity; power generated at a level corresponding to receiver noise makes r-f attenuators unnecessary. The usefulness of noise generated is limited because it is found difficult to generate noise signals much above the thermal noise of a resistor at room temperature. Methods capable of generating substantial noise power involve phenomena which contain uncertain theoretical factors. As a result, receivers with poor sensitivity cannot be tested accurately and often not at all.

b. Standard Signal Generators. A block diagram of a representative standard signal generator is illustrated schematically in Fig. 1.57. The main components are:

1. Tunable laboratory oscillator (or an oscillator-amplifier system)
2. Power supplies
3. Modulating circuits
4. Power monitor
5. Frequency monitor
6. R-f attenuator
7. Shielding and power-line filters
8. Optional external power bridge for initial power calibration

An ideal standard signal generator delivers output signals at a frequency and power level which can be determined from direct-reading dials controlling the r-f attenuator setting and the oscillator tuning, respectively. Ideally, the r-f signals at the output can be reduced indefinitely by adding sufficient attenuation; in practice, this is impossible as the r-f shielding of the signal generator components cannot be perfect, causing small signals to radiate into the surrounding space. The shielding requirements depend upon various factors, such as the sensitivity of apparatus under test and its own shielding.

The r-f source in the signal generator closely resembles the laboratory oscillator previously described. For most applications, it is desirable to provide tuning over a wide frequency range such as the bandwidth of the output transmission line. For various practical reasons, the tuning range becomes progressively smaller at the higher frequencies. It is usually advisable to keep the output at a constant level as the tuning is

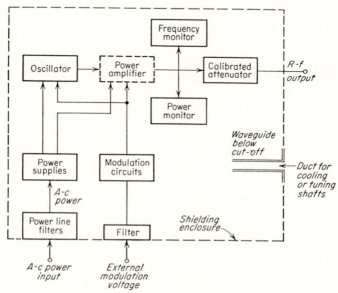

FIG. 1.57. Block diagram of a standard signal generator.

varied. As this may be difficult to attain, a power monitor is often connected at the input terminals to the r-f attenuator, permitting visual observation of the power level. The frequency of the signal generator can be determined from the setting of the tuning control of the oscillator or, more carefully, by means of a frequency monitor of the cavity wavemeter type described in Chap. 7.

Power supplies and modulating circuits needed for the r-f oscillator depend upon the various factors previously discussed. The leads bringing the a-c power for the power supplies and other circuits contained within the shielding enclosure must be carefully filtered to prevent leakage of r-f power. Even though microwave oscillators employ cavity resonators, substantial leakage occurs because of imperfect construction of cavities or output connectors; the various interconnecting cables inside of the enclosure may pick up some of this leakage power and radiate it externally unless low-pass filters are provided. Suitable filters can be constructed using lumped-parameter filter sections, distributed-parameter cavity filters, or artificial transmission lines employing high-loss dielectric material, such as powdered iron. In addition, the shielding enclosure around the entire chamber must be sufficiently continuous to prevent leakage at the various joints. Difficulties in joint design can be resolved by various methods, such as gaskets, fingers, or nearly perfect mechanical joints. These practical considerations do not warrant further discussion because the performance of a given method depends upon mechanical perfection.

It is often necessary to pierce the shielding enclosure to provide holes for tuning shafts for the oscillator, attenuator, and other adjustments; or, to provide holes for circulation of air for cooling. Tubular ducts, permanently attached to the shielding enclosure as shown in Fig. 1.57, will cause negligible leakage if the tube diameter is small enough to cause

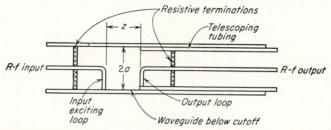

FIG. 1.58. Simplified drawing of the TE_{11} waveguide-below-cutoff attenuator.

the duct to act as a waveguide below cutoff and if the duct is made sufficiently long. Ducts of this type can be used to provide mechanical coupling between inside and outside as needed for various tuning adjustments. Tuning rods passing through the duct must be constructed of dielectric material to insure that the duct continues to act as a waveguide below cutoff in the presence of the rod. Simpler mechanical methods can be used if shielding requirements are not excessively severe.

The remaining important component of the standard signal generator is the r-f attenuator. In many applications it is necessary to reduce the power level from about 1 mw to 10^{-15} watt or less, requiring a range of 120 db or more. The needed attenuation can be easily provided by passing the signal through a waveguide whose transverse dimensions are too small to permit normal propagation.[1] Consider, for example, the behavior of a typical waveguide or *piston* attenuator shown in Fig. 1.58.

[1] Problems pertaining to design and construction of waveguide below cutoff attenuators are described in C. G. Montgomery (ed.), "Technique of Microwave Measurements," pp. 685–719, McGraw-Hill Book Company, Inc., New York, 1947.

It consists of a section of a waveguide (usually cylindrical) operated below cutoff. The fields excited in the waveguide in some convenient manner must decay exponentially with distance. Figure 1.58 shows a coaxial line terminated in an inductive post which can be regarded as an input exciting loop. Attenuated fields establish an output signal by means of a similar coupling mechanism. At both input and output terminals some form of resistive termination is usually needed to make the input and output impedances equal to characteristic impedances of the lines used. Circular waveguides are invariably used since telescoping tubing easily permits simple mechanical adjustment of loop separation. The diameter of the attenuating waveguide must be accurately known and should remain constant over the entire usable region of loop separation.

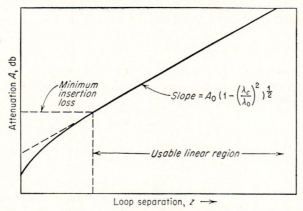

Fig. 1.59. Insertion loss of a waveguide-below-cutoff attenuator as a function of loop separation.

The insertion loss of the piston attenuator can be accurately predicted from simple theory and waveguide dimensions. Typical behavior of the attenuator as a function of loop separation is shown in Fig. 1.59. For small loop separation attenuation A (expressed in decibels) varies non-linearly with displacement; this is due to the presence of extraneous modes excited by the input loop. Beyond a certain loop separation, the attenuation becomes linear with distance and easily predictable from the dimensions of the waveguide and the operating wavelength. The attenuation A beyond minimum insertion loss is given by[1]

$$A_{\mathrm{db}} = 16.0 \frac{z}{a} \left[1 - \left(\frac{\lambda_0}{\lambda_c} \right)^2 \right]^{1/2} \tag{1.60}$$

where z is the loop displacement beyond the point of minimum insertion

[1] These results can be obtained as follows. The propagation of a given mode through a waveguide can be represented by means of a traveling wave of magnitude

loss, a is the waveguide radius, λ_0 is the free-space wavelength, and λ_c the cutoff wavelength. For $\lambda_0 \gg \lambda_c$, Eq. (1.60) becomes

$$A_{db} = 16.0 \frac{z}{a} \qquad (1.61)$$

E. If initial excitation is E_0, the field E will be given by

$$E = E_0 e^{j(\omega t - \beta z)} \qquad (1.62)$$

where the symbols are as defined in Chap. 4 (cf. Eq. 4.26). Omitting time factors,

$$E = E_0 e^{-j\beta z} \qquad (1.63)$$

Using Eq. (4.36),

$$\frac{E}{E_0} = e^{-j\frac{2\pi z}{\lambda_0}\left[1 - \left(\frac{\lambda_0}{\lambda_c}\right)^2\right]^{\frac{1}{2}}} \qquad (1.64)$$

If $\lambda_0 > \lambda_c$, the radical is imaginary and Eq. (1.64) becomes

$$\frac{E}{E_0} = e^{-\frac{2\pi z}{\lambda_c}\left[1 - \left(\frac{\lambda_c}{\lambda_0}\right)^2\right]^{\frac{1}{2}}} \qquad (1.65)$$

indicating exponential attenuation of the exciting wave. The cutoff wavelength of a waveguide depends upon its transverse dimensions. Thus, using Eq. (7.15) and Table 7.1, Eq. (1.65) becomes

$$\frac{E}{E_0} = e^{-u'_{m,n}\frac{z}{a}\left[1 - \left(\frac{\lambda_c}{\lambda_0}\right)^2\right]^{\frac{1}{2}}} \qquad (1.66)$$

Taking the logarithm of Eq. (1.66),

$$\begin{aligned} A_{db} &= 8.686 \ln \frac{E}{E_0} \\ &= 8.686 u'_{m,n} \frac{z}{a} \left[1 - \left(\frac{\lambda_c}{\lambda_0}\right)^2\right]^{\frac{1}{2}} \\ &= A_0 \left[1 - \left(\frac{\lambda_c}{\lambda_0}\right)^2\right]^{\frac{1}{2}} \end{aligned} \qquad (1.67)$$

where $A_0 = 8.686 u'_{m,n}$. The lowest or *dominant* mode is TE_{11} for which $u'_{m,n} = 3.42$. Substitution of this value leads to Eqs. (1.60) and (1.61). Attenuation for other modes can be obtained by substituting appropriate values for $u'_{m,n}$ from Table 7.1 or Appendix A. It will be observed that the attenuation of TE_{11} mode is smaller than of any other mode. Thus, with sufficient distance, the TE_{11} field will always become predominant. The initial nonlinearity of attenuation with distance shown in Fig. 1.59 is principally due to the presence of higher-order modes. Beyond the point labeled *minimum insertion loss*, other modes become too small to be important and the remaining field is due to TE_{11} mode alone. Practical problems include detection of the presence of fields due to residual undesirable modes, reduction of the magnitude of undesirable modes at small loop separations, and other important questions which are discussed in the reference cited.

Derivation of the above formulas neglects the skin effect which effectively increases the waveguide dimensions. At microwave frequencies, this correction is negligibly small but becomes important at very low r-f frequencies. For further discussion of second-order effects see J. Brown, Corrections to the Attenuation of Piston Attenuators, *Proc. IEE (Radio and Communications)*, vol. 96, pt. III, p. 191, November, 1949.

These equations are applicable for waveguides excited to emphasize the TE_{11} mode. Attenuators of this type are sometimes referred to as *inductive* because the coupling between the input and output circuits is due to linkage by magnetic flux. Although coupling by other modes of propagation is also possible, their use is not recommended because their attenuation is not so great as for the TE_{11} mode; excitation of the waveguide in any other mode will excite the TE_{11} mode to some extent, causing it to become predominant with sufficient separation and result in serious error. Carefully constructed inductive attenuators can be regarded as standards of attenuation, since their accuracy depends only upon the measurement of mechanical dimensions.

Several other types of attenuators can be used when the needed measurement accuracy does not justify the expense of the precision inductive attenuator. Several successful forms of resistive attenuators have been devised for this purpose.[1]

c. Noise-signal Generators. Substantial noise power can be generated in various ways. To insure accurate calibration, it is imperative to be able to predict the generated power level from some aspect of the natural phenomenon. Among devices found to be successful for the purpose of testing receivers are: resistors generating thermal noise at elevated temperatures; gas discharge in fluorescent-type lamps; and noise induced in standardized microwave cavities due to temperature-limited electron beams. Power available from these sources increases in the order mentioned. Other methods of noise generation are also known, but have not been sufficiently perfected.

As previously mentioned, the use of noise-signal generators for testing radio receivers eliminates the possibilities of error which tend to accumulate when large attenuation is used to reduce the power from a relatively high-power laboratory oscillator. Another advantage of the noise generator (assuming that the bandwidth of the noise source is appreciably larger than that of the receiver under test) is the fact that the noise can be compared directly against the receiver noise without a subsidiary measurement of its bandwidth. The comparison of noise against noise avoids certain theoretical uncertainties in comparison of sinusoidal signals against noise which may arise as a result of the detection process.

The use of a noise source for testing receivers is illustrated schematically

---

[1] For example, see B. P. Hand, A Precision Wave Guide Attenuator Which Obeys a Mathematical Law, *Hewlett-Packard J.*, vol. 6, no. 5, January, 1955. This paper describes a rotary attenuator capable of providing 0 to 50 db, with errors not exceeding 1 db. A circular TE_{11} waveguide carries a resistive septum; rotation of this waveguide with respect to fixed input and output sections provides attenuation depending upon *orientation* of the septum with respect to plane of polarization of the incident wave. Calibration is independent of frequency and the specific resistance of the septum.

in Fig. 1.60. A receiver under test is connected (perhaps through an impedance transformer) to a resistance R which, for the moment, can be assumed to be any suitable resistor terminating the r-f transmission line in its characteristic impedance. The noise power P_n generated by the resistor R is due to thermal agitation; it is often called *thermal*, or *Johnson*, noise. The magnitude of the noise is given by

$$P_n = \frac{\bar{e}_n{}^2}{R} \tag{1.68}$$

$$P_n = 4kT \, \Delta f \tag{1.69}$$

where $\bar{e}_n{}^2$ is the mean-square noise voltage produced by the resistor R, k is the Boltzmann constant, T is the temperature of the resistor in degrees

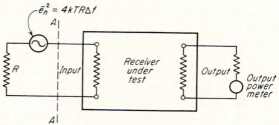

Fig. 1.60. Equivalent circuit of the noise generator connected to a receiver under test.

Kelvin, and Δf is the bandwidth over which the power is measured. The mean-square noise voltage can be written as

$$\bar{e}_n{}^2 = 4kTR \, \Delta f \tag{1.70}$$

Substituting the value of Boltzmann constant, the noise power becomes

$$P_n = 1.6 \times 10^{-20} \frac{T}{290} \, \Delta f \tag{1.71}$$

Thus, noise signals can be generated by placing the r-f terminating impedance R into a suitable oven and raising its temperature to T. The noise power is often specified by stating the temperature T, which is sometimes referred to as the *noise temperature*. It is often given in decibels, determined from the ratio of T to some reference temperature, usually 290°K.

A simple method of generating noise signals consists of merely heating the input resistance R as indicated above. A suitable arrangement of components is illustrated in Fig. 1.61. A long glass lamp is placed inside a coaxial line with the tungsten wire becoming the inner conductor. A suitable impedance transformer is used to match the resistance of the lamp to the characteristic impedance of the r-f input. If the loss per unit length of the coaxial line formed by the tungsten lamp is small but the lamp is long enough, the r-f input impedance to the lamp will remain constant regardless of its temperature.   The lamp can be heated by means of external d-c connections as indicated.   A similar arrangement can be provided in the waveguide; for example, the tungsten lamp can be placed diagonally across the waveguide replacing the fluorescent lamp in Fig. 1.62.   If the r-f impedance remains independent of lamp temperature, the noise temperature can be accurately predicted from Eq. (1.71). The temperature of the lamp can be determined by means of an optical pyrometer or other means.

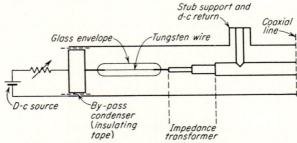

FIG. 1.61. Simplified drawing of a noise generator utilizing a heated resistor.

The usefulness of the thermal noise method is limited because of the relatively low melting point of all common materials.   The temperature T cannot exceed approximately 2900°K, thus limiting the noise temperature to approximately 10 db.   Since this value is too low for most applications, the thermal noise method is generally used only for standardization.[1]

Certain types of gas discharge result in a higher and more easily obtainable source of power.   It has been found that ordinary fluorescent lamps containing mercury vapor produce a discharge which emits random noise.   Figure 1.62 shows a typical arrangement of the lamp in a waveguide.   Diagonal placement of the lamp assures that the r-f input to the waveguide is nearly matched.   Experiments conducted by various workers have shown that the discharge is relatively independent of all operating conditions, resulting in effective temperature of 11,400°K or 15.8 db.*

[1] E. H. Ullrich and D. C. Rogers, An Absolute Method of Measurement of Receiver Noise Factors, *J. IEE (Proc. Radiolocation Convention)*, vol. 93, pt. IIIA, no. 8, pp. 1347–1351, March–May, 1946.   The use of long lamps to avoid variation of input resistance is due to W. W. Hansen.   Another example employing a heated polyiron termination is described by R. H. Dicke, The Measurement of Thermal Radiation at Microwave Frequencies, *Rev. Sci. Instr.*, vol. 17, no. 7, pp. 268–275, July, 1946.

* The discovery of the usefulness of fluorescent lamps as a noise source is due to Mumford.   See W. W. Mumford, A Broad-band Microwave Noise Source, *Bell*

The striking uniformity of fluorescent lamps, constant output, broadband operation, and extreme simplicity make receiver measurements simple and reliable. The principal limitation is due to the relatively low available noise temperature making it difficult to measure receiver noise figures in excess of 20 db.

Another form of noise generator employs the shot effect in a temperature-limited electron beam. It can be employed in the form of diodes placed across r-f transmission lines or by passing the electron stream through an r-f cavity as shown in Fig. 1.63.[1] The cavity method is more suitable because the higher impedances result in larger noise output.

Figure 1.63 shows a resonant cavity specifically designed for generation of noise.[2] The cathode is placed close to the anode, permitting substantial

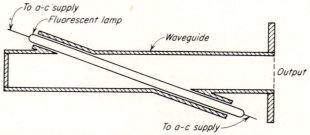

FIG. 1.62. Simplified drawing of a fluorescent-lamp noise generator in a waveguide holder.

temperature-limited current to be drawn. The current is controlled by varying the cathode temperature. The collector is placed immediately adjacent to the exit grid and is built in the form of a Faraday cage to prevent escape of secondary electrons. The magnitude of the noise generated by the beam can be predicted as follows: The mean-square shot noise current in an electron beam is given by

$$\bar{i}_n{}^2 = 2eI_0\Gamma^2\,\Delta f \tag{1.73}$$

System Tech. J., vol. 28, no. 4, pp. 608–618, October, 1949. Mumford hypothesizes that a gaseous discharge radiating monochromatic light at the wavelength λ_m causes microwave noise energy to be radiated as if it emanated from a black body radiating its maximum energy at a wavelength λ_m. Thus, employing Wien's displacement law, the wavelength of maximum radiation is given by

$$\lambda_m T = 0.289 \text{ cm-deg} \tag{1.72}$$

Substituting the characteristic wavelength of mercury discharge ($\lambda = 2,536 \times 10^{-8}$ cm), the temperature is found to be 11,400°. This closely corresponds to the observed results. The validity of the hypothesis is not known.

[1] The use of diodes as microwave noise generator has been studied by several workers. See, for example, R. Kompfner, J. Hatton, E. E. Schneider, and L. A. G. Dresel, The Transmission-line Diode as Noise Source at Centimeter Wavelengths, *J. IEE*, vol. 93, pt. IIIA, no. 9, pp. 1436–1442, March–May, 1946.

[2] After unpublished work of B. Auld, Stanford University, 1949–50.

where e is the charge on the electron, I_0 the d-c current passing through the gap, Γ is the space-charge noise-reduction factor (it is unity when the temperature limitation reduces the space-charge current by a factor of 20 or more), and Δf is the bandwidth. The noise power supplied by the current to the cavity will be

$$P_s = \beta^2 \bar{i}_n{}^2 R \, \Delta f \tag{1.74}$$

where β is the beam-coupling coefficient given by Eq. (1.1) and R is the

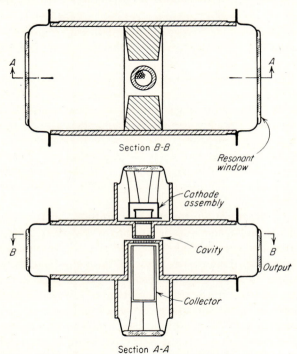

Section B-B

Resonant window

Cathode assembly

Cavity

Output

Collector

Section A-A

FIG. 1.63. Simplified diagram of a noise source employing shot effect in an electron beam. Method of tuning of the cavity is not shown.

shunt impedance of the cavity under operating conditions. Substituting the value of e,

$$P_s = 3.2 \times 10^{-19} \beta^2 I_0 R \, \Delta f \tag{1.75}$$

The effective noise temperature can be computed by taking the ratio of the noise generated in the cavity to the noise due to thermal noise as given by Eqs. (1.69) and (1.71). Thus, the effective noise temperature is

$$T = \frac{P_s}{P_n}$$
$$= 20 \beta^2 I_0 R \tag{1.76}$$

If d is the gap spacing between grids in the cavity, and f is the frequency, Eq. (1.76) can be shown to become

$$T = \frac{340}{fd} RI_0 V_0^{1/2} \tag{1.77}$$

Equation (1.77) neglects the effect of space-charge debunching and impedance change due to beam loading; these effects may become appreciable at large values of current. Experimental tests of the noise generator of the type illustrated have shown an agreement with theoretical expectations to an accuracy of about one decibel. Careful design at 3,000 Mc can lead to a noise temperature of about 40 db, with 2 per cent bandwidth. The obtainable noise temperatures will decrease with frequency as indicated by Eq. (1.77).

A reflex klystron structure can be used for generation of noise as it contains all the elements needed. However, ordinary reflex klystrons are not suitable in accurate work because the magnitude of the available current is not large enough, especially when the cathode temperature is limited to a sufficient degree. The reflector electrode does not permit the incident current to be read accurately because of the uncertain effect of secondary emission. Under ordinary circumstances, the Q value of the resonator is also excessive, making the noise bandwidth smaller than is usually needed.

1.15. Crystal Rectifier Harmonic Generators. Harmonic generation by means of nonlinear elements is useful for a variety of reasons. Frequency multipliers are needed, for example, in frequency-multiplying chains in generation of standard frequency sequence signals for frequency measurements as discussed in Chap. 8. Harmonic generators also permit experimental work in the frequency region beyond the high-frequency oscillation limit of available tubes. Aside from these principal applications, it is sometimes convenient to use harmonic generators to increase the frequency coverage of an oscillator by using it at one-half or one-third of the desired frequency. For instance, klystron tubes operating at about 6 mm have a relatively narrow tuning range and low power output. Similar power at this wavelength can be obtained from a 2 or 3 to 1 multiplier, thus providing a considerably greater tuning range.

A typical harmonic generator employing a standard crystal rectifier is shown in Fig. 1.64. Power from a K-band oscillator is introduced into the crystal through a waveguide-to-coaxial line transition. A suitable arrangement of r-f chokes permits the d-c rectified current to be monitored in the course of initial adjustments. The plunger in the K-band waveguide acts to match the impedance of the crystal to the waveguide. The inner conductor of the coaxial transition passes through the smaller waveguide causing radiation of the harmonics into the output waveguide. On one end of the smaller waveguide a shorting plunger is used to maximize the radiated power for a particular harmonic. Although numerous variations of this scheme are possible, a successful design will need to provide all of the functions in the device shown. Specifically, these consist of impedance matching for input and output waveguides and some means to filter out the fundamental and all harmonics lower than the one desired.

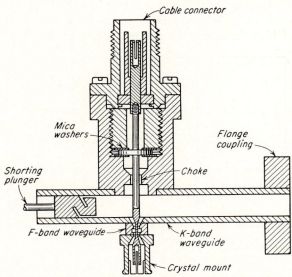

Fig. 1.64. Simplified drawing of a harmonic generator intended for use with IN-26 crystal rectifier. (*Reprinted with permission from "Microwave Spectroscopy," by W. Gordy, W. V. Smith, and R. S. Trambarulo. Copyright, 1953. John Wiley & Sons, Inc., New York.*)

The cross-guide design shown in Fig. 1.64 is intended to be used with commercially available rectifiers. At the higher frequencies, the performance of the harmonic generator can be improved by placing the semiconductor wafer and the cat whisker directly into the output waveguide.[1]

---

[1] For further details pertaining to design and construction of crystal rectifier harmonic generators, see A. G. Smith, W. Gordy, J. W. Simmons, and W. V. Smith, Microwave Spectroscopy in the Region of Three to Five Millimeters, *Phys. Rev.*, vol. 75, no. 2, pp. 260–263, Jan. 15, 1949; C. M. Johnson, D. M. Slager, and D. D. King, Millimeter Waves from Harmonic Generators, *Rev. Sci. Instr.*, vol. 25, no. 3, pp. 213–217, March, 1954; A. H. Nethercot, Jr., Harmonics at Millimeter Wavelengths, *Trans. IRE, PMTT*, vol. MTT-2, no. 3, pp. 17–20, September, 1954; W. Gordy, W. V. Smith, and R. F. Trambarulo, "Microwave Spectroscopy," pp. 48–53, John Wiley & Sons, Inc., New York, 1953; W. C. King and W. Gordy, One-to-Two Millimeter Wave Spectroscopy. IV. Experimental Methods and Results for OCS, CH$_3$F, and H$_2$O, *Phys. Rev.*, vol. 93, no. 3, pp. 407–412, Feb. 1, 1954; W. C. King and W. Gordy, One-to-Two Millimeter Wave Spectroscopy, *Phys. Rev.*, vol. 90, no.

The typical observed behavior of a crystal rectifier harmonic generator is shown in Fig. 1.65, which indicates the conversion loss from fundamental versus harmonic number.[1] The conversion loss increases rapidly with harmonic number, which indicates that the best performance is obtained with low multiplication. However, since available power from an oscillator also decreases rapidly with frequency, maximum power output at a given frequency will be obtained by selecting a harmonic number in conjunction with highest available power at the fundamental. The importance of high fundamental power is illustrated in Fig. 1.66, which

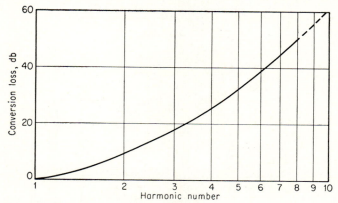

FIG. 1.65. Experimental curve showing the conversion loss of a crystal harmonic generator vs. harmonic number. (*Used by permission of the Columbia Radiation Laboratory, where it was produced in the course of research supported jointly by the Signal Corps, the Office of Naval Research, and the Air Research and Development Command under the Signal Corps Contract* DA-36-039 sc-42519.)

shows harmonic output versus fundamental power input for the second, third, and fourth harmonic.[2]

1.16. Sources of Radiation above the High-frequency Limit of Electron Oscillators. Vacuum-tube oscillators which employ interaction between electron beams and circuits have a high-frequency limit above which oscillations are impossible. This frequency limit differs somewhat from one type of oscillator to another and depends upon the exact nature of

---

2, pp. 319–320, Apr. 15, 1953; J. A. Klein and A. H. Nethercot, Jr., Microwave Spectrum of DI at 1.5 Mm Wavelength, *Phys. Rev.*, vol. 91, no. 4, p. 1018, Aug. 15, 1953; C. A. Burrus and W. Gordy, Sub-millimeter Wave Spectroscopy, *Phys. Rev.*, vol. 93, no. 4, pp. 897–898, Feb. 15, 1954. The last reference reports usable output at 12th, 13th, and 14th harmonics of the 1.23-cm fundamental, resulting in signals at 1.03, 0.95, and 0.88 mm.

[1] A. H. Nethercot, Jr., and B. Rosenblum, *Columbia Radiation Laboratory Tenth Quarterly Progress Report*, 1955.

[2] A. H. Nethercot, Jr., Harmonics at Millimeter Wavelengths, *Trans. IRE*, vol. MTT-2, no. 3, pp. 17–20, September, 1954.

the interaction and other practical details. While exact analysis of the problem is complicated, it is helpful to understand the qualitative reasons that preclude the generation of signals below a certain wavelength.

Consider, for example, the high-frequency limit of the reflex klystron for which the starting current is given by Eq. (1.37). If a klystron is scaled to shorter wavelengths by a proportional decrease of all dimensions, the shunt impedance R_s will be proportional to the square root of the wavelength. Under simplified assumptions, the current available from this cathode will be proportional to $(\lambda/a)^2$, where a is the radius of

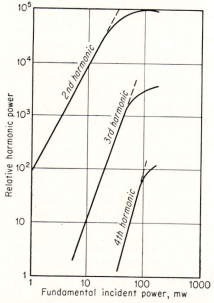

Fig. 1.66. Relative power output from crystal harmonic generator vs. incident fundamental power. (*By permission from Harmonics at Millimeter Wavelengths, by A. H. Nethercot, Jr., Trans. IRE, MTT-2, no. 3, September, 1954.*)

the interaction gap.[1] Thus, with decreasing wavelength, the available current decreases rapidly as the current required to produce oscillations increases; there will be a wavelength below which oscillations will be impossible. At the present stage of development, it appears that the short-wavelength limit for the reflex klystron is about 3 to 5 mm. The short-wavelength limit for magnetrons and traveling-wave tubes is somewhat lower; however, because of difficulties involved with mechanical tolerances in fabrication, it is not likely that this limit will be reached in practical tubes.

[1] This is an oversimplification; it neglects important effects due to thermal velocities of the electron at the cathode.

By means of harmonic generators described in the preceding section higher frequencies can be derived.   But due to poor conversion efficiency, small available fundamental power, and limited heat dissipation in crystals, this method permits the extension of laboratory signals to higher frequencies by only a moderate factor.

A number of experimental methods are being explored currently to breach the region between infrared black-body radiation and the electronic oscillators.   Several of these make use of radiation from relativistic electrons.   Substantial signals have been observed from high-velocity electrons injected longitudinally into waveguides.   The radiation spectrum appears to be harmonically related to the frequency used to bunch the electrons in the process of acceleration in a linear electron accelerator prior to the injection of electrons into the waveguide.[1]

Small, incoherent signals can be generated by numerous devices at very high frequencies.   For instance, spark gaps used to excite radiating bodies, such as tiny needles or spheres, emit weak signals because of the random process involved and low Q values of the radiating bodies.   The peak of the radiation spectrum can be controlled by adjusting the size of the radiating bodies.   Another form of incoherent radiation can be created by Cerenkov radiation in which the electrons injected into a dielectric medium at a velocity greater than the velocity of electromagnetic waves in the region cause radiation.   In one experiment, propagation of an electron beam adjacent to titanium dioxide dielectric at a velocity 0.15 times the velocity of light and a current of 0.4 ma produced detectable radiation.[2]

In another experiment, visible radiation was produced by allowing an electron beam to pass tangentially to an optical diffraction grating, causing the induced charges in the wires of the grating to radiate electromagnetic energy.   The wavelength of the radiation is determined by the grating spacing and the angle of observation.   It has been suggested that the generated frequency can be controlled by employing reflecting plates placed at an angle with respect to the grating.[3]

For comparison purposes, it may be of interest to compute power radiated by a black body at an elevated temperature.   Power flow in watts per square centimeters in a bandwidth Δf may be determined from

[1] K. B. Mallory and H. Motz, Generation of Sub-millimeter Waves, *J. Appl. Phys.*, vol. 26, no. 11, p. 1384, November, 1955.

[2] M. Danos and H. Lashinsky, Millimeter Wave Generation by Cerenkov Radiation, *Trans. IRE*, vol. MTT-2, pp. 21–22, September, 1954.

[3] E. M. Purcell and S. M. Smith, Visible Light from Localized Surface Charges Moving across a Grating, *Phys. Rev.*, vol. 92, no. 4, Nov. 15, 1953.   For further details of this method of generating and controlling the frequency, see W. W. Salisbury, U.S. Patent No. 2,634,372, Apr. 7, 1953.

the Rayleigh-Jeans formula, giving:

$$P = \frac{8\pi k T \, \Delta f}{\lambda^2} \times 10^{-7} \tag{1.78}$$

where k = Boltzmann constant
   T = absolute temperature of black body
   Δf = frequency interval, cycles
   λ = wavelength, cm

If the bandwidth Δf is (arbitrarily) $f/1{,}000$, the radiated power per square centimeter becomes

$$P = \frac{75kT}{\lambda^3} \tag{1.79}$$

Substituting suitable values, $T = 2{,}500°\mathrm{K}$, $\lambda = 0.1$, $k = 1.37 \times 10^{-16}$, the radiated power P is found to be 2.5×10^{-8} watts/sq cm.

Sources of radiation in the submillimeter range have not yet been developed sufficiently to permit satisfactory experimentation. In addition, the difficulties in the generation of power are no greater than those pertaining to detection. Some exploratory experiments, however, are possible if sufficient bandwidth is used.

CHAPTER 2

DETECTION OF MICROWAVE POWER

2.1. Introduction. In all microwave experiments it is necessary to detect the presence of signal power. This chapter will be concerned with methods which are useful to indicate the presence of microwave signals and the measurement of their relative magnitudes. It is essential in some cases to determine the absolute magnitude of the power flowing through the system, but this topic will be reserved for discussion in connection with the more fundamental question of power measurement.

In order to detect microwave signals it is necessary to convert the signal power, directly or indirectly, into some form of mechanical or visible energy. Among the indicating devices which have been tried are the following:

1. Mechanical devices—force operated indicators, such as the gold-leaf electroscope[1,2] or direct measurement of radiation pressure[3]

[1] Gold-leaf electroscopes intended for operation at 10 and 3 cm have been described by Collard. By inserting a narrow strip of gold foil along a longitudinal slot in a coaxial line, an electroscope can be formed. It can be calibrated at low frequencies and used up to a limiting frequency beyond which the length of the gold leaf becomes appreciable when compared to the operating wavelength. Collard found that a sensitivity of about 20 volts could be obtained. By employing resonance methods, he could measure a power of 50 μw at 10 cm and 500 μw at 3 cm. The equipment is rather delicate and requires the use of a microscope for measurement of deflection. The effect of a gold foil in the slot on the resultant distribution of fields has not been studied in detail. However, for high-power measurements, such voltmeters could be made practical. For further description of the electroscope, see J. Collard, The Measurement of Voltage at Centimeter Wavelengths, *J. IEE*, March–May, 1946, p. 1393.

[2] A variation of the electroscope principle has been explored by Norton. As in the previous method, use is made of forces developed by electromagnetic fields upon the walls of the transmission line. If part of the wall is made in the form of a thin diaphragm, resonant at some audio frequency, then a modulated signal source will cause vibration of the diaphragm. The amplitude of the oscillations can be measured in several ways; one method makes the diaphragm a part of a condenser microphone arrangement. Forces acting upon the diaphragm are due to the electric and magnetic fields. Since the two are in opposite directions, the design must take this into account and emphasize one or the other. As in the electroscope, the forces are independent of the signal frequency subject to the limitation stated above. Norton has been able

108

2. Visual indicators—neon glow tubes, lamps, etc.[1]

3. Thermoelectrical indicators—various forms of thermometric devices,[2] thermocouples, thermistors, bolometers

4. Electrical rectifiers—various types of nonlinear elements, such as diodes, crystal rectifiers, triodes, klystrons, etc.

---

to obtain satisfactory measurements, without the use of resonance, of microwave power in the vicinity of 1 mw with nearly constant sensitivity over the wavelength range of 3 to 30 cm. For further details, see L. E. Norton, Broad-band Power Measuring Method at Microwave Frequencies, *Proc. IRE*, p. 759, July, 1949.

[3] The radiation pressure of an electromagnetic wave impinging upon a plane surface can be measured by mechanical means. If a perfectly reflecting plane surface is placed normally to the direction of propagation, the pressure exerted on the surface will be equal to the total energy density in front of it. Such an effect was first anticipated by Kepler in 1619 and measured by Lebedew and also by Nichols and Hull in 1901 using visible radiation. (For a description of the theory and of the apparatus suitable for use in the optical range, see G. P. Harnwell and J. J. Livinggood, "Experimental Atomic Physics," chap. 1, McGraw-Hill Book Company, Inc., New York, 1933.) Cullen made use of radiation pressure as a basis for absolute power measurements at microwave frequencies. He suspended a reflecting vane in a waveguide so that the pressure of the radiation would cause a mechanical force, measurable directly in terms of mass, length, and time, without introducing secondary electrical standards, and obtained excellent agreement with a balanced calorimeter when measuring power in the range of 10 to 50 watts. However, the equipment is delicate and limited in accuracy by the same difficulties that confront the optical methods. These limitations are usually caused by the radiometer effect, i.e., heating of the reflecting vane which, in turn, causes convection of air and other complicated effects. For a detailed discussion, see A. L. Cullen, Absolute Power Measurements at Microwave Frequencies, *Proc. IEE*, vol. 99, pt. IV, p. 100, 1952. See also Sec. 3.12.

[1] Neon glow tubes, incandescent lamps, fluorescent lamps, etc., are often used to indicate the presence of microwave power. While it is satisfying to see a lamp glow in response to microwave power, such indications are seldom sufficiently accurate to be useful in actual measurements. Various attempts have been made to make glow lamps into quantitative indicators—such as the measurement of the length of an ionized column in a fluorescent lamp. In another application a visual pattern of standing waves has been obtained by inserting a row of identical glow tubes into a long longitudinal slot in a transmission line. As the strength of the field determines the length of ionization in each of the tubes, it is possible to give an immediate, though rough, idea of the standing-wave pattern.

[2] For example, Golay describes a pneumatic cell in which an expansion of a gas is caused by absorption of incoming radiation in a resistive film. A movable membrane, by mirror action, activates an optical detection system, and produces electrical signals from a photocell. A cell, 3 mm in diameter, may have a typical time constant of 0.003 sec and a minimum detectable power of approximately 10^{-9} watt. Use of helium, instead of air, results in a shorter time constant at the expense of sensitivity. These cells are suitable for use throughout the infrared region and up to several millimeters. For details, see M. J. E. Golay, A Pneumatic Infra-red Detector, *Rev. Sci. Instr.*, vol. 18, no. 5, pp. 357–363, May, 1947; M. J. E. Golay, Theoretical Consideration in Heat and Infra-red Detection, with Particular Reference to the Pneumatic Detector, *Rev. Sci. Instr.*, vol. 18, no. 5, pp. 347–356, May, 1947.

The first two of these detecting devices (1 and 2), are not generally useful for practical reasons and are mentioned merely for completeness. Thermoelectric devices, on the other hand, involve principles which are common to the entire electromagnetic spectrum and are useful in absolute measurements.   One specific form of the thermoelectric detector is a device called a *bolometer*.   A bolometer is a wire which, subjected to microwave radiation, changes its resistance because of the resultant heating.   This resistance change can be easily detected by means of suitable circuits.   In practice, bolometers need to be biased by direct currents; as long as the signal power is much smaller than the biasing power, the resultant output voltage signals are directly proportional to the incoming power.   Such bolometers are useful in measurements in which accuracy is of importance, but they have comparatively low sensitivity.   Thermometric methods are described here only to the extent that they are useful as indicating devices; a more complete description will be found in the discussion of power measurements in Chap. 3.

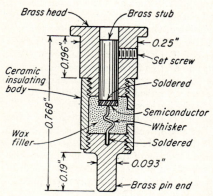

FIG. 2.1.   Cross-sectional view showing the elements of a crystal rectifier.   Details of construction differ among various manufacturers.

The electrical methods make it possible to convert microwave signals to d-c or low frequencies—which can then be measured by conventional methods.   Such nonlinear elements can be used either as rectifiers or frequency converters. Rectifier-type detectors are relatively the most important because of their simplicity, versatility, sensitivity, and availability, and are the principle subject of discussion in this chapter.

2.2. Crystal Rectifiers.   The modern crystal rectifier is the most sensitive and the simplest of all rectifying devices.   In spite of various defects, such as uncertain response law and the variation of sensitivity with temperature, it has many applications in measurement practice.   The cross section of a typical rectifier is shown in Fig. 2.1.   This consists of a fine wire (cat whisker) touching a suitable semiconductor, such as silicon, germanium, galena, or iron pyrite.   Present-day crystals are usually made of germanium or silicon.   The tungsten wire is carefully pointed and brought into contact with the semiconductor; by controlling the pressure against the semiconductor, the area of contact is adjusted to a desired value.   This contact area determines the resistance of the barrier contact and its capacity, as well as the power-handling ability of the device.[1] The area is made either small or large depending upon the intended use of the crystal.   The volume surrounding the point contact

[1] Aside from the critical nature of the contact between the wire and the semiconductor, the gross features of the rectifier depend upon the nature of the latter. Semiconductors are materials having a high electrical resistance, intermediate between metals and insulators.   It has been found that the addition of small amounts of suitable impurities improves the rectification properties of pure semiconductors.   The work functions of the whisker and the semiconductor are generally different, which is believed to create a potential barrier to the flow of electrons.   Figure 2.2 shows dia-

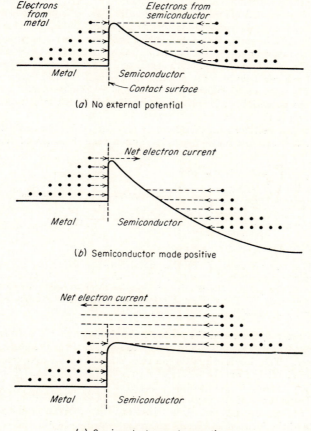

FIG. 2.2. Diagrammatic illustration showing the potential barrier between the metal and germanium semiconductor for three different conditions of applied potential. The illustration is drawn for the case in which the semiconductor work function is less than that of metal.   In (a) no external potential is applied.   In (b) the potential of the semiconductor is raised, and in (c) the semiconductor is made negative.   Substantial current can flow only in case (c).   (*Courtesy of Crystal Rectifiers, by W. E. Stephens, Electronics, McGraw-Hill Publishing Company, Inc., New York, July, 1946.*)

is usually filled with a wax to prevent the penetration of moisture and to provide some additional mechanical stability.

The static characteristic of a representative crystal detector is shown in Fig. 2.4. The nonlinear characteristic makes it possible to use the crystal detector either as a low-level detector or as a frequency converter. When used as a frequency converter, a local oscillator signal is supplied to the crystal in addition to the signal, and mixed currents flow in the output. One of the resultant components is the difference frequency

---

grammatically the potential barrier between the metal whisker and the semiconductor for three values of applied potential. The potential barrier is presumed to decrease slowly with distance on the semiconductor side because of the space charge created by the unneutralized impurity ions. While electronic conduction is possible both in the metal and the semiconductor, the barrier between the two effectively prevents the flow of electrons. If the potential of the semiconductor is raised as shown in Fig. 2.2b, few electrons can flow into the metal. However, if the electronic potential is lowered as in Fig. 2.2c, a slight flow of electrons from the semiconductor becomes possible. Thus, the potential barrier allows conduction of current in one direction, but nearly none at all in the other.

The action of the rectifier can, therefore, be represented by the equivalent circuit shown in Fig. 2.3. Resistance R represents the nonlinear action of the potential

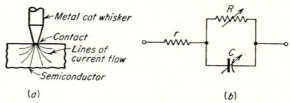

(a)   (b)

FIG. 2.3. Diagrammatic view of (a) the metal-semiconductor contact and (b) its equivalent circuit. r is the bulk resistance of a semiconductor (often called *spreading resistance*); R and C represent the nonlinear action of the potential barrier. (*Courtesy of Crystal Rectifiers, by W. E. Stephens, Electronics, McGraw-Hill Publishing Company, Inc., New York, July, 1946.*)

---

barrier and C the capacitance at the contact. Resistance r is the bulk resistance of the semiconductor, taking into account the spreading nature of the current from the whisker contact. The circuit constants can be obtained from low-frequency measurements, or approximately from the theory of the rectification process. The equivalent circuit can then be used to predict the behavior of the crystal rectifier at high frequencies. The presence of the capacity C makse it obvious that the high-frequency performance of the crystal cannot be predicted (or checked) by low-frequency measurements of the forward and backward resistance alone. Since the thickness of the barrier layer is small, on the order of 10^{-6} cm, the transit-time effects of electrons are not important.

For a more complete discussion of the properties of crystal rectifiers, see R. V. Pound, "Microwave Mixers," McGraw-Hill Book Company, Inc., New York, 1948; Technical Staff, Bell Telephone Laboratories, "Radar Systems and Components," pp. 710–739, D. Van Nostrand Company, Inc., Princeton, N.J., 1949; W. E. Stephens, Crystal Rectifiers, *Electronics*, July, 1946.

signal, whose amplitude is strictly proportional to the signal voltage as long as the local oscillator level is much larger than the signal level.   For the low-level detector, a signal is introduced into the crystal causing the rectified current.   Because in most measurement problems the crystal is used as a low-level detector, much of the following material is devoted to this topic.

2.3. Crystals as Low-level Detectors.   When a crystal detector is used as a low-level detector, its output terminals are connected to a d-c meter, or an audio or video amplifier, depending upon the type of signal modulation.   From the viewpoint of basic characteristics, it makes little difference what indicating device follows the detector. For simplicity, consider a circuit consisting of a load resistance and a d-c meter in series with the crystal.   When a microwave signal is applied, a d-c signal will appear in the load circuit.   The magnitude of the current will depend upon the characteristics of the crystal, r-f source impedance, and the d-c load impedance.   As seen from its output terminals, the crystal acts as a current generator with a certain dynamic impedance.   The important parameters of the crystal are *the response law, the dynamic impedance,* and *the sensitivity.*

Response Law. When the r-f signal is applied to some nonlinear device, the resultant current can be

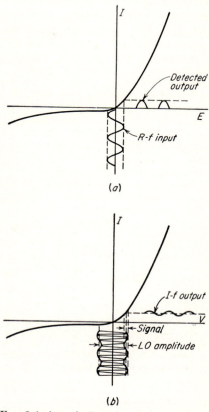

(a)

(b)

FIG. 2.4. A typical static characteristic of a silicon crystal rectifier when used (a) as a rectifier, (b) as a converter.

predicted as follows: The nonlinear characteristic can be expressed analytically in the form of a Taylor series expansion about the operating point (the origin, if there is no d-c bias).   If the current is expressed in this manner as a function of voltage, the series will begin in a linear term in voltage followed by quadratic and higher-order terms.   The linear term does not contribute to rectification and is of no importance.   If the signal voltage is small enough, higher-order terms will be negligible in comparison to the quadratic term; therefore, the rectified current must be strictly proportional to the square of applied voltage. Because of this, the low-level detectors are often called *square-law detectors*.

The low-level detector can be represented as a constant-current generator as shown in Fig. 2.5 with an internal dynamic impedance R_0. The magnitude of the current i will be proportional to the signal power. The dynamic impedance R_0 will also become a constant at low levels but will be a function of the signal power at higher levels. Rectification properties of a typical crystal rectifier are shown in Fig. 2.6.[1] This shows short circuit and open circuit d-c current and voltage, respectively, plotted as a function of r-f power, and the variation of the dynamic impedance of the crystal. It can be seen that above about 10 μw the square-law response is violated. In some crystals, the deviation from square-law may take place at power levels as low as 1 μw.

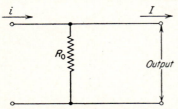

FIG. 2.5. Equivalent circuit of a low-level rectifier in constant-current form. The rectified current i is proportional to r-f power; R_0 is independent of r-f power at sufficiently low level.

It is also found that the response law above 1 μw can be affected by the r-f source impedance. Assume that the rectified current is expressed in the form $i = V^n$, where n is expected to be a function of voltage V and the r-f source impedance Z. In a series of tests conducted on about 25 silicon-tungsten rectifiers, the exponent n was observed to have the following properties.[2] If the rectified current is 1 μamp or less, n does not deviate from 2 for a wide range of source impedances. If Z is small compared to the crystal impedance (at low level), then n will increase with V and may reach a value of 3 at about 100 μamp. If Z is much higher than the impedance of the crystal, n will decrease with increasing V and may fall to 1.5 or less at current levels of about 100 μamp. For intermediate values of the source impedance, the exponent n may at first increase and then decrease.

Thus, it is apparent that, when using crystal current above approximately 1 μamp, one must calibrate the crystal under the precise conditions in which it is to be used. For example, in standing wave detector measurements probe adjustments must not be made once the crystal is calibrated—since such adjustments determine the r-f source impedance. It is also found that deviations of crystal response from square-law are

[1] H. C. Torrey and C. A. Whitmer, "Crystal Rectifiers," p. 334, Massachusetts Institute of Technology Radiation Laboratory Series, McGraw-Hill Book Company, Inc., New York, 1948.

[2] R. C. Robbins and F. W. Black, An Investigation into the Use of Crystal Rectifiers for Measuring and Monitoring Purposes, *J. IEE*, p. 1343, March–May, 1946.

least when the load impedance is in the vicinity of 2,000–3,000 ohms. The methods of calibrating the crystal detector are described in Sec. 2.10.

Sensitivity. The current sensitivity of the detector is defined as the ratio of rectified current to the absorbed r-f power. It depends upon the nature of the semiconductor material and the contact area. The sensitivity of crystals does not vary greatly from crystal to crystal as

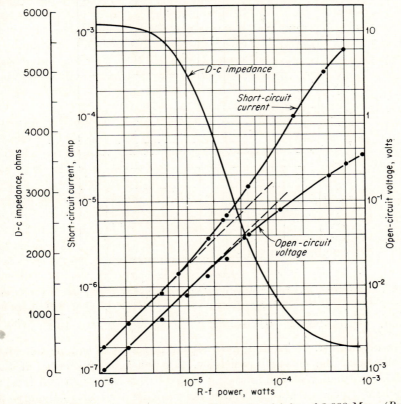

FIG. 2.6. Behavior of a silicon crystal rectifier in the vicinity of 3,000 Mc.   (*By permission from "Crystal Rectifiers," by H. C. Torrey and C. A. Whitmer.   Copyright*, 1948. *McGraw-Hill Book Company, Inc., New York.*)

might be suspected.   Figure 2.7 shows the sensitivity for a few crystals as a function of frequency.   The curves shown were computed on the basis of the equivalent circuit shown in Fig. 2.3, using the values of circuit parameters as determined by low-frequency impedance measurements.[1]   Although sketchy experimental evidence does not permit verification of the theory, the trends are well indicated.

[1] For more complete discussion of the sensitivity of crystal rectifiers, see Torrey and Whitmer, *op. cit.*, pp. 335–340.   They show that current sensitivity β can be

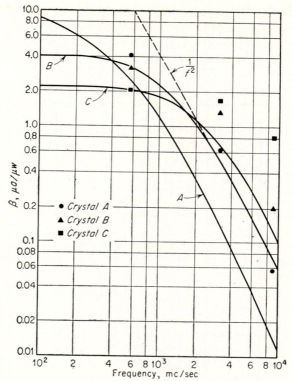

FIG. 2.7. Dependence of current sensitivity upon frequency. The curves were computed from approximate theory using Eq. (2.1). The points are measured values for three crystals. (*By permission from "Crystal Rectifiers," by H. C. Torrey and C. A. Whitmer. Copyright, 1948. McGraw-Hill Book Company, Inc., New York.*)

Figure of Merit. The minimum signal power that can be detected depends upon the current sensitivity, the dynamic impedance of the crystal, the quality of the following amplifier, and the required intelligence bandwidth. Figure 2.8 shows the equivalent circuit of the crystal connected to the grid circuit of an amplifier. The resistance R_A is the

represented by

$$\beta = \frac{\alpha}{2} \frac{1}{1 + \omega^2 C^2 rR} \tag{2.1}$$

where the circuit constants are those shown in Fig. 2.3, and α is related to the curvature of the static characteristic at the origin, as found from the theoretical expressions of the type

$$i = i_0 f(V)$$
$$i = i_0(e^{\alpha V} - 1) \tag{2.2}$$

While not at all accurate, these expressions do indicate the general behavior of crystals with frequency, and the dependence of β upon the contact characteristics.

equivalent noise resistance of the first tube and corresponds to the resistance which would give rise to thermal noise of the magnitude actually generated by the first stage.[1] The signal current i generated by the rectifier at the first tube is given by

$$i = \beta P \tag{2.3}$$

where P is the signal power absorbed by the crystal. With the aid of Fig. 2.8, the signal-to-noise voltage ratio can be shown to be

$$\frac{V_s}{V_n} = \frac{\beta P R_0}{\sqrt{4kT \Delta f (R_0 + R_A)}} \tag{2.4}$$

where k is Boltzmann's constant, T is the absolute temperature, V_s is the signal voltage at the first grid, and V_n is the noise voltage due to thermal noise generated by the combined crystal impedance R_0 and the equivalent noise resistance R_A; Δf is the bandwidth of the amplifier system. Equation (2.4) can be rewritten for clarity as

$$\frac{V_s}{V_n} = \frac{P}{\sqrt{4kT \Delta f}} M \tag{2.5}$$

in which M is called the *figure of merit* of the crystal and is equal to

$$M = \frac{\beta R_0}{\sqrt{R_0 + R_A}} \tag{2.6}$$

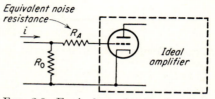

FIG. 2.8. Equivalent circuit of a low-level rectifier connected to an amplifier. R_A is a fictitious resistance representing the noise generated by the first amplifier tube.

M involves the tube parameter R_A and is, therefore, not entirely dependent upon the crystal. However, using $R_A = 1{,}200$ ohms, a value not greatly different from the best that can be obtained with a pentode amplifier, permits using M to compare crystals against each other. It is found that the figure of merit for good crystals generally lies between 50 and 100.

Equation (2.5) can be used to compute the minimum detectable power. Consider a special case: assuming $V_s/V_n = 1$, $\Delta f = 100$ cycles, $M = 50$, $4kT = 1.6 \times 10^{-20}$ watts/cycle, the minimum detectable signal is found to be 2.5×10^{-12} watts.

Effect of D-C Bias. The current sensitivity of a crystal can be increased by introducing d-c bias in series with the crystal. Quali-

[1] For further discussion of tube noise see F. E. Terman, "Radio Engineering," pp. 578–584, McGraw-Hill Book Company, Inc., New York, 1947. For triodes, R_A is approximately equal to $2.5/g_m$, where g_m is the transconductance of the tube. In pentodes, the noise is higher because of shot effect reintroduced by current captured by the positive screen grid.

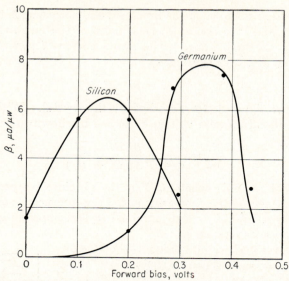

Fig. 2.9. Improvement in the current sensitivity of a crystal rectifier with applied d-c bias. (*By permission from "Crystal Rectifiers," by H. C. Torrey and C. A. Whitmer. Copyright, 1948. McGraw-Hill Book Company, Inc., New York.*)

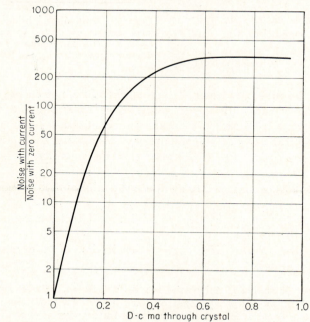

Fig. 2.10. Typical low-frequency noise generated by d-c current flowing through a crystal.

tatively, this is merely a process of selecting the point on the characteristic curve of the crystal where curvature is the greatest.   Substantial
improvement in current sensitivity can be obtained, as shown in Fig. 2.9.
However, associated with the resultant d-c current there is generated
large low-frequency noise which makes biasing generally undesirable.
Figure 2.10 shows experimentally observed variation of noise in a crystal
detector as a function of d-c current through the crystal.   The abscissa
represents *either* d-c component of rectified (10 cm) power or d-c current
furnished by a battery; the nature of this noise seems to be largely independent of the polarity of the current or its source.   Sensitive crystals
show more noise than less sensitive ones.   The maximum noise developed

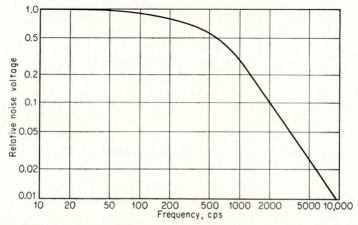

FIG. 2.11. Experimentally determined frequency distribution of noise in a crystal
detector.   D-c current of about 10 μa was furnished to the crystal by a battery.   The
relative noise voltage was measured in a four-cycle band as a function of frequency.

by the crystals is often found to be from 50 to 500 times the noise existing with zero d-c current.   The frequency distribution of such noise is
shown in Fig. 2.11.   As in the case of the carbon microphone, the noise
decreases with increasing frequency.   While available data do not allow
generalization, it can be observed that the mean-square noise voltage
developed by a carbon microphone varies as df/f, where f is frequency
and df is the frequency bandwidth in which the noise is measured; the
crystal detector probably behaves in a similar manner.[1]

Thus, biased crystal detectors are poor if the detected output is at
audio frequencies.   Above 20,000 cycles, the "resistance fluctuation"
noise voltage rapidly diminishes and approaches the thermal level.

[1] Many other theories have been proposed to explain the observed noise.   See
Torrey and Whitmer, *op. cit.*, p. 186; also L. I. Schiff, Noise in Crystal Rectifiers,
University of Pennsylvania, NDRC 14–126, Mar. 10, 1943.

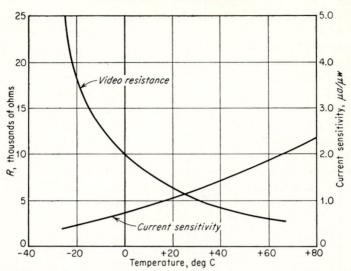

Fig. 2.12. Dependence of sensitivity and crystal resistance upon temperature as calculated from approximate theory. (*By permission from "Crystal Rectifiers," by H. C. Torrey and C. A. Whitmer. Copyright, 1948. McGraw-Hill Book Company, Inc., New York.*)

There is evidence that resistance fluctuation noise at 30 Mc contributes not more than 1 db over thermal noise.

Dependence of Sensitivity on Temperature. Since crystal detection involves electronic conduction through the barrier layer, it may be expected that temperature will affect the performance of the rectifier in much the same way as it affects ordinary diodes.[1] Under controlled conditions it is found that the circuit constants of the rectifier depend

[1] It can be shown on theoretical grounds that the conduction through the barrier layer should be analogous to the results obtained by Schottky for a thermionic diode. Thus, rewriting Eq. (2.2) in the more complete form,

$$i = A e^{-\frac{e\phi}{kT}} (e^{\frac{eV}{kT}} - 1) \qquad (2.7)$$

where A = a constant of the semiconductor
ϕ = barrier contact potential difference
k, T = as previously defined
Differentiating with respect to V, and computing dV/di at zero bias ($V = 0$),

$$R_0 = \frac{dV}{di} = \frac{kT}{eA} e^{\frac{e\phi}{kT}} \qquad (2.8)$$

This predicts exponential dependence of R_0 upon temperature. The main effect of temperature on sensitivity is apparently due to the change of R_0. It is usually found that the product of current sensitivity and dynamic resistance is a constant. Calculations of this type lead to Fig. 2.12. For further details, see Torrey and Whitmer, *op. cit.*, pp. 342–344.

upon the temperature in a manner consistent with simple thermionic theory. The theoretical variation of the sensitivity and dynamic impedance of a crystal rectifier can be computed from such theoretical considerations. Calculated dependence of β and R_0 upon temperature are shown in Fig. 2.12.

In practice, the behavior of a crystal will depend upon environmental conditions in an unpredictable manner. In crystals in which the contact is stabilized by means of a wax filler, the effects are often erratic and sometimes show hysteresis behavior. Most of the troublesome effects occur below room temperature. Above room temperature it is generally found that the theoretical increase in sensitivity is obeyed, presumably because of the lowered forward resistance. In one series of tests it was found that the rectified current changed by about 1.6 per cent/°C.* When crystal detectors are used for relative measurements during short periods of time, the changes in sensitivity are seldom important.

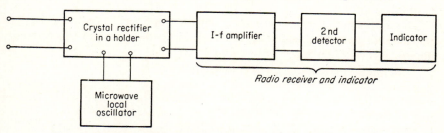

FIG. 2.13. Block diagram of microwave superheterodyne receiver.

2.4. Crystals as Converters. A crystal detector can be used as a heterodyne converter or mixer by supplying it with a source of local oscillator power. The output voltage of a heterodyne converter is strictly proportional to its input signal as long as the signal is much smaller than the voltage supplied by the local oscillator.[1] Crystal rectifiers can be used to convert microwave signals to low frequencies, where conventional methods can be applied for final detection and measurement. The advantages of a converter system are that the response is linear and the sensitivity is much greater than can be obtained with a square-law detector. The added complexity of the additional microwave source, however, seldom justifies the use of the heterodyne principle in measurement applications. When occasionally needed, such methods do provide increased sensitivity simultaneously with added benefits of stability without requiring the determination of response law.

A heterodyne system of detection, shown in Fig. 2.13, consists of the

* Robbins and Black, *op. cit.*

[1] For a description of the heterodyne principle of detection, see any standard text in radio engineering. For example, Terman, *op. cit.*, pp. 535–540.

following main elements: A crystal holder is arranged so that signal and local oscillator power can be introduced to the crystal simultaneously; nearly all of the signal power should be dissipated in the crystal without escaping into the local oscillator. The local oscillator need only supply a few milliwatts of power; its frequency should differ from the signal frequency by the desired intermediate frequency, perhaps in the vicinity of a few megacycles. The local oscillator should be capable of delivering appreciably more power than is required for proper mixing action in order to allow it to be only loosely coupled to the crystal. The resultant difference frequency is introduced into the intermediate frequency amplifier which may take the form of any conventional low-frequency radio receiver. The difference frequency is detected by the "second" detector, and finally measured by an appropriate indicator. The action of the heterodyne system is just that of the conventional superheterodyne receiver and differs from it only in details of characteristics of the crystal converter.

The important parameters of a crystal rectifier when used in this service are: conversion efficiency, noise, r-f impedance, and i-f impedance. These are described more fully below.[1]

Conversion Efficiency. Conversion efficiency is defined as the ratio of power delivered to the i-f network to the power absorbed by the converter at the signal frequency. The behavior of the converter can be understood qualitatively with the aid of the d-c characteristic as shown in Fig. 2.4b. A large local oscillator signal and a relatively small signal are superposed and applied to the crystal. In response to these, rectified current will flow through from the crystal, through a low-pass filter, permitting only the d-c and the difference-frequency component to appear at the output. Thus, the output signal, shown in Fig. 2.4b, does not contain high-frequency components. The magnitude of the difference-frequency component depends upon the slope of the characteristic at the peaks of the local oscillator signal. If the characteristic is strongly asymmetrical, the difference-frequency component will be large. As long as the magnitude of the local oscillator voltage is large enough, the output signal will be largely independent of the local oscillator voltage. A typical curve showing the dependence of conversion efficiency upon local

---

[1] For a comprehensive discussion of the properties of the crystal converter, see Torrey and Whitmer, *op. cit.*, pp. 111–195. Phenomenological analysis of diode-type converters is given by E. W. Herold, Some Aspects of Radio Reception at Ultra-high Frequency—Frequency Mixing in Diodes, *Proc. IRE*, vol. 31, p. 575, October, 1943. This analysis, in simplified form, is to be found in Terman, *op. cit.* The use of crystal rectifiers as microwave mixers is described by Pound, *op. cit.*

The relation between the r-f source impedance, i-f impedance, and the conversion loss is discussed by W. L. Pritchard, Notes on a Crystal Mixer Performance; *Trans. IRE*, vol. MTT-3, no. 1, pp. 37–39, January, 1955; also P. D. Strum, Some Aspects of Crystal Mixer Performance, *Proc. IRE*, vol. 41, no. 7, pp. 876, 889, July, 1953.

oscillator level is shown in Fig. 2.14. The performance of the converter does not depend upon the curvature of the characteristic at the origin; therefore, a crystal rectifier can be good as a low-level detector but not as converter, and vice versa.

Crystals used for microwave applications require the local oscillator power to be in the vicinity of 1 mw for best performance; it has been found that an adequate way to specify the proper operating point is in terms of the d-c rectified current. A value of 0.6 ma is generally considered as best.

Noise Temperature. It has been found that crystal rectifiers, when supplied by a local oscillator signal, produce noise in excess of that

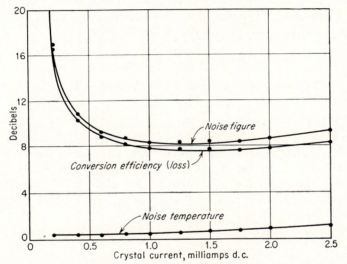

FIG. 2.14. Conversion efficiency and noise temperature of a typical microwave crystal converter. The data shown were experimentally obtained on a 10-cm rectifier, but the result is not representative of the best available crystals.

expected from thermal agitation alone. This *excess* noise is often measured in terms of quantity t called the *noise temperature.* It is defined as the ratio of noise power available from a crystal (under some specific condition of operation) to the noise that would be available from a resistor at room temperature; the value of the resistor being equal to the resistance of the converter as seen from the i-f terminals. The noise temperature of the crystal rectifier is nearly proportional to the d-c crystal current, as shown in Fig. 2.14. As mentioned in the preceding section, the excess noise of a crystal at high i-f frequencies is not large. The value shown in Fig. 2.14 is typical.[1]

[1] For further discussion, see Sec. 2.3; for greater detail, see Pound, *op. cit.*, pp. 93–96; also Torrey and Whitmer, *op. cit.*, chap. 6.

R-F and I-F Impedances. The impedance of the converter as seen from the microwave signal terminals is called the r-f impedance. The source impedance of the converter as viewed from the i-f terminals is called the i-f impedance. The two are interdependent in a complicated way, and the exact behavior of the crystal cannot be predicted without knowledge of details of the microwave circuit in which it is used. It can be shown that the impedance of the signal generator at the *signal* and the *image* frequencies affect the performance of the crystal.[1] None of these factors is of basic importance unless the ultimate in sensitivity is desired.

Noise Figure.[2] The over-all sensitivity of the heterodyne detector system depends upon the above factors and, in addition, upon the quality of the i-f amplifier. The sensitivity is usually measured in terms of the quantity called the *noise figure*, defined as follows:

$$NF = \frac{NF_{\text{i-f}} + t - 1}{G}$$

or

$$NF_{\text{db}} = 10 \log \frac{NF_{\text{i-f}} + t - 1}{G} \tag{2.9}$$

where NF is the noise factor of the heterodyne detector expressed as a power ratio, and NF_{db} when expressed in decibels; NF_{if} is the noise factor of the i-f amplifier expressed as a power ratio, t is the noise temperature of the converter as defined above, and G is its conversion efficiency. The noise factor expresses the ratio between the minimum detectable signal of an ideal receiver and the signal which is actually required to produce an output equal to the receiver noise.

The minimum power that can be detected by a heterodyne system is

$$P_{\text{min}} = (kT \, \Delta f)NF \tag{2.10}$$

where $kT = 4 \times 10^{-21}$ watts per cycle at room temperature, Δf is the i-f bandwidth, and NF is the noise figure as defined above.

For example, the following numbers are typical of a crystal converter operation: $G = 0.125$, $t = 1.25$, $\Delta f = 10^6$ cps, $NF_{\text{i-f}} = 4$. This corresponds to a noise figure of 40 or 16 db. The minimum detectable power is then 1.6×10^{-13} watts.

[1] Torrey and Whitmer, *op. cit.*, pp. 148–152; for greater detail, see Pound, *op. cit.*, chap. 2.

[2] H. T. Friis, Noise Figure of Radio Receivers, *Proc. IRE*, vol. 32, no. 7, pp. 419–422, July, 1944; R. Berringer, C. G. Montgomery, R. A. Howard, and S. Katz, chap. 4, pp. 221–226, in C. G. Montgomery (ed.), "Techniques of Microwave Measurements," McGraw-Hill Book Company, Inc., New York, 1947; Terman and Pettit, *op. cit.*, pp. 360–362; S. Roberts, Some Considerations Governing Noise Measurements on Crystal Mixers, *Proc. IRE*, vol. 35, no. 3, pp. 257–265, March, 1947; H. Goldberg, Some Notes on Noise Figures, *Proc. IRE*, vol. 36, no. 10, pp. 1205–1214, October, 1948.

Since the conversion efficiency does not change rapidly with local oscillator level, and since the noise temperature is generally low, the noise figure of the entire system does not change appreciably with moderate changes in local oscillator level.

Comparison of Low-level Detectors and Converters.   It is of interest to compare the minimum detectable power for the same bandwidth when the signal is detected by linear and square-law detectors.   Assuming that the signal-to-noise ratio is *unity* in both cases, the minimum detectable power can be found from Eqs. (2.5) and (2.10).   For the square-law case it is

$$P_{min} = \frac{\sqrt{4kT\,\Delta f}}{M} \tag{2.11}$$

and for the converter,

$$P_{min} = (kT\,\Delta f)\text{NF} \tag{2.10}$$

Taking the ratio of the two,

$$\frac{\text{Minimum detectable power with linear detector}}{\text{Minimum detectable power with square-law detector}} = \frac{\text{NF }M}{2}\sqrt{kT\,\Delta f} \tag{2.12}$$

Using typical values of $M = 50$, $\text{NF} = 40$, this ratio becomes of the order $10^{-7}\sqrt{\Delta f}$.   Thus, for a bandwidth of 10,000 cycles, the heterodyne detector is capable of detecting signals about 10^5 times weaker than the square-law detector.

2.5. Crystal Types.   As mentioned above, the desirable characteristics are not the same for a crystal rectifier when intended for low-level or converter service.   In addition, the higher the frequency of operation, the more important is the role of barrier-layer capacity.   A group of crystals has been developed for the various types of service, whose general properties are given in Table 2.1.   For higher-frequency operation it is necessary to reduce the area of the point contact, leading to more delicate structures, both electrically and mechanically.

Two types of cartridges which have been standardized are shown in Fig. 2.15.   The standard unit for wavelengths above 3 cm is shown in Fig. 2.15a.   Below 3 cm the dimensions become too large a fraction of the operating wavelength, so a smaller unit, shown in Fig. 2.15b, has been developed.

In column 2 of Table 2.1, the crystal shown in Fig. 2.15a is referred to as A and that shown in Fig. 2.15b as B.   The third column in this table shows the intended use of the crystal.   The fourth indicates the intended frequency, this being the frequency at which the crystal must pass manufacturing specification tests.   Columns 5 to 10 pertain to the use of the crystals as converters: column 5 lists the local oscillator power at which the crystals are tested; column 6, the minimum rectified current that is expected; column 7 lists the conversion efficiency, expressed in decibels; column 8 gives the maximum acceptable noise temperature expressed as a numerical factor; column 9 shows the i-f resistance, being the value of the resistance used in determining the conversion efficiency; and column 10 gives the over-all noise figure (in decibels) of a heterodyne receiver assuming a noise figure of the i-f amplifier of 5 db.

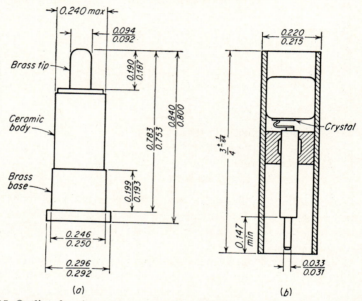

FIG. 2.15. Outline drawings of two crystal cartridges.   (a) Useful at 3 cm and above; (b) outline drawing of coaxial crystal cartridge useful for wavelengths shorter than 3 cm.   All dimensions are in inches.

Columns 11 and 12 in Table 2.1 pertain to low-level rectifiers. While converter or mixer crystals can be used as low-level detectors, their characteristics vary greatly, and the crystals especially designed for this service are better. Column 11 gives the minimum figure of merit M, while column 12 gives the expected range of dynamic resistance R_0.

Column 13 gives the burnout-test specifications. Each crystal must withstand the listed energy in ergs when applied in a single pulse approximately 0.003 μsec in duration. A burnout test is performed before the crystal is subjected to the operating tests for determination of conversion efficiency and the noise temperature. These tests simulate the initial spike present in a radar receiver due to the failure of the transmit-receive switch to act instantaneously. Although the low-level detectors are not

TABLE 2.1

Type of crystal (1)	Type of cartridge (Fig. 2.15) (2)	Converter use								Low-level use		Burnout (13)	Remarks (14)
		Use (3)	Test frequency, kMc (4)	Local-oscillator power, mw (5)	D-c minimum current, ma (6)	Maximum conversion efficiency, db (7)	Maximum noise temperature t (times) (8)	I-f or video impedance (test), ohms (9)	NF (5-db i-f), db (10)	Minimum figure of merit M (11)	Impedance R₀, ohms (12)		
1N21	A	Mixer	3.06	0.5	0.4	−8.5	4	400*	16.4	......	......	0.3 erg	Obsolete S band
1N21A	A	Mixer	3.06	0.5	0.4	−7.5	3	300	14.6	......	......	2.0 ergs	Standard S band
1N21B	A	Mixer	3.06	0.5	0.4	−6.5	2	400	12.7	......	......	2.0 ergs	Improved S band
1N21C	A	Mixer	3.06	0.5	0.4	−5.5	1.5	400	11.1	......	......	2.0 ergs	Most sensitive S band
1N23	A	Mixer	9.375	1.0	...	−10.0	3	300*	17.1	......	......	0.3 erg	Standard X band
1N23A	A	Mixer	9.375	1.0	...	−8.0	2.7	300	14.9	......	......	1.0 ergs	Improved-sensitivity X band
1N23B	A	Mixer	9.375	1.0	...	−6.5	2.7	300	13.4	......	......	0.3 erg	Most sensitive S band
1N25	A	Mixer	1.0	0.9	...	−8.0	...	200	14.7	......	......	6.5-watt pulse†	High-burnout L band
1N26	B	Mixer	24	1.0	0.5	−8.5	2.5	300	15.2	......	......	0.1 erg	Standard K band
1N27	A	Detector	3.295	...	...	...	...	...	...	60	4,000 max	......	Pulse-discrimination S band
1N28	A	Mixer	3.06	0.4	0.4	−7.0	2.0	250*	13.2	......	......	5 ergs	High-burnout S band
1N30	A	Detector	9.375	...	...	...	...	...	...	55	7,000–21,000	0.3 ergs	Original X band
1N31	B	Detector	9.375	...	...	...	...	...	...	55	6,000–23,000	0.02 watt‡	Improved-stability X band
1N32	A	Detector	3.295	...	...	...	...	...	...	100	5,000–20,000	0.36 watt‡	Improved-sensitivity S band
1N33	A	Detector	2.880	...	...	...	...	...	...	40 min 140 max	2,000–10,000	2.3 watts‡	Improved-burnout S band
1N53	B	Mixer	35	1.0	0.5	−8.5	2.5	400–800	16	......	......	0.15 erg	Ka band, useful as harmonic generator

* Approximate.
† Applied in 1-µsec d-c pulse.
‡ Design test value.

used in this way, they can still be damaged by leakage from high-power transmitters in the vicinity of the receiver, or by overloading in measurement applications. The burnout tests are, therefore, applied in longer pulses, usually one μsec in duration.

Stability and Handling of Crystals. Present-day crystals are subjected to rugged mechanical, electrical, and exposure tests at the factory.

The mechanical tests involve dropping the crystal from a height of 30 in. onto a wooden block, twisting the crystal with a torque of 1.5 in.-lb, and applying other forces. It must withstand immersion in water and also temperature cycling between 70 and $-40°C$.

In spite of the apparent ruggedness of the crystal unit, it can be easily damaged in handling, storage, and in use. It has been found that the static accumulated by a person's body is often sufficient to permanently damage the crystal when inserting it into its holder. It is, therefore, advisable to ground one's hand just before inserting the crystal into equipment. Crystals have also been damaged when stored in the vicinity of high-power systems. In such cases, it is advisable to keep crystals in shielded capsules when not in use.

When using crystals to monitor relatively high power, it is best to use low-impedance indicating devices; this prevents the development of high back voltages across the crystal. Crystal currents of 10 to 20 ma are generally safe if connected to a meter of low internal resistance.

Checking Crystal Characteristics. While it is impossible to determine the high-frequency behavior of a crystal rectifier by any method other than complete high-frequency measurement, it is possible to tell whether the crystal has deteriorated from the time it was known to be acceptable at the factory. A simple way to check the crystal for deterioration is to measure its back resistance at a standard voltage of 1 volt. A simple d-c crystal checker is shown in Fig. 2.16, together with instructions for its use. The results of a d-c check depend upon the particular crystal type but not upon the manufacturer. Limits for back resistance of several crystals are shown in Fig. 2.16.

2.6. Crystal Holders. The function of a crystal holder is to introduce the terminals of the crystal rectifier into the microwave circuit so that r-f power is absorbed in the crystal but without escaping through the output terminals. It is usually desirable to prevent unnecessary loss of signal power which can occur because of poor electrical connections, because some of the signal power can escape together with the detected output signal, or because of reflections. Several types of crystal holders are illustrated in Fig. 2.17.

The crystal holder, whether it is used as a low-level detector or as a frequency converter, should be arranged to transform the r-f crystal impedance to equal the impedance of the input transmission line in order to avoid reflections.   Many types of transformer circuits are possible, both of resonant and nonresonant type.   Resonant circuits are often desired to provide a degree of r-f preselection, i.e., tuning.   On the other hand, for some applications it is desirable to make the crystal holder as nonresonant as possible in order to provide constant sensitivity over a

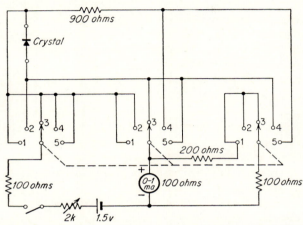

FIG. 2.16. Circuit diagram of a d-c crystal checker.   It is used as indicated in switch diagram.   Accept crystals if (1) forward resistance is less than 500 ohms, (2) back-to-front ratio is more than 10:1, and (3) the back current at −1 volt is less than:

Crystal type	Back current, ma
IN21	0.40
IN21A	0.175
IN21B	0.125
IN23	0.40
IN23A	0.30
IN23B	0.175

Switch position	Circuit function
1	Ohmmeter—calibration
2	Ohmmeter—forward resistance
3	Ohmmeter—back resistance
4	Set voltage across crystal to −1 volt
5	Read back current through crystal at −1 volt

band of frequencies.   In general, it is not hard to provide resonant circuits of a suitable kind, but it is more difficult to eliminate various unwanted resonances in a broadband holder.

The mixer-type and the low-level holders differ principally because of the necessity of introducing (a variable amount) local oscillator power. The coupling between the mixer and the local oscillator can be of some simple kind, providing loose coupling since the local oscillator power usually greatly exceeds the power required for proper converter action. Because the low-level crystal has an r-f impedance quite different from that of the mixer, the details of holder design will be different in the two cases.

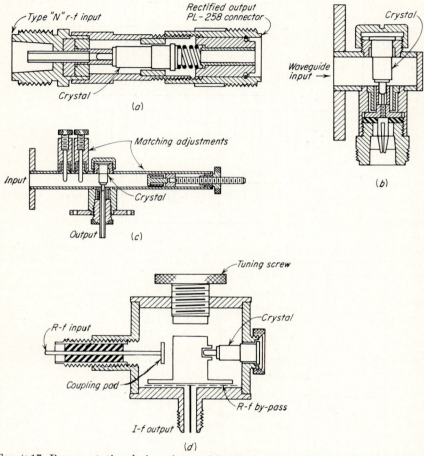

FIG. 2.17. Representative design of crystal holder.   (a) A coaxial holder suitable for general use at 10 cm and longer.   (b) Waveguide mount, fixed-tuned for use at 3 cm.   (*By permission from "Microwave Mixers," by R. V. Pound. Copyright, 1948. McGraw-Hill Book Company, Inc., New York.*)   (c) A 3-cm holder tunable over the range of the waveguide.   (*By permission from "Microwave Mixers," by R. V. Pound. Copyright, 1948.   McGraw-Hill Book Company, Inc., New York.*)   (d) A cavity-type low-Q design suitable for use at 10 cm.

The design of crystal holders for microwave receiver converter service is a complicated matter.   However, the various problems do not present unusual difficulties in the measurement service, since the ultimate sensitivity is seldom a major problem.   In most of the converter crystal holders required for measurement purposes, the crystal is exposed to the incoming microwave power in a simple manner, as indicated in Fig. 2.18. The r-f impedance of such a structure depends upon the details of construction and usually is frequency sensitive. This sensitivity can be minimized by either of two methods: providing some kind of an impedance matching device, such as suitably disposed reactance stubs or their

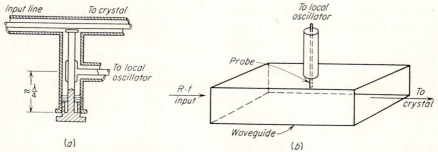

FIG. 2.18. Two methods of introducing local oscillator power into crystal holders. (a) Coaxial capacity coupling; (b) probe coupling from a local oscillator to the waveguide.

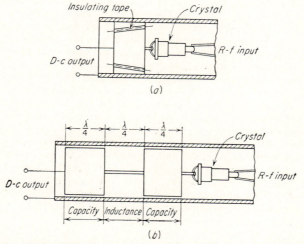

FIG. 2.19. Two methods of coupling crystal to outside terminals. (a) Lumped-capacity method; (b) distributed filter system consisting of quarter-wave filter sections.

equivalent; or by introducing a lossy element between the holder and the equipment terminals. A loss of several decibels does not usually matter, but it does eliminate the possibility of sharp resonances.

The detected signal can be taken from the crystal holders through a suitable bypass condenser or a system of microwave filter chokes. Both methods are illustrated in Fig. 2.19.

The design of the crystal holder intended for low-level operation must be tested, of course, at the low level.   The mixer-type holder must be checked under normal operating conditions with the local oscillator power supplied to the holder.   Since the local oscillator power will usually be flowing away from the holder into the signal terminals, determination of the impedance of the crystal holder requires special techniques.[1]

2.7. Vacuum-tube Detectors.   At low frequencies, several types of vacuum tube detectors are useful.   Diodes and biased triodes can be used at microwave frequencies but are not as satisfactory as the crystal rectifiers described above.   Vacuum tubes of the diode and triode type have been devised for microwave applications and in some cases have been arranged so that their elements are a part of the microwave circuit. The interelectrode spacings must be small in order to minimize the transit time of electrons across the cathode-anode gap.   Figure 2.20 shows a typical diode useful for microwave applications.

Diode and triode circuits are relatively poor at microwave frequencies because the noise level is generally higher than that of crystals.   Vacuum tubes are relatively expensive and require the use of resonant circuits.

---

[1] To determine the impedance of a heterodyne converter, a low-level signal source must be used.   A standing-wave detector is connected between the signal source and the crystal converter under test.   Power will flow from the signal source into the converted crystal, and local oscillator power from the crystal toward the signal generator.   A moving probe in the standing-wave detector will, therefore, have two signals varying in magnitude with the position of the probe.   If this standing-wave detector probe is connected to an i-f amplifier (operating at a frequency corresponding to the difference in frequency between the signal and the converter frequency), a detected signal will be available which will be a measure of the impedance of the converter crystal holder.   If the signal generator source impedance is equal to the characteristic impedance of the transmission line, then the probe amplifier will indicate the correct value of the converter impedance.   This is because the local oscillator signal introduced into the standing-wave detector from the crystal converter will remain constant in magnitude as the probe is moved, and the only variations in probe signal will be due to the standing waves present because of the mismatched converter. It is also possible to override the varying local oscillator signal in the probe detector by introducing an external source of local oscillator power into the probe.   In order to make this measurement, the signal power in the standing-wave detector line should be small compared to the local oscillator signal.

Another variation of the above experiment is based upon the reciprocity theorem. In the apparatus described above, the low-level signal source and the probe detector can be interchanged.   The r-f signal source is connected to the moving probe, and the detector crystal is connected to the former signal-source terminals.   Motion of the probe along the slot will cause changes in the detector i-f amplifier output; the resultant detected signals have identical meaning with the results obtained in the conventional manner.   However, because the probe is, by necessity, strongly decoupled from the main transmission line, the signal power reaching the converted crystal is greatly reduced (as it must be for meaningful results) without reducing the sensitivity of the impedance measuring apparatus.   For further details, see Sec. 5.13.

For these reasons, vacuum-tube detectors have not been widely accepted in general microwave applications. This, in turn, has limited their availability for measurement applications. Vacuum-tube detectors are superior to crystal because their characteristics are likely to remain more constant with time, temperature, and other laboratory conditions.

Klystrons with biased detector elements, as shown in Fig. 1.1g, can be used as detectors or convertors. However, such klystrons have not been accepted in microwave applications for the reasons described in Chap. 1 and immediately above.

Many types of nonlinear electronic processes can be conceived which would operate as detectors. While many experimental models of various

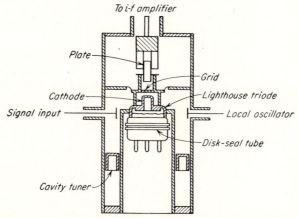

FIG. 2.20. Schematic diagram showing a coaxial cavity arrangement for a vacuum-tube triode mixer circuit. Both the signal and local oscillators are fed into a single low-Q resonant cavity. The i-f or detector terminals are connected to the plate circuit (in a manner not illustrated).

ideas have been tried in the past, none has proved to be sufficiently promising to remain competitive with the crystal rectifier.

2.8. Bolometers. A bolometer is a device for detecting electromagnetic radiation by converting it to heat and measuring the subsequent change of electrical resistance. Bolometers are generally used for microwave power measurements and are discussed in Chap. 3. One form of a bolometer is the *barretter*, consisting of a fine wire whose resistance changes can be readily measured. Its use in a demodulator application is illustrated in Fig. 2.21. The barretter is supplied with d-c bias power connected in series with the input transformer of an amplifier. The barretter can be placed in a holder similar to the crystal mountings discussed above. The r-f signal will cause the d-c current flowing through the transformer to fluctuate in accordance with the modulation envelope.

The resultant signal can be amplified and measured by an audio-frequency voltmeter.

When so used, the barretter exhibits square-law response provided the r-f power is sufficiently small compared to the d-c bias power. The time constant of the barretter must be small compared to the modulation period. Although the sensitivity of the barretter-amplifier combination

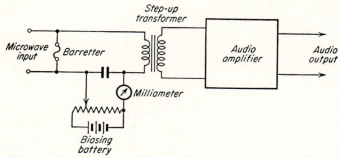

FIG. 2.21. Main elements of a circuit for the use of a barretter as a demodulator of microwave signals.

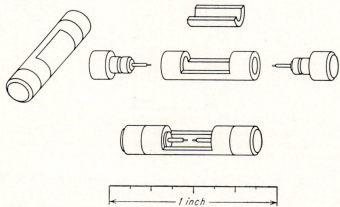

FIG. 2.22. Elements of a Sperry 821 barretter cartridge. The invisible Wollaston wire is connected across the terminals of the cartridge. (*By permission from "Technique of Microwave Measurements," edited by C. G. Montgomery. Copyright, 1947. McGraw-Hill Book Company, Inc., New York.*)

is appreciably lower than that of the crystal rectifier, it has the important advantages of stability, precisely known response law, and relative ruggedness.

Several types of barretter elements are available for measurement applications. The 0.01-amp common fuse (intended for protection of small electric meters) is the simplest and the least expensive. Commercial fuses, such as Littelfuses or Buss fuses, are readily available and are satisfactory for relative measurements. However, they do not have terminals suitable for microwave circuits and this tends to cause losses and reflections. A barretter designed specifically for use in microwave applications is shown in Fig. 2.22. It was developed to meet the requirements of microwave design. The terminals of the 821 barretter are arranged so that capacity joints can be made easily to the remaining circuit and there are no unnecessary wires or supports to complicate the microwave behavior of the circuit.

Characteristics of Barretters. Some of the more important characteristics of a typical (Sperry type 821) barretter are illustrated in Figs. 2.22–2.25. This barretter was intended primarily for use in holders in 3-cm waveguides. As shown in Fig. 2.22, it consists of an air-filled plastic

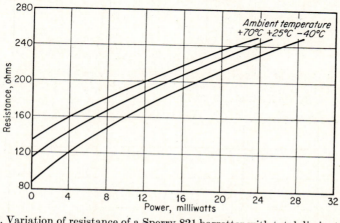

FIG. 2.23. Variation of resistance of a Sperry 821 barretter with total dissipated power. (*Reproduced by permission of the Microwave Electronics Division, Sperry Gyroscope Company, Division of the Sperry Rand Corporation.*)

cartridge with metal end caps supporting a bare platinum wire 0.00006 in. in diameter. Figure 2.23 shows the variation of resistance with the total dissipated power for several values of ambient temperature. Figure 2.24 shows the resistance vs. d-c current. Figure 2.25 shows the modulation frequency response of the same unit.[1]

The operating characteristic of the barretter shown in Fig. 2.23 can be expressed with sufficient accuracy by

$$R - R_0 = JP^n \tag{2.13}$$

where R_0 is the cold resistance of the unit, R the resistance of the barretter corresponding to a power P being dissipated, J and n are con-

[1] E. E. Eberle, The Sperry Type 821 Barretter for Microwave Power Measurements and Detection, unpublished Sperry Gyroscope Company Rept. 5224–1042, July 24, 1945; also Montgomery (ed.), *op. cit.*, pp. 161–169.

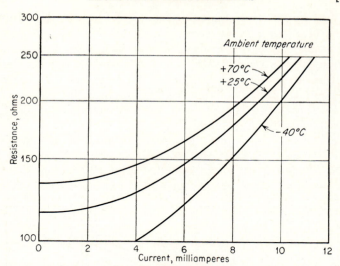

FIG. 2.24. Variation of resistance of a Sperry 821 barretter with d-c current.   (*Reproduced by permission of the Microwave Electronics Division, Sperry Gyroscope Company, Division of the Sperry Rand Corporation.*)

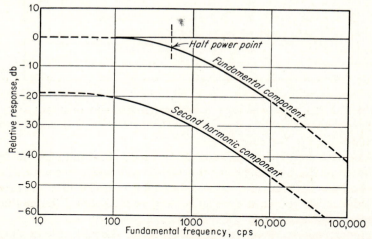

FIG. 2.25. Frequency response of a Sperry 821 barretter.   (*Reproduced by permission of the Microwave Electronics Division, Sperry Gyroscope Company, Division of the Sperry Rand Corporation.*)

stants.[1]   For the Sperry type 821 barretter, these have the values: $R_0 = 115$ ohms, $n = 0.9$, and $J = 7.57$.   The sensitivity β of the bar-

[1] E. Peskin, Microwave Power Measurements with Bolometers, Polytechnic Institute of Brooklyn, NDRC Rept. 14-529, Oct. 31, 1945.   This report is summarized in Montgomery (ed.), *op. cit.*, pp. 161–162.

retter can be found by differentiating Eq. (2.13) with respect to P, giving

$$\beta = \frac{dR}{dP} = \frac{n(R - R_0)}{P} \tag{2.14}$$

Using the recommended operating point of 200 ohms at 15 mw, the sensitivity is found to be 5 ohms/mw. (Data taken on 60 Sperry type 821 units have resulted in the average value of 4.45 $\pm$ 0.12 ohms/mw. The dependence of the barretter sensitivity on room temperature can be predicted from curves shown in Fig. 2.23.)

Comparison of Sensitivity of Crystals and Barretters. It is of interest to compare the sensitivity of the barretters and the crystal rectifiers. Since both of these devices convert microwave power to signals of low frequency which must be amplified in identical fashion, the noise problem does not need to be considered explicitly. If d-c current I flows through the barretter, the signal voltage V_s produced is

$$V_s = I\beta \, dP \tag{2.15}$$

Using the characteristics of the barretter stated above and assuming $P = 10^{-6}$ watts, the output voltage V_s is found to be about 50×10^{-6} volts. Referring to Fig. 2.6, it can be seen that the open-circuit voltage produced by the crystal rectifier with 10^{-6} watts is about 10^{-3} volts, or 20 times greater.

If the amplifier bandwidth is in the neighborhood of 100 cycles, the limiting thermal noise in the 200-ohm resistor of the barretter at its *elevated* temperature is about 2.5×10^{-8} volt. This means that the barretter of the 821 type will have a limiting sensitivity of about 10^{-8} watt for 100-cycle bandwidth. Greater sensitivity can be obtained by further reducing the amplifier bandwidth.

The dependence of barretter sensitivity upon room temperature is predictable from the curves shown; it is not large enough to be serious.

To summarize, bolometer-type detectors are desirable when accurate knowledge of the response law and general stability are of greater importance than the sensitivity. If the barretter current is always maintained at a predetermined value, and if the amplifier circuits are stabilized by negative feedback, the resultant combination will have reproducible sensitivity that cannot be attained with crystals. Although far inferior to the crystal converter in sensitivity, the barretter has a comparable dynamic range and superior stability.

2.9. Amplifier and Metering Circuits. Metering circuits useful with crystal rectifiers and bolometers vary in complexity depending upon the sensitivity and stability desired. The metering methods can be roughly divided into three groups, as follows, in order of their complexity:

1. D-c galvanometers in conjunction with crystal rectifiers for detecting unmodulated signals

2. High-gain audio amplifiers used with either crystal rectifiers or bolometers, for detecting modulated r-f signals

3. Superheterodyne receivers, converting microwave signals into low-frequency ones with conventional r-f methods used for final detection and measurement

The general features of these systems have been discussed above with a comparison of their sensitivity. Examples of satisfactory metering systems in each group will be given below.

The use of a sensitive d-c meter or a galvanometer represents the ultimate in simplicity. The crystal rectifier is a sensitive device and, if used carefully, will produce good accuracy. For rough measurements, a d-c meter can be connected to the crystal directly; this enables one to use the combination as a monitor, or for relative measurements when the various currents can be read on the single scale. The range of measurable currents can be extended by adding a variable T-pad attenuator between the crystal and the meter. It is often convenient to use a precision three-decade attenuator. If the galvanometer impedance is adjusted by padding to match the impedance of the attenuator, the sensitivity of the galvanometer can be changed over wide limits, keeping the impedance presented to the crystal at a constant value.[1]

For most laboratory applications a sensitive vacuum-tube amplifier is more satisfactory than the galvanometer arrangement described. The sensitive galvanometers are mechanically delicate and sluggish in

[1] Commercial attenuators are available with convenient 10-, 1-, and 0.1-db ranges. The characteristic impedance of a variable attenuator is not likely to match the galvanometer impedance. Neither is the attenuator impedance likely to provide the critical damping impedance that the galvanometer requires. It becomes desirable,

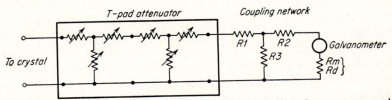

FIG. 2.26. Elements of the coupling network between a T-pad attenuator and the galvanometer; R_m is the internal impedance of the galvanometer, R_d is the critical damping resistance.

then, to add an unsymmetrical T pad between the galvanometer and the attenuator so designed that the attenuator sees its characteristic impedance, while providing the critical damping impedance to the galvanometer. Such unsymmetrical T pads can be designed with the aid of the following relations: Referring to Fig. 2.26, let R_0

response; in addition, any random r-f signals picked up by interconnecting cables will be rectified by the crystal and can be mistaken for signals or in other ways produce interference. The use of a vacuum-tube amplifier necessitates modulation of the r-f source. Although one must be aware of the possible presence of frequency modulation (see Sec. 1.5), modulation with square-wave audio signals is not difficult. The sensitivity of a narrowband amplifier is about equivalent to the most sensitive galvanometers. It also provides rapid response, rugged construction, and general flexibility. It has become customary to modulate the frequency sources with 1,000-cycle square-wave voltages. An audio amplifier sharply tuned to 1,000 cycles will respond to the fundamental and, by virtue of its narrow band, will reject a large fraction of the noise. Spurious signals are also discriminated against, unless they happen to be related to the modulation frequency.

A typical amplifier circuit is shown in Fig. 2.27. An input step-up transformer can be used between the low-impedance detector and the high-impedance of the grid circuit of the first amplifier stage. One or two stages of preamplification are needed before the variable attenuators are inserted to provide the large dynamic range. The variable attenuator, the subsequent amplifier stages, and the metering circuit all closely resemble the circuits of an ordinary vacuum-tube voltmeter. The amplifier bandwidth can be reduced in several ways. Either high-Q tuned circuits or negative-feedback circuits can be used. Extreme narrowband response can be obtained by means of the phase-detector circuit shown in Fig. 2.28 in place of the ordinary rectifier meter.

Some input circuit details shown in Fig. 2.27 require special mention. The use of bolometers requires d-c current to be supplied in series with

---

be the characteristic impedance of the variable T-pad attenuator; R_m the impedance of the galvanometer; and R_d the critical damping impedance of the galvanometer. R_1, R_2, and R_3 are the three arms of the unsymmetrical matching pad. Then, if $(R_m + R_d) > 2R_0$, use

$$R_1 = 0$$
$$R_2 = R_d - R_0 \sqrt{\frac{R_d + R_m}{R_d + R_m - 2R_0}} \qquad (2.16)$$
$$R_3 = R_0 \sqrt{\frac{R_d + R_m}{R_d + R_m - 2R_0}}$$

If $(R_m + R_d) < 2R_0$, use

$$R_1 = \frac{R_0}{2} \left(\sqrt{5 - \frac{8}{R_0} \frac{R_m R_d}{R_d + R_m}} - 1 \right)$$
$$R_2 = 0 \qquad (2.17)$$
$$R_3 = R_0 \frac{\sqrt{1 - \frac{2}{R_0} \frac{R_d R_m}{R_d + R_m}} - \frac{2R_m}{R_d + R_m}}{\left(1 - \frac{2R_0}{R_d + R_m} \right)}$$

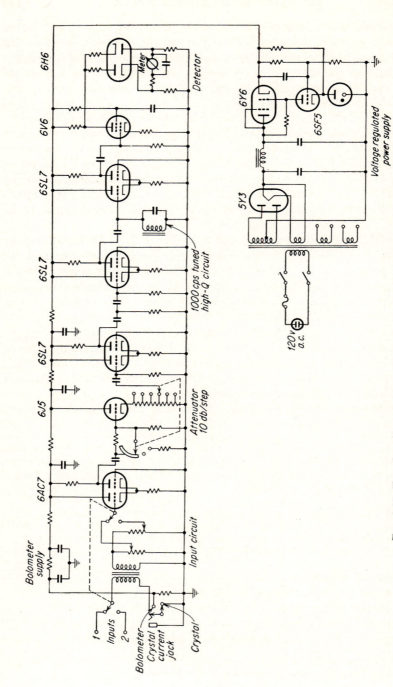

FIG. 2.27. Tuned audio amplifier suitable for use with crystals and barretters.

the bolometer and the amplifier.[1]   Generally the d-c bolometer current does not need to be adjusted.   If, however, it is desirable to keep the over-all sensitivity constant, a suitable d-c meter may be added to monitor the current and adjust it to a desired value.   The monitor jack should be provided to measure the magnitude of the d-c crystal current.   The

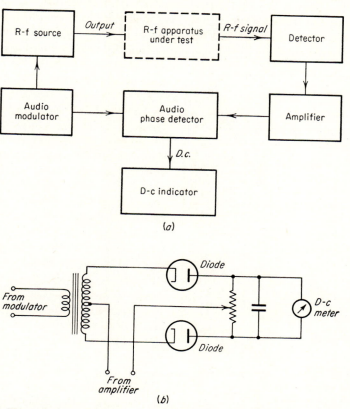

(a)

(b)

FIG. 2.28. Phase-detector circuit for providing narrowband response without tuned amplifiers.   (a) The arrangement of the principal pieces of apparatus; (b) a representative phase-detector circuit using conventional diodes.   The effective bandwidth of the system depends upon the time constant of the meter circuit.

knowledge of maximum crystal current, together with Fig. 2.6, enables one to avoid nonlinear regions of the response characteristic.

The output meter should have a linear scale to permit calibration of the detector, as described in Sec. 2.10.   If the amplifier is to be used for standing-wave ratio measurements, it is convenient to have the output

[1] As the crystal rectifier is likely to be damaged by d-c bias, the user must be careful not to switch to the bolometer terminals while using the crystal.

scale calibrated directly in units of VSWR. This is simple if the response law of the detector-amplifier is assumed to be equal to 2.

The most sensitive detecting systems employ the superheterodyne principle as well as the largest dynamic range. Such converter systems have been described above in so far as the crystal rectifier element is involved. Two forms of these systems are found useful. The first is like the conventional radio receiver in which the local oscillator operates near the frequency signal and heterodynes it to an i-f frequency. The second system employs the instrument called the *spectrum analyzer* which still is a superheterodyne receiver but with the local oscillator frequency sweeping over a desired narrowband at some audio frequency. The spectrum analyzer usually has an internal oscilloscope. This makes it possible to display the input signals by introducing them to the vertical deflection plates of the oscilloscope with the horizontal plates being supplied by the audio voltage sweep which is proportional to frequency. This particular arrangement makes it unnecessary to tune the local oscillator to precisely the signal frequency. Frequency converter systems of these types are ideal for detection and measurement of radio signals. Their only disadvantage is the relative complexity and cost.[1]

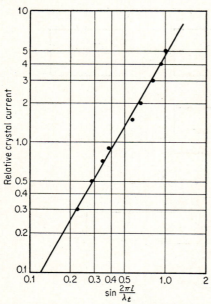

FIG. 2.29. Typical data obtained in calibration of a crystal rectifier by the method described in Sec. 2.10.

2.10. Calibration of Detectors.

It is usually necessary to know accurately the response law of the detecting device. Many methods can be devised for calibration of detectors, but the following is recommended because of its accuracy and simplicity.

If standing waves with infinite standing-wave ratio are created in a low-loss transmission system, the electric field of any one half-loop will closely approximate half-sine curves. A probe loosely coupled to the transmission line and arranged to sample this field along its length will have a voltage induced in it proportional to $\sin 2\pi l/\lambda_t$, where l is the dis-

---

[1] Some of the complexity of the superheterodyne system is compensated by the fact that its use makes the modulator for the signal source unnecessary. The design of spectrum analyzers and their general features are given in detail in Montgomery (ed.), *op. cit.*, chap. 7, pp. 408–455.

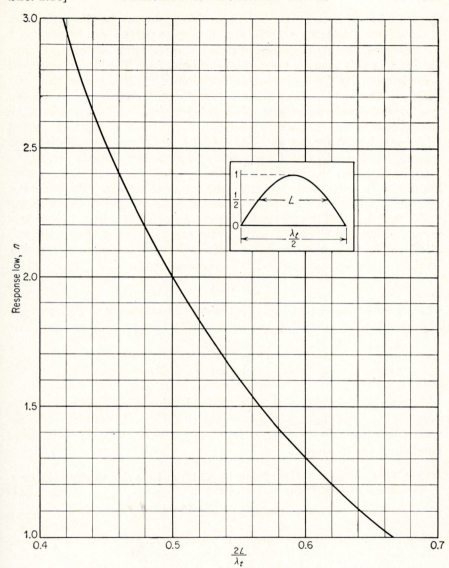

FIG. 2.30. Relation between the response law of a rectifier and the distance between half-response points.

tance measured from the voltage minimum, and λ_t is the transmission line wavelength. If this movable probe is connected to the detecting device under test, the response of the detector meter can be recorded as a function of distance l. The slope of the curve of output from the detector vs. $\sin 2\pi l/\lambda_t$ when plotted on log-log graph paper will give the response law of the device. The movable probe can be the probe of a standing-wave detector, and the standing-wave pattern can be produced by either shorting or opening the receiving terminals. Sample data obtained in this manner are plotted in Fig. 2.29. The largest source of error is generally due to inaccurate location of the "reference" position of the voltage node. This position should be found by averaging the positions of equal response on the two sides of the voltage node. Care should be taken to calibrate the detector in the range of signals expected in the anticipated application. Also, in the case of crystals, the response law may be dependent upon circuit conditions as described in Sec. 2.3.

The calibration procedure can be considerably simplified if the detecting device is to be used over a limited range of signals. By using the described method for furnishing known relative voltages to the detector under test, first find the meter reading corresponding to the voltage maximum. Then find the two positions, one on each side of the maximum, at which the meter reading is one-half of the voltage maximum. It can be shown that if the response law is described by

$$I = kV^n \tag{2.18}$$

where I is the meter reading, V is the applied voltage, and k a constant of proportionality, that the exponent n can be found from the expression[1]

$$n = \frac{\log(\tfrac{1}{2})}{\log \cos \dfrac{\pi}{2} \dfrac{2L}{\lambda_t}} \tag{2.19}$$

This expression is plotted in Fig. 2.30, showing the exponent n for a range of values of $2L/\lambda_t$. In these expressions, λ_t is the transmission line wavelength, and L is the distance between points at which the response is one-half of the maximum.

---

[1] This is arrived at as follows: Using Eq. (2.18) and the sinusoidal voltage form $V = \cos 2\pi z/\lambda_t$, the rectified current will be

$$I = k \left(\cos \frac{2\pi z}{\lambda_t} \right)^n \tag{2.20}$$

Let I_{max} be the current corresponding to its maximum value at $z = 0$. Hence, $I_{max} = k$. If the position z_0 is found at which $I = I_{max}/2$, then

$$\frac{I_{max}}{2} = I_{max} \left(\cos \frac{2\pi z_0}{\lambda_t} \right)^n \tag{2.21}$$

which leads to Eq. (2.19) if $L = 2z_0$.

CHAPTER 3

MEASUREMENT OF MICROWAVE POWER

3.1. Introduction. The various methods of *detecting* the presence of microwave power were discussed in the last chapter. Special attention was paid there to the accuracy of making relative measurements, to sensitivity, and to other relevant factors. In this chapter, a different aspect of the same problem will be considered, that of determining the absolute power flowing through a given system. Such absolute measurements are important, for example, in determining the power output from a transmitter, in establishing the sensitivity of a radio receiver, or in measuring the power gain of an amplifier. It is obvious that the measurement of power is as important at microwave frequencies as it is elsewhere in the radio domain. In addition, by and large, the measurement of power replaces the measurement of voltage and current in numerous relative measurements, as these quantities tend to lose their meaning in the distributed circuits encountered in typical microwave applications.

Since the microwave applications deal with both transmission and reception of signals, the range of power measurements extends from the measurement of many kilowatts down to the thermal agitation level in resistors. Sometimes the power is continuous, sometimes it is pulsed, or otherwise modulated. Many methods have been devised to accomplish the necessary measurements, and these differ greatly from one another. Furthermore, the applicability of many of these changes with frequency in a manner which is too complicated to be discussed here. This chapter will be limited to discussion of the methods which have proved to be convenient and accurate and which are most applicable in the microwave spectrum. Interested readers are referred to the literature for examples of ingenious techniques and description of their usefulness and limitations.[1]

The meaning of the word *power* is, of course, the usual one, and refers to the average value of power taken over a single cycle. However, since

[1] A survey of power measuring methods useful in the microwave region is to be found in the following references: R. N. Griesheimer, Microwave Power Measurements, chap. 3 in C. G. Montgomery (ed.), "Technique of Microwave Measurements," McGraw-Hill Book Company, Inc., New York, 1947; E. A. Yunker, H. C. Early,

145

in many applications microwave sources are pulsed, it is necessary to introduce two useful definitions. *Peak power* refers to the average taken over a period of the pulse. *Average power* refers to the average taken over a period between consecutive pulses. Most of the devices for measuring power have time constants of one-thousandth of a second or longer. Thus, in the case of radar-like applications, the power meter provides a measure of the average power directly. The peak power must then be computed from knowledge of the *duty cycle*, i.e., the ratio of pulse length of the repetition period. Thus, peak power P can be computed from the average power P_0 if the pulse length τ and the repetition frequency n are known. These factors are related by

$$P = P_0 \frac{1}{\tau n} \qquad (3.1)$$

Among desirable characteristics of a power-measuring device or a wattmeter are the following: The value of power indicated should be absolute in the sense that no further calibration should be required against any other microwave method. The power measuring device should be in the form of a standard microwave transmission system so that it can be directly connected to the apparatus under test; it should present a purely resistive load, equal in magnitude or the characteristic impedance of the line in which it is used; and it should remain *matched* in this manner at all frequencies at which power measurements are likely to be made. Although such matching conditions are hard to meet, the ideal device would be properly matched without the use of additional impedance transformers or other r-f adjustments. An ideal device for pulse applications would be one which indicated pulse power directly. The extent to which practical wattmeters meet these general requirements will become apparent below.

In the discussion of the various methods of measuring power, the reader should focus his attention on three separate subjects of basic importance:

1. The method of converting microwave power to other forms of energy (heat, light, force) which may be observed directly
2. The method of indicating such measurable quantities
3. The method of extending the useful range of the device to high and low values of power

---

G. Hok, and G. R. Bridgeford, "Very High Frequency Techniques," chap. 24, McGraw-Hill Book Company, Inc., New York, 1947; A. C. Matthews, Radio-frequency Power Measurements, *Radio* (New York), pp. 23–27, September, 1944; R. A. Schrack, Radio-frequency Power Measurements, *Natl. Bur. Standards Circ.* 536, March, 1953. The last reference contains an extensive bibliography.

The useful range of any device can be extended in the upward direction by suitable power dividers or other sampling methods. The devices can be made more sensitive only by increasing the sensitivity of the indicating device. The problem of sampling power is a simple one and corresponds to the general concept of current shunts at low frequencies.

In general, the methods available for power measurement at microwave frequencies are capable of good accuracy. However, the methods are all fairly elaborate, and many sources of error are possible in each one. The user must be aware of possible difficulties if errors are to be avoided.

One of the most reliable methods of checking the validity of power measurement is to compare the power readings of several types of measuring devices at one time. Checking the bolometer-type device against the calorimeter is one of the surest ways of satisfying oneself of the reliability of the power measuring methods. Such a comparison is not simple to make under usual laboratory conditions because of the different power levels to which bolometers and calorimeters respond. The use of separately calibrated directional couplers makes it possible to operate the bolometer in a power range at which common calorimeters produce good accuracy. Agreement to within a few per cent can usually be obtained by proper attention to details.

It is easily possible to check various types of bolometer wattmeters against each other. Thermistor and barretter elements are very different from one another in construction and operation, and a cross check of one against the other can usually be taken as proof of the satisfactory operation of both. Excellent agreement can be obtained at wavelengths of 10 cm and longer. Shorter wavelengths usually entail greater apparatus difficulties and invariably result in greater errors.

3.2. Methods of Power Measurement. For the sake of convenience, the power level below 10^{-2} watt will be referred to as low power; the range between 10^{-2} and 10 watts will be called medium power; and above 10 watts, high power.

Microwave power can be measured either by absorbing all of the available power in the measuring device or by sampling a known fraction of power from a transmission line which carries most of its power to some external load. In the discussion below, it will be assumed that all of the available power is absorbed in the measuring device, unless otherwise stated. This limits the maximum power to the dissipation limit of the measuring device. However, the range of any device can be extended in the upward direction by the sampling method. The devices for sampling power and their calibration will be described in Sec. 3.8.

A number of the methods most commonly used to measure microwave power are briefly described in this section, and more completely in subsequent pages. Less common methods will be mentioned in Secs. 3.12 and 3.13.

The bolometric method already mentioned in Chap. 2 is most useful in the low and medium power ranges and is illustrated in Fig. 3.1. A bolometer element, either a barretter, a lamp, or a thermistor, is placed into a microwave holder and subjected to the heating effect of incoming power. It is assumed that the resistance of such an element will change when heated. The holder is designed in the same manner as the crystal holders described in Chap. 2, so that the d-c terminals of the bolometers are available externally without allowing the microwave power to escape. The d-c terminals of the bolometer are connected to a suitable Wheatstone bridge. The bridge is supplied with power from a battery through an ammeter and an adjustable resistance R_1. In the absence of microwave power, enough d-c power is supplied from the battery so that the resistance of the bolometer is equal to the remaining arms of the bridge. When microwave power is applied, the bolometer becomes hotter and the bridge

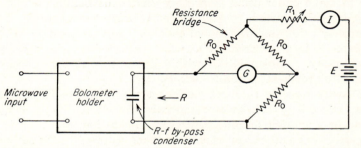

FIG. 3.1. Main elements of a bolometric wattmeter. Resistance R_1 is used to adjust d-c power input to the bridge. Galvanometer G indicates the bridge balance. R-f bypass condenser symbolically represents the design feature of the bolometer holder which prevents microwave power from escaping the holder into the bridge circuit.

unbalances. The balance can be restored by decreasing the d-c power supplied by the battery. The change in d-c power to the bolometer is taken as a measure of the microwave power. The conditions under which this substitution process is valid are described in Sec. 3.3.

The use of barretters constructed with Wollaston wire (as described in Sec. 2.8) in conjunction with sufficiently sensitive resistance bridges makes it possible to detect and measure power as low as 10^{-8} watt, provided ambient temperature changes are eliminated or compensated. Because the dissipation of power must usually be restricted to a wire length which is small compared to the wavelength, the dissipation limit of barretter elements cannot be made very high. The dissipation limit of the sensitive Wollaston-wire barretters is low, in the range of 10 to 20 mw. Tungsten lamps can be used for higher power. A medium-power (0.0012-cm diameter) tungsten barretter intended for use at 10 cm should not exceed about 1 cm in length; when evacuated such a lamp will safely dissipate about 1 watt. Filling this lamp with hydrogen increases its dissipating power limit to about 20 watts.*

Another form of the bolometer is the thermistor shown in Fig. 3.2. It is a small bead of semiconducting material supported between two wires. It acts as a resistor with large negative temperature coefficient. The useful range of measurement provided by available thermistors approximates that of the Wollaston-wire barretters.

While thermistors and Wollaston-wire barretters can be made to operate over nearly the same range of power, they are not equivalent in their usefulness. The thermistor is sluggish in its response and is, therefore, less desirable than the barretter in many applications in which rapid observations are important. The same features, however, make the thermistor invaluable in measuring pulse power, as its long time constant provides averaging automatically and avoids some errors which happen to be proportional to resistance excursion during the pulse. The thermistor is more sensitive than the barretter, making it more desirable in some applications. Simultaneously, however, it is more sensitive to changes in ambient temperature, creating additional problems in the design of bridge circuits and their use. The thermistors can also be made in extremely small sizes, which permits direct comparison of microwave power with d-c power. Thermistors are also less delicate and less subject to burnout. On the other hand, barretters can be made with remarkable uniformity with regard to their r-f and d-c characteristics. A defective unit can be replaced by a new one without readjusting any of the r-f matching conditions. In the use of barretter elements the question of validity of substitution process must be analyzed carefully.

In addition to barretters and thermistors, bolometer elements can be made in other forms. Thin metallic films deposited over glass supports can be arranged to provide geometrical structures which are ideal from the viewpoint of r-f design. Because of their geometrical shape, such film resistors can be used over very wide frequency ranges and are superior in this regard to the other elements mentioned above. They have other advantages which will be discussed more completely in Sec. 3.6.

The microwave circuits intended for housing bolometer devices are usually called *bolometer mounts*. In principle, the bolometer mounts are the same as the crystal and barretter holders discussed in Chap. 2. Because the bolometer elements suitable for power measurements are

---

* Hydrogen increases the cooling of a hot wire by a complicated process involving disassociation of molecular hydrogen and formation of atomic hydrogen. The latter recombines into molecular hydrogen at the wall of the lamp, giving off heat there. See E. G. Linder, The Use of Gas-filled Lamps as High Dissipation, High-frequency Resistors, Especially for Power Measurements, *RCA Rev.*, vol. 4, no. 1, p. 83, 1939.

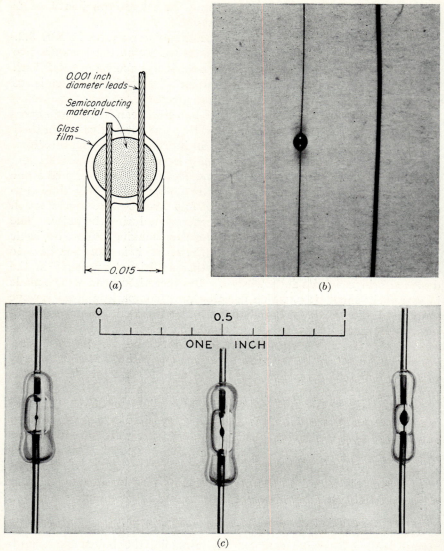

FIG. 3.2. The bead thermistor. (a) The semiconductor bead resistor between the 0.001-in. lead-in wires. The bead is covered with a glass layer for protection. (b) A photograph of Western Electric type 23A open-bead thermistor next to a human hair for comparison. (c) Three thermistors, mounted in a glass envelope for protection. *Left to right:* Western Electric 28A, Western Electric D162046, and Bell Telephone Laboratory experimental type. The smallest easily responds to power charge of 0.1 mw; the largest is capable of dissipating up to 200 mw. For high frequencies, the uncased thermistors shown in (b) are more satisfactory. (*Photographs, courtesy of Bell Telephone Laboratories, Inc.*)

designed with microwave applications in mind, their impedances are made roughly equal to the characteristic impedance of the transmission lines for which they are intended.   In many cases, however, the method of connecting the bolometer element to the transmission system involves geometrical discontinuities which produce local fringing fields.   These are equivalent to lumped reactances and result in reflections of the incoming power.   It is usually necessary to introduce matching devices or other reactive elements so as to eliminate these reflections.   Sometimes broadband bolometer mounts can be devised with fixed-tuned matching elements.   In other cases, it is simpler to provide tunable adjustments in order to allow the desired impedance matching at a particular frequency.   The use of both fixed-tuned and tunable matching devices is equivalent to the use of resonant circuits at lower frequencies and may introduce appreciable loss due to circulating currents.   The poor contacts in movable joints further increase the possibility of such losses. Methods of estimating such losses are discussed in Sec. 3.9.

Bolometers are usually used in bridge circuits in the manner described above.   Alternatively, the bridge unbalance may be used as an indication of r-f power.   A variety of bridge circuits has been developed to facilitate the measurement of power.   Control circuits have been devised which balance the bridge automatically and present the measured power on a direct-reading meter.   Compensation for changes in resistance of the bolometer due to ambient temperature changes is often necessary. This can be done by incorporating in the bridge circuit another temperature-sensitive resistor which is not exposed to r-f power.   The problem of compensation is more important with thermistors than barretters and is more acute at the lower power ranges.   In the milliwatt range and above, temperature compensation is less important for obvious reasons. Examples of bridge circuits and methods of temperature compensation are given in Sec. 3.7.

Above the power capacity of the bolometers, calorimetric methods can be used.   The heart of a microwave calorimeter is a device, generally called the *load*, in which the incoming power is dissipated completely. The dissipating medium may take the form of a transmission line partially filled with water, a liquid-cooled resistor, or a suitable gas.   Once the power is dissipated, ordinary calorimetric methods can be employed to determine the quantity of heat and, therefore, the microwave power. True calorimetric methods, making use of the first law of thermodynamics, produce the results in terms of basic physical quantities; i.e., mass, time, and temperature.

However, ordinary calorimetry is awkward since it involves measuring the rate of flow of liquids, which is time-consuming and subject to many errors.   There are several substitution techniques which make the calorimetric method convenient and simple. These will be described in Sec. 3.11. The main difficulties in calorimetric measurements are encountered at low power levels. Heat losses from the load and the cooling medium are difficult to avoid and become serious when the rates of flow of the liquid are small. Several methods have been devised to minimize and compensate heat losses and are briefly mentioned in Sec. 3.11.

Although the bolometric and calorimetric methods are the most common and convenient ones for determining microwave power, there are many other possible methods; some of these possess excellent accuracy but are complicated and the equipment is too delicate for general use. Others are convenient and simple, but are not susceptible to absolute calibration in the sense used here. To the first of these groups belong such methods as the measurement of radiation pressure, and the measurement of voltage or current, which were mentioned briefly in Chap. 2. To the second belong such devices as thermocouples, gas-discharge devices, and temperature-limited diodes, many of which are useful as power monitors, and, if calibrated, have many applications. An interested reader is referred to the literature for details[1] and to a brief introduction in Secs. 3.12 and 3.13.

3.3. Validity of the Substitution Process in Barretters. The use of barretter elements in the absolute power-measuring process involves the assumption that the d-c resistance of the barretter is a uniquely defined function of the power dissipated in the wire irrespective of whether this power is d-c, microwave, or a mixture of the two. The validity of this assumption will be examined in this section by considering certain limiting situations.

It will be assumed that the only sink of power within the bolometer mount is the temperature-sensitive element itself. The losses due to dielectric enclosures, poor contacts, and lossy impedance transformers will not be considered. Such losses, if present, can be detected by a variety of tests as discussed in Sec. 3.9.

In general, the discrepancy between d-c resistance changes caused by d-c and r-f heating is due to the different current distribution along the wire caused by the presence of standing waves. The skin effect may also, in part, be responsible for this difference. The end cooling of the wire can be different in the two cases as well, but this is generally not serious. The questions which will be examined below relate to possible errors arising when the diameter of the barretter wire is comparable to the skin depth in the material and when its length is an appreciable fraction of the wavelength. The details of the problem depend upon the relation between the resistance of the wire and the dissipated power.

[1] Schrack, *op. cit.;* Yunker et al., *op. cit.*

The change in d-c resistance of a barretter element will be proportional to the total change in power irrespective of the source of the additional power or its spatial distribution if the following criteria are satisfied:

1. The resistance of the barretter element is proportional to its absolute temperature.

2. The temperature rise at any point along the wire is proportional to the power dissipation at that point.

3. The constant of proportionality in (2) is independent of position along the wire.

Consider, for example, a hypothetical case of a long, slender wire cooled entirely by convection. If the end effects are negligible and if the principal heating is due to direct current, the resistance and temperature along the wire will be everywhere the same. The presence of a small amount of r-f power will result in changes in resistance which may be different from point to point because of possible standing waves, but because the changes in resistance will be small, they can be considered to be proportional to the power change at each point. Hence, the total resistance change will be proportional to the summation of power change along the length, irrespective of the source of additional power or its spatial distribution.

Such a situation, however, represents a special case and will not be true in general. If, for instance, a large fraction of heating is due to r-f power, the current distribution, resultant heating, temperature, and resistance will all vary with the position along the wire in a manner which depends upon the nature of the cooling process. In general, the criteria stated above cannot all be satisfied, and therefore the validity of the power substitution must be examined in some detail. It is necessary to determine how the resistance of a barretter wire changes with r-f power at each point along the wire. The change in total resistance of the wire can be computed and compared to the change in resistance due to direct current alone. In several cases considered below, the power-resistance relationship is not linear, and is dependent upon the particular cooling process. The nature of the cooling process, in turn, depends upon the construction of the barretter element, its size and geometry, and the power level at which it is operated. The following cases are of practical importance and are discussed more fully.

1. Very thin platinum wire, such as the Wollaston-wire barretter described in Secs. 2.8 and 3.2, when mounted in air is useful in the milliwatt range. Convection losses are predominant under all practical conditions.

2. Evacuated barretters made, for example, of tungsten wire, 0.001 cm in diameter and 1 cm long, are useful in the milliwatt range. The cooling process is due to conduction along the wire.

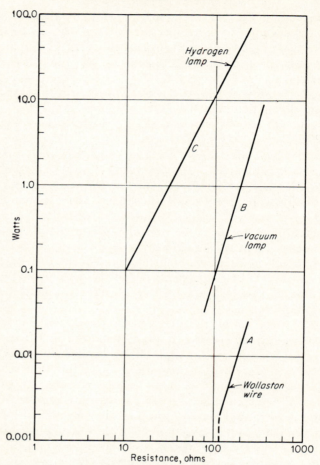

FIG. 3.3. Relation between resistance and power for three different types of barretter elements.

3. Evacuated tungsten barretters, as described above, are useful if operated at incandescence at power levels up to 1 watt. The cooling is due to radiation.

4. If a similar tungsten barretter is operated in hydrogen gas, the cooling process at incandescence is due to disassociation of molecular hydrogen.

The relation between resistance and power is different in these cases and is shown plotted in Fig. 3.3.[1]

---

[1] The relation between d-c resistance and power dissipated in a resistive rod has been studied theoretically for several cases of interest. See E. Peskin and E. Weber, The D-C Thermal Characteristics of Microwave Bolometers, *Rev. Sci. Instr.*, vol. 19, no. 3, p. 188, March, 1948.

It is necessary to know how the d-c power and r-f power compare if each (either separately or together) is used to heat the barretter to produce the same d-c resistance.   This relation has to be considered for a variety of possible standing-wave conditions and for the various conditions of cooling.

The conclusions which will be reached in this section may be summarized as follows:

1. The skin effect in barretters is of no practical importance in so far as the substitution process is concerned.

2. If r-f power is very small compared to the initial d-c heating, all residual questions of wire length, cooling process, etc., are not important; the substitution process can be trusted.

If the r-f power is at all appreciable in comparison with the initial d-c heating, a number of errors are possible.   The salient conclusions are then as follows:

1. The errors are absent if the relation between power and resistance is linear.   Convection-cooled Wollaston wires approximate this condition closely.

2. In radiation and gas-cooled conditions, the resistance-power relation is not linear.   The barretter wire must be short compared to the wavelength.

3. Even with short lengths, serious errors can occur if r-f power is too large a fraction of total power *and* if the wire happens to be located near a current node or loop of the standing-wave pattern.

4. If the cooling process is due to conduction, it is possible to use special wire lengths for which the substitution process happens to be valid even though r-f power is not small compared to d-c power.

The various effects of importance will be considered briefly below. The material follows the work of Feenberg,[1] Bleaney,[2] Carlin and Sucher,[3] and Gainsborough.[4]

---

[1] Skin effect, end corrections, and the general problem of spatial distribution of current along a barretter wire when the latter is cooled by radiation or hydrogen are considered in two reports: E. Feenberg, The Frequency Dependence of the Power-Resistance Relation in Hot-wire Wattmeters, Sperry Gyroscope Co. Rept. 5220–108, Mar. 10, 1943.   [The skin effect problem as treated by Feenberg is summarized in Montgomery (ed.), *op. cit.*, pp. 166–167.]   E. Feenberg and R. Kahal, Apparent R-F Power as a Function of Filament Length in Nodal Position in a Hot-wire Wattmeter, Sperry Gyroscope Co. Rept. 5224–1031, Apr. 23, 1945.

[2] The conduction-cooling problem is considered in the following paper: B. Bleaney, Radio-frequency Power Measurement by Bolometer Lamps at Centimeter Wavelengths, *J. IEE*, vol. 93, pt. IIIA, no. 9, March–May, 1946.

[3] The convection-cooled problem is considered in detail by H. J. Carlin and M. Sucher, Accuracy of Bolometric Power Measurements, *Proc. IRE*, vol. 40, no. 9, p. 1042, September, 1952.

[4] G. F. Gainsborough, Some Sources of Error in Microwave Milliwattmeters, *J. IEE*, vol. 95, pt. III, no. 36, p. 229, July, 1948.

Skin Effect. It may be thought that the skin effect, causing the current to flow near the surface of the wire, would make the d-c resistance of the wire differ when heated by r-f and d-c. However, in wires suitable for use as barretter elements, the difference in the two cases is extremely small. To understand this, one needs to know the radial temperature distribution in the wire in the two cases.

The skin effect causes the heating to concentrate at the surface of the wire. Under steady-state conditions the interior of the wire becomes heated to the temperature of the skin so that the temperature distribution can be considered to be constant over the cross section. In the d-c case, however, the heat is dissipated uniformly over the area of the wire, causing heat to flow outwardly. The center of the wire must, therefore, be hotter than the surface. The difference in temperature between the center and the outside of the wire can be calculated by solving the heat-flow equation in cylindrical coordinates. The resistance of the wire can then be computed, taking into account the variation of electrical conductivity with temperature. If the d-c resistance of an element of wire is R_a when heated by r-f power, and R when heated only by d-c power, the difference between the two is

$$\frac{R - R_a}{R_a} = 0.10 \frac{P}{lT_ak} \tag{3.2}$$

where P is the power dissipated in the length l of the wire, T_a is its outside temperature, and k is its thermal conductivity in cal/(°C)(sec)(cm).* Substitution of typical values appropriate to various barretter elements shows that this difference is usually a small fraction of 1 per cent.

The fact that the *d-c resistance* of a thin wire when heated by d-c and r-f is nearly the same does not imply that the r-f impedance of the barretter is equal to its d-c resistance. Because of the skin effect, both the resistance and the inductance of the wire change with frequency. This change in r-f impedance of the barretter does not affect the power measuring process but is important in considering the matching of the element to its r-f structure and in other questions such as those discussed in Sec. 3.9.

Effect of Wire Length and Standing Waves. The effect of wire length and spatial distribution of current along the wire due to standing waves is considered in the following special cases. It is assumed that the barretter elements are held in coaxial mounts of the type shown in Fig. 3.4, permitting standing waves to exist along the wire. For simplicity, it is assumed that losses along the heated wire are negligible, resulting in sinusoidal distribution of current.

In the first two cases below, the resistance-power relation is nearly linear. In the first, this is so by virtue of the fact that the r-f power is

* Feenberg, *op. cit.;* Gainsborough, *op. cit.*

very small compared to d-c; in the second, the convection-cooling process assures this linear relation without requiring the r-f power to be small. In both cases, the criteria stated at the beginning of this section are satisfied simply.   In the third case, the conduction cooling causes the temperature to vary with position along the wire, violating the criteria for validity in general.   Special conditions on wire length must be satisfied in order to make the barretter useful.   In the last two cases, the cooling process assures uniform cooling along the wire, but the power-resistance relationship is nonlinear.   This imposes restrictions on wire length as well as upon the fraction of d-c power that may safely be displaced by r-f power.

CASE 1.   R-F POWER SMALL COMPARED TO D-C POWER.   The simplest and one of the most important cases is one in which the r-f power is small compared to the d-c power.   Under these circumstances, the current is everywhere the same and, assuming negligible end cooling, the heat production and temperature will be independent of position along the wire.

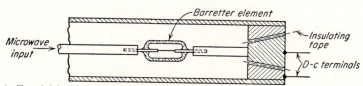

FIG. 3.4. Coaxial holder for barretter elements.   The microwave input terminals are assumed to have a d-c connection so that the resistance of the barretter elements can be measured at the d-c terminals.

It can then be assumed that the resistance of a given incremental length of wire will be proportional to the total power dissipated in this element. Because of this linear dependence, the total change in the wire resistance is simply the summation of the changes in the resistance along the length; therefore, a measure of the barretter resistance is a measure of the power producing it, irrespective of whether it is d-c or r-f power.   Hence, the presence of r-f power is correctly measured even though the wire length is not small compared with the wavelength.

CASE 2.   WOLLASTON WIRE—CONVECTION COOLING.   Many of the barretters commercially available are made of platinum Wollaston wire mounted directly in air.   In this case it is found that the process of cooling is almost entirely due to convection, even at temperatures approaching the melting point of platinum.   Aside from the negligible effects at the ends, the convection process insures uniform cooling.   It is also found that the convection results in a nearly linear dependence of resistance upon power [see Sec. 2.8; Eq. (2.13)].   Thus, the criteria for the validity of the power substitution process mentioned above are approximately satisfied.

Careful studies have shown that Wollaston-wire barretters can be used to measure continuous wave power throughout the microwave region with an accuracy approaching low-frequency practice.   Small errors due to the end effects and departure of the resistance-power relation from linearity are described in the literature.[1]

CASE 3.   R-F POWER EQUAL TO D-C POWER—CONDUCTION COOLING.   If power of the order of 10^{-4} to 10^{-3} watt is dissipated in a vacuum tungsten lamp (1 or 2 cm long and 10^{-3} cm in diameter), the absolute temperature of the wire changes by no more than a factor of 2.   The cooling is found to be due to conduction of heat to the wire terminals with radiation losses being negligibly small.   The temperature and, therefore, the resistance

TABLE 3.1. MAXIMUM LENGTH OF A WOLLASTON-WIRE BARRETTER AS A FUNCTION OF ITS DIAMETER FOR THE CONDITION THAT THE ERROR IN POWER MEASUREMENT BE LESS THAN 2 PER CENT

$\dfrac{Length}{Diameter}$	$Maximum\ \dfrac{length}{wavelength}$
10	0.11
50	0.11
100	0.12
200	0.13
500	0.16
1,000	0.19
2,000	0.28
5,000	0.50

are proportional to the power dissipated in the wire.   However, the presence of sinusoidally distributed r-f currents causes the heating and temperature to depend upon position along the wire.   This effect, in general, causes the d-c resistance to be different under d-c and r-f heating in a manner which depends upon the ratio of d-c power to r-f power, and upon the exact distribution of the current in the wire, as well as upon the properties of the wire itself.   Under certain special conditions, it is still possible to use the substitution process correctly, even without enforcing the restriction that the r-f power should be small compared to d-c.   It is found possible to use the bolometer by first measuring a change in its resistance due to r-f, and later determining the d-c power required to produce the same d-c resistance in the absence of r-f.   However, it is

[1] Carlin and Sucher, *op. cit.*   It is found that the residual errors in Wollaston-wire barretters are principally due to axial flow of heat along the wire and a sheath of air immediately adjacent to it.   Table 3.1 shows the maximum length of a barretter as a function of its diameter if the errors are to be limited to 2 per cent or less.

For example, a Sperry 821 barretter has a length-to-diameter ratio of about 2,000 and a length of approximately 3 mm.   From Table 3.1 the error is less than 2 per cent even if it were used at wavelengths as short as 1 cm.   This is well below the wavelength for which this barretter is intended (because of r-f circuit considerations).

necessary to keep the wire length either very short compared to the wavelength, or else to select special wire lengths.[1]

[1] Bleaney, *op. cit.* This paper considers theoretically the effect of finite length and describes the construction and use of long tungsten lamps suitable for service at 10 and 3 cm. Although long bolometer elements can be used with success in coaxial and waveguide mounts, it should be remembered that the specific results obtained are applicable only when the lamp is a part of a coaxial structure. The current distribution along a wire mounted in a waveguide cannot be assumed to be sinusoidal. For a coaxial structure, the analysis proceeds as follows:

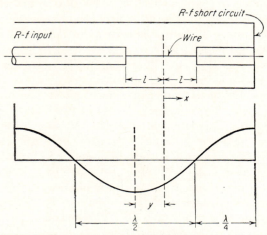

Fig. 3.5. Barretter wire in a coaxial holder showing distribution of r-f current along its length. The position of the standing wave along the wire depends upon the length of the wire and its distance from the r-f short circuit.

Consider the barretter wire mounted in a coaxial structure, as shown in Fig. 3.5. A current of magnitude $i \cos 2\pi(x + y)/\lambda$ is flowing through the wire of length $L = 2l$, and with $x = 0$ at the middle of the wire. The appropriate temperature distribution along the wire can be obtained by solving the heat-flow equation:

$$kA \frac{\partial^2 T}{\partial x^2} + i^2 r_0 \cos^2 \frac{2\pi}{\lambda} (x + y) = 0 \qquad (3.4)$$

where k = thermal conductivity of the wire
A = cross section of the wire
i = rms current at current maximum
r_0 = r-f resistance per unit length
y = distance of current maximum from the center of the wire
T = increase of temperature above the surroundings and supports

and
$$\delta = \frac{2\pi y}{\lambda}$$
$$\phi = \frac{2\pi L}{\lambda} \qquad (3.5)$$

The solution of Eq. (3.4) leads to the following temperature distribution along

It can be shown that the ratio of r-f power to d-c power for equal changes in r-f and d-c resistance is

$$\frac{\Delta P_{r-f}}{\Delta P_{d-c}} = \frac{1 + \cos 2\delta \dfrac{\sin \phi}{\phi}}{1 + \dfrac{3}{\phi^2} \cos 2\delta \dfrac{\sin \phi}{\phi} - \cos \phi} \tag{3.3}$$

This equation is plotted in Fig. 3.6. It is of interest to note that the ratio of resistances is unity periodically. The maximum error takes place when the center of the wire is located either at the current maximum or the current minimum. The error is zero when the wire length happens to be 0.92 wavelength long. If the center of the wire is halfway between the current maximum and current minimum, the error is zero for any length.

CASE 4. HIGH-POWER LAMPS—RADIATION AND GAS COOLING. In the two cases considered, the resistance change in the barretter was proportional to r-f power. This is not true in general, as can be verified from Fig. 3.3. Experimentally obtained data show that the resistance of a tungsten filament in vacuum (of the type described above but operating at incandescence) varies as $P^{0.33}$. The resistance of a similar filament in the hydrogen is proportional to $P^{0.5}$. Such nonlinearity between power and resistance causes the barretter d-c resistance to be dependent upon current distribution and other factors. This problem has been studied

---

the wire:

$$T = \frac{i^2 r_0}{2kA} \left\{ \frac{l^2 - x^2}{2} + \frac{\lambda^2}{16\pi^2} \left[\cos \left(\frac{4\pi x}{\lambda} + 2\delta \right) - \cos 2\delta \cos \frac{4\pi l}{\lambda} \right] \right.$$
$$\left. + \frac{x\lambda^2}{16\pi^2 l} \sin 2\delta \sin \frac{4\pi l}{\lambda} \right\} \tag{3.6}$$

The corresponding power input is obtained by integrating $i^2 r_0$ losses along the length of the wire; it is found to be

$$P = i^2 r_0 \left(l + \frac{\lambda}{4\pi} \cos 2\delta \sin \frac{4\pi l}{\lambda} \right) \tag{3.7}$$

The fractional change in the d-c resistance of the wire when heated by r-f current is computed on the assumption that change in resistance is proportional to the temperature of the wire. The fractional change in resistance is

$$\left(\frac{\Delta R}{R} \right)_{r-f} = \frac{1}{2l} \int_{-l}^{+l} \alpha T \, dx \tag{3.8}$$

$$= \frac{\alpha i^2 r_0 L^2}{24kA} \left[1 + \frac{3}{\phi^2} \cos 2\delta \left(\frac{\sin \phi}{\phi} - \cos \phi \right) \right] \tag{3.9}$$

in which α is a temperature coefficient of resistivity.

The change in resistance in the wire due to d-c heating is related to the power dissipated in the wire. It is assumed that the change in resistance of the wire in the two cases is equal. The final result expressed as a ratio of r-f power to d-c power for equal-resistance changes leads to Eq. (3.3).

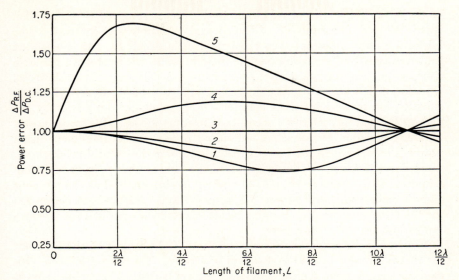

FIG. 3.6. Fractional error in power measurement for conduction-cooled barretter as a function of its length.   The curves shown are plotted for five different positions of current loop along the wire.   (1) $y = 0$, (2) $y = \lambda/12$, (3) $y = \lambda/8$, (4) $y = \lambda/6$, (5) $y = \lambda/4$.

by Feenberg and Kahal.[1]   Their work can be summarized in Figs. 3.7 and 3.8.

It is assumed that the resistance of the barretter is adjusted to the same d-c value whether heated by r-f or d-c power or a combination

[1] The results are obtained as follows, referring to Fig. 3.5 and the symbols

I_0 = initial d-c current in filament
i_0 = increment of d-c current
P_0 = initial d-c power
$\Delta P_{d\text{-}c}$ = increment of d-c power
R_0 = initial d-c resistance of wire
r_0 = initial d-c resistance per unit length = R_0/L
R = total d-c resistance of wire
$R_{d\text{-}c} = R_0 + (\Delta R)_{d\text{-}c}$
$R_{r\text{-}f} = R_0 + (\Delta R)_{r\text{-}f}$

The current distribution is assumed to be sinusoidal.   Neglecting the end effects, the d-c resistance due to total d-c current $I = I_0 + i_0$ on a per-unit-length basis is

$$r_0 = \beta \sqrt{P} = \beta \sqrt{I^2 r_0} \qquad (3.10)$$

or

$$r_0 = \beta^2 I^2 \qquad (3.11)$$

where β is an empirical constant determined from Fig. 3.3.   Total resistance is

$$R_{d\text{-}c} = L\beta^2(I_0 + i_0)^2 \qquad (3.12)$$

If, instead of d-c current, an increment of r-f current is added, the d-c resistance of

of the two. The ratio of r-f power to d-c power required to accomplish this is plotted as a function of the several parameters of interest. The initial d-c power dissipated in the barretter is called P_0. It is assumed that additional r-f and d-c power is introduced to the barretter, one at a time, in such a way that the d-c resistance is the same in both cases. Curves labeled $P_0 = 0$ mean that the initial d-c power is zero, i.e., the substitution process involves complete replacement of d-c power by r-f. Curves labeled $\Delta P_{r-f}/P_0 = 1$ mean that to some initial value of d-c power P_0 there is added an equal amount of r-f power. This increment in r-f power is compared to the increment of d-c power that would produce the same d-c resistance. The ordinate in the curves shown is the ratio of r-f power to d-c power, $\Delta P_{r-f}/\Delta P_{d-c}$ and can be interpreted as the per cent error in measurement of power. Figures 3.7 and 3.8 have been computed for the hydrogen lamps. Similar results have been obtained for vacuum lamps but are not shown here.

Figure 3.7 shows the error as a function of the length of the filament for three different positions of standing waves. The curves labeled with capital letters refer to the complete power substitution while curves labeled with small letters correspond to the case of r-f power being equal to d-c power. Curves A and a are plotted for the case in which the center of the filament is located at the current node; curves B and b, for the case of the current maximum at the center of the filament; curves C and c, for the case of the current maximum being located at the input

---

the wire will be

$$R_{r-f} = L\beta^2 \left[I_0^2 + i^2 \overline{\cos^2 \frac{2\pi}{\lambda} (x - y)} \right] \tag{3.13}$$

where the bar indicates an average taken over the length of the wire.

The power dissipated can be computed by taking the product I^2R in the two cases. These are

$$P_0 + (\Delta P)_{d-c} = L\beta^2(I_0 + i_0)^4 \tag{3.14}$$

$$P_0 + (\Delta P)_{r-f} = \beta^2 \int_{-l}^{l} \left[I_0 + i^2 \cos^2 \frac{2\pi}{\lambda} (x - y) \right]^2 dx \tag{3.15}$$

$$= L\beta^2 I_0^4 \left[1 + 2\left(\frac{i}{I_0}\right)^2 C_2 + \left(\frac{i}{I_0}\right)^4 C_4 \right] \tag{3.16}$$

in which

$$C_n = \frac{1}{L} \int_{-l}^{l} \left[\cos \frac{2\pi}{\lambda} (x - y) \right]^n dx \tag{3.17}$$

Eqs. (3.14) and (3.16) can be combined and solved for $\Delta P_{r-f}/\Delta P_{d-c}$; i and i_0 can be related by equating the d-c resistances R_{d-c} and R_{r-f}. This leads to the equation

$$\frac{\Delta P_{r-f}}{\Delta P_{d-c}} = \frac{1 + \left(\frac{1}{2} + \frac{C_4}{C_2^2}\right)\frac{i_0}{I_0} + \frac{C_4}{C_2^2}\left[\left(\frac{i_0}{I_0}\right)^2 + \frac{1}{4}\left(\frac{i_0}{I_0}\right)^3\right]}{1 + \frac{3}{2}\frac{i_0}{I_0} + \left(\frac{i_0}{I_0}\right)^2 + \frac{1}{4}\left(\frac{i_0}{I_0}\right)^3} \tag{3.18}$$

This equation contains the information shown in Figs. 3.7 and 3.8.

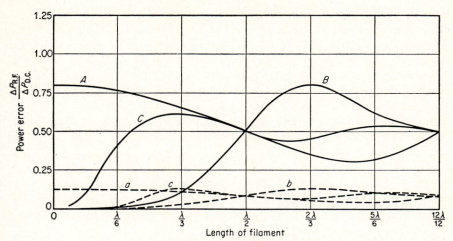

FIG. 3.7. Error in power measurement in a hydrogen-cooled lamp as a function of the length of the filament.   Curves labeled with capital letters correspond to complete replacement of r-f power; curves labeled with small letters correspond to the case of r-f and d-c power being equal.   Curves A, a correspond to the case when the filament is located at current node; curves B, b for the case when the current loop is at the center; curves C, c when the current loop is at the input end of the filament.

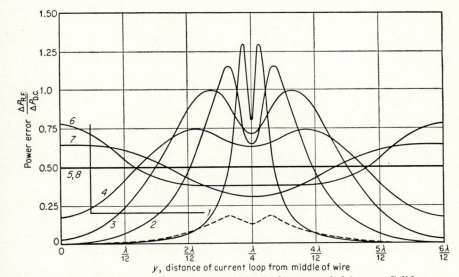

FIG. 3.8. The power measurement error in the hydrogen-cooled lamp.   Solid curves show the error plotted as a function of position of standing waves along the wire for eight different lengths of wire with complete replacement of d-c by r-f power.   Key: (1) $x = \lambda/24$, (2) $x = \lambda/8$, (3) $x = \lambda/4$, (4) $x = 3\lambda/8$, (5) $x = \lambda/2$, (6) $x = 5\lambda/8$, (7) $x = 13\lambda/8$, (8) $x = \lambda/8$.   The dashed curve is plotted for $x = \lambda/8$, for r-f power being equal to d-c power.

end of the filament. The behavior in all cases is substantially different from the situation resulting from conduction heating. The possible error is larger and there is no wire length for which the error is zero. Furthermore, for the case of complete substitution, even short lengths can produce large errors, as can be emphasized by examining the error for the filament length of $\lambda/8$ as a function of position of standing waves. The computed results are shown in Fig. 3.8. The error can be large over a substantial range of possible locations of the current node as long as the r-f power is a large fraction of the initial d-c power.

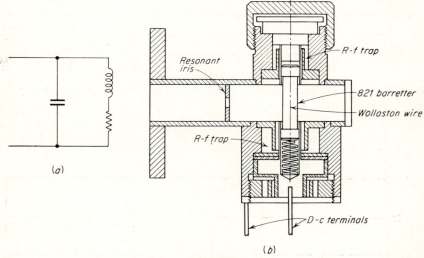

Fig. 3.9. (a) Equivalent circuit of Sperry 821 barretter usable up to about 6,000 Mc. (b) A waveguide mount for Sperry 821 barretter. A resonant window is used as a matching element. (*Adapted by permission of the Microwave Electronics Division, Sperry Gyroscope Company, Division of the Sperry Rand Corporation.*)

The last result has been qualitatively verified in a series of experiments.[1] Measurements show that for a certain range of adjustments of the tuning mechanisms in the lamp holder, very large errors are observed of the type predicted by Feenberg and Kahal.

The conclusion reached from these calculations is that improper use of high-power lamps can lead to serious difficulties. It is best to avoid lamp length in excess of $\lambda/8$. A barretter mount should be carefully adjusted

[1] T. Moreno and O. C. Lundstrom, Microwave Power Measurement, *Proc. IRE*, vol. 35, p. 514, May, 1947. The errors in power measurement reported in this paper are appreciably larger than the theoretical values computed by Feenberg and Kahal. These are believed to be the result of losses associated with the bolometer holder. The losses are accentuated by very high standing-wave ratio encountered due to the improper location of the current maximum along the filament.

to avoid current nodes or loops near the filament center.   Impedance matching systems should be selected in which resonances are minimized or eliminated entirely.   (Some barretter elements have been designed to make this possible.[1])   The most important precaution is to limit the r-f power to a small fraction of the initial d-c power.

3.4. Typical Barretter Elements.   The use of barretter elements for power measurement was discussed in the preceding sections.   Several barretter elements developed for bolometric applications are described more completely below.

The 821 barretter, as described in Chap. 2, was originally designed for measuring power at the wavelength of 3 cm and longer.   Its length and

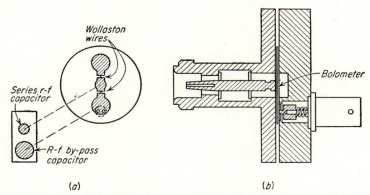

FIG. 3.10. Disk-mounted twin barretter.   (a) The barretter wires mounted between metallized terminals on a mica disk; (b) a coaxial holder.   (*Courtesy of Polytechnic Research and Development Company, Inc.*)

construction were specifically selected for mounting it in a 3-cm waveguide without introducing unnecessary electrical discontinuities.   Various types of holders have been developed to make this barretter useful for longer wavelengths.   An equivalent circuit of the barretter is shown in Fig. 3.9, together with a typical mount.

Another version of the barretter using Wollaston wire is shown in Fig. 3.10.   Two identical bolometer elements are placed in opposite directions from the inner conductor to the outer conductor.   This procedure minimizes the residual inductance of the bolometer termination and facilitates matching over a wide band.[2]   The barretter wires are attached across metallized contacts on mica plates.   The Wollaston wire is etched, leaving exposed platinum wires as indicated in Fig. 3.10a.

[1] Moreno and Lundstrom, *op. cit.*

[2] These barretters are manufactured by Polytechnic Research and Development Co.   The type shown is PRD 630A.   When housed in suitable holder, similar to one shown in Fig. 3.10, a bandwidth of 1,000 to 4,000 Mc can be obtained.

A series of lamplike barretters have been developed to extend the power measuring range into the medium-power region. These are the vacuum and hydrogen-filled lamps discussed in Sec. 3.3, and shown in Fig. 3.11. These lamps necessitate lamp holders of the type illustrated in Fig. 3.12. The shorted section of coaxial line in series with the wire is necessary to adjust the r-f impedance of the holder to the desired value. The movable short also adjusts the position of standing waves along the

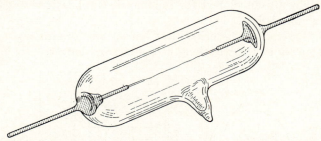

FIG. 3.11. Early hydrogen-filled lamp suitable for use in coaxial holders. (*Adapted by permission of the Microwave Electronics Division, Sperry Gyroscope Company, Division of the Sperry Rand Corporation.*)

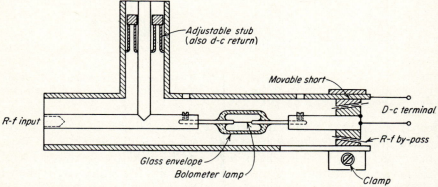

FIG. 3.12. Main features of a high-power bolometer lamp holder. An adjustable stub and a movable short are used to help match the bolometer lamp to the main transmission line. The movable elements are clamped in place as shown after initial adjustment.

wire element to minimize errors resulting from nonuniform heating of the wire, as discussed in Sec. 3.3. In addition, a quarter-wave stub is usually placed at the input end of the lamp to help adjust the r-f impedance of the holder. The two shorted coaxial stubs, however, make the structure frequency sensitive and difficult to adjust. Furthermore, any one set of possible adjustments may result in a matched condition but may be improper in the sense that the current distribution in the lamp results in nonuniform heating.

An improved type of barretter element which uses a carbon filament is shown in Fig. 3.13.[1]   The location of the carbon wire is such that the heating is essentially uniform throughout the length of the wire.   This minimizes the possibility of errors of the type discussed in Sec. 3.3.   If the resistance of the element is near the characteristic impedance of the coaxial line, the lamp in its holder will present a nearly matched load at all frequencies at which the inductance of the filament is not important. Resonant stubs are not required for matching, and the bandwidth is much greater than that of the type in Fig. 3.12.   At frequencies at which the inductance of the filament begins to be important, the impedance of the barretter element will differ from its d-c resistance.   This inductance, however, can be resonated by introducing a suitable additional capacity in the form of a mechanical discontinuity as shown in Fig. 3.13.

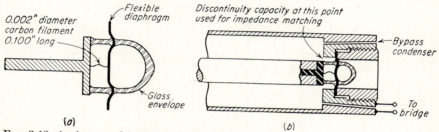

FIG. 3.13. An improved barretter lamp using a carbon filament.   (a) The details of the barretter element; (b) the salient features of the bolometer holder.   (By permission from Microwave Power Measurement, by T. Moreno and O. C. Lundstrom, Proc. IRE, vol. 35, no. 5, May, 1947.)

The barretter element shown in Fig. 3.13 can be made to match a standard 46-ohm coaxial line with only small reflections for all frequencies below 3,000 mc.

Other types of barretter elements have been described in the literature,[2] but are not readily available.

3.5. Thermistors.   Another form of a resistive element suitable for bolometric use is the *thermistor*.   As manufactured for microwave power measurements, the thermistor is made in the form of a small bead of semiconducting material suspended between two fine lead-in wires.   It is usually enclosed in a glass envelope as shown in Fig. 3.2.   The tiny bead, about 0.04 cm in diameter, is composed of a mixture of oxides of manganese, cobalt, nickel, and copper.   It constitutes a resistor with a very high negative temperature coefficient.[3]

[1] Moreno and Lundstrom, *op. cit.*

[2] Matthews, *op. cit.*

[3] R. R. Badger, Thermistors in Electronic Circuits, *Electronic Inds.*, vol. 4, p. 76, January, 1945; J. A. Becker, C. B. Green, and G. L. Pearson, Properties and Uses of

The resistance of the thermistor can be controlled in manufacture by the addition of finely dispersed metallic copper. In use, the resistance of the thermistor can be adjusted over wide limits by controlling the d-c power bias. The d-c characteristics of the common thermistor are shown in Fig. 3.14. It is easily possible to adjust its resistance to equal the characteristic impedance of typical microwave transmission lines. Because of its very small size, it can be assumed that resistance changes

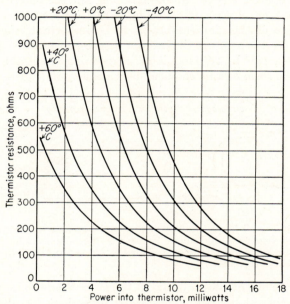

FIG. 3.14. Resistance-power characteristics of a V-519 thermistor. The curves are plotted for six different ambient temperatures. The curves are all similar according to the approximate theory. (*Adopted by permission from "Technique of Microwave Measurements," edited by C. G. Montgomery. Copyright, 1947. McGraw-Hill Book Company, Inc., New York.*)

in the thermistor are the same function of electrical heatin gpower, irrespective of frequency (in the microwave region); thus, the bothersome question of the validity of the substitution process examined in the case of barretters does not arise with the thermistor.

The thermistor is convenient for numerous applications. Its reactance is low compared with its r-f resistance, making it relatively easy to construct broadband holders. In spite of its small size, it is relatively

Thermistors—Thermally Sensitive Resistors, *Trans. AIEE*, vol. 65, no. 11, 1946; W. Rosenberg, Thermistors, *Elec. Eng.*, vol. 19, no. 232, p. 185, June, 1947. Extensive description of the use of thermistors in microwave applications is given in Montgomery (ed.), *op. cit.*, pp. 89–156.

rugged and not as easily damaged (electrically) as the barretter.   This is partially due to the fact that the thermistor resistance changes rapidly with power, thus mismatching it to the r-f line in case of an accidental overload.   As mentioned previously, its rather long time constant is both advantageous and bothersome depending upon the specific application. Its high sensitivity to changes in heating power makes it superior in applications in the milliwatt range, but also creates difficulties in temperature compensation if it is intended for measurement at very low power levels.

In addition to the bead thermistors, other geometrical shapes are often made for nonmicrowave applications.   Some of them, in the form of disks, can be used in bridge circuits to help compensate the bridge against ambient temperature changes.

Examination of Fig. 3.14 shows that the resistance of the bead thermistor can be varied over an extremely large range; however, the practical

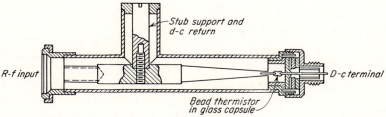

Fig. 3.15. Example of a coaxial line thermistor mount for 10-cm applications. (*Adopted by permission from "Technique of Microwave Measurements," edited by C. G. Montgomery.   Copyright, 1947.   McGraw-Hill Book Company, Inc., New York.*)

operating range is not nearly as large as it appears at first.   If the thermistor is selected to operate at too high a resistance, an increase in ambient temperature may make it impossible to balance the bridge.   For example, if the initial resistance is selected to be 700 ohms, at 20°C, it becomes impossible to retain this resistance, if the ambient temperature reaches 50°C.   If the initial resistance is 500 ohms, the bridge can be balanced at any reasonable temperature, but the d-c bridge current may become small at the higher temperature, reducing the resultant sensitivity.   If the resistance is much too low, the bead becomes overheated and is dangerously close to burning out.   It has been found best to operate thermistor units of the type shown in Fig. 3.2 in the range of 100 to 300 ohms, to optimize the conditions of bridge sensitivity, ease of matching to r-f circuits, and to provide a margin of safety against overloads.

Aside from the differences in d-c characteristics and other obvious parameters, the thermistor can be used for power measurements in nearly the same way as the barretter elements described previously. The details of thermistor-holder construction closely resemble the barretter mounts. Examples of two holders are shown in Figs. 3.15 and 3.16. The problems pertaining to bridge compensation against room temperatures are more difficult in the case of the thermistor. These problems have received much attention and are described in the available literature.[1] Both larger and smaller thermistors have been developed; beads large enough to allow safe dissipation up to 200 mw have been made.

3.6. Resistance-film Bolometers. Another form of temperature-sensitive resistor suitable for bolometric applications is an element consisting of thin metal films deposited on a suitable base, such as glass or mica. The advantage of the film resistor is that a desired resistance, approaching the characteristic impedance of transmission lines, can be obtained without resorting to extremely thin wires. Resistance elements whose shape and dimensions correspond to those of the r-f transmission line permit their insertion into the r-f structure with a minimum of physical discontinuities. This reduces or eliminates the need for resonant matching elements which are needed to compensate for the geometrical discontinuities and the self-inductance of the wire elements. Resistance films, when made to avoid geometrical discontinuities, can be used to obtain extremely broadband performance. It is found that molecularly thin layers of platinum can be deposited over glass and mica to produce the desired characteristics. The skin depth, even at the highest frequencies for which the resistor elements are designed, is always greater than the thickness of the film. Therefore, the resistor elements can be assumed to have the same r-f and d-c resistance. Because the elements are usually made to bridge across the transmission line, they are physically short when compared to the wavelength. The current distribution is nearly uniform over the length of the element.

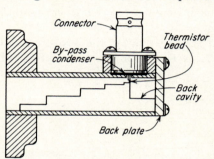

FIG. 3.16. Broadband thermistor mount. Open-type thermistor is soldered between the top of a stepped ridge and the connector. The stepped-ridge waveguide provides impedance matching between the thermistor and the waveguide. (*Courtesy of Polytechnic Research and Development Co., Inc.*)

The sensitivity of film bolometers depends upon the details of construction and the materials chosen. The base materials are important as they determine the heat capacity of the element and, consequently, its time constant.

[1] Montgomery (ed.), *op. cit.*

One form of metallized-film resistor is shown in Fig. 3.17.* Electrically it consists of two resistors intended to be placed from the center conductor of a coaxial line to diametrically opposite points on the outer conductor. The r-f currents flow in opposite directions through the two resistors, minimizing their inductance. The resistance holder can be so designed that the d-c resistance of the two elements is in series, thus increasing the response sensitivity. Metallized resistors of this particular type are suitable for use up to 100 mw.

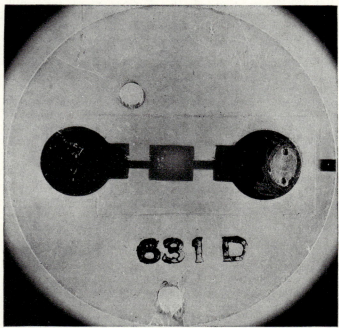

FIG. 3.17. Photograph of Polytechnic Research and Development Co. bolometer 631D. An evaporated metal film connects metallized terminals on a mica sheet which can be used to terminate a coaxial line as shown in Fig. 3.10.

Another type of metallized resistor uses pyrex tubing with an outside diameter of 0.04 cm and wall thickness of 0.008 cm, the length being 0.7 cm. When coated with platinum to produce a d-c resistance of about 300 ohms, this element safely dissipates about 0.1 watt and has a time constant of about 5 sec.

Still other types of film resistors have been tried. Figure 3.18 shows a film element made of tellurium-zinc. Because of its high resistance, nearly all of the power is transmitted and only a small fraction dissipated in the film. This makes it possible to measure power in the order of

* Catalogue of Polytechnic Research and Development Co.

25 mw over a band of frequencies from 1,000 to 10,000 Mc without any impedance-matching devices.[1]

In another device, shown in Fig. 3.19, the wall of a waveguide is replaced by a metallized film on a glass sheet so arranged that its d-c resistance can be measured.[2] The r-f continuity in the waveguide is accomplished by utilizing r-f choke joints between the film and the walls of the waveguide; the d-c resistance of the film can be measured because it is isolated from the waveguide.   It is possible to demonstrate that the substitution process is valid.   As in the previous case, the film absorbs only a small fraction of the total power, requiring initial calibration. Instruments of this type can be made to cover the entire band of the waveguide.   Because the device presents no significant obstruction, the reflections are small and no special matching is required.   This device has, in common with other film elements, a large thermal mass and,

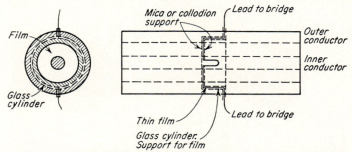

Fig. 3.18. Tellurium-zinc thin-film bolometer in a coaxial line. (*Adopted by permission from Broad-band Power-measuring Methods at Microwave Frequencies, by L. E. Norton, Proc. IRE, vol. 37, no. 7, July, 1949.*)

consequently, is sluggish in response.   This disadvantage can be minimized by establishing a procedure of reading the bridge output after a specified number of seconds and comparing this to the final value.   Film bolometers of this kind can be fabricated to respond to a wide power range.

3.7. Bolometer-bridge Circuits.   It is common practice to detect bolometer-resistance changes by means of a Wheatstone-bridge circuit such as is shown in Fig. 3.1.   There are two ways to obtain the desired information from the bridge.   One of these involves the measurement of the bridge unbalance due to r-f heating of the bolometer, and the second requires the measurement of the d-c increment of power required to rebalance the bridge.

[1] L. E. Norton, Broad-band Power-measuring Methods at Microwave Frequencies, *Proc. IRE*, vol. 37, no. 7, p. 759, July, 1949.

[2] J. Collard, The Enthrakometer, an Instrument for the Measurement of Power in Rectangular Waveguides, *J. IEE*, vol. 93, pt. IIIA, no. 9, p. 1399, 1946.

Numerous circuits have been devised to facilitate the adjustment and use of the basic bridge circuit. The simplest circuit is the one shown in Fig. 3.1. The d-c bridge current is read before and after introduction of the r-f power into the bolometer. The r-f power is then computed in the obvious way. More elaborate circuits make use of calibrated attenuators to vary and indicate the change in d-c power; still more elaborate devices balance the bridge automatically.

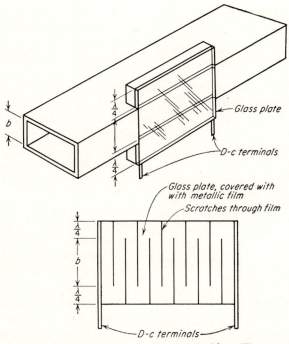

FIG. 3.19. Thin-film bolometer for use in the waveguide. The narrow side of the waveguide is removed and replaced by a thin film of metal deposited on a glass sheet. The latter is connected to the waveguide through choke joints but is isolated for d-c.

To compensate for changes in bolometer resistance due to changes in the ambient temperature, two kinds of features are often added to the simple Wheatstone bridge. One method of temperature compensation is illustrated in Fig. 3.20. The bridge elements consist of three standard resistors, the fourth being the usual bolometer element. A normal d-c source is used to operate the bridge, the unbalance being detected by the galvanometer G. An auxiliary low-frequency oscillator (say, 100 kc) introduces an adjustable amount of power into the bolometer. The presence of this additional low-frequency voltage does not affect the galvanometer directly, but makes it possible to heat the bolometer to

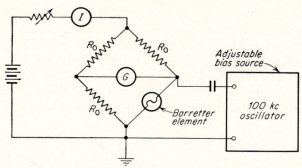

FIG. 3.20. Modified Wheatstone bridge using a 100-kc supply to compensate for ambient temperature changes.

some predetermined resistance value. This arrangement makes it possible to balance the bridge in the absence of r-f power by compensating for variable heat losses in the bolometer due to changes in room temperature. This standardization procedure does not alter the normal operation of the bridge or the methods of computing the r-f power.

The second and more conventional method of temperature compensation is shown in Fig. 3.21. Two of the bridge elements are standard resistors, the third is the bolometer element, and the fourth is a combination of resistors selected so that their effective temperature coefficient equals the thermal coefficient of the bolometer. The temperature-sensitive resistors are not exposed to r-f currents, but are mounted in intimate contact with the bolometer holder. In this manner, temperature changes in the room affect the bolometer and the temperature compensating resistor in nearly the same way. With sufficient thermal insulation around the entire device, excellent results can be obtained.

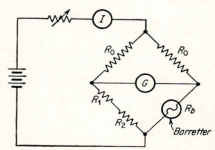

FIG. 3.21. Circuit for compensating the barretter bridge against ambient temperature changes. Resistors R_1 and R_2 are selected so their effective temperature coefficient is equal to the temperature coefficient of the barretter. Conditions for bridge balance are

$$R_1 + R_2 = R_b$$

If R_1 = constant and

$$R_b = R_0(1 + a_1 T)$$
$$R_2 = R_2(1 + a_2 T)$$

then

$$R_1 = R_0 \left(1 - \frac{a_1}{a_2}\right)$$
$$R_2 = R_0 \left(\frac{a_1}{a_2}\right)$$

Several variations of the bridge circuits will be described by way of illustration. Figure 3.22 shows a bridge which is supplied with d-c power

through a series of T-pad attenuators. The initial power to the bridge
is computed from the measured d-c current and known impedance of the
system. It is assumed that the bridge elements, the bolometer and the
attenuators, all have identical impedance. The bridge is rebalanced upon
the introduction of r-f power by suitable adjustment of the T-pad attenuators. The decrease in power is read directly from the calibrated attenuators; the r-f power equals one-fourth of the power increment.

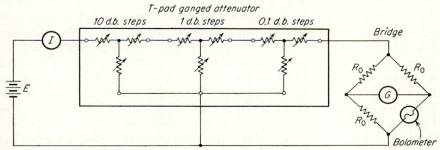

Fig. 3.22. Improved method of controlling the d-c power in a simple bridge.

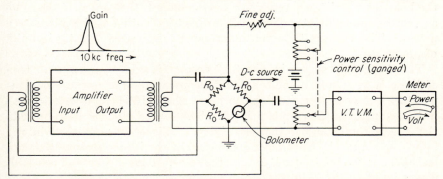

Fig. 3.23. Example of an automatically balancing, direct-reading bolometer bridge.

Because balancing and rebalancing procedures and corresponding calculations are time-consuming, circuits have been developed to do these
functions automatically.[1] An example of the basic elements of an automatically balancing, direct-reading bridge is shown in Fig. 3.23. The
operation of the circuit is as follows: The bolometer element is placed
in the bridge circuit in a conventional way. An output of an audio
amplifier is connected to the bridge as shown. When the system is first
turned on, the bolometer is cold, the bridge is unbalanced, and positive

[1] W. W. Hansen, J. R. Woodyard, and E. L. Ginzton, Automatic Power Bridge, U.S.
Patent No. 2,525,901; C. C. Bath and H. Goldberg, Self-balancing Thermistor Bridge,
Proc. Natl. Electronics Conf., vol. 3, p. 47, November, 1947; Montgomery (ed.), *op.
cit.*, pp. 127, 169.

feedback exists between the output and input of the amplifier. This causes the amplifier to oscillate and to supply audio-frequency power to the bridge. The bolometer becomes heated and its resistance increases until the bridge is nearly balanced. More specifically, oscillations continue to increase until the product of the gain of the amplifier and the degree of bridge unbalance equals unity. If the gain of the amplifier is 1,000, the bolometer resistance will be within 0.1 per cent of the remaining arms of the bridge. (The amplifier should contain a frequency-determining element so that oscillations will take place at a predetermined frequency. The frequency should be high enough so that the resistance of the bolometer does not change appreciably during the period of one cycle.) A vacuum-tube amplifier connected across the bolometer will indicate the initial power required to balance the bridge. This reading on the voltmeter is the reference value and is labeled as zero on the power scale. Introduction of microwave power into the bolometer will heat the bolometer, requiring a smaller amount of power to be delivered by the oscillating amplifier. Since the balance must be nearly perfect in all cases, the substitution process is completed automatically. Because the bolometer resistance remains nearly constant, the square of the voltage across the bolometer element is a direct indication of the microwave power. The vacuum-tube voltmeter can be calibrated directly in units of power.

The d-c supply shown in Fig. 3.23 accomplished two purposes. One of these is to supply a small amount of power for the purpose of temperature compensation (taking the place of the 100-kc source discussed in the example of the simple bridge). The second purpose is to provide the means for changing the sensitivity. This is accomplished in the following way: The automatic balancing of the bridge assures that the resistance of the bolometer is always the same. This means that the total power input to the bolometer from all sources must be constant. Consider, for example, an arbitrary case in which the balance is obtained with 11 mw of total power, obtained with 1 mw of d-c and 10 mw of audio power. Introduction of 0 to 10 mw of r-f power will result in a change in audio power from 10 to 0 mw. A voltmeter, properly calibrated, will indicate this power range. If the d-c power is changed to 10 mw, only 1 mw of audio will be required to balance the bridge initially. Therefore, variation of r-f power from 0 to 1 mw produces a variation of 1 to 0 mw of audio power. If the audio voltmeter sensitivity is changed simultaneously in proportion, a new scale of power is provided, increasing the sensitivity of the meter by a factor of 10. Other sensitivity ranges can be provided in a similar manner. The use of 10.9 mw of d-c power would provide 0.1 mw r-f power scale.

In use, the operation of such a device is as follows: The *voltmeter* scale is switched to the desired power range and d-c bias is changed simultaneously by approximately the correct amount. A fine adjustment of d-c bias is then made so that, in the absence of r-f power, the proper audio voltage is developed across the bolometer as indicated by "zero" reading on the power scale in question. Assuming that the voltmeter is accurately calibrated, this completes the standardization on the given scale. The accuracy of the instrument depends only upon the stability of the circuit components.

3.8. Methods of Extending the Range of Bolometric Devices. The power-handling capacity of bolometric devices is necessarily very limited. Although some bolometric loads have been developed that can dissipate tens of watts, most of the readily available devices are restricted to the low-power level, in the vicinity of a few milliwatts. A given device has a dissipation limit which depends upon its size and method of cooling. To measure power above the dissipation limit, sampling methods are necessary. These are analogous to the use of current shunts and voltage dividers at the low frequencies.

Two classes of devices are available for this purpose. In the first of these, a series or shunt circuits divert a small amount of power into an auxiliary line. The division of power in T junctions is inversely proportional to the impedance of the two lines as seen at the junction. It is simple to divert relatively large fractions of the total power to the branch line, such as 0.5 or 0.1. This makes it possible to increase the range of any given power measuring device by corresponding factors. Larger division ratios are difficult to obtain because it is difficult to accurately construct transmission lines of drastically different impedance.

A T junction can easily be designed to provide a known division of power and can be calibrated easily.[1] Two suitable structures are shown in Figs. 3.24 and 3.25. In the coaxial version, the impedance of a transmission line as seen from the generator is gradually decreased by increasing the size of the inner conductor. Tapering is exponential in principle, and, if sufficiently gradual, no significant reflections would be expected. In practice, the exponential taper can be replaced by a series of quarterwave steps as indicated in Fig. 3.24. At the junction there is a slight decrease in the size of the inner conductor which increases the impedance by some desired amount. The tapering then continues in the opposite direction, returning the impedance of the main line to its nominal value. The branch line is tapered in the opposite direction as shown, starting with a high impedance. Its impedance at the junction can be chosen so that the parallel impedance of the two arms as seen from the generator is equal to the impedance looking toward the generator. This insures a

[1] The theory of microwave T junctions is discussed by J. C. Slater, "Microwave Electronics," chap. 7, D. Van Nostrand Company, Inc., Princeton, N.J., 1950.

continuous "match" through the junction; the power flow in the two arms is inversely proportional to the impedances at the junction. Thus, if the generator, load, and the wattmeter are all matched, a known fraction of the total power is delivered to the wattmeter with the remainder of the power absorbed by the useful load (such as an antenna).

An example of a waveguide T junction is shown in Fig. 3.25a. The branch is joined to the main waveguide at some angle which determines the division of power flow. The equivalent circuit of the junction is shown in Fig. 3.25b, in which the variable angle is represented by the variable turn ratio of the transformer. Due to the discontinuity at the

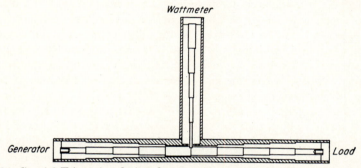

FIG. 3.24. Coaxial T junction designed to provide a 10:1 power division. The steps are quarter-wavelength in length, approximating exponential tapering. Method of supporting the inner conductor is not shown.

junction, shunting reactance exists in the equivalent circuit. This undesirable reactance, together with the change in impedance due to the power flow into the branch, can be matched by means of a suitable iris.

Another form of a T junction is a probe (of either capacitive or inductive type) inserted into the transmission line. Variable insertion permits wide range of power division, but accurate calibration is difficult and generally unreliable.

The simple T-junction method is incapable of providing very high division ratios. In addition, it is sensitive to errors caused by impedance mismatched at the load.[1]

[1] It can be shown that the net power transfer from the generator to load is proportional to the product of maximum and minimum voltage in a transmission line. The presence of accidental standing waves in the main line can cause serious errors in power measurement if the division of power is accomplished by the T-junction method. It can be shown that the error in power measurement will lie within the limits of $r - 1$ and $1/r - 1$, where r is VSWR of the load line. Thus, a standing-wave ratio $r = 1.1$ can cause errors of ± 10 per cent.

In the directional coupler method to be discussed below, assuming two-hole coupler with $\lambda_t/4$ separation of coupling holes, the possible errors are much smaller. It can be shown that the error will lie within the limits $(r - 1)^2/2r$ and $(r - 1)^2/4r$. For a standing-wave ratio of 1.1, the error will lie between 0.25 and 0.5 per cent.

Another method of sampling and measuring the power in a transmission line involves the use of a standing-wave detector. If the indicator of a standing-wave detector is calibrated in units of power with the aid of known power flow, it can then be used to indicate power transferred to a load in spite of the possible presence of standing waves. The errors found in the T junction can be completely eliminated. The use of a bolometer element makes calibration reliable as long as probe adjustments are not disturbed.[1]   For this purpose, the standing-wave detector

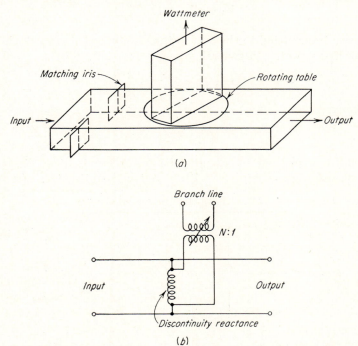

FIG. 3.25. Waveguide T junction as a power divider. Power-division ratio can be controlled by adjusting the angle between the two waveguides. A matching iris is required to compensate for the discontinuity in impedance and reactance. (a) A possible configuration; (b) the equivalent circuit.

is used as follows: It is first calibrated by connecting it between a generator and a power meter. If the power meter is "matched," the probe meter will indicate the same reading regardless of the position of the probe. It is assumed that the probe detector (bolometer) is a square-law device. If V is the transmission-line voltage, Z_0 is the characteristic impedance of the line, and I is the probe output, then $I = kV^2$, where k is a constant. Let power flow P_0 (as registered on the power meter) cause the probe current I_0. Hence $kZ_0 = I_0/P_0$. This calibrates the

[1] Schrack, *op. cit.;* Yunker et al., *op. cit.*

probe. The probe can now be used to indicate the presence of standing waves. If V_1 and V_2 represent incident and reflected waves, respectively, the voltage maximum and voltage minimum as indicated by the probe are

$$I_{max} = k(V_1 + V_2)^2 \qquad (3.19)$$
$$I_{min} = k(V_1 - V_2)^2 \qquad (3.20)$$

from which

$$V_1 + V_2 = \sqrt{\frac{I_{max}}{k}} \qquad (3.21)$$

$$V_1 - V_2 = \sqrt{\frac{I_{min}}{k}} \qquad (3.22)$$

The power transmitted to the load is the difference between the incident and reflected power. In general, power P is

$$P = (V_1{}^2 - V_2{}^2) \frac{1}{Z_0} \qquad (3.23)$$

Combining,

$$P = \frac{P_0}{I_0} \sqrt{I_{max} I_{min}} \qquad (3.24)$$

This relation allows one to compute the power flow to an arbitrary load, using the calibration obtained with a matched wattmeter. (It should

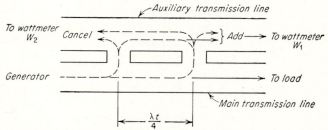

FIG. 3.26. Two-hole directional coupler as a power sampler. Wattmeters W_1 and W_2 indicate the incident and reflected waves in the main transmission line, respectively.

be obvious that a matched wattmeter is not essential to the calibration process.)

Another form of a power divider is the directional coupler. It is a device for sampling separately the forward and reflected waves in a transmission line. One form is illustrated in Fig. 3.26. Suppose two identical transmission lines are placed adjacent to each other and are coupled at two points separated by one-quarter wavelength. The coupling mechanism is immaterial and can take the form of simple holes, loops, or probes. Assuming that the coupling is weak, each hole will couple power equally and symmetrically as indicated in the illustration. A traveling wave propagating from left to right in the main line causes the induced waves in the auxiliary line to reinforce in the forward direction and cancel completely in the backward direction. This makes it possible to sample the forward and reflected waves separately.

The power introduced into the auxiliary line depends upon the mechanism of coupling. There is no limit to the power-division ratio that can be obtained in practice, except that small division is sometimes difficult to attain. Matched power meters, W_1 and W_2, allow the measurement of the power of forward and returning waves directly.

Since the magnitude of the coupling between the two lines depends upon the dimensions of accurately made holes or other simple geometrical objects, the coupling mechanism can be made to be reliable and constant with time. Many types of directional couplers have been developed and are described in the literature.

The range of power measuring devices can also be extended by inserting a suitable r-f attenuator between the source of r-f power and the bolometer mount. Several types of r-f attenuators have been developed for this purpose.[1] Some use resistive material distributed throughout a section of the transmission line with matching end sections. Others are built with three separate resistive elements constructed to approximate the conventional T-pad attenuator. The former can easily be made adjustable by moving the absorbing material into or out of the region of strong electric field. An example of this is the waveguide flap attenuator in which the resistive card is inserted through a longitudinal slot in the broad side of a rectangular waveguide. Attenuators using metallized film resistors can be accurately calibrated and remain stable.

For higher power applications, it is possible to use transmission lines partially or entirely filled with lossy dielectric material. Possible lossy substances are common transite, a mixture of sand and carbon, and other similar materials. These high-power attenuators are often useful in the laboratory, but it is generally found that the loss varies appreciably with temperature and humidity, making their calibration unreliable.

3.9. Measurement of Bolometer-mount Losses. As mentioned previously, r-f circuit elements used to connect the bolometer to its r-f terminals may cause an appreciable amount of energy loss. The loss in r-f matching networks may be either due to unavoidable resistive losses in the walls of the transmission lines and bolometer casing, or because of

---

[1] Numerous examples of available coaxial and waveguide attenuators are described by J. Ebert, *PRD Repts.*, Polytechnic Research and Development Co., Inc., vol. 1, no. 3, October, 1952. The principles of design of microwave attenuators and extensive examples of devices developed in the past are given by R. N. Griesheimer, Microwave Cut-off Attenuators, chap. 11, p. 679, in Montgomery (ed.), *op. cit.*; E. Weber and R. N. Griesheimer, Microwave Attenuators—Resistive Attenuators, chap. 12, p. 720, in Montgomery (ed.), *op. cit.*

the poor contacts in adjustable elements. Since bolometer mounts cannot be perfect, it is necessary to be able to estimate the losses involved. This section will be concerned with a description of an experimental method by means of which bolometer mount losses may be evaluated.[1]

The losses in the bolometer mount are usually described in terms of mount efficiency η, defined as

$$\eta = \frac{\text{power absorbed by the bolometer}}{\text{power delivered to bolometer mount}} \qquad (3.25)$$

The method of measuring mount efficiency is based upon the assumption that the bolometer mount can be treated as a four-terminal network. Figure 3.27 shows the r-f transmission line leading to the bolometer element. The r-f terminals of the mount are selected at some convenient

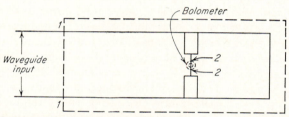

FIG. 3.27. Symbolic representation of the bolometer mount. Terminals 1-1 are in the main waveguide at some convenient reference plane through which all of the input power passes. Terminals 2-2 are at the bolometer terminals.

reference plane, such as 1-1 in the transmission line. A small volume is indicated around the bolometer element proper, enclosing only the temperature-sensitive element and excluding all other parts, such as its glass casing, lead-in wires, etc. The terminals of the bolometer element as they pierce the indicated bounding surface are called terminals 2-2. It is assumed that the r-f impedance of the bolometer element is equal to its d-c value. This assumption has been discussed previously and must be satisfied if this method is to be valid.[2]

The behavior of the network defined by the four terminals as shown in Fig. 3.27 is predictable in terms of network theory. The input and out-

[1] This method was described by D. M. Kerns, Determination of Efficiency of Microwave Bolometer Mounts from Impedance Data, *Natl. Bur. Standards Rept.* CRTL-9-6, August, 1948. Equivalent circuit, approximate formulas, and sample data were provided by R. Winkler, Stanford University Microwave Laboratory, 1950.

[2] There are several exceptions to be considered. The power measurement process involves the substitution of r-f power for d-c power, the equality being determined by measurement of d-c resistance of bolometer in the two cases. It is not necessary that the r-f impedance be equal to d-c impedance in order to satisfy the conditions of validity. For example, if the skin depth is smaller than the diameter of the barretter

put impedances of such a network are related by a linear fractional transformation

$$z = \frac{aw + b}{cw + d} \tag{3.26}$$

in which a, b, c, and d are constants of the network, z is the r-f impedance as measured in the r-f transmission line, and w is the r-f impedance of the bolometer. Since this equation contains three independent constants, the network can be completely specified by performing three suitable experiments. These may take the form of measuring three sets of impedances, i.e., r-f impedance z_1 at terminals 1-1 corresponding to a particular value of bolometer resistance, w_1, etc. Three such impedance determinations make it possible to write three specific equations, the unknowns in which are the three network constants.

The knowledge of the network constants makes it possible to compute the circuit losses in the following manner: The r-f voltage and current, respectively, at terminals at 1-1 are related to corresponding quantities at the bolometer terminals 2-2 by the following set:[1]

$$V_1 = aV_2 - bI_2 \tag{3.27}$$
$$I_1 = cV_2 - dI_2 \tag{3.28}$$

where V_1 and I_1 are peak values and I_1^* is the complex conjugate of I_1. (For the sake of simplicity, the reader at this point may wish to assume that these are the ordinary peak values of voltage and current of a coaxial line. The results, however, are valid for any transmission line.) The voltages V_2 and I_2 are peak values measured at the boundaries of the small volume enclosing the bolometer element. Because the linear dimensions of this volume are very small compared to the wavelength, the voltage and current values at this boundary carry the conventional connotation.

The convention of choosing voltage and current sets is as follows. The voltage and current are both positive when one is looking into the network, resulting in a positive value of impedance. When one looks out of the network, however, the impedance is assumed to be negative. This means that the impedance of the bolometer w_0 is $V_2/I_2 = -w_0$. This symbolism is explained further in Chap. 4.

---

wire, the r-f impedance will be different from its d-c value. Nonetheless, the power measuring process can still be accurate. However, the method of measuring mount losses cannot be used directly under these circumstances. It is possible to adapt the method by calculating the relationship between d-c resistance and r-f impedance. In the case of the barretter wires, this is done using the Kelvin skin-depth factor.

[1] The r-f voltage and current, V_1 and I_1, are the normalized quantities in the sense discussed in Chap. 4, i.e., the power flow in the transmission line is obtained from $P = \frac{1}{2}V_1I_1^*$.

Since $w_0 = -V_2/I_2$,

$$V_1 = \left(a + \frac{b}{w_0}\right) V_2 \tag{3.29}$$

$$I_1 = -(cw_0 + d)I_2 \tag{3.30}$$

If the first of these equations is multiplied by the complex conjugate of the second, the left-hand side will be the complex power input to the network.   It is

$$W_1 = \tfrac{1}{2} V_1 I_1^* \tag{3.31}$$

$$= -\frac{1}{2}\left(a + \frac{b}{w_0}\right)(cw_0 + d)^* I_2^* V_2 \tag{3.32}$$

But the output of the network is W_2,

$$W_2 = -\tfrac{1}{2} V_2 I_2^* \tag{3.33}$$

Hence the efficiency of the network is given by

$$\eta = \frac{\text{Re } W_2}{\text{Re } W_1} \tag{3.34}$$

$$= \frac{\cos \phi}{N \cos (\theta + \phi)} \tag{3.35}$$

where ϕ, N, and θ are defined from

$$\left(a + \frac{b}{w_0}\right)(cw_0 + d)^* = N e^{j\theta} \tag{3.36}$$

$$W_2 = |W_2| e^{j\theta} \tag{3.37}$$

The mount efficiency can be computed from these relations if the network constants are determined in the manner indicated above.

Detailed calculations can be simplified and actual determination of network constants can be avoided if the bolometer mount is nearly matched at some specific bolometer resistance.   If three r-f impedances in a nearly matched mount are measured for three values of bolometer resistance, and if all values are normalized to unity, then the efficiency can be shown to be[1]

$$\eta = \frac{(1 - z_1)(1 - z_2)(w_2 - w_1)}{(1 - w_1)(1 - w_2)(z_2 - z_1)} \tag{3.38}$$

The above procedure can be made clearer by considering a special case. A thermistor was mounted in 1.5- by 3-in. waveguide with a quarter-wave short and a screw tuner for matching as shown in Fig. 3.28a.   Its r-f impedance was measured as the function of the d-c resistance of the thermistor.   By referring the r-f impedance to a voltage minimum, it was

[1] Kerns, *op. cit.*

found that the r-f impedance remained resistive over a substantial range of thermistor resistances.   Sample data is shown plotted in Fig. 3.28b. This can be represented by

$$z = Z_i + Sw \tag{3.39}$$

in which Z_i and S are real constants.   The linear dependence of r-f impedance on bolometer resistance makes it simple to determine the network

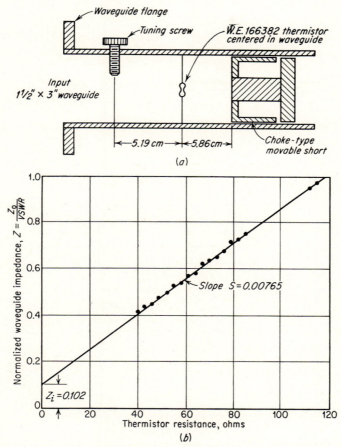

FIG. 3.28. (a) A tunable waveguide thermistor holder. (b) The normalized r-f impedance as a function of thermistor d-c resistance.

constants.   These, from comparison with Eq. (3.26), are: $c = 0$, $a/d = S$. Since reciprocity condition now states that $ad = 1$ the mount efficiency becomes

$$\eta = \frac{W_2}{W_1} = \frac{1}{1 + Z_i/wS} \tag{3.40}$$

This relation can be represented by the equivalent circuit shown in Fig. 3.29. The effect of the bolometer matching elements is to step up the thermistor impedance through an ideal transformer by a turn ratio of $n:1$. The resistor Z_i accounts for the losses in the network due to losses,

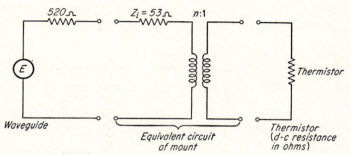

FIG. 3.29. Equivalent circuit of the bolometer mount shown in Fig. 3.28a.

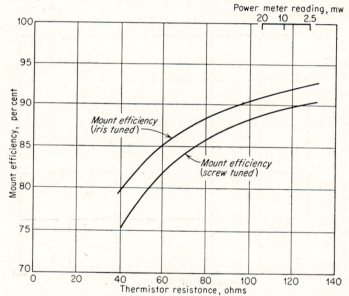

FIG. 3.30. Mount efficiency η for two thermistor mounts.

poor contacts between the thermistor and the mount, and losses in the tuning element.

The efficiency of the two thermistor mounts obtained in the above manner is shown in Fig. 3.30. In one of these the r-f matching is obtained by means of a screw as described and in the other by means of an inductive iris. In the operating range there is about 10 per cent power lost in the thermistor mount. It is usually found that bolometer losses cannot be made completely negligible, except by exercising unusual precautions.

3.10. Measurement of Pulsed Power by Means of Bolometers. In the previous sections, it was tacitly assumed that the power being measured is continuous. It is, of course, possible to measure pulsed power as well. Since bolometers have time constants in the order of 100 μsec. or longer, the measurement of the usual radarlike short pulses provides an automatic averaging process. However, the measurement of pulsed power by means of bolometers entails special considerations. Certain errors in measurement can arise because the bolometer resistance during the measurement is not constant but may vary appreciably during the time of the applied pulse.[1] The time average of resistance variation does not strictly correspond to the time average of power because of the following factors:

In the analysis of the behavior of bolometers under pulsed applications it is assumed for simplicity that the bolometer is used in a simple Wheatstone-bridge circuit shown in Fig. 3.1. Some of the errors associated with pulsed applications are due to the specific circuit arrangements. The understanding of the use of a simple Wheatstone bridge can be easily extended to more elaborate circuits.

In this qualitative discussion, it is assumed that the time constant of the bolometer element is appreciably greater than the duration of the pulse and that the repetition period is longer than the time constant of the bolometer. Under these conditions, the temperature of the bolometer will rise linearly during the pulse and will decay exponentially to a constant value before the arrival of the subsequent pulse. If the bolometer resistance were strictly proportional to temperature, the time average of the bolometer response would be directly proportional to average power. The first source of error arises because the resistance of a bolometer is not strictly proportional to temperature. As a result, the indicated average power will be different from the true power. The second source of error is related to the circuit problems. In the typical bridge arrangement, such as Fig. 3.1, the galvanometer deflection is not a linear function of the resistance unbalance of the bridge. Because of this, an observed balance does not represent the correct value of the average bolometer resistance. This error makes the apparent power lower than the true value.

The third source of error is due to the fact that the d-c power supplied to the bolometer during the length of the pulse is not constant. As the

---

[1] M. Sucher, L. Sweet, and H. J. Carlin, The Operation of Bolometers under Pulsed Power Conditions, *Polytechnic Institute of Brooklyn Microwave Research Institute Rept.* R-291-52, PIB-230, May 4, 1953. Some aspects of this report are summarized by C. Solomon, see Polytechnic Research and Development Co., *PRD Repts.*, vol. 1, no. 4, January, 1953.

impedance of the bolometer changes, the bridge impedance changes accordingly and causes fluctuation of the d-c bias power. An error results because of nonlinearity between bolometer resistance and power supplied from the d-c source.

The fourth source of error is due to the change of the r-f impedance of the bolometer mount with change in bolometer resistance. If the r-f impedance of the mount is matched to the generator at some initial continuous-wave level, it will be progressively mismatched during the pulse. Therefore, the measured power absorbed by the bolometer mount is less than it would be under continuous operation.

All of the described errors are present because the bolometer resistance changes during the pulse and becomes larger in proportion to the magnitude of the resistance changes. The errors are most serious with Wollaston-wire barretters, which have a relatively short time constant. It has been empirically found that the measurement error with Wollaston-wire barretters is directly proportional to resistance excursion during the

TABLE 3.2. OPERATION OF WOLLASTON-WIRE BARRETTERS UNDER PULSED CONDITION

Barretter type	Sperry 821	PRD 630A
Resistance excursion, ohms/μj	15	105
Per cent power error (per 10-ohm excursion)	1.4	1.5
Approximate excursion at burnout, ohms	40	150
Approximate pulse burnout energy, μj	2.6	1.4
Approximate power error at burnout point, %	5.5	22

pulse. The resistance excursion can be either measured or be computed from known physical dimensions and properties of the sensitive element. Table 3.2 summarizes the pertinent factors and gives the measurement error at the burnout point for two typical barretters. Since in practice the resistance excursions must be smaller than that corresponding to burnout conditions, it is seen that the error is not very large. The more sensitive PRD 630A barretter produces the larger error because it is made of smaller wire and has smaller heat capacity; its resistance excursion for a given pulse energy measured in microjoules is appreciably larger, causing greater errors.[1]

Since thermistor and film bolometers have longer time constants than barretters, they are more suitable for application in pulse measurements.

3.11. Microwave Calorimetry. The most fundamental method of measuring microwave power is based upon the principle of conservation of energy. By means of calorimetric methods, the incoming power is

[1] Sucher et al., *op. cit.*

measured in terms of the basic physical quantities, namely, mass, time, and temperature.   This differs from the substitution methods described above because it depends neither upon the validity of the substitution process nor upon subsidiary determination of low-frequency or d-c power. The true calorimetric method consists of dissipating all of the incoming power in some convenient medium and determining the resultant effect by ordinary calorimetry.

The rate of production of heat can be measured by observing the rise in the temperature of the dissipating medium itself, or the heat can be transferred to another medium before measurement.   The first of these is known as the *direct* heating method, and the second, the *indirect* heating method.   In both cases, the measurement process can be of the *static* type or the *circulating* type.

In spite of the ease with which such absolute power measurements can be made, in many applications it is more convenient to modify the calorimetric procedure in order to eliminate the necessity of measuring the rate of flow of thermometric medium by combining it with the substitution method.   If a d-c or low-frequency dissipating element is added to the calorimetric equipment with the cooling medium common to both, the temperature rise due to microwave power can be compared to the temperature rise due to d-c.   This substitution process leads to a group of methods which differ only in detail and are known as *adapted* or *balanced* calorimetry.

Calorimetric methods are most useful at high power.   High power permits the rate of flow of liquid to be high, minimizing the various practical difficulties.   The temperature rise is easily measured, the laminar flow of liquid in temperature-measuring regions can be avoided, and heat losses from various pieces of apparatus can be made small. All of these problems become more serious as the power level is decreased. It is relatively simple to obtain good accuracy even at the milliwatt level if proper attention is paid to details.[1]

The description of the calorimetric methods is divided into two topics: first, the physical arrangements and the main principles; second, the types of microwave loads in which the energy exchange takes place.

[1] Schrack, *op. cit.*, p. 5.   A direct calorimetric method of measuring microwave power in the milliwatt range has been developed at the National Bureau of Standards. See A. C. Macpherson and D. M. Kerns, Microwave Microcalorimeter, *Rev. Sci. Instr.*, vol. 26, no. 1, pp. 27–33, January, 1955; another example is given by W. M. Sharpless, A Calorimeter for Power Measurements at Millimeter Wavelengths, *Trans. IRE*, vol. MTT-2, no. 3, pp. 45–47, September, 1954.   An indirect heating calorimeter designed for use as a portable instrument was also developed by T. F. Turner of Alto Scientific Co., Palo Alto, California (private communication to the author) in 1954.   Both methods are reported to be capable of about 1 per cent accuracy at 1-mw level.

Static Calorimeters. If the microwave power is dissipated in a load which has sufficient thermal isolation from its surroundings, the temperature rise as a function of time will be a measure of power input. The average power input P during a time interval t is given by

$$P = \frac{4.187 m c_p T}{t} \tag{3.41}$$

where m is the mass of the thermometric medium in grams, c_p is its specific heat in calories per gram, T the temperature rise in degrees centigrade, t time in seconds, and P is the power in watts. If adequate care is used to thermally isolate the load, the remaining apparatus can be quite simple. Numerous variations of static calorimetry have been tried and are described in the literature.[1]

An example of an indirect heating method is one in which a microwave dissipating load is placed into a bath of cooling liquid, the temperature rise of which is a measure of power.[2] Static calorimeters are among the oldest known methods of measuring r-f power and with the usual well-known precautions produce excellent accuracy.

Circulating Calorimeters. The circulating or flow calorimeter differs from the static calorimeter because the calorimetric fluid is constantly flowing through the device. The heat introduced into the fluid makes the exit temperature higher than the input temperature. Measurement of this temperature difference under steady-state conditions enables one to compute the average power. It is computed from the relation

$$P = 4.187 v d c_p \, \Delta T \tag{3.42}$$

where v = rate of flow of calorimetric fluid, cu cm/sec

  d = specific gravity of fluid, g/cu cm

  c_p = specific heat, cal/g

  ΔT = temperature rise, °C

Fluid flow can be provided in the calorimeter in two ways. In the open type, water is introduced from the mains into an elevated tank

---

[1] In one version, ammonia gas was used as a thermometric medium; the temperature of the gas is measured by the rate of rise of pressure. At 3 cm and below, various gases can be found with high absorption properties, making such devices practical. See, for example, Montgomery (ed.), *op. cit.*, p. 214. In another variation, the power is measured by the rate of phase change in a suitable medium. Ice, for example, if exposed to microwave power will melt, the amount of melting being a measure of average power during the interval. This is described by D. C. Ginnings and R. J. Corruccini, An Improved Ice Calorimeter, *J. Natl. Bur. Standards Research*, vol. 38, p. 583, 1947.

[2] A. C. Matthews, Radio-frequency Power Measurements, *Radio* (New York), vol. 20, no. 9, p. 23, September, 1944; G. Pession and T. Gorio, Measurement of Power and Efficiency of Radio Transmitting Apparatus, *Proc. IRE*, vol. 19, no. 3, 1931.

which is always overflowing. Water from this tank is introduced into the calorimeter and discharged into the drain. This system requires neither pumping nor cooling and is simple to assemble and adjust. But, because it requires connection to the plumbing, it is not easily portable nor convenient under all laboratory conditions. The alternative system uses recirculation of the fluid. Although more complicated to construct, it is self-contained, portable, and allows fluids other than water to be used.

The salient features of the flow calorimeter are shown in Fig. 3.31. The r-f power is dissipated in a suitable r-f load, and either directly or indirectly transfers the energy to the flowing fluid. The difference in temperature across the fluid terminals of the r-f load is measured as shown. Thermopiles are most suitable for indicating the temperature difference, as they are inherently temperature-difference measuring

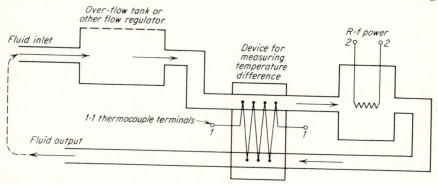

FIG. 3.31. Elements of a circulating calorimeter. R-f power is dissipated in the load indicated by resistor at terminals 2-2. The temperature difference is measured by a thermocouple or other suitable thermometers. The use of a thermopile is indicated by the multiple thermoelectric junctions between terminals 1-1.

devices. They are also more convenient than thermometers, having a high sensitivity and a short time constant. Some method must be provided for metering the fluid flow; the simplest method is to divert the flow into a separate container to determine the quantity of fluid accumulated in a given time. Constancy of the fluid flow is of paramount importance.

The construction of a calorimeter of this type requires care in the design of numerous details. The simple formula for the calculation of power given by Eq. (3.42) neglects heat transfer that may occur between various parts of the calorimeter and also several types of heat losses. Heat may escape from the r-f load or the connecting tubing between the load and the temperature measuring elements. These heat losses can be minimized by design but need to be evaluated in any given case. All such losses depend upon the rate of flow of the fluid, and can be detected by measuring power at several different flow rates. There are also several ways in which these heat losses can be compensated for, as will be discussed below.

The problem of heat transfer between various parts of the calorimeter can be illustrated by considering one specific case. Suppose that the r-f load and its immediate surroundings are at room temperature, and the entering fluid from water mains is at a lower temperature. The water, in passing through the r-f load, even in the absence of r-f power, will become heated and the exit temperature will be higher than that of the input. Similar errors would occur if the input temperature were higher than the ambient temperature. A convenient way to avoid this effect is merely to circulate the input water around the r-f load structure before introducing it into the thermopile.

Another error can occur if the temperature difference is measured by means of thermopiles. The usual thermopile construction uses two parallel channels through which the input and exit fluid flow. A series of wires are placed from one channel into the other, as shown in Fig. 3.31. These wires form the thermopile, and provide a simple yet sensitive difference-measuring system. The larger the number of thermoelectric junctions, the greater the sensitivity but not in proportion to the number of junctions. This is because heat transfer through the wires must be avoided by increasing the length of the wires between the two fluid channels, by making the wires thinner, or both. This causes the internal resistance of the thermopile to increase as the number of junctions is increased.

For greatest accuracy the fluid rate should be adjustable. Regardless of the amount of power to be measured, the temperature rise should be within limits which are known to be reasonable. Excessive flow rates make the temperature rise small, causing errors in the temperature measurement. Insufficient rates cause the temperature rise to be high, and accentuate heat-transfer errors. Slow rates can also lead to erratic performance, because of the inadequate mixing of the fluid in the load, or of the laminar flow of fluid through temperature measuring tubes.[1] Some method should also be provided to minimize the formation of air

---

[1] Turbulence should be maintained in the tubing in order to eliminate the possibility of laminar flow and consequent gradients of temperature over the cross section of the tubing. Flow of fluid will be turbulent if the Reynolds number exceeds 2,000. The Reynolds number R_n for water is given by (see any text on fluid dynamics)

$$R_n = 56vD(1 + 0.033T + 0.0002T^2)$$

where v = velocity of water, cm/sec
$\quad\ D$ = diameter of tubing, cm
$\quad\ T$ = average water temperature, °C

bubbles, whose presence tends to change the flow rate and modify the effective specific heat of the fluid.

Examples of satisfactory flow calorimeters can be found described in the literature.[1] Errors as low as 1 per cent have been reported.[2]

Balanced Calorimetry. It is possible to use the calorimetric method indirectly to avoid several practical difficulties of ordinary calorimetry. The principle of *balanced* or *adapted* calorimetry consists of adding a comparison calorimeter in which power is dissipated from a d-c or low-frequency source. Thus, if the same cooling fluid passes through both calorimeters, a comparison of the temperature difference across the two calorimeters will indicate the r-f power. If the d-c power is adjusted so that the temperature difference is the same, measurement of the d-c power by ordinary methods will be a measure of the r-f power. This avoids the measurement of the rate of flow of liquids and the use of physical quantities in the determination of power; instead, a known quantity of heat is substituted. This raises the practical question of validity of the substitution process, in view of the possible heat leakages and other related problems. It can be demonstrated, however, that not only can such difficulties be avoided, but in addition, some of the heat leakages present in the ordinary calorimetry can be balanced out, increasing the potential accuracy. It is possible to arrange the equipment so that the temperature comparison can be made largely independent of the rate of flow of calorimetric fluid.

Two examples of adapted calorimetric systems are shown schematically in Figs. 3.32 and 3.33. The first illustrates an arrangement used in direct substitution manner. In addition to the usual elements of an r-f calorimeter, a heater is added as shown, where power is determined by a suitable low-frequency wattmeter. The device is used as follows: A reference power P_1 is introduced into the heater, and temperature difference is measured by the thermopile after steady-state conditions have

[1] Montgomery (ed.), *op. cit.*, pp. 208–211; R. C. Shaw and R. J. Kircher, A Coaxial-type Water Load and Associated Power Measuring Apparatus, *Proc. IRE*, vol. 35, no. 1, p. 84, 1947; W. R. Rambo, A Coaxial Load for Ultra-high Frequency Calorimeter Wattmeters, *Proc. IRE*, vol. 35, no. 8, p. 827, 1947; G. H. Brown and J. W. Conklin, Water-cooled Resistors for Ultra-high Frequencies, *Electronics*, vol. 14, no. 4, 1941; M. C. Crowley-Milling, D. S. Gordon, C. W. Miller, and G. Saxon, The Measurement of Power at Centimetric and Decimetric Wavelengths, *J. IEE*, vol. 93, pt. IIIA, no. 9, p. 1452, March–May, 1946; E. Kettlewell, A Wide-band Calorimeter for R-F Power Measurements at Three Cm, *J. IEE*, vol. 93, pt. IIIA, no. 9, p. 1431, March–May, 1946; J. Dyson, A New Differential Thermometer for Use in R-F Power Measurements, *J. Sci. Instr.*, vol. 24, no. 8, p. 208, August, 1947; J. W. Tiley, Microwave Power Measuring Apparatus, U.S. Patent No. 2,453,645, 1948; O. H. Schmitt, Radio-frequency Power Meter, U.S. Patent No. 2,442,619, 1948.

[2] H. M. Huckelberry, UHF and VHF Power Measurement, *Bendix Radio Eng.*, vol. 1, no. 4, 1945.

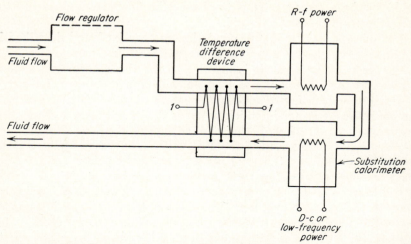

FIG. 3.32. Principal elements of a substitution-type calorimeter. Low-frequency power, measured by an ordinary wattmeter, delivers power to a substitution calorimeter.

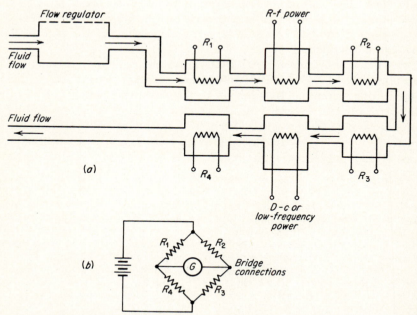

FIG. 3.33. Main elements of a balanced calorimeter. (a) The arrangement of the main components; (b) electrical connection of the temperature-sensitive resistors.

been reached. The r-f power is then introduced, and the heater power decreased so that the previous temperature difference is again established. The heater power P_2 is then lower than P_1 by an amount corresponding to the r-f power.

Although the measurement of power in the above manner is simple, the rate of flow of fluid must be constant throughout the entire procedure. Figure 3.33 shows an arrangement to avoid this requirement. The temperature is measured just before and after the fluid passes each calorimeter. In the illustration, it is assumed that the temperature is indicated by temperature-sensitive resistors, such as platinum coils or thermistors which are connected in a bridge circuit, allowing the comparison of the temperature difference across the two calorimeters. Since the fluid is common to the two calorimeters, equal temperature rise indicates that r-f power is equal to the low-frequency power. If the temperature-sensitive elements are identical, the balance should be independent of the rate of flow of the fluid. If the usual precautions in regard to construction and use of the calorimeters are observed, this method can lead to excellent accuracy. Over-all accuracy can be further improved by

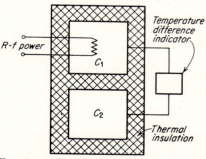

FIG. 3.34. Comparison calorimetric system. C_1 and C_2 are identical calorimetric bodies insulated from the outside and from each other.

arranging the various elements so that the heat leakage from the r-f calorimeter just cancels the heat leakage from the balancing calorimeter. Examples of calorimeters of this type are found in the literature.[1]

Another type of a comparison scheme is shown in Fig. 3.34. Two identical calorimetric bodies are enclosed in a common insulated box. One of these is used to measure r-f power; the second, as a reference body. If the power flow into the calorimeter is constant, the temperature difference T between the two bodies, under suitable conditions, can be shown to be

$$T = PR(1 - e^{-t/RC}) \qquad (3.43)$$

[1] L. B. Turner, Balanced Calorimeters for 3,000 and 10,000 Mc/sec with Tapered Loads for H_{01}-rectangular Pipes, *J. IEE*, vol. 93, pt. IIIA, no. 9, p. 1467; I. R. Neilsen, "A Flow Calorimeter for Radio-frequency Power Measurement in the Ten-centimeter Microwave Region," M.S. thesis, Stanford University, 1948; W. A. Penton and I. Overton, A Balanced Water-flow Calorimeter for Centimeter Wavelengths, *New Zealand J. Sci. Technol.*, vol. 29, sec. B, no. 4, p. 215, 1948; C. C. Wang, UHF Power Measurement, U.S. Patent No. 2,398,606, 1946; J. Evans, Super-high Frequency Wattmeter, U.S. Patent No. 2,427,094, 1947.

where P is the power input, R is the thermal resistance of the calorimetric bodies to their surroundings, C is their heat capacity, and t is time. The constants R and C can be determined by subsidiary experiments involving the use of d-c power only. Once the constants are known, the r-f power level can be determined by observing the temperature rise with time. This arrangement has been used in the measurement of power in the milliwatt range and has produced accuracies in the order of 1 per cent. This arrangement can be used at any reasonable power and at any frequency.[1]

Calorimetric Loads. The purpose of a calorimetric load is to dissipate completely the incoming r-f power and to allow some thermometric fluid to carry the resultant heat away. Many types of loads have been devised for this purpose. It is convenient to divide them into two classes, the direct and indirect heating types. In the first, the r-f power is dissipated directly in the thermometric fluid. In the second, the r-f power is dissipated in some element, such as a resistor, which is cooled by the thermometric fluid. At microwave frequencies, it is simple to use the direct heating method because ordinary water is ideal both as a dissipating medium and a calorimetric fluid. The loss tangent of water[2] is sufficiently high, in the range of 100 Mc to 30,000 Mc, making it practical to use it as a lossy element in transmission lines.

At longer wavelengths, the length of the water load may become inconveniently long. It is possible, however, to increase the conductivity of water by simple additives, such as common salt. It has been suggested that an oil suspension of carbon particles be substituted for water. However, at the lower frequencies, it is generally more convenient to use the indirect heating method.

The problems of the design of r-f load involve several considerations. Among the principal ones are the following· From the viewpoint of r-f problems, the dissipating medium must be introduced into the transmission line gradually. This is desirable in order not to change the characteristic impedance of the loaded line appreciably from its unloaded value. If this procedure is used, and if the load is long enough, all the power can be absorbed without additional impedance matching. Alternatively, the dissipating medium can be introduced discontinuously into

---

[1] Schrack, *op. cit.;* Macpherson and Kerns, *op. cit.*

[2] It is found that in the frequency range up to 10 Mc the loss tangent decreases with frequency. This is a consequence of nearly constant conductivity up to this frequency. Above 10 Mc, the dipole moment of water molecules becomes important, and the loss tangent begins to increase with frequency. In the frequency range of 100 to 10,000 Mc, the loss tangent is high enough to make the absorption of microwave power relatively simple. The attenuation of a coaxial line filled with ordinary water is roughly proportional to frequency of operation. It has been found that tap water at 22°C produces approximately 1.5 db/cm at 9.2 cm and approximately 0.35 db/cm at a wavelength of 29.6 cm. (See Shaw and Kircher, *op. cit.*)

the line.   In this case, it becomes necessary to add a suitable impedance matching device to transform the impedance of the loaded line to the natural characteristic impedance.   In addition to the problem of imped- ance discontinuities, it is also important to pay attention to the geometri- cal structure in regard to possible dielectric breakdown and to leakage of r-f power through the holes that introduce the calorimetric fluid.

From the viewpoint of calorimetric problems, it is desirable that the dissipation be uniform throughout the length of the dissipating medium. Failure to so do can result in excessive heating in small areas, which can cause errors due to local heat conduction, radiation, or other effects. Very large errors can result if the water becomes superheated to the extent of forming steam bubbles.   To avoid stagnant regions the calori- metric fluid should mix thoroughly in passing through the load.   In order to minimize heat leakages from the thermometric fluid prior to measure- ment of its temperature, it is desirable to enclose the calorimetric fluid

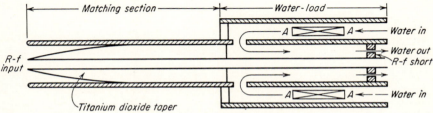

Fig. 3.35. Coaxial water load utilizing dielectric taper for matching.   Space *A-A* is reserved for a low-frequency heater for substitution calorimetry.

in a casing which has poor thermal conductivity to the walls of the r-f structure.   It is also desirable to minimize the volume of the calorimetric fluid exposed to the r-f power to reduce the thermal time constant.   Some examples of water load are shown in Figs. 3.35 to 3.37.

Figure 3.35 shows a coaxial structure intended for use in the wave- length range of 10 to 30 cm.*   Because the dielectric constant of water is still in the neighborhood of 80 in this frequency range, the character- istic impedance of the water-filled line is reduced by about a factor of 9. The water-filled section is matched to the main line by means of a gradu- ally tapered dielectric bushing so designed that a broadband impedance transformation is obtained over the entire frequency interval.   This design is intended for use in the coaxial line $5/16$ in. in diameter, with a water length of 9 in. and a volume of water of 15 cu cm.   It is adequate up to about 150 watts, but permits the power measurement of a few watts with fairly good accuracy.   The response time was found to be in the vicinity of 10 to 15 sec.

Figure 3.36 shows a structure suitable for use in waveguides.   It con-

* W. R. Rambo, A Coaxial Load for Ultra-high-frequency Calorimeter Wattmeter, *Proc. IRE*, vol. 35, no. 8, p. 827, August, 1947.

sists of a low-loss glass tube inserted across the waveguide. By slanting the tube and by decreasing its size slightly toward the front end of the load, it is possible to obtain uniform impedance match over a substantial frequency band together with a reasonable distribution of power along the length of the water column.   Because the water occupies but a small fraction of the waveguide cross section, the loads need to be long to provide adequate attenuation at the end of the waveguide.   The advantages of the slanted tube device are simplicity, low-heat capacity, and excellent inherent r-f matching.   Variations of this approach are described in the literature.[1]

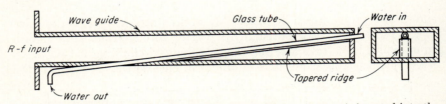

FIG. 3.36. Waveguide calorimeter.   The glass tube carrying water is inserted into the waveguide next to the tapered ridge.   This concentrates the electric field in the water and also helps to provide broadband performance.

Another structure useful for high power is shown in Fig. 3.37.   It consists of a polystyrene or lucite box tapered to a point at the side of the waveguide.   Except for its large heat capacity, it satisfies the design requirements for a satisfactory water load.   Mixing of water is accomplished by use of suitable baffles.[2]

Indirect heating calorimetric loads use resistors of various types with provisions for proper cooling.   These resistors are convenient for measuring power at the lower frequencies where absorption in water loads becomes impractical.   Resistors suitable for this application are described in the literature.[3]

3.12. Force-operated Devices.   A number of methods mentioned in Sec. 2.1 can be used to measure radio frequency power by observing the

[1] Montgomery (ed.), *op. cit.*, p. 199; E. Kettlewell, A Wide-band Calorimeter for R-F Power Measurements at Three Cm, *J. IEE*, vol. 93, pt. IIIA, no. 9, p. 1407, March–May, 1946; E. A. Yunker, H. C. Early, G. Hok, and G. R. Bridgeford, "Very-high Frequency Techniques," p. 588, McGraw-Hill Book Company, Inc., New York, 1947.

[2] L. B. Turner, *op. cit.;* Neilsen, *op. cit.*

[3] Yunker et al., *op. cit.*, p. 581; D. R. Crosby and C. H. Pennypacker, "Radio-frequency Resistors as Uniform Transmission Lines," *Proc. IRE*, vol. 34, no. 2, pp. 62–66, February, 1946; G. H. Brown and J. W. Conklin, Water-cooled Resistors for Ultra-high Frequencies, *Electronics*, vol. 14, no. 4, p. 2428, April, 1941; J. W. Tiley, Microwave Power Measuring Apparatus, U.S. Patent No. 2,453,645, 1948; O. H. Schmitt, Radio-frequency Power Meter, U.S. Patent No. 2,442,619, 1948; P. J. Ovrebo, High Power Radio-frequency Air Calorimeter Wattmeter, U.S. Patent No. 2,421,758, 1947.

physical forces exerted upon some part of the transmission line through which the r-f energy is being transmitted. Although these methods are basically absolute in the sense that they depend only upon the measurement of physical quantities, they are not generally useful for laboratory applications. Many sources of error are possible because the forces developed are small and require delicate measuring apparatus. None-theless, with care, they can be constructed in practical form to provide an alternate form of a power standard. In addition, some of these methods, such as the response to the radiation pressure, do not require the use of microwave resonance phenomena nor any other physical limitation restricting their use to a narrow frequency range.

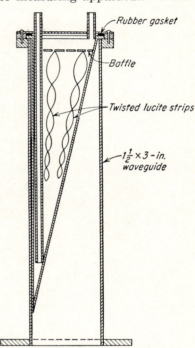

An example of an absolute power measuring device based upon measurement of force, developed by the electrostatic fields, is shown illustrated in Fig. 3.38. A vertical section of a waveguide contains two vanes supported on a thin glass rod and suspended by a quartz fiber. The metal vanes are initially placed at an angle of 45° with respect to the normal electric field in the waveguide. The r-f power flowing through the waveguide produces a torque on the vanes which can be detected by observing the rotation of the mirror with the aid of a light source and a

FIG. 3.37. Waveguide calorimeter using water circulating through a tapered lucite box. The water is mixed by means of twisted lucite strips.

distant scale. The position of the vanes can be restored by applying torsion through the shaft *D* shown in Fig. 3.38. The r-f power can be measured in terms of the shaft rotation.

The electrical discontinuity in the waveguide caused by the vanes can be compensated by placing inductive irises near each of the vanes. Two vanes are used to make the instrument less sensitive to standing waves in the waveguide. Furthermore, any residual reflections from the vane-iris combination tends to cancel since the two vanes are spaced one-quarter wavelength apart. The oil-filled dashpot at the bottom of the glass rod provides critical damping to the instrument. The clamping lever *E* is used to lock the suspension in place when the instrument is not in use.

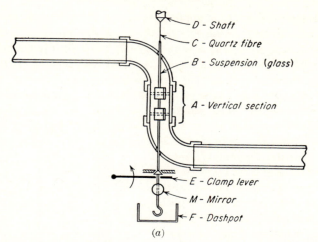

(b)

FIG. 3.38. Force-operated wattmeter.　(*a*) Schematic diagram.　*A*, vertical section of the waveguide containing two thin metallic vanes; *B*, glass suspension rod; *C*, quartz fiber suspension; *D*, suspension shaft; *E*, clamping lever; *M*, mirror; *F*, an oil-filled dashpot.　(*b*) Photograph of the device.　(*Photograph, courtesy of Wayne-Kerr Laboratories, Ltd., New Malden, Surrey, England.*)

According to the manufacturer, the device can be accurate to ± 2 per cent in the frequency range of 8,955 to 9,680 Mc when the average power is in the range of 10 to 200 watts.　At a reduced accuracy the device is useful to a power level as low as 0.5 watt.　The presence of the vanes reduces the power handling capacity of the waveguide, but 50 kw can be measured.　The insertion loss of the device is only slightly greater than a corresponding length of the ordinary waveguide.[1]

[1] The instrument described is manufactured by The Wayne-Kerr Laboratories, New Malden, Surrey, England.　See also A. L. Cullen, Absolute Power Measure-

3.13. Miscellaneous Methods. Many devices have been invented which respond to the presence of microwave power and produce physical effects which can be used as a measure of power. Some of these are mentioned below for the sake of completeness, although none has proved as useful as those described in the previous sections.

The thermocouple is one of the most useful instruments at the lower radio frequencies for measuring r-f currents. Its usefulness can be extended into the microwave region by proper construction. The advantage of thermocouples is the extreme simplicity of the indicating system, requiring nothing but an ordinary galvanometric meter. A variety of thermocouple elements have been developed which have d-c resistance values suitable for use in the usual microwave transmission circuits.[1] Two types of thermocouple elements are shown in Fig. 3.39. The first of these consists of a resistive element which dissipates the r-f power and heats a thermocouple junction imbedded in a suitable insulating body. This type is not especially useful in microwave applications because of the difficulty of incorporating four-wire elements in microwave circuits. The second type, the "straight-through" variety, uses heaters in series with the thermocouple wires.

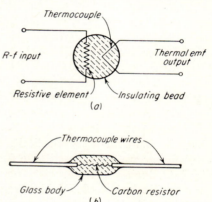

FIG. 3.39. Two types of thermocouples. (a) The indirect-heating type, not generally useful at microwave frequencies; (b) a direct-heating thermocouple ideally suited for microwave circuits.

This type can be incorporated into microwave circuits similarly to the thermistor.

Evacuated thermocouples possess excellent sensitivity and are especially useful as power monitors. Approximate calibration is simple by means of direct currents, but absolute calibration is difficult because of the probable presence of standing waves. The resistance of the thermocouple necessarily changes with temperature, causing difficulties in impedance matching to microwave circuits.

Another group of devices uses a filament-type lamp for dissipation of power, as in a bolometer, but depends upon different indicating means.

ment at Microwave Frequencies, *Proc. IEE*, vol. 99, pt. IV, pp. 100–111, February, 1952; A. L. Cullen, A General Method for the Absolute Measurement of Microwave Power, *Proc. IEE*, vol. 99, pt. IV, pp. 112–120, February, 1952; A. L. Cullen and I. M. Stephenson, A Torque-operated Wattmeter for 3-cm Microwaves, *Proc. IEE*, vol. 99, pt. IV, pp. 294–301, July, 1952; A. L. Cullen, B. Rogal, and S. Okamura, A Wideband Double-vane Torque-operated Wattmeter for 3-cm Microwaves, submitted for publication in *Proc. IRE*, 1956.

[1] Montgomery (ed.), *op. cit.*, pp. 187–191; Schrack, *op. cit.*, p. **9**.

If a bolometer-like lamp is placed in a suitable microwave holder, and if the power is sufficient to raise the temperature of the lamp to incandescence, several methods can be devised to indicate the magnitude of the r-f power.   One consists of measuring the total emitted light with a photometer.   An alternative one consists of constructing two identical lamps in the same vacuum envelope.   The r-f power is fed into one filament and calibrating d-c power is introduced into the other.   Photometric methods can be used to compare the light intensity in the two lamps.

The temperature of a lamp can also be determined by causing it to act as an electron emitter.   An anode plate, supplied with a d-c voltage, will collect the electrons and provide a measure of the temperature of the filament.   Sufficiently high anode voltage makes it possible to employ Richardson's equation directly to determine the temperature of the filament.   The lamp can be calibrated by d-c power.   Automatic balancing systems using diodes are possible.[1]

Aside from the difference in the indicating systems, this group of methods corresponds closely to the bolometric method previously described, both in its advantages and limitations.

Another wattmeter, suitable for use at high power, has been devised by introducing in series with the waveguide a short section of identical waveguide but made of high resistance material, such as constantan. I^2R losses in the constantan waveguide cause it to be elevated to a temperature above that of the main waveguide.   Resistance thermometers attached to the low-loss waveguide and the constantan section indicate the difference in temperature and the power dissipated.   It is possible to calibrate this device against a calorimeter, or by merely passing d-c power through the constantan section from one end to the other.[2]

Neon lamps and other gas-discharge devices can be arranged to respond to microwave power as mentioned in Sec. 2.2.   Gas-discharge lamps can be inserted into the waveguide to indicate the relative power flow.   Alternatively, a slender glass tubing inserted into a slot in the waveguide will ionize, the length of ionized column being approximately proportional to the power in the waveguide.[3]

Various types of rectifiers used to indicate microwave power were discussed in Chap. 2.   For reasons discussed there, these are not suitable for measurement of absolute power.   The principal problems are those of stability and uncertain response law.

[1] R. D. Campbell, The Diotron, An Aid to RMS Instrumentation, *Electronics*, vol. 23, no. 7.

[2] This device was invented by M. H. Johnson and is described in Montgomery (ed.), *op. cit.*, pp. 216–217.

[3] Yunker et al., *op. cit.*, p. 607; Montgomery (ed.), *op. cit.*, p. 218.

CHAPTER 4

IMPEDANCE CONCEPTS AT MICROWAVE FREQUENCIES

4.1. Introduction. The word *impedance* has a general connotation in the various branches of science as a constant of proportionality relating the physical forces and the response they create. The word began to be used in connection with electrical systems after Oliver Heaviside introduced it as a term for the ratio of voltage to current in a circuit. It may be of interest to note that the presently accepted meaning of the word *impedance* evolved gradually with time. It was not over fifty years ago that serious proposals were made to use the word *impedance* for the impedance of the circuit containing resistance and inductance only, and to coin other expressions for circuits of a different type. Fortunately, the generalized impedance concept was adopted and, as a complex ratio of voltage to current, forms the foundation of circuit analysis and transmission theory.

However, it is the absolute clarity of the term and its convenience in circuit analysis that have finally led to an unnecessarily restrictive interpretation of physical phenomena and to ambiguities which have to be resolved before the concept of impedance can play its usual important role in microwave applications. In ordinary electrical circuits one always knows the meaning of voltage and current, and the ratio of the two has a simple meaning. However, in microwave circuits one will be concerned with propagation of waves from point to point, from one bounded region to another, and in ways in which the ordinary concept of current and voltage can no longer play an important role. In many instances, it is not possible to state simply what the voltage is across a pair of points in a microwave circuit. Because the fields are distributed, the magnitude of the voltage depends upon the particular path chosen from one point to another. An example of this is a waveguide, where the field can vary sinusoidally with transverse coordinates. Thus, since both voltage and current can no longer be identified uniquely, no single ratio can be found which would carry with it the conventional connotation of impedance. In spite of this apparent difficulty, there are still simple relationships between cause and response; only more care is required in identifying the meaning of the terms *cause* and *response*.

The electric and magnetic intensities are vector quantities; their vector product is also a vector, giving the magnitude and direction of power flow. In many applications one is not concerned with this vector directly, but only with certain of its components. For example, in the transmission of power from the generator to the load, one often is not interested in the components of power flow in the transverse direction, as these do not contribute to the net power transfer. In this case, one can take the product of E_x and H_y to compute the power flow in the z direction and neglect the other components of **E** and **H**.

There are many possibilities in trying to formulate a definition of impedance. Several of the possible definitions do not have any practical significance in certain problems, but are important in others. In some cases one may be interested in considering the power flowing along the transmission line as a cause, and the resultant *maximum electric field* as the response; this is of importance if one is concerned with the problem of electrical breakdown in the transmission line. But if one wishes to understand the interaction of the fields with an electron stream, then one may consider the power as the cause, and the integral of the electric field along the electron path as the response. In a still different situation, one may find the axial electric field of importance, as is the case in the traveling-wave tube and the linear accelerator. Thus, depending upon the particular quantities of importance in a given problem, one may be selected as the cause and another as the response. The relationship between them can be established by some convenient method which includes the constant of proportionality. This constant, for the problem in question, can be called the *impedance*.

Consider a circuit at low frequencies containing an impedance Z with a current I flowing due to a source of voltage V. According to the usual circuit theory, the following relations can be written

$$V = IZ \tag{4.1}$$
$$W = \tfrac{1}{2}VI^* = \tfrac{1}{2}ZII^* \tag{4.2}$$
$$W = \frac{VV^*}{2Z^*} \tag{4.3}$$

in which the values of current and voltage are peak values, W is the complex power, and the asterisk denotes the conjugate of the complex quantities. Each one of these equations may be used as a definition of the impedance of the circuit, and the measurement of any two corresponding quantities can be used to determine the impedance of the circuit. Suppose the equations are rewritten with a subscript after Z to identify the pair of quantities used to define the impedance. The above equations become

$$Z_{V,I} = \frac{V}{I} \tag{4.4}$$

$$Z_{W,I} = \frac{2W}{II^*} \tag{4.5}$$

$$Z_{W,V} = \frac{VV^*}{2W^*} \tag{4.6}$$

This formal procedure yields nothing new in the case of ordinary circuit analysis, as all values of Z, no matter how computed, lead to the same numerical result. But at microwave frequencies the definitions of voltage and current cannot be unique. A pair of quantities selected, because of the specific requirements of a problem, lead to values of impedance which are different depending upon the particular set chosen. In stating the value of the impedance, then, one has to simultaneously state the basis upon which this impedance is defined. The use of subscripts, as was done above, is convenient and in many classes of problems is sufficiently descriptive.

Consider, for example, the rectangular waveguide shown in Fig. 4.1. In certain applications, it is of interest to define the voltage V across the waveguide as the line integral of the electric field at the midpoint of the waveguide, and the current I as the total longitudinal current flowing in the wide surface of the guide. It can be shown that these particular definitions lead to the following formulas:[1]

$$Z_{V,I} = \frac{\pi b}{2a} Z_0 \tag{4.7}$$

$$Z_{W,I} = \frac{\pi^2 b}{8a} Z_0 \tag{4.8}$$

$$Z_{W,V} = \frac{2b}{a} Z_0 \tag{4.9}$$

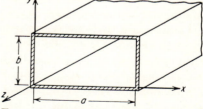

FIG. 4.1. Rectangular waveguide and the coordinate system.

where Z_0 is the *wave impedance* of the waveguide; its meaning will be discussed in Sec. 4.3. Its value for an air-filled rectangular waveguide for the TE_{10} mode is given by [see also Eqs. (4.45) and (4.46)]

$$Z_0 = \left(\frac{\mu_0}{\epsilon_0}\right)^{1/2} \left(1 - \frac{\lambda^2}{4a^2}\right)^{-1/2} \tag{4.10a}$$

$$= 377 \left(1 - \frac{\lambda^2}{4a^2}\right)^{-1/2} \tag{4.10b}$$

[1] S. A. Schelkunoff, Impedance Concept in Waveguides, *Quart. Appl. Math.*, vol. 2, no. 1, April, 1944. This paper discusses the problem of the junction of waveguides of dissimilar proportions and some other applications of the waveguide impedance concept.

It is apparent that the three definitions given by Eqs. (4.7), (4.8), and (4.9) differ from each other by a numerical constant whose value depends upon the dimensions and proportions of the waveguide.

Most of the problems in which the impedance concept is found to be useful fall into two classes. The first of these deals with the question of the propagation of electromagnetic waves along transmission lines. In general, all questions in this class pertain to the existence of standing waves as a consequence of reflections. In these problems, the exact numerical value of an impedance is often of no importance, because it is always possible to express the final meaningful result in a normalized form in which the impedance itself does not appear. For example, suppose one measures the standing-wave ratio in a transmission line by means of a moving probe which responds to the transverse electric field. The standing-wave ratio is determined by taking the ratio of the sum of two traveling waves divided by their difference.[1] Since it does not matter if each term in the numerator and the denominator is multiplied by the same constant, the numerical value of the impedance is of no consequence. The final result is expressed in an unambiguous form, i.e., the standing-wave ratio. As is shown in the following sections, the measurement of standing-wave ratio compares the magnitude of the impedance being measured to the impedance of the transmission line used in the detector section; i.e., the unknown impedance is *normalized* with respect to the impedance of the standing-wave detector line.

Occasionally it is necessary to determine the numerical value of the impedance instead of the normalized value. The conversion of the standing-wave ratio into an absolute value of impedance can be carried out simply. The proper definition of impedance is formed, as discussed above, and its value for the geometry of standing-wave detector line is computed from the geometry and dimensions of the line. With the aid of the standing-wave ratio, the value of the unknown is determined as described in Sec. 4.7. Just what is meant by the *proper* definition of impedance depends upon the quantities considered as the cause and response.

The main part of this chapter is concerned with the problems of the first class, i.e., where reflections are caused by arbitrary obstacles in uniform transmission lines and whose nature one wishes to study. In this discussion, neither the numerical value nor the exact basis of the definition of impedance is of particular concern.

The second class of problems is one in which the *numerical* value of the impedance of a microwave circuit is of primary importance. Among examples of these cases are the shunt impedance of a klystron cavity,

---

[1] Using absolute values of the quantities only. For more complete definition, see Sec. 4.7.

the impedance of a ridged waveguide, and the helix impedance of the traveling-wave tube. All of these devices, to be sure, could be connected to a standing-wave detector, and relative measurements of several kinds could be made. But the connection between the device in question and the particular set of points across which the impedance is measured involves, as a minimum, an ideal transformer whose turn ratio is not known. Thus, the impedance information obtained by means of the standing-wave detector cannot be sufficient to obtain the numerical values of the impedance. The specific problem of measurement of impedance of microwave circuits (resonant cavities, waveguides, etc.) will be discussed in Chap. 10.

4.2. Transmission Lines and Wave Concepts. Before starting to discuss the various available methods for the measurement of impedance, it is desirable to describe the salient features of the transmission lines that can be used to connect the various pieces of microwave equipment, and the general nature of traveling electromagnetic waves inside of such lines.

Transmission lines may be defined in a general way, following the definition to be found in the IRE Standards: "A transmission line is a system of material boundaries forming a continuous path from one place to another, and capable of directing the transmission of electromagnetic energy along the path."[1] This definition does not distinguish between the various possible forms of transmission lines, such as parallel wires, coaxial lines, waveguides, dielectric rods, dielectric-coated single conductor wires, etc. In all cases, propagation from one point to another can be affected by exciting the lines with permissible forms of electromagnetic fields. The field configuration surrounding the material boundaries is entirely dependent upon the material and the shape of the boundaries; the permissible set of field configurations can be found by obtaining suitable solutions of Maxwell's equations.[2] Associated with each permissible field configuration, or mode, is a characteristic number, called the *cutoff wavelength*, which must also be determined from solutions of Maxwell's equations. Once this number has been determined, the phase velocity of the particular mode can be found for the frequency in question.

The knowledge of the phase velocity for a given mode and frequency permits the expression for the propagation of electromagnetic waves along the transmission line to be written. The formal appearance of this expression is identical to the familiar telegrapher's equation but will

[1] IRE Standards on Antennas and Waveguides: Definition of Terms, 1953, *Proc. IRE*, pp. 1721–1728, December, 1953.

[2] For common boundary shapes, many such solutions have been carried out and can be found in the literature. A list of common field configurations will be found in Appendix A.

differ from it because the velocity of propagation (in the general case) will be different from the velocity of light, and the numerical coefficients will not simply be the voltage and current. The purpose of the following material is to give a clearer picture of the behavior of electromagnetic waves in transmission lines and to establish an analogy between the telegrapher's equation and the wave equation derived directly from Maxwell's theory. The understanding of the analogies and differences will enable one to follow the usual practice of borrowing the results of the familiar transmission-line theory in treating the problems in microwave transmission. In particular, it will be shown that it is possible to identify certain coefficients in the general expression for traveling electromagnetic waves as if they were voltage and current of the ordinary parallel-wire line. These coefficients, taken together with the velocity of propagation of the particular mode, are all that is needed to solve the general transmission-line problem using the symbolism of the ordinary parallel-wire line theory.[1]

To make the following discussion simple, it is convenient to make certain restrictive assumptions. Although a transmission line can have material boundaries of either metallic or dielectric type, it will be assumed that the transmission line has metallic boundaries. Many of the following results are, however, applicable to other types of transmission lines. Also, unless otherwise stated, it is assumed that the geometrical dimensions and constants of materials are identical in all transverse sections of the line and that the dissipative losses are negligible. The last two assumptions simplify the equations because the traveling waves will be independent in magnitude of the axial position. Aside from the obvious attenuation of the waves as they progress along the line, there are other consequences of dissipation which are not of general importance, but which can complicate the simple picture of single mode propagation.[2] Neglecting the losses does not cause serious errors in anything that follows, but the reader must be aware of this approximation.

Although this book does not make extensive use of Maxwell's theory, it is essential to understand the basic principles which govern the propagation of electromagnetic waves through bounded regions. It must be remembered that the fields in any region must satisfy Maxwell's equations and not merely the wave equation which is derived from them. Thus, the general solution of the long-line or telegrapher's equation is

---

[1] For more complete discussion, see S. A. Schelkunoff, Conversion of Maxwell's Equations into Generalized Telegraphist's Equations, *Bell System Tech. J.*, vol. 34, no. 5, pp. 995–1043, September, 1955.

[2] If losses are present, the true modes do not have the same field distribution as the ideal modes of the lossless waveguide, but are certain linear combinations of these. Excitation of an "ideal" mode in a lossy guide can, therefore, excite additional modes.

not a general solution of Maxwell's equations, although there is a great deal of similarity.   In the material below, the differences and similarities between solutions of Maxwell's equations and the telegrapher's equation are examined.

Since losses are neglected, there are no magnetic or electric fields within the conducting walls.   Under these conditions, the electric field must be normal to the boundary surface, and the magnetic field must be tangential.   These are the well-known *boundary* conditions, often referred to by this name.

The fields must satisfy the following Maxwell equations:[1]

$$\text{curl } \mathbf{E} = -\mu_0 \frac{\partial \mathbf{H}}{\partial t} \tag{4.11}$$

$$\text{curl } \mathbf{H} = \epsilon_0 \frac{\partial \mathbf{E}}{\partial t} \tag{4.12}$$

$$\text{div } \mathbf{B} = 0 \tag{4.13}$$

$$\text{div } \mathbf{D} = 0 \tag{4.14}$$

which are true for a transmission line in vacuum.

[1] These are written in rationalized mks system.   The units are: $\mathbf{E}$ is in volts per meter, $\mathbf{H}$ is in ampere-turns per meter, and

$$\epsilon_0 = 8.85 \times 10^{-12} \text{ farads/m}$$
$$\mu_0 = 4\pi \times 10^{-7} \text{ henry/m}$$

from which
$$(\mu_0/\epsilon_0)^{1/2} = 377 \text{ ohms}$$
$$(\epsilon_0\mu_0)^{-1/2} = 2.99793 \times 10^8 \text{ m/sec} \tag{4.15}$$

The boldface symbols represent vector quantities.   The reader who is unfamiliar with vector notation may wish to simplify these relations by rewriting some of them in differential form for the one-dimensional case; some vector formulas which will be found helpful are given in Appendix B.

Derivation of the wave equation for the one-dimensional case can be carried out as follows: Assuming propagation in the z direction, E_y and H_x are the only components present.   The following relations can be written as

$$\text{curl } \mathbf{E} = -\mathbf{k}_x \frac{\partial E_y}{\partial z} \tag{4.16}$$

$$\text{curl } \mathbf{H} = \mathbf{k}_y \frac{\partial H_x}{\partial z} \tag{4.17}$$

The first two Maxwell equations then become

$$\mathbf{k}_x \frac{\partial E_y}{\partial z} = \mu_0 \frac{\partial H_x}{\partial t} \tag{4.18}$$

$$\mathbf{k}_y \frac{\partial H_x}{\partial z} = \epsilon_0 \frac{\partial E_y}{\partial t} \tag{4.19}$$

Differentiating the first of these with respect to z and the second with respect to t and combining, one obtains the wave equation for $\mathbf{E}$ in one dimension.   This is

$$\frac{\partial^2 E_y}{\partial z^2} = \epsilon_0\mu_0 \frac{\partial E_y{}^2}{\partial t^2} \tag{4.20}$$

It is of interest to compare these with the telegrapher's equations applicable to the two-

The first two Maxwell equations can be combined by eliminating between them the electric and magnetic fields, one at a time. This results in the general wave equations

$$\nabla^2 \mathbf{E} - \frac{1}{c^2} \frac{\partial^2 \mathbf{E}}{\partial t^2} = 0 \tag{4.24}$$

$$\nabla^2 \mathbf{H} - \frac{1}{c^2} \frac{\partial^2 \mathbf{H}}{\partial t^2} = 0 \tag{4.25}$$

In the usual way, a general solution to these differential equations is found assuming sinusoidal variation in space and time:

$$\mathbf{E} = \mathbf{E}_0 e^{j(\omega t - \beta z)} \tag{4.26}$$
$$\mathbf{H} = \mathbf{H}_0 e^{j(\omega t - \beta z)} \tag{4.27}$$

where $\omega = 2\pi f$, and β is the propagation constant. Since lossless uniform lines have been postulated, $\mathbf{E}_0$ and $\mathbf{H}_0$ will not be dependent upon the axial coordinate z, but will be functions of x and y, varying in such a way that the boundary conditions are satisfied. These assumed solutions represent waves traveling in the z direction. If at a particular set of values of t and z, $\mathbf{E}$ and $\mathbf{H}$ have certain values, then at a later time another position can be found where they will have the same value. Hence, the assumed solutions correspond to traveling waves, the velocity of propagation for which is

$$v_p = \frac{\omega}{\beta} \tag{4.28}$$

where v_p is called the *phase velocity*. By substituting Eqs. (4.26) and (4.27) into Eqs. (4.24) and (4.25), the following equations are obtained:

$$\frac{\partial^2 \mathbf{E}_0}{\partial x^2} + \frac{\partial^2 \mathbf{E}_0}{\partial y^2} + \left(\frac{\omega^2}{c^2} - \beta^2 \right) \mathbf{E}_0 = 0 \tag{4.29}$$

$$\frac{\partial^2 \mathbf{H}_0}{\partial x^2} + \frac{\partial^2 \mathbf{H}_0}{\partial y^2} + \left(\frac{\omega^2}{c^2} - \beta^2 \right) \mathbf{H}_0 = 0 \tag{4.30}$$

---

wire transmission line for the case of zero losses. Instead of Maxwell's equation, equations relating the voltage and current are

$$\frac{\partial v}{\partial x} = -L \frac{di}{\partial t} \tag{4.21}$$

$$-\frac{di}{\partial x} = C \frac{\partial v}{\partial t} \tag{4.22}$$

where L and C are inductance and capacitance per unit length, and v and i are voltage and current, respectively. When combined together by eliminating the current, these give

$$\frac{\partial^2 v}{\partial x^2} = LC \frac{\partial^2 v}{\partial t^2} \tag{4.23}$$

The similarity between Eqs. (4.20) and (4.23) is readily apparent.

These differential equations must be satisfied if the traveling wave set is to be a possible one.

As its name implies, the wave equation is concerned with the axial propagation of the fields whose transverse dependence is arbitrary. However, the transverse variation of the fields is dependent upon the boundary conditions at the walls of the transmission line. If some field configuration is found which satisfies the boundary conditions, then it is possible to calculate the phase velocity of the waves of this configuration by substituting the expressions for the fields into the wave equation. Thus, the particular dependence of $\mathbf{E}_0$ and $\mathbf{H}_0$ upon transverse coordinates will determine the velocity of the propagation of the waves.

It is convenient to adopt certain notation for the various quantities. Let λ_0 be the free-space wavelength, λ_t be the wavelength as measured inside the transmission line,[1] and λ_c be the cut-off wavelength. The cutoff wavelength is known as the wavelength beyond which propagation of the mode, i.e., the field configuration in question, becomes impossible. The reason for this will become apparent below.

In terms of these symbols, Eqs. (4.29) and (4.30) become

$$\frac{\partial^2 \mathbf{E}_0}{\partial x^2} + \frac{\partial^2 \mathbf{E}_0}{\partial y^2} + \left(\frac{2\pi}{\lambda_c}\right)^2 \mathbf{E}_0 = 0 \tag{4.31}$$

$$\frac{\partial^2 \mathbf{H}_0}{\partial x^2} + \frac{\partial^2 \mathbf{H}_0}{\partial y^2} + \left(\frac{2\pi}{\lambda_c}\right)^2 \mathbf{H}_0 = 0 \tag{4.32}$$

in which (with $\beta = 2\pi/\lambda_t$ and $\omega/c = 2\pi/\lambda_0$)

$$\left(\frac{2\pi}{\lambda_c}\right)^2 = \left(\frac{2\pi}{\lambda_0}\right)^2 - \left(\frac{2\pi}{\lambda_t}\right)^2 \tag{4.33}$$

$$= \frac{\omega^2}{c^2} - \beta^2 \tag{4.34}$$

Rearranging Eq. (4.33), the transmission-line wavelength is found to be

$$\lambda_t = \frac{\lambda_0}{\sqrt{1 - (\lambda_0/\lambda_c)^2}} \tag{4.35}$$

from which[2]

$$\beta = \frac{2\pi}{\lambda_0} \sqrt{1 - (\lambda_0/\lambda_c)^2} \tag{4.36}$$

---

[1] The wavelength in the transmission line is the ratio of phase velocity of the waves to the frequency. Thus, the transmission-line wavelength can be computed from Eq. (4.28), and is found to be

$$\lambda_t = \frac{v_p}{f} = \frac{2\pi v_p}{\omega} = \frac{2\pi}{\beta}$$

[2] Should the transmission line be filled with a dielectric material, these equations contain

$$\sqrt{\frac{\epsilon}{\epsilon_0} - \left(\frac{\lambda_0}{\lambda_c}\right)^2} \qquad \text{instead of} \qquad \sqrt{1 - \left(\frac{\lambda_0}{\lambda_c}\right)^2}$$

and $$v_p = \frac{c}{\sqrt{1 - (\lambda_0/\lambda_c)^2}} \qquad (4.37)$$

$$= c(\lambda_t/\lambda_0) \qquad (4.37a)$$

These equations show the following things: The propagation constant β of the assumed set of traveling waves is not necessarily equal to its value in free space but depends upon conditions imposed by the

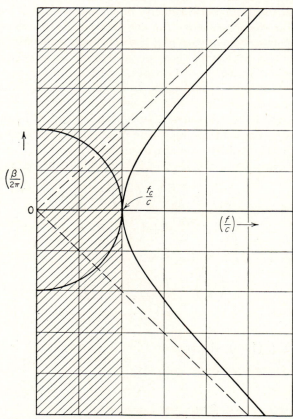

FIG. 4.2. Variation of propagation constant with frequency. In the shaded region propagation constant is imaginary. To the right of the cutoff frequency, propagation constant is real.

boundary in a manner not yet discussed. Thus, the wavelength of the propagated wave depends upon the free-space wavelength (or, more precisely, upon the frequency) and a certain quantity λ_c. As will be shown below, the cutoff wavelength is a characteristic constant of the physical boundaries and the particular field configuration within these boundaries. When the free-space wavelength is much less than the cutoff wavelength, the transmission-line wavelength approaches the free-space wavelength. But as the free-space wavelength approaches the cutoff wavelength, the transmission-line wavelength approaches infinity, and the propagation constant β approaches zero.   Exactly at cutoff, $\lambda_0 = \lambda_c$, and $\beta = 0$, and from Eqs. (4.26) and (4.27) it is seen that the fields become periodic in time but independent of distance.   When λ_0 is larger than λ_c, β becomes imaginary, and Eqs. (4.26) and (4.27) show that the fields become exponentially attenuated with distance.[1]

It is illuminating to consider further the dependence of propagation constant β on frequency.   Using Eq. (4.36) and replacing $1/\lambda_0$ by f/c,

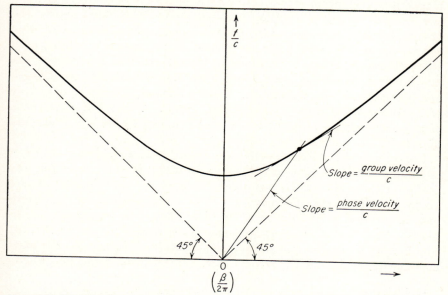

Fig. 4.3. Propagation constant vs. frequency diagram, showing graphically the meaning of the group and phase velocities.

Figs. 4.2 and 4.3 can be drawn.   In Fig. 4.2, the shaded region corresponds to cutoff, in which the waves are exponentially attenuated.   To the right of the cutoff frequency, the curve is hyperbolic and is symmetric about the frequency axis.   The negative values of the propagation constant merely imply the propagation of waves in the negative z direction.   For frequency considerably above the cutoff, the curve approaches the 45° line from the origin, which means that the velocity of propagation becomes independent of frequency.   The same curve is plotted again in Fig. 4.3.   The slope of the radius vector to any point on the curve is

[1] Near cutoff, the effects of the neglected dissipation become important.   The reader is referred to standard texts for further details.

equal to v_p/c; it can be seen that for large values of frequency the phase velocity becomes constant. The slope of the radius vector at the origin approaches infinity, as previously described. The slope of the curve itself is equal to v_g/c, where v_g is the group velocity, i.e., the velocity with which any signal can propagate along the transmission line.[1]

To compute the phase or group velocity of a particular field configuration it is necessary to find the cutoff wavelength. The dependence of the cutoff wavelength upon boundary conditions is determined directly from Maxwell's equations as discussed in the next section.

4.3. Modes of Propagation. The characteristic behavior of electromagnetic waves propagating through transmission lines depends upon two related things. First, any possible set of fields must satisfy the boundary conditions imposed by Maxwell's equations. This restriction can be satisfied by an infinite set of field configurations or *modes*, each characterized by a cutoff wavelength. Second, each of the modes must also satisfy the wave equation; this condition determines the wavelength and phase velocity for each mode. In this manner, the complete picture of the propagating waves becomes established. The cutoff wavelength of any field configuration or mode is determined by factors which are discussed in this section.

Consider again the wave equations, Eqs. (4.31) and (4.32). Since it is assumed that the transmission line is uniform in the z direction, the field quantities E_0 and H_0 are independent of z. Both E_0 and H_0 are vector quantities and each may have three components along the coordinate axes which may, in general, be functions of the transverse coordinates. Each one of these components must satisfy the wave equation. Let E_t and H_t be the transverse components and E_z and H_z the axial components of E_0 and H_0, respectively. In terms of these, Eqs. (4.31)

---

[1] v_g is given by

$$v_g = \frac{1}{d\beta/d\omega} \qquad (4.37b)$$

It can be found from the slope of the curve in Fig. 4.3. Differentiating Eq. (4.36) with respect to ω,

$$v_g = c\left(\frac{\lambda_0}{\lambda_t}\right) \qquad (4.37c)$$

Hence, the product of v_p and v_c is

$$v_p v_g = \left(\frac{\omega}{\beta}\right) c\left(\frac{\lambda_0}{\lambda_t}\right)$$
$$= c^2$$

However, this result is applicable only to uniform transmission lines. For nonuniform structures, such as periodically loaded waveguides, the group and phase velocities are independent of each other.

Further discussion of group velocity can be found in any standard text on electromagnetic theory.

and (4.32) become

$$\frac{\partial^2 \mathbf{E}_t}{\partial x^2} + \frac{\partial^2 \mathbf{E}_t}{\partial y^2} + \left(\frac{2\pi}{\lambda_c}\right)^2 \mathbf{E}_t = 0 \qquad (4.38)$$

$$\frac{\partial^2 E_z}{\partial x^2} + \frac{\partial^2 E_z}{\partial y^2} + \left(\frac{2\pi}{\lambda_c}\right)^2 E_z = 0 \qquad (4.39)$$

$$\frac{\partial^2 \mathbf{H}_t}{\partial x^2} + \frac{\partial^2 \mathbf{H}_t}{\partial y^2} + \left(\frac{2\pi}{\lambda_c}\right)^2 \mathbf{H}_t = 0 \qquad (4.40)$$

$$\frac{\partial^2 H_z}{\partial x^2} + \frac{\partial^2 H_z}{\partial y^2} + \left(\frac{2\pi}{\lambda_c}\right)^2 H_z = 0 \qquad (4.41)$$

Assuming that the transmission line consists of tubular metallic conductors of infinite conductivity, the boundary conditions require that at the surface of such conductors (1) the axial component of $\mathbf{E}$ be zero and (2) the normal (transverse) component of $\mathbf{H}$ be zero. The requirement that E_z vanish at the surface can be satisfied in two ways. Either E_z can be zero everywhere, or it must vary with transverse coordinates in such a way that it vanishes at the boundary. The second condition can be met, similarly, either by H_z being zero everywhere or by having a vanishing gradient at the surface.[1] If E_z is zero everywhere, the only possible components of $\mathbf{E}$ are entirely in the transverse plane, and this class of solutions is known as the *transverse electric* modes, abbreviated TE. Similarly, if H_z is zero, all of the magnetic field lines lie in the transverse plane, and the resultant modes are referred to as *transverse magnetic* modes, called TM. Under these conditions, it is easily shown from Maxwell's equations that the remaining transverse and axial components are all interrelated.[2] For the TE case, it is found that

$$\operatorname{grad} H_z = 2\pi j \frac{\lambda_t}{\lambda_c^2} \mathbf{H}_t \qquad (4.42)$$

and for TM,

$$\operatorname{grad} E_z = 2\pi j \frac{\lambda_t}{\lambda_c^2} \mathbf{E}_t \qquad (4.43)$$

[1] As will be seen from Eq. (4.42), the normal component of the magnetic field is related to the gradient of the axial component. Thus, the second boundary condition can be satisfied in the manner stated. The transverse component cannot be zero everywhere, since this would imply zero-power transfer.

[2] The following two equations can be derived as follows: using Maxwell's equations, Eqs. (4.11) and (4.12), expand the two curl equations into the vector component form (see Appendix B), and substitute time and z derivatives of the assumed fields. For the TE case, $E_z = 0$, which greatly simplifies the original equations. Taking x, y, and z components separately, from curl $\mathbf{E}$ equation one finds

$$E_y = -\mu_0 f \lambda_g H_x$$
$$E_x = \mu_0 f \lambda_g H_y$$

Substituting these into curl $\mathbf{H}$ equation, and writing the result in vector form, one obtains Eq. (4.42). The procedure for the TM case is identical.

These equations state the obvious fact that if the magnitude of the transverse components of a wave is known, the axial components are determined as well.

Ordinary transmission-line theory predicts that the voltage and current in a traveling wave are related to each other through the characteristic impedance of the line. A similar situation must exist for the general case. Continuation of the analysis of the preceding footnote leads to the result that

$$\mathbf{H}_t = \frac{\mathbf{k}_z \times \mathbf{E}_t}{Z_0} \tag{4.44}$$

where Z_0 is, for TE waves,

$$Z_0 = \left(\frac{\mu_0}{\epsilon_0}\right)^{1/2} \frac{\lambda_t}{\lambda_0} \tag{4.45}$$

and, for TM waves,

$$Z_0 = \left(\frac{\mu_0}{\epsilon_0}\right)^{1/2} \frac{\lambda_0}{\lambda_t} \tag{4.46}$$

The quantity Z_0 is known as the *wave impedance* and relates the magnetic and electric fields in a way which makes it similar to the characteristic impedance of the ordinary transmission line. It is not exactly the same, however, and this difference will become apparent in Sec. 4.5.

Having observed that the field quantities $\mathbf{E}_t$, E_z, $\mathbf{H}_t$, and H_z, are all related, it is necessary only to discuss in detail the solutions of one of the differential equations of the set Eqs. (4.38) to (4.41). Consider the TE case. Since E_z is zero by definition, the only boundary condition left to be satisfied is that $\mathbf{H}_t$ be zero at the walls of the transmission line. Equation (4.40) has an infinite set of possible solutions for any value of λ_c, but not all of these satisfy the required boundary condition. Any one solution of the infinite set can be made to satisfy the boundary condition by selecting a proper value of λ_c.* This leads, then, to an infinite set of constants λ_c, with a specific value for each one of the possible solutions. Each solution with its particular field configuration is known as a *mode* of transmission, and the value of λ_c which is required to make this solution satisfy the boundary conditions is known as the cutoff wavelength

---

* Consider, for example, the rectangular waveguide shown in Fig. 4.1. The transverse components of $\mathbf{H}_t$ must be zero at all surfaces of the waveguide. A simple form of the possible fields is one for which $H_y = 0$. H_x can be of the form $H_x = B \sin mx$, as can be easily verified by substituting this into Eq. (4.40); such solutions are possible for *any* value of m. However, in order to meet the boundary conditions, H_x must vanish at $x = 0$ and at $x = a$. This can be done by letting $m = \pi n/a$, with $n = 1, 2, 3, \ldots$ This leads to the result that λ_c must have *specific* values, i.e.,

$$\lambda_c = \frac{2a}{n} \qquad n = 1, 2, 3, \cdots \tag{4.47}$$

for this mode. Such solutions have been carried out for the most common geometrical shapes of transmission lines and can be found in the literature. A few of the common modes, together with their cutoff wavelengths, are listed in Appendix A. For any one geometrical shape the possible cutoff wavelengths start with a certain value, called the *dominant mode*, and can be listed in the order of diminishing magnitude. All of the shorter-wavelength modes are referred to as the *higher-order modes*. Certain of these modes will belong to the TE set, others to the TM set.

If the transmission line has two conductors (such as the coaxial line), the dominant mode has an infinite cutoff wavelength. Modes for which this happens are called *principal modes*, and, under these conditions, both E_z and H_z are zero. These modes are sometimes referred to as transverse electromagnetic modes (TEM), since both the electric and the magnetic fields are entirely in the transverse plane. Single conductor waveguides have no principal modes, as they cannot support a potential difference at direct current.

A source of a single frequency can excite the transmission line in all possible modes. Propagation of any one mode is possible only if the cutoff wavelength of the particular mode is greater than the free-space wavelength. Thus, if the free-space wavelength happens to be shorter than several of the possible cutoff wavelengths, those particular modes will be propagated. The remaining modes of the infinite set will be attenuated. In practice, waveguides are usually used in the dominant mode. The excitation of this mode, and this mode only, is possible over a narrow range of frequencies lying between the cutoff wavelength of the dominant mode and the cutoff wavelength of the next higher order mode. Propagation of the dominant mode is possible at shorter wavelengths, but propagation of other modes can then occur. This greatly complicates the control of the desired dominant mode, especially if the physical structure is not geometrically simple. From a practical viewpoint, the waveguide can be considered as a bandpass transmission line. The coaxial line, in the same sense, is a low-pass device, being useful from direct current up to a frequency at which higher-order modes become possible.

4.4. Identification of Modes. A certain practice has been established to identify the field configuration in the common waveguides. For the rectangular and circular waveguides the field configuration inside the guide is described by adding subscripts to the abbreviated symbols, TE and TM, as follows: The modes are called TE_{mn} or TM_{mn}, in which m and n are determined from the following conventions:

a. Waves in Rectangular Waveguides. If a single wave is being transmitted in a rectangular waveguide, the field quantity that is entirely in the transverse plane can be resolved into two components, parallel to the wide and narrow walls. In any transverse plane, these components vary periodically with distance along a path parallel to one of the walls. One then defines m as the total number of half-period variations of either component of the field along a path parallel to the wide wall; and n as the total number of variations of either component of the field along the path parallel to the narrow wall.

b. Waves in Circular Waveguides. If a single wave is transmitted in a circular waveguide, the transverse field may be resolved into two components, radial and angular. These components can vary along a circular path concentric with the wall, and vary in a manner related to the Bessel functions of order n along a radius. The subscripts m and n are defined as follows: m is the total number of full-period variations of either component of the field along a circular path concentric with the wall; and n is one more than the total number of reversals of sign of either component along a radial path.

This system can be used only if the observed wave form is known to correspond to a single mode.

4.5. Normalized Voltage and Current: Power Flow. The electric and magnetic field quantities representing traveling waves as given by Eqs. (4.26) and (4.27) can be rewritten in a form which makes it appear that certain coefficients behave as if they were voltage and current in the sense that their product is equal to the power flow. The ratio of these coefficients is an impedance equal to the *wave impedance* previously defined.

The power flow at any point inside of a transmission line is given by Poynting's vector, defined as the vector product of the electric and magnetic fields at the point in question. The total power flow is obtained by integrating Poynting's vector over the cross section of the guide, taking its component in the direction of the guide, and computing the time average. In the following, the subscript t means the *transverse component of* the quantity in question, while the second subscript n refers to the nth mode of transmission. An asterisk after the quantity means the complex conjugate of the quantity.

If W_s represents the power flow per unit area in the z direction and W the total power, then

$$W_s = \tfrac{1}{2}\mathbf{E}_{t,n}\mathbf{H}^*_{t,n} \tag{4.48}$$

The transverse components of the electric and magnetic fields are related through the wave impedance. Using Eq. (4.44) and using the quantities as if they were scalars, W_s becomes

$$W_s = \tfrac{1}{2}Z_{0,n}H_{t,n}H^*_{t,n} \tag{4.49}$$
$$= \tfrac{1}{2}Y^*_{0,n}E_{t,n}E^*_{t,n} \tag{4.50}$$

where $Y_0 = 1/Z_0$ = wave admittance. The total power is obtained by integrating W_s over the area of the transmission line. It is helpful to normalize the field quantities by rewriting them in the following form. Let

$$E_{t,n} = V_n F_n(x,y) \tag{4.51}$$
$$H_{t,n} = I_n F_n(x,y) \tag{4.52}$$
where
$$\iint [F_n(x,y)]^2 \, dx \, dy = 1 \tag{4.53}$$

The function $F_n(x,y)$ is chosen so that its dependence upon the transverse coordinates is identical to that of the transverse components of the fields. Further, its magnitude is adjusted so that Eq. (4.53) becomes true. The constants V_n and I_n are then adjusted so that the right-hand sides of Eqs. (4.51) and (4.52) give the known field quantities. Using this form in carrying out the integration of the Poynting's vector over the area of the guide, the total power flow becomes

$$W = \tfrac{1}{2} Z_{0,n} I_n I_n^* = \tfrac{1}{2} Y_{0,n}^* V_n V_n^* \tag{4.54}$$

This means that if appropriate normalization is carried out for a given transmission line, the coefficients V_n and I_n can be found which can be identified as voltage and current in an ordinary transmission line, i.e., their product gives the power flow. For this reason, the coefficients V_n and I_n are known as *normalized voltage* and *current*, respectively. In mks units, V_n and I_n have the physical dimensions of volts and amperes, respectively. Their product gives the power flow in watts. The ratio of the normalized voltage and normalized current remains equal to the wave impedance of the transmission line.

4.6. Application to Traveling Waves. The formal solutions of Maxwell's equations for the transmission line can be rewritten with the help of normalized voltage and current to make them appear mathematically identical to the solutions of the telegrapher's equations.

The normalized voltage and current coefficients in Eqs. (4.51) and (4.52) depend upon the magnitude of the actual field; they are also time and z dependent in the same way as the electric and magnetic fields themselves. Thus, normalized voltage and current can be written as

$$V_n = A_n e^{j(\omega t - \beta z)} \tag{4.55}$$
$$I_n = \frac{A_n}{Z_{0,n}} e^{j(\omega t - \beta z)} \tag{4.56}$$

where A_n is a numerical coefficient which depends upon the magnitude of the fields, and is obtained by means of the normalization procedure. These equations are applicable to any uniform transmission line, and can be considered as a direct formulation of the long-line transmission-line theory. In form, these are identical with the voltage and current traveling-wave solutions of the telegrapher's equations.

The impedance which appears in these equations is the *wave impedance* for the nth mode. However, the use of this particular impedance is not essential in the formulation of the voltage and current concept. It is possible, for example, to multiply the voltage and to divide the current by the same constant. This does not change the power flow, but it changes the magnitude of the impedance. This unavoidable ambiguity in the value of impedance leads to the necessity of defining it in a way best suited to the individual problem.

This ambiguity in the meaning of impedance should not be of serious concern. As stated in the introduction, there are many possible definitions of cause and response, and it becomes necessary to choose a sensible set of variables for the given problem. The normalized voltage and current set is consistent with respect to power flow and is based directly upon the use of wave impedance, which is a fundamental parameter arising directly from the application of Maxwell's equations. In spite of the arbitrariness in the choice of voltage, current, and impedance in some problems, these quantities must be self-consistent with regard to power flow; as a result, the impedance only differs from the wave impedance by a constant. Furthermore, in most problems of concern in this text the actual choice of the impedance basis is immaterial as the principal quantities of interest will be expressions such as the standing-wave ratio in a transmission line and the total power flow. In these cases, the choice of the impedance basis is irrelevant for similar reasons.

4.7. Standing Waves in Transmission Lines. In the previous section it was shown that solutions of Maxwell's equations for uniform transmission lines can be considered from the viewpoint of conventional transmission-line theory. Adapting the usual transmission-line technique, the complete behavior of propagating waves is obtained by considering the effect of reflected waves caused by an arbitrary obstacle in the uniform transmission line. The complete set of waves consists of waves propagating in both directions with the relative magnitude and phase of the two sets of propagating waves being determined by the nature of the obstacle, e.g., the value of the terminating impedance.

The interference between the two sets of propagating waves gives rise to the familiar standing-wave phenomenon. The magnitude and position of the standing-wave pattern are easily observable; it is of considerable practical importance to be able to study the properties of these standing waves and to be able to connect the observable facts with the characteristics of the obstacle which creates the reflection. Many excellent reference books are available which treat these topics fully; the following material is limited to the extent required to connect physical observations with the nature of the discontinuity.

The solution of a general transmission-line problem is obtained by considering two waves traveling in opposite directions.   Cartesian coordinates are used in the following discussion as a matter of convenience, and x and y coordinates shall refer symbolically to the transverse coordinates of any suitable coordinate system.   Also, it is assumed that the generator produces a single frequency and excites the transmission line in a single mode.   These conditions are always desired in practice; if they are not satisfied, the resultant phenomenon becomes too complicated to be understood in general.

Let V_1 and I_1 be the voltage and current, respectively, of a wave propagating to the right in the coordinate system shown in Fig. 4.4, and V_2 and I_2 be the voltage and current of another wave propagating from right to left.   The two sets of traveling waves can be written as follows: The incident (forward) wave set is

$$V_1 e^{j(\omega t-\beta z)}$$
$$I_1 e^{j(\omega t-\beta z)} \qquad (4.57)$$

and the reflected (backward) wave set is

$$V_2 e^{j(\omega t+\beta z)}$$
$$I_2 e^{j(\omega t+\beta z)} \qquad (4.58)$$

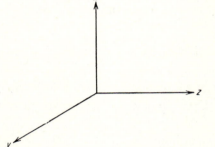

For a given change in z, these sets have the same value when t changes by $\omega z/\beta$; ω/β, the phase velocity of the wave, is positive for the first set and negative for the second.

FIG. 4.4. Coordinate system used in the analysis of traveling waves.   The transverse coordinates are x and y; direction propagation is in the z direction.

As stated in Sec. 4.5, the voltage and current of a traveling wave set are not independent.   Using Eq. (4.44), the two sets become

Forward wave:

$$V_1 e^{j(\omega t-\beta z)}$$
$$\frac{V_1}{Z_0} e^{j(\omega t-\beta z)} \qquad (4.59)$$

Reflected wave:

$$V_2 e^{j(\omega t+\beta z)}$$
$$-\frac{V_2}{Z_0} e^{j(\omega t+\beta z)} \qquad (4.60)$$

The voltage and current waves in the reflected wave are $180°$ out of phase, as indicated by the negative sign.   If the direction of propagation is reversed, then for a given direction of the electric field the magnetic field must reverse, and so must the associated current quantity.

The voltage and current distribution in the transmission line can be explored with the aid of a moving probe which responds to total fields due to the sum of the two traveling waves.   The total voltage and current at any point on the transmission line is the sum of the corresponding quantities given by the sets of Eqs. (4.59) and (4.60). The ratio of the *total* voltage to the *total* current, Z, is

$$Z = Z_0 \frac{1 + \dfrac{V_2}{V_1} e^{j2\beta z}}{1 - \dfrac{V_2}{V_1} e^{j2\beta z}} \qquad (4.61)$$

The time factor is canceled, having appeared in all terms. If the transmission line is terminated by an impedance Z_L at $z = l$, $Z = Z_L$, and

$$Z_L = Z_0 \frac{1 + (V_2/V_1)e^{j2\beta l}}{1 - (V_2/V_1)e^{j2\beta l}} \qquad (4.62)$$

and solving for V_2/V_1,

$$\frac{V_2}{V_1} = \frac{Z_L - Z_0}{Z_L + Z_0} e^{-j2\beta l} \qquad (4.63)$$

Hence, at any other place along the line, the impedance Z is

$$Z = Z_0 \frac{Z_L + jZ_0 \tan \beta(l - z)}{Z_0 + jZ_L \tan \beta(l - z)} \qquad (4.64)$$

Equation (4.64) relates the impedance located at $z = l$ to the impedance that can be observed at any point along the transmission line. This is an important relation, and will be used in several ways.

Suppose that a certain point along the transmission line is to be regarded as the *load*. It can be an actual load, such as an antenna, a resistive termination, or a mere discontinuity in shape or dimensions. Or, it may be desirable to consider an arbitrary point as the *reference point* for some problem even though there may not be anything unique about it. It is necessary to relate standing-wave observations to the load impedance at the point in question.

Many ways are conceivable by means of which proper observations can be made. The simplest and the most illuminating measurement is one in which the intensity of the fields is observed along the length of the transmission line. As a consequence of reflections at the load, there will result the familiar standing waves, with maximum and minimum values being produced between the two waves by constructive and destructive interference, respectively. Although it does not matter which quantity is measured, assume that some detecting device is available which permits a measurement of relative values of the total voltage.

Let the reading of the voltage maximum be called V_{max} and the voltage minimum, V_{min}. The quantity r is defined as the *voltage standing-wave ratio*, often abbreviated as VSWR:

$$r = \frac{V_{max}}{V_{min}} \qquad (4.65)$$

It should be noted that r is a ratio of two numbers, the values of voltage maximum and minimum, and is always real.   Expressed in terms of the incident and reflected waves, it is

$$r = \frac{|V_1| + |V_2|}{|V_1| - |V_2|} \tag{4.66}$$

$$= \frac{1 + \left|\dfrac{V_2}{V_1}\right|}{1 - \left|\dfrac{V_2}{V_1}\right|} \tag{4.67}$$

The ratio V_2/V_1 given by Eq. (4.63) is called the *reflection coefficient*, Γ. It is, in general, a complex number.   Equation (4.67) can be written as

$$r = \frac{1 + |\Gamma|}{1 - |\Gamma|} \tag{4.68}$$

When Γ is different from zero, reflections occur, which are evident from the observed standing waves.

Equation (4.63) can be written as

$$\Gamma = \left|\frac{Z_L - Z_0}{Z_L + Z_0}\right| \underline{/-2\beta l + \phi} \tag{4.69}$$

where ϕ is the angle of the vector quantity in the absolute brackets. The absolute value of Γ depends only upon the ratio Z_L/Z_0, but its phase depends both upon the nature of the load and the distance from the load. Using Eq. (4.69), Eq. (4.68) can be written as

$$r = \frac{|Z_L + Z_0| + |Z_L - Z_0|}{|Z_L + Z_0| - |Z_L - Z_0|} \tag{4.70}$$

or
$$r = \frac{|Z_L + Z_0| + |Z_0 - Z_L|}{|Z_L + Z_0| - |Z_0 - Z_L|} \tag{4.71}$$

These two equations are mathematically identical, but are written in this form to emphasize that Z_L can be either greater or smaller than Z_0.

The special case when the load impedance is purely resistive is important.   In this case, the absolute brackets may be removed, giving

$$R_L > Z_0 \qquad r = \frac{R_L}{Z_0} \tag{4.72}$$

$$R_L < Z_0 \qquad r = \frac{Z_0}{R_L} \tag{4.73}$$

4.8. Some Properties of Standing Waves.   Suppose that the incident voltage wave has magnitude equal to unity.   Leaving the time factors out for simplicity, the total voltage V_t becomes

$$V_t = e^{-j\beta z} + \Gamma e^{j\beta z} \tag{4.74}$$

The first term has an amplitude of unity and a phase angle of $-\beta z$. The second term has a magnitude Γ and an opposite phase angle. These two vectors are shown in Fig. 4.5. When the phase angle $\beta z = 0$, the two vectors add, producing the voltage maximum. When $\beta z = \pi/2$, the voltages subtract, giving rise to the voltage minimum. The corresponding current equation has the form

$$I_t = e^{-j\beta z} - \Gamma e^{j\beta z} \tag{4.75}$$

Because of the negative sign in the current equation, the current maxima occur at the points of voltage minima and vice versa. At either place, the ratio of voltage to current is a real number and corresponds to a pure resistance.

At the points of voltage minima and maxima the impedance is a pure resistance, which makes it possible to evaluate it in terms of the easily measured standing-wave ratio. Thus, if a load Z_L is considered located at a voltage minimum, then all the terms in Eq. (4.70) are real numbers. Calling $Z = Z_L$ at the voltage minimum,

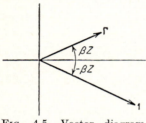

$$Z_L = \frac{Z_0}{r} \tag{4.76}$$

FIG. 4.5. Vector diagram showing the relation between reflected and incident waves.

Or, at a voltage maximum,

$$Z_L = rZ_0 \tag{4.77}$$

Obviously there is nothing special about any point along a uniform transmission line, including the points of voltage minima and maxima, as the waves travel continuously in both directions. However, these points are easily identified, and mathematical manipulations become especially simple if such points are chosen as *points of reference* for the various calculations that may need to be made.

The load impedance at the end of a transmission line can be determined experimentally from these results. The required information is the standing-wave ratio r and a distance d, the distance between some voltage minimum and the load. From the above considerations, it is known that at the point $l - z = d$, $Z = Z_0/r$. Using the general expression given by Eq. (4.64) and solving it for Z_L, it is found that

$$Z_L = Z_0 \frac{1 - jr \tan \beta d}{r - j \tan \beta d} \tag{4.78}$$

This important relation makes it possible to evaluate the unknown impedance from data which are readily available from laboratory observations.

The measurement of impedance resolves itself into the determination of the three quantities which appear in Eq. (4.78).   Transmission-line wavelength is first determined, either from the separation of two voltage minima, with the end of the line shorted, or from the known frequency of the generator and the cutoff wavelength of the propagating mode. From this, β can be computed.   The experimental determination of r and d is simple, as discussed in Chap. 5.

The physical interpretation of r is very simple as it is a measure of the resistive component of the load.   The physical meaning of d is less simple, because it is not a quantity which is absolutely defined; it is a distance from some voltage minimum to some arbitrary point chosen by the observer as the place where the load is considered to be located.   At low frequencies, there is seldom any doubt as to the location of the terminals of the load.   At microwave frequencies, however, the definition of the terminals of the load, i.e., the reference point, must often be completely arbitrary.   But having established a reference point, even though arbitrarily, the distance d assumes a physical meaning.   It is essentially a phase factor which determines the transformation of the resistance Z_0/r to its final value Z d units of length away.

It is interesting and often convenient to be able to recognize the nature of the relation between Z_L and the distance d, at which the impedance is a pure resistance.   This can be done easily for a few special cases. Consider first the case when Z_L is a pure resistance.   Then

$$\frac{Z_0}{r} = Z_0 \frac{Z_L + jZ_0 \tan \beta d}{Z_0 + jZ_L \tan \beta d} \tag{4.79}$$

Rationalizing the right hand side,

$$\frac{Z_0}{r} = Z_0 \left[\frac{1 + \tan^2 \beta d}{\dfrac{Z_0}{Z_L} + \dfrac{Z_L}{Z_0} \tan^2 \beta d} + j \frac{\tan \beta d \left(\dfrac{Z_0}{Z_L} - \dfrac{Z_L}{Z_0} \right)}{\dfrac{Z_0}{Z_L} + \dfrac{Z_L}{Z_0} \tan^2 \beta d} \right] \tag{4.80}$$

The left-hand side of the equation is a pure resistance.   Therefore, the imaginary term on the right must be zero.   This can happen under the following three conditions:

1. $Z_L = Z_0$; there are no standing waves.
2. $\tan \beta d = 0$ or $d = 0$, $\lambda_t/2$, λ_t, etc., and, from this, $Z_L = Z_0/r$.   This means that at this value of d the load resistance is less in value than Z_0.
3. $\tan \beta d = \infty$ or $d = \lambda_t/4$, $3\lambda_t/4$, etc., and this gives $Z_L = Z_0 r$, which means that the load resistance is greater in value than Z_0.

Therefore, when the load impedance is a pure resistance, the minima can occur at two sets of points:

$$d = 0, \frac{\lambda_t}{2}, \lambda_t, \ldots \qquad \text{or} \qquad d = \frac{\lambda_t}{4}, \frac{3\lambda_t}{4}, \ldots$$

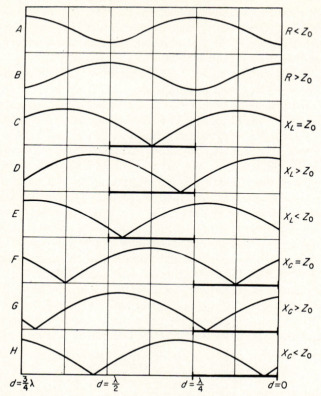

Fig. 4.6. Position of the standing-wave pattern for various load terminations located at $d = 0$. Cases A and B correspond to resistive terminations; the remaining, to purely reactive loads.

depending upon whether or not $Z_L > Z_0$ and, inversely, the minima cannot occur anywhere else.

If the load impedance is a pure inductance, $r = \infty$ and the position of the minima can be determined as before. Let $Z_L = jX_L$,

$$\frac{Z_0}{r} = Z_0 \frac{jX_L + jZ_0 \tan \beta d}{Z_0 - X_L \tan \beta d} \tag{4.81}$$

which must be equal to zero. This can happen if

$$X_L + Z_0 \tan \beta d = 0$$

or if

$$\tan \beta d = -\frac{X_L}{Z_0}$$

This situation is different from the resistive case; the position of the minima depends upon the ratio X_L/Z_0.

If X_L approaches zero, d approaches the values $\lambda_t/2$, $3\lambda_t/2$, ... If X_L approaches ∞, d approaches $\lambda_t/4$, $3\lambda_t/d$, $5\lambda_t/4$, ... In the special case when $X_L = Z_0$, $d = 3\lambda_t/8$, $11\lambda_t/8$, ... Thus, when Z_L is purely inductive, the minima will lie between

$$\frac{\lambda_t}{4} \text{ and } \frac{\lambda_t}{2} \qquad \frac{3\lambda_t}{4} \text{ and } \lambda_t \qquad \text{etc.}$$

Conversely, if the standing-wave ratio is infinite, and the minima are

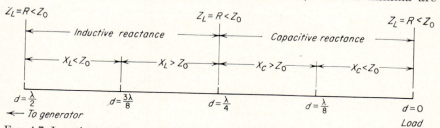

FIG. 4.7. Location of the voltage minima with respect to the position of the load for purely resistive and reactive terminations.

located between the above limits, the load is a pure inductance, whose magnitude can be computed from the relation

$$X_L = -Z_0 \tan \beta d$$

If the load is a pure capacitive reactance, $Z_L = -jX_c$, and $r = \infty$.

$$\frac{Z_0}{r} = \frac{-jX_c + jZ_0 \tan \beta d}{Z_0 + X_c \tan \beta d} \qquad (4.82)$$

This is zero when

$$\tan \beta d = \frac{X_c}{Z_0}$$

When X_c approaches zero, $\tan \beta d$ approaches 0, and d approaches values of 0, $\lambda_t/2$, ... When X_c approaches ∞, d approaches values $\lambda_t/4$, $3\lambda_t/4$, ... In the special case when $X_c = Z_0$, $d = \lambda_t/8$, $9\lambda_t/8$, $17\lambda_t/8$, ... Thus, if it is found that the standing-wave ratio is infinite and d is located in the regions

$$0 \text{ to } \frac{\lambda_t}{4} \qquad \frac{\lambda_t}{2} \text{ to } \frac{3\lambda_t}{4} \qquad \text{etc.}$$

the load must be a pure capacitive reactance, whose magnitude can be computed from

$$X_c = Z_0 \tan \beta d$$

The three cases discussed are summarized in the charts shown in Figs. 4.6 and 4.7. The first of these is self-explanatory; the second shows the regions where the voltage minima will be found for the three types of load terminations shown.

4.9. Graphical Representation of Impedance Relations. In the previous sections a number of equations were found which relate one set of impedance parameters with another. In one case the impedance at any point along a transmission line was found in terms of the load impedance and the line length between the load and the point in question. In another case, it was shown how the load impedance can be computed

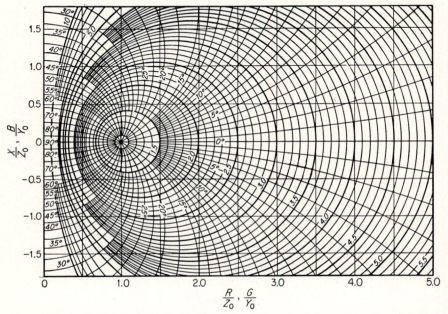

$$\frac{X}{Z_0}, \frac{B}{Y_0}$$

$$\frac{R}{Z_0}, \frac{G}{Y_0}$$

FIG. 4.8. Rectangular impedance (or admittance) chart useful in solving transmission-line problems.

in terms of laboratory measurements. These equations are fairly complicated, making it difficult to perceive the physical relations between the various factors. For this reason, it is often convenient to solve transmission-line problems by graphical methods. Having once established the relationship between a mathematical equation and its graphical form, it is possible to use the latter to obtain information from geometrical considerations with relative ease. Such graphs are useful both for routine transformations and plotting data. They are also useful for intuitive analysis, making use of certain graphical rules obtained from the defining equations.

There are a number of ways to present impedance relations graphically. Two of these which have been found to be the most useful are discussed here. These are known as the *rectangular* chart, and the *hemisphere* chart, often called the *Smith* chart, based upon Eqs. (4.64) and (4.69) respectively.

Figure 4.8 shows the rectangular chart in cartesian form. The coordinates of this chart are the vector components of the impedance Z that can be observed at any point along the transmission line. If the transmission line is terminated with an impedance Z_L and the distance from the load allowed to vary, the resultant variations in Z can be found from the contour lines of the chart.[1]

[1] The mathematical justification of the various statements can be obtained as follows: Equation (4.64) can be rationalized and the imaginary part can be plotted as a function of the real part. The resultant chart is a family of circles. Stated analytically,

$$Z = R + jX \tag{4.83}$$

Letting $p = Z_L/Z_0$ and $q = \tan \beta l$, R and X are

$$R = \frac{p(1 + q^2)}{1 + p^2 q^2} \tag{4.84}$$

$$X = \frac{q(1 - p^2)}{1 + p^2 q^2} \tag{4.85}$$

If p and q are eliminated one at a time between Eqs. (4.84) and (4.85), the following relations are obtained:

$$\left(R - \frac{p^2 + 1}{2p}\right)^2 + X^2 = \left(\frac{p^2 - 1}{2p}\right)^2 \tag{4.86}$$

$$R^2 + \left(X - \frac{q^2 - 1}{2q}\right)^2 = \left(\frac{q^2 + 1}{2q}\right)^2 \tag{4.87}$$

The first of these is the locus of points having the same ratio Z_L/Z_0, but at different positions along the transmission line. The second is the locus of points at the same place on the line but shows the dependence of X and R upon Z_L/Z_0.

Equation (4.86) represents a family of circles with centers at $(p^2 + 1)/2p$, 0 and whose corresponding radii are $(p^2 - 1)/2p$. In terms of impedances, these become

Centers at: $$\frac{(Z_L/Z_0)^2 + 1}{2(Z_L/Z_0)}, 0 \tag{4.88}$$

Radii: $$\frac{(Z_L/Z_0)^2 - 1}{2(Z_L/Z_0)} \tag{4.89}$$

These circles have their centers on the R axis, and surround the point $(1,0)$.

In a similar way, Eq. (4.87) represents another family of circles whose centers lie on the X axis, with

Centers at: $$0, \frac{\tan^2 \beta l - 1}{2 \tan \beta l} \tag{4.90}$$

Radii: $$\frac{\tan^2 \beta l + 1}{2 \tan \beta l} \tag{4.91}$$

An important property of this family of circles is that they all pass through the point $(1,0)$; this can be shown as follows: If two circles, distinguished from each other by different values of q, are to intersect, this intersection can be found as the simul-

The use of the rectangular chart can be seen more clearly by considering a specific illustration. Suppose the load impedance Z_L is known; then the normalized resistance and reactance components can be computed and located on the chart as a point R/Z_0, X/Z_0. This point will fall at the intersection of two curves corresponding to a certain value of βl and Z_L/Z_0. To determine the impedance at some other position along the line, one follows the circle of the constant Z_L/Z_0 from the starting point until the βl factor has been increased (or decreased) by the desired value.

An important property of the rectangular chart is that the circles of constant Z_L/Z_0 intersect the real axis at two points whose geometric mean is the center of the circle. The maximum value of the normalized resistance is also equal to the value of standing-wave ratio r, as can be seen from Eqs. (4.72) and (4.73). This means that if the standing-wave ratio is measured in the laboratory, the rectangular chart can be entered by identifying the circle whose maximum resistance value is equal to r. All other possible impedances along the transmission line can be found by moving along the appropriate circle through the electrical distance βl, as specified by the orthogonal circles giving the parametric values of length. The points of voltage minimum and maximum, readily identifiable in the laboratory, can be located as the extremal positions of the given VSWR circle.

The sense of rotation on a rectangular chart can be easily established by imagining that the load is terminated in a short circuit. Moving a small distance toward the generator from a short circuit results in an inductive reactance, and, therefore, in positive values of reactance on the chart.

An obvious property of the rectangular chart is that impedances can be represented as vectors directly. The angle between the vector and the real axis is equal to the electrical angle between voltage and current in the corresponding impedance; the length of the vector is the ratio of the magnitudes of the voltage and current. When impedances are connected in series, the operations are described by the parallelogram law of addition of vectors.

---

taneous solution of

$$R^2 + X^2 + X\left(\frac{1}{q_1} - q_1\right) = 1$$

$$R^2 + X^2 + X\left(\frac{1}{q_2} - q_2\right) = 1 \tag{4.92}$$

This requires that

$$X\left(\frac{1}{q_1} - q_1\right) = X\left(\frac{1}{q_2} - \frac{1}{q_2}\right) \tag{4.93}$$

which is true only when $X = 0$ and, therefore, at $R = 1$.

The above equations can be written in the admittance form, and are useful in problems involving impedances connected in parallel. A set of circles is obtained which is identical with those in the impedance chart.

It is impossible to represent all of the values of impedance on any given rectangular chart because the area of the impedance plane is infinite and a given piece of paper can cover only a small part of it. This is often a disadvantage. A transformation of a low impedance through $\lambda/4$ gives rise to a high one, and the resultant impedance often lies beyond the edges of the chart.

The hemisphere and the Smith charts can be formed by graphical representation of Eq. (4.69). Any possible value of Γ can be represented in polar coordinates by plotting absolute value of Γ as the radius at an angle of $2\beta l$ (or $-2\beta l$, depending upon the direction in which the distance is measured). The advantage of this chart is immediately obvious. Regardless of the value of Z_L, all possible transformed values of Z_L lie either within the circle of $|\Gamma| = 1$, or on its periphery.

The Smith chart is a polar plot on which two families of orthogonal circles are drawn; these identify the resistance and reactance components, and correspond to abscissae and ordinates of the rectangular chart. A sample of the Smith chart is shown in Fig. 4.9.[1]

A point on the chart corresponding to a given load can be located directly from the knowledge of the standing-wave ratio r and the position of the minimum (from the load), since

$$|\Gamma| = \frac{r - 1}{r + 1} \tag{4.94}$$

The measured values of r and $2\beta l$ are the polar coordinates, locating the impedance on the Smith chart. The impedance seen at any other point on the transmission line is located by rotating the point representing the load impedance about the center at a uniform angular displacement for a distance corresponding to twice the electrical distance from the load to the point considered. The motion of the impedance point follows a path of a constant radius, determined by r.

An analysis of the behavior of the traveling waves gives a further insight into the geometry of the Smith chart. Referring to Sec. 4.8, the voltage on the line can be written in the form

$$V_t = V_1 e^{-j\beta l} + V_2 e^{j\beta l} \tag{4.95}$$

or, if normalizing with respect to V_1,

$$V_t = 1 + \frac{V_2}{V_1} e^{-2j\beta l} \tag{4.96}$$

[1] P. H. Smith, A Transmission Line Calculator, *Electronics*, vol. 12, no. 1, p. 29, 1939.

where the second term is the reflection coefficient Γ.   Figure 4.10 shows
this graphically.   The sum of the two vectors is the total voltage on the
line.   The variation of the voltage with the position along the line can be
visualized immediately as the end of the Γ vector rotates uniformly with
the angle 2βl.   Since the standing-wave ratio r does not depend upon βl,

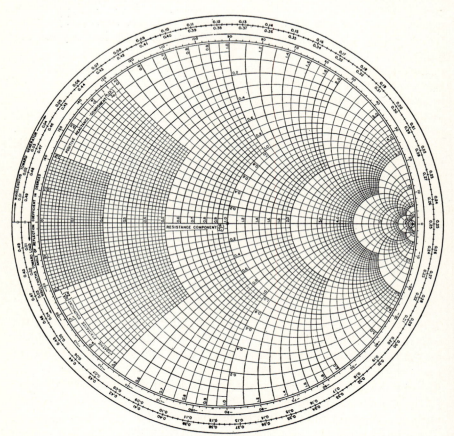

Fig. 4.9. Smith or hemisphere impedance (or admittance) chart.

the Γ vector follows a circle of a constant r.   The variation of the current in the line can be represented in the same way, remembering that
the current associated with a reflected wave has a negative sign.

The coordinate circles drawn on the Smith chart are lines of constant
resistance and reactance components of the impedance Z.   These lines
may be regarded as distortion of the rectangular coordinates of the rectangular chart.   It is possible to perform this distortion mathematically
by means of the linear fractional transformation.   If W represents the

impedance on the Smith chart, and Z the impedance on the rectangular chart, the transformation from one plane to the other can be obtained from

$$W = \frac{AZ + B}{CZ + D} \tag{4.97}$$

by proper selection of the complex constants A, B, C, and D. This transformation is conformal, i.e., the angles between lines are preserved in going from W to Z planes. Therefore, the coordinate circles of the Smith chart intersect at right angles. Also, a circle in W plane transforms into a circle in Z plane.

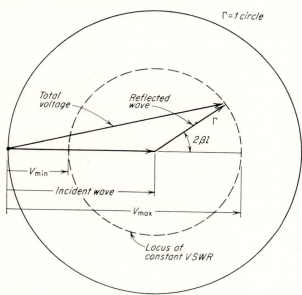

FIG. 4.10. Vectors useful in understanding the reflection coefficient representation of the Smith or hemisphere chart.

The sense of rotation in the Smith chart can be verified by applying the rule given above in using the rectangular chart, i.e., in remembering that a small length of shorted line results in a positive reactance.

The rectangular chart is usually found more convenient than the Smith chart for problems involving additions of vectors and related intuitive analysis; such as in understanding the behavior of multiple stub transformers. The Smith chart is usually better for recording the laboratory data because:

1. All possible impedances lie within the area of the chart.

2. Laboratory data plotted on a Smith chart representing variation of impedance with some parameter have the same geometric configuration

and size regardless of the point of reference, whereas the appearance of data on the rectangular chart is strongly dependent upon the choice of the reference point.

3. Variation of impedance with position along the line is presented uniformly as a function of position. In the rectangular chart certain sections are greatly compressed while others are expanded.

4. Attenuation, if present, can be compensated readily by an appropriate change in the radius with rotation.

The choice between the rectangular and Smith charts can often be made on the basis of obvious characteristics of the problem. This choice is often affected by the extent of one's familiarity with the geometrical properties of the chart. As it happens, the Smith-chart graph paper is more readily available. Principally for this reason, the Smith chart is the most frequently used for recording of data, while the rectangular chart is used for graphical intuitive processes or analysis, usually by sketching the coordinates and representative circles.

CHAPTER 5

MEASUREMENT OF IMPEDANCE

5.1. Types of Impedance Measurements. On the surface the subject of impedance measurements appears simple and straightforward; however, not only is the topic important and diversified, but it is also extremely complicated. Because at microwave frequencies the apparatus can be made either smaller or larger than the corresponding wavelength, there are many techniques available for making the necessary measurements, each having its advantages and limitations. Furthermore, there are many indirect uses for impedance measurements, involving either a unique way of using the standard equipment or an ingenious way of interpreting the conventional data. This subject is further complicated by the multiplicity of errors which exist in all of the possible measurements so that a good understanding of the principles of operation of the various devices is indispensable to their successful use. This chapter is devoted to the general subject of impedance measurements where the desired result is the knowledge of the impedance itself. Indirect uses of impedance measurements, such as the determination of attenuation, are discussed in later chapters.

The conventional method of measuring impedances, illustrated in Fig. 5.1a, is based upon the exploration of the standing-wave pattern by means of a standing-wave detector. Not only is this the most common method, but it is also possible to think of the standing-wave detector as the impedance standard. The unknown impedance is connected to the standing-wave detector and a moving probe, equipped with a suitable indicator, allows the exploration of the standing-wave pattern. The detailed study of the standing-wave pattern provides a measure of the unknown in terms of the impedance of the standing-wave detector line. As discussed in Chap. 4, it is seldom necessary to know more than the standing-wave ratio and the position of the minimum, i.e., the normalized value of the impedance. Occasionally it is necessary to know the absolute value of the impedance. This can be computed from the characteristic impedance of the standing-wave detector, which depends upon its geometry, dimensions, mode of propagation, the particular set of field components of interest, and the operating frequency. Once the characteristic impedance is computed, the normalized measured impedances can be converted into absolute values.

The accuracy of the measurements obtained with the standing-wave detector method is dependent upon several factors related to details of the construction of the standing-wave detector. Ideally, and almost so in practice, the characteristic impedance of the standing-wave detector depends upon geometrical factors, so that the measurement of an unknown impedance by observation of the standing-wave phenomenon

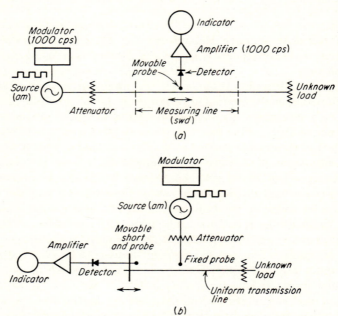

FIG. 5.1. Two possible methods for detection of standing waves in transmission lines. (a) The conventional standing-wave detector; (b) the Chipman method.

can be construed to be a direct comparison against the standard of impedance. In contrast to the usual low-frequency measurements, auxiliary impedance standards are not needed. Careful construction and reasonable attention to numerous operating details usually result in excellent accuracy.

The standing-wave detector is not the only means of exploring the standing-wave pattern in a transmission line. The existence of the standing waves can be ascertained by several related techniques. For example, a series of fixed probes can be used to sample the field; simple methods can be established to aid in interpreting the data. Another example is a single fixed probe separated from the load by a length of line containing a variable (reflectionless) phase shifter. This arrangement can be thought of as an equivalent to the moving probe since the standing-wave pattern can be made to sweep past the probe and it represents a convenient method for rapid observation of the standing-wave pattern.[1] Still another variation of the standing-wave method consists of an unusual arrangement of the components illustrated in Fig. 5.1b. A loosely coupled probe introduces a signal into a uniform transmission line which is connected to the unknown on one end and to a shorting plunger on the other. The detector is carried by the moving plunger. The motion of the plunger results in maxima and minima in the detected output which can be interpreted as if they were the conventional standing-wave detector data. This method avoids the slot in the transmission line and minimizes the possibility of distortion of the transmission line due to its presence.

It is possible to separate the traveling waves in a transmission line and to measure each one independently by devices called directional couplers.[2] These allow one to measure the magnitudes of the reflected and incident waves. Provided the equipment is constructed carefully, this method represents a simple, rapid, and accurate means of measuring the absolute value of the unknown impedance. With the addition of simple auxiliary equipment, phase information can also be derived.

Microwave bridge circuits can be constructed which, at least in part, correspond to the conventional low-frequency Wheatstone impedance bridge. With bridge techniques it is possible to compare an unknown impedance against a standard without the necessity of accurately reading relative voltages. The bridge methods require impedance standards which are not generally available.

Dynamic presentation of impedance data is possible by modification of some of the above techniques. Automatic measurements are often valuable when elaborate measurements as a function of some parameter of the microwave system are needed.

Finally, the usual elements of the impedance-measuring system can be used in unconventional ways. For example, it is often necessary to measure small reflections in transmission lines. It will be found that it is

---

[1] This method is also adaptable to precision measurement of impedance. The signal source, the detector, and the unknown impedance can be joined together by an arbitrary T junction with a provision to vary the phase of the unknown by a variable phase shifter. It can be shown that the variation in phase of the unknown causes the detector current to vary periodically and this enables the maxima and minima to be interpreted to provide the impedance information. For further details, see A. C. Macpherson and D. M. Kerns, A New Technique for the Measurement of Microwave Standing-wave Ratios, *Proc. IRE*, vol. 44, no. 8, pp. 1024–1030, August, 1956.

[2] For description of directional couplers, their theory, construction, and characteristics, see R. Kyhl, chap. 14 in C. G. Montgomery (ed.), "Technique of Microwave Measurements," McGraw-Hill Book Company, Inc., New York, 1947.

possible to extend some of the common low-frequency methods into the microwave region. The conventional low-frequency short-circuit–open-circuit measurement can be adopted directly and results in a variety of methods, often referred to as the nodal-shift techniques. To apply these methods, the region beyond the discontinuity under study is shorted with a movable plunger; on the input side the standing-wave pattern is explored with a moving probe. All that is required in this method is to locate the voltage zeros on the input side for various positions of the short circuit. This method may be further modified by replacing the standing-wave detector by another short circuit locating it at the position of one of the voltage zeros. The final impedance information can be determined from *length* measurements alone, i.e., the separation between the two short circuits.

The above remarks are but a brief summary of the topics covered in this chapter. The principal emphasis will be upon the conventional methods of impedance measurements and the errors which are likely to arise rather than the theory and design of the various pieces of apparatus; these interesting topics are beyond the scope of this book.

5.2. The Standing-wave Detector. It was assumed in Chap. 4 that a method exists for investigating the nature of the standing-wave pattern inside the transmission line. This section is concerned with the practical aspects of obtaining the information needed to evaluate the load and other impedances along the transmission line. In particular, it was assumed that it is possible to investigate the field distribution in the transmission line without disturbing the natural fields, and that the relative magnitude of the fields along the line can be recorded.

In principle, this problem is simple. A section of transmission line identical to the line where the standing waves are to be investigated is provided. This section contains a longitudinal slot several half-wavelengths long. The slot is placed parallel to the lines of current flow so that it does not disturb the natural fields if it is narrow enough. A probe is inserted into the slot and responds to the fields inside the transmission line and picks up a small fraction of the energy flowing by the probe. The probe is connected by a suitable r-f transmission line to a detector which converts radio frequency into direct current; this is measured by an appropriate meter as discussed in Chap. 2. A mechanical drive mechanism is provided to move the probe along the length of the line, always maintaining the translational symmetry, i.e., a fixed orientation of the probe with respect to the slotted line. A scale attached to either the probe or the transmission line makes it possible to determine the position of the probe with respect to some specific point. In this manner, all the required information is obtained. It is now necessary to examine these basic components more carefully to consider the requirements that must be imposed upon the mechanism, arrangement, and performance of each part if the device is to provide the desired information with accuracy.

a. Transmission Line. The section of transmission line where standing-wave measurements are to be made must be properly related in cross section to the transmission line under test. Preferably, the mode of propagation and transverse dimension of the two lines should be identical. Since this is sometimes impossible, the junction of similar transmission lines having different dimensions can be made through gradual and carefully constructed tapered adapters. In this case, or in the event of the more abrupt discontinuity formed by the junction of two entirely dissimilar lines, the presence of the junction should be recognized as an impedance transformer whose characteristics must be determined by a suitable calibration procedure (as described in Sec. 5.7).

The cross section of the slotted line must be uniform throughout the length where the measurements are to be made. If the dimensions inadvertently vary from place to place, the measurement of the field intensity will not accurately indicate the magnitude of the incident and reflected traveling waves as they exist beyond the slotted section. In practice, it is usually necessary to manufacture the slotted line by precision methods, such as machining from solid metal, electroforming, honing, or broaching of annealed commercial tubing. If the line has an odd shape—rectangular waveguides, for example—electroforming techniques are recommended.

If possible, the slotted section should be designed to permit only the desired mode of propagation to exist at the operating frequency. Simultaneous presence of higher-order modes makes it very difficult to interpret the resultant standing-wave pattern. If it is impossible to choose the cross section to limit the propagation to the proper mode, careful adjustment of the entire system must be made to prevent the higher-order modes from occurring in the slotted section.

b. The Slot. A suitable slot must be provided in order to be able to insert the probe into the transmission line. The location of the slot must be chosen so that its presence does not significantly disturb the normal propagation of the energy. The proper location of the slot depends upon the mode of propagation. In all transmission lines carrying TEM (such as coaxial lines) and TM waves, the current flow is everywhere parallel to the axis of the transmission line. A slot formed by removing a narrow strip of metal parallel to current flow does not seriously disturb the fields as there is no tendency for the axial current to cross the longitudinal gap. In TE modes, however, the position of the slot must be chosen carefully because the current flow is more complicated. For example, in the rectangular waveguide propagating the $TE_{1,0}$ mode the slot can be placed only in the middle of the wide face.

The length of the slot depends upon the transmission-line wavelength. Since it is necessary to measure the relative intensity at two points $\lambda_t/4$ apart (the values of maximum and minimum), and since the position of the minima will shift by $\lambda_t/4$ for different phase angles of the load, a length of at least $\lambda_t/2$ must be provided. A slot the length of a full wavelength is desirable, if possible, so that several minima and maxima can be observed to ascertain whether they repeat in magnitude and position.

The presence of the slot in the line can make itself evident in several different ways. First, the slot makes the characteristic impedance different from that of the unaltered line; this change is usually small but can be of importance in accurate work. The change in the characteristic impedance due to the slot in a coaxial line is given by

$$\frac{\Delta Z_0}{Z_0} = \frac{1}{4\pi^2} \frac{w^2}{b^2 - a^2} \tag{5.1}$$

where w is the width of the slot, a and b are the radii of the inner and outer conductor respectively, and $\Delta Z_0/Z_0$ is the fractional change in the characteristic impedance. Similarly, for a rectangular waveguide, shown in Fig. 4.1, the change in the wave impedance is given by

$$\frac{\Delta Z_0}{Z_0} = \frac{1}{2\pi} \frac{w^2}{ab} \left(\frac{\lambda_t}{2a}\right)^2 \tag{5.2}$$

where λ_t is the transmission-line wavelength, and a and b are the width and the height of the waveguide respectively.

Second, if the slot ends abruptly, the fields in the slotted and unslotted lines will be somewhat different. As a consequence, local waves will be produced at the geometrical discontinuity which can be represented by a small reactance shunting the transmission line. Because of the change in impedance and the discontinuity reactance, there will be reflections at the beginning and end of the slotted section. These reflections are indistinguishable from small reflections from the load, and lead to errors that depend upon the magnitude and phase of the load impedance. It is desirable to compensate for or remove these discontinuity effects. The change in impedance due to the slot can be compensated by changing some other dimensions in the slotted section. For example, in the coaxial line this can be done by changing the radii of the conductors, or by providing a small ramp attached to the inner conductor. The discontinuity reactance can be compensated by introducing a small geometrical discontinuity at the end of the slot as shown in Fig. 5.15. An alternative procedure transforms the slotted section into the unaltered section by gradually tapering the width of the slot in a distance comparable to the wavelength.

Third, accompanying the change in impedance, the slot also changes the wave velocity. For example, in the rectangular waveguide shown in Fig. 4.1 the effect of the slot is to increase the guided wavelength which can be approximately predicted by assuming that the guide of width a acts as a guide with an altered width a' given by

$$a' = a\left(1 - \frac{w^2}{2\pi ab}\right) \tag{5.3}$$

The corresponding change in guided wavelength is seldom important. In the usual practice the guided wavelength is measured directly in the slotted section by noting the distance between successive voltage minima when the output terminals of the slotted section are shorted. This procedure automatically eliminates errors in the uncertain dimensions of the guide, and simultaneously it provides a reference point in the slotted region corresponding to the location of the short. If the measured impedance as determined in the slotted section must be referred to some point in the unaltered line, this guide wavelength must not be used directly. Methods of studying the discontinuity effects created by the slot and experimental techniques for determining the difference between guided wavelength in the slotted and in the unaltered sections are discussed in Sec. 5.7.

Under unusual conditions the presence of the slot can cause radiation of energy into free space. This occurs if the slot is too large or if current crosses it due to improper placement. Thus, energy can either escape into free space or be coupled from free space into the transmission line. The first results in an energy loss and in disturbing effects due to the motion of various parts; for example, an operator's hands may affect the detected current. The second causes difficulties if the slotted line is operated in the vicinity of powerful signals such as a nearby transmitter. However, with a properly placed slot and with finite wall thickness, these effects are negligible.

The presence of the slot in the transmission line also changes the boundary conditions, making it possible to excite modes which are normally impossible in the unaltered line. Consider, for example, the exaggerated situation in the rectangular waveguide shown in Fig. 5.2 where the fields, due to some mechanical asymmetry, excite a mode which cannot normally exist. These fields are similar to those existing in the klystron resonator; this mode cannot exist beyond the ends of the slot, so that a complete reflection must occur at each end. A frequency can be found which will excite the slot into integral multiple of half-wavelengths of the slot mode so that strong fields will appear in the slot and completely alter the apparent standing-wave pattern. This situation is not unlikely for any arbitrary frequency; because the moving probe in the slot produces strong reflections, it adjusts the "length" of the slot continuously so that at some point of its travel resonances can occur. The slot resonance is usually damped by the radiation into free space, and the resultant Q is not likely to be high.

Slot resonances can be eliminated by preserving symmetry throughout the slotted section to avoid excitation of the slot mode. It is also advisable to provide damping of the slot mode by inserting small pieces of absorbing material (such as powdered iron) into the slot at each end.

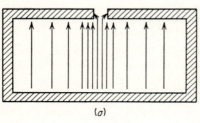

(a)

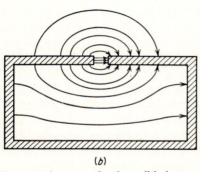

(b)

FIG. 5.2. An example of possible interfering slot waves. (a) The normal fields in rectangular waveguide; (b) the general configuration of possible slot fields.

Regardless of the care used in avoiding the slot resonances and related defects, the fields near the end of the slot are not representative of the fields in the unaltered line. The local waves excited by the transition between the slotted and unslotted line are attenuated exponentially with distance, and under normal circumstances are negligible at a distance roughly equal to the transverse dimensions of the guide. Therefore, it is not good practice to use the portion of the slot within this distance from the ends.

Thus, consideration of the distortion of the natural fields in the transmission line dictates that the width of the slot be made as small as possible. If the slot is narrow and properly located, and if the symmetry of the transmission line is carefully preserved, the effect of the slot on the characteristic properties of the line is generally negligible. Unfortunately, the narrow slot is not compatible with the requirements imposed upon it by the environmental requirements of the probe, as discussed below.

c. The Probe. This name is commonly given to the device which responds to the fields inside the transmission line and delivers the sample to the indicating device. There are several kinds of probes, but only two are used extensively. One of these is the *probe* which responds only to the electric field in the line; the other is the *loop* which, in principle, responds only to the magnetic field; both are shown in Fig. 5.3, being sections through the line along the axis of propagation without specifically indicating in the lower portion the type of transmission line.

The electric field probe is the most useful. Because of its small geometrical size, the field in the transmission line is not disturbed appreciably. The fact that it responds to the electric field alone is important, as interpretation of results is complicated by response to both fields. The loop has the disadvantage, because of its self-inductance, of responding to both fields to some extent. Some situations, however, require the use of the magnetic probe. In $TE_{0,n}$ modes, for example, there is no radial electric field and the loop must be used to explore the fields. Here, however, the self-inductance of the loop is of no consequence, as there are no electric fields at the loop.

Under ideal conditions, the probe would provide an accurate indication of the relative fields in the transmission line. There are several conflicting conditions which may make the detected output deviate appreciably from the true reproduction of the standing-wave pattern. The fact that the detecting element, such as the crystal detector, may not have a simple response law will not be considered here, since this topic was discussed in Chap. 2.

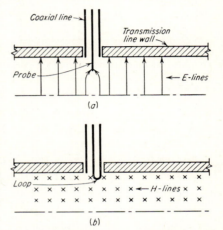

FIG. 5.3. Schematic representation of the probe and loop coupling. Coupling to the (a) electric field, (b) magnetic field.

Two kinds of difficulties arise in the use of sampling probes. The first has to do with the fact that the probe, in sampling the field, extracts a nonnegligible amount of power from the transmission line. The second is due to the difficulty in maintaining sufficient mechanical accuracy in the construction of the important parts of the small sampling mechanism.

The distortion of the standing-wave pattern, due to the power absorbed by the probe, can be explained by considering the effect of an equivalent impedance shunting the transmission line. The resistive component of this impedance represents the power absorbed by the probe; the reactive component is due to the reflections caused by the probe and is affected by probe tuning. The equivalent circuit of the transmission line, shunted by the equivalent probe impedance, is shown in Fig. 5.4. It can be seen that the effect of the probe impedance depends upon the relative values of the generator, probe, and load impedances and upon the position of the probe with respect to the load. The general situation is too complex to be understood readily. Consider, therefore, several simplified situations, all of considerable practical importance.

First, assume that the generator impedance is equal to Z_0. If the load impedance is also matched, there will be no standing waves; the probe will correctly indicate that the standing-wave ratio is unity. However, if the load impedance is zero, perfect standing waves will exist. Placing

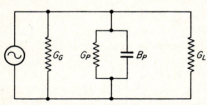

the probe at a voltage zero does not disturb the standing-wave pattern because at this point the impedance is zero. The voltage maxima, however, are disturbed because the probe both absorbs the power and places a reactance across the line. The magnitude of the maximum is changed in value, and its position is shifted from its proper location. The magnitude of this shift depends upon the

FIG. 5.4. An equivalent circuit representing the interaction between the generator, probe, and the load admittances.

adjustment of the probe tuning elements. In the case of an arbitrary load impedance, both maxima and minima are shifted from their true positions, and their values change.[1] These changes can be predicted analytically by considering the circuit of Fig. 5.4. If B_p and G_p are both

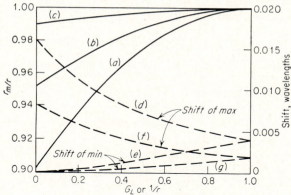

FIG. 5.5. Effect of the probe admittance on measured VSWR, r_m, and on position of the voltage minimum and maximum. Solid curves are calculated from Eq. (5.6). Curves a, b, and c are for $G_p = 0.1$, 0.05, and 0.01, respectively. Dashed curves indicate the change in position of voltage minimum and maximum; curves d and e are for $B = 0.1$. Curves f and g correspond to $B = 0.05$. (*By permission from "Technique of Microwave Measurements," edited by C. G. Montgomery. Copyright, 1947. McGraw-Hill Book Company, Inc., New York.*)

[1] Equations (5.4), (5.5), (5.6), and Fig. 5.5 have been taken from Montgomery (ed.), *ibid.*, pp. 486–487. The reader is referred to this material for further discussion. See also W. Altar, F. B. Marshall, and L. P. Hunter, Probe Error in Standing-wave Detectors, *Proc. IRE*, vol. 34, no. 1, pp. 33–44, January, 1946. This paper demonstrates that the probe can be represented as a simple shunt admittance across the transmission line. It also gives a method of obtaining exact results from badly

small, and assuming that $G_L \leqq 1$, the shifts in the position of minima and maxima, $\delta_{\min}$ and $\delta_{\max}$, respectively, are

$$\frac{\delta_{\min}}{\lambda_t} = \frac{G_L{}^2 B_p}{(1 + G_L)^2} \tag{5.4}$$

$$\frac{\delta_{\max}}{\lambda_t} = \frac{B_p}{(1 + G_L)^2} \tag{5.5}$$

The true standing-wave ratio r is altered due to both B_p and G_p. For simplicity, only the case $B_p = 0$ is described; the measured value of r is called r_m given by

$$\frac{r_m}{r} = \frac{1 + G_L + G_p G_L}{1 + G_L + G_p} \tag{5.6}$$

Equations (5.4), (5.5), and (5.6) are plotted in Fig. 5.5 for a few selected cases.

These results show that large probe penetrations can seriously affect impedance measurements. The maximum shifts more than the minimum; for this reason, the location of the minimum rather than the maximum should be used to determine the phase of the reflection coefficient. The larger the standing-wave ratio, the smaller is the displacement of the voltage minimum.

Consider the second special case in which the generator impedance is not equal to Z_0. The motion of the probe along the slot produces periodic variations in the impedance at the generator terminals which cause fluctuation in the power delivered by the generator. If the load impedance is matched, the *apparent* standing-wave ratio r_a is given by

$$r_a = \frac{1 + G_G + G_p}{1 + G_G + G_p G_G} \tag{5.7}$$

which is valid for generator conductance $G_G < 1$. The worst case arises when the generator impedance $G_G = 0$. Equation (5.7) then becomes

$$r_a = 1 + G_p \tag{5.8}$$

The probe conductance G_p is an important parameter because it determines the power abstracted by the probe. If the source and the load impedances are both matched, the value of the probe conductance is numerically equal to the fraction of the power diverted to the probe circuit. For this reason the probe conductance G_p is sometimes called the *coupling coefficient*. Since the characteristics of the probe are determined by its conductance and susceptance, the electrical behavior of two

---

distorted patterns. These procedures permit deeper penetration without loss of accuracy; this is helpful in cases where sufficient power is not available to limit the perturbing effects of the probe.

probes with the same electrical constants will be identical, despite any differences in their physical configuration.

Unless the data are to be corrected later, the precision required in the measurement of relative fields specifies the maximum value of the probe conductance. This, in turn, specifies the fraction of the power available for detection. If the minimum detectable power is known (see Sec. 2.4), this determines the lower limit on generator power required for the specified accuracy.

The probe susceptance B_p can be made zero by tuning the probe for maximum output by a reactive tuner in shunt (or in series) with the probe. The presence of the probe loading can be detected easily by moving the probe under test and reducing its penetration until its motion

TABLE 5.1. ABSORPTION CHARACTERISTICS OF A PROBE IN A 3- BY 1-IN.
RECTANGULAR WAVEGUIDE AT 3,000 MC

Probe length, % of waveguide height	Power absorbed, %	Probe conductance G_p
0	0	0
2.5	0.0025	0.000025
5	0.023	0.00023
10	0.14	0.0014
15	0.55	0.0055
20	1.8	0.018
25	4.3	0.045
30	8.3	0.090
35	12.5	0.14
40	17	0.20
45	22	0.27
50	27	0.43

no longer affects the fields in the waveguide as indicated by means of an additional standing-wave detector ahead of the probe. For any given penetration, its conductance can be measured with this auxiliary standing-wave detector. An alternate way to measure the probe conductance is based upon the observation of the apparent standing-wave ratio caused by the probe when operated between a completely mismatched generator and a matched load; with the aid of Eq. (5.8) G_p can be computed. Table 5.1 shows the typical values of probe conductance (obtained experimentally) as a function of the probe penetration in a rectangular waveguide.

The preceding discussion indicates the magnitude of possible probe errors. In the usual laboratory practice, the operator should determine if the probe penetration and its adjustment are within acceptable limits.

It is relatively simple to provide sufficiently sensitive indicators and adequate power to keep the probe penetration from introducing appreciable errors under most typical conditions. It is good practice to insert an attenuating pad between the generator and the slotted section because the various errors are minimized with a matched generator.

The second source of difficulties due to the probe mechanism arises from certain mechanical irregularities in construction of the standing-wave detector. Figure 5.6 shows the detecting system and its equivalent circuit referred to the edge of the transmission line looking into the detecting system. The main transmission-line voltage acts upon this circuit through the small capacity C_1 which represents the capacity of

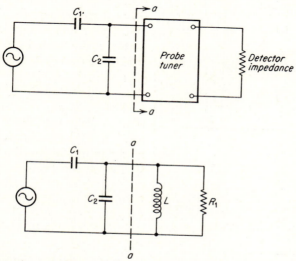

FIG. 5.6. Schematic representation of the probe circuit and its equivalent circuit. C_1 represents the coupling capacity; C_2, the probe-to-slot capacity.

the probe to the opposite side of the transmission line. Capacity C_2 represents the capacity of the probe to the slot and is very much greater than C_1. The detecting element is usually connected to the probe through an impedance transformer which can be adjusted to provide a maximum transfer of power to the detector. The effect of tuning the probe can be understood by the application of Thévenin's theorem at the points marked a-a in Fig. 5.6. To obtain maximum output (if $C_2 \gg C_1$), the tuner is adjusted so that the parallel-tuned circuit consisting of C_2, L, and R_1 is resonant at the operating frequency. For a given probe depth, this adjustment assures maximum sensitivity, and is nearly equivalent to making the probe susceptance $B_p = 0$. However, tuning the probe for maximum output also places a restriction on the construction of the device; for not only must the coupling capacity be constant, but the capacity of the probe to its surroundings must remain constant as it moves along the slot. This additional requirement on the accuracy of construction is difficult to meet in practice, because small transverse displacement makes an appreciable change in the effective capacity C_2.

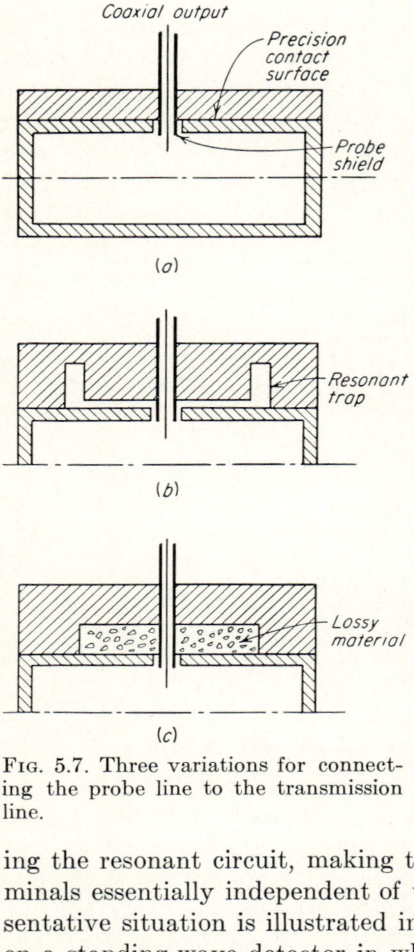

Coaxial output

Precision contact surface

Probe shield

(*a*)

Resonant trap

(*b*)

Lossy material

(*c*)

FIG. 5.7. Three variations for connecting the probe line to the transmission line.

Either of two possible methods can be used to counteract such defects; one can be applied in the design of the standing-wave detector, and the other resorted to in the case of inadequate performance of a given device. In the design of a standing-wave detector, a skirt can be made to protrude into the slot to shield the probe wire from its environs. The probe shield must be electrically connected to the transmission line; several effective methods are illustrated in Fig. 5.7. If this and other precautions in manufacture fail to eliminate the detuning of the probe circuit, erratic changes in the detected output or failure of maxima and minima to repeat will be observed. If these are due to variation of the capacity C_2, the probe tuning mechanism can be *detuned* to reduce the detected current by some large factor, such as 10. Referring to the equivalent circuit of Fig. 5.6, this is equivalent to detuning the resonant circuit, making the impedance across the detector terminals essentially independent of the probe-slot capacity C_2. A representative situation is illustrated in Fig. 5.8, which shows the data taken on a standing-wave detector in which the variations in C_2 are not negligible. It will be noted that random variations in detected output are substantially reduced when the probe output is reduced by detuning of the probe.

To summarize, it can be seen that to minimize the probe difficulties the slot should be wide to reduce the slot-probe capacity, preferably wide enough to accommodate a probe skirt. If the probe penetration is appreciable, the probe tuner should be adjusted for maximum output to minimize the distortion effects of the probe susceptance upon the standing-wave pattern; but to keep the disturbing effect of probe-to-slot capacity to a minimum, the probe may need to be detuned significantly. These conditions, as well as those imposed by consideration of the slot problem, are mutually contradictory. The situation can be greatly improved in regard to accuracy if the power output of the generator and the detector sensitivity are both high. If the sensitivity is not a problem, the probe penetration can be kept small and the probe mechanism can be detuned if necessary. It is most important that there be adequate precision in the manufacture of the entire device to preserve translational symmetry of the line and the fixed orientation of probe in the slot.

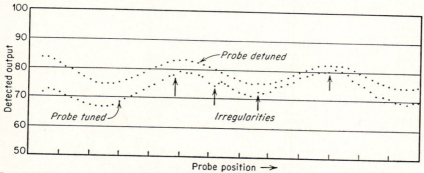

FIG. 5.8. The effect of variation in the probe-slot capacity. For the same standing-wave pattern the probe is shown tuned for maximum output and also detuned. Note irregularities in the former: the maxima and minima do not repeat, and local irregularities are found.

Standing-wave detectors are unavoidably expensive and delicate. The operator should treat them with adequate care. Regular cleaning and oiling, as recommended by the manufacturer, are important. They should be protected from mechanical damage as well as from dust when not in use. Dust and dirt cause wear, and, in addition, produce fluctuations in output which are undistinguishable from the probe errors.

Methods of examining the behavior of a standing-wave detector and separating the sources of probe error are described in Sec. 5.7.

5.3. Typical Standing-wave Detectors. Numerous standing-wave detectors are available for the various types of transmission lines. However, it is sometimes necessary for the user to make his own devices, either because of the special size of transmission line or an unusual mode of propagation. The following examples of successful designs illustrate most of the desirable features, both electrical and mechanical. Appreciation of these features by the user is desirable, both from the viewpoint of proper choice of equipment and its successful use.

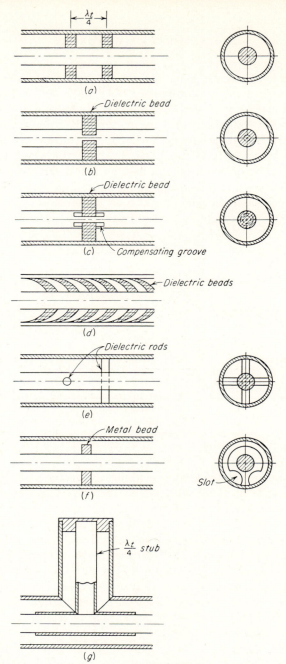

Fig. 5.9. Methods of supporting the inner conductor in coaxial lines. (*a* to *e*) Various forms of dielectric supports; (*f, g*) the use of resonant metallic supports. (*a*) Paired bead, (*b*) undercut bead, (*c*) undercut bead with series inductance added, (*d*) continuous beads for flexible lines, (*e*) dielectric rod supports. In (*f*) a slot is cut in the metallic bead to be resonant at operating frequency. (*g*) A resonant quarter-wavelength stub support.

a. Coaxial-line Standing-wave Detector. Coaxial lines are generally used for frequencies up to 3,000 Mc, and sometimes higher. Some coaxial lines are flexible and use solid dielectric insulation to support the inner conductor. Some lines are rigid with dielectric beads or resonant stubs used to support the inner conductor. Various methods of supporting the inner conductor are shown in Fig. 5.9. Three types of connectors used to join coaxial lines are illustrated in Fig. 5.10.

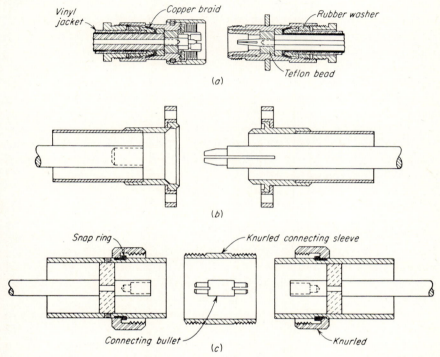

FIG. 5.10. Three types of microwave coaxial-line connectors. (a) Type N connector for flexible coaxial cable such as UG-21B/U. (*By permission from "Technique of Microwave Measurements," edited by C. G. Montgomery. Copyright, 1947. McGraw-Hill Book Company, Inc., New York.*) (b) A rigid connector for 7/8-in. 50-ohm coaxial line. (c) A sexless connector for laboratory use.

The type of connector and inner conductor support is of paramount importance in impedance measurements. Rigid-type connectors, even when precision made and individually inspected, will seldom have reflections of less than 1 per cent and, under unfavorable circumstances, can be appreciably higher. Connectors for smaller lines, especially those used with flexible lines, are not suitable for precision instruments. Type N connectors often produce reflections of about 10 per cent, causing uncertainties in the impedance in the order of 20 per cent.

The support of the inner conductor is equally important.   Undercut bead supports can be made without causing measurable reflections.   Supports of this design are essentially low-pass pi-filter elements, in which the discontinuity capacities at each end of the bead form the shunt elements, and the undercut inner conductor provides the series inductance. These filter sections are designed experimentally and can be tested by the nodal-shift method discussed in Sec. 5.8.   It is sometimes desirable to avoid supporting the inner conductor in the standing-wave detector but to use the load under test to supply the required mechanical constraints.

Accurate precision in fabrication is important for both the inner and outer conductors.   The inner conductor should be smooth, uniform in cross section, straight, and accurately centered.   The radial displacement of the inner conductor is especially important; displacements can be caused either by inaccuracies of the supporting beads at the ends or by natural bending or sagging.   Unless the connectors are accurately made, it is also possible to bend the inner conductor by transmitting axial forces in the process of attaching the load.   The change in the electric field at the probe (located in the slot in the outer conductor) can be computed from the following formula:[1]

$$\frac{dE}{E}\bigg|_{r=b} = \frac{2b}{b^2 - a^2}\, dr \qquad (5.9)$$

where dE/E is the fractional change in the electric field at the probe due to the displacement of the inner conductor by a distance dr, and b and a are outer and inner radii, respectively.   For $\frac{7}{8}$-in. 50-ohm line, the field changes by 0.625 per cent per 0.001-in. displacement.   The smaller the size of the line, the more critical the problem becomes.

Figure 5.11 shows one form of commercially available standing-wave detectors.   The translational symmetry is accurately maintained by making the probe-carriage slide directly on the outer conductor of the slotted section.   The inner conductor is supported only at the ends, by means of thin dielectric beads.   The beads and the inner conductor are designed to keep the probe penetration constant to within ± 2.5 per cent. The slot length is 50 cm, long enough to allow measurements from 300 Mc; reflections from the connectors and other residual errors are small enough to allow it to be useful up to about 5,000 Mc.   The carriage is moved by a friction-drive knob; the position of the probe is indicated directly

---

[1] From the unpublished work of J. K. Mann, Stanford University, 1947.   The formula is derived by obtaining solutions of Laplace's equation in bipolar coordinates. The change in the electric field at the inner conductor due to its displacement by a distance dr is similarly

$$\frac{dE}{E}\bigg|_{r=a} = \frac{2a}{b^2 - a^2}\, dr \qquad (5.10)$$

by a stationary scale.   A convenient feature is the separate mechanical drive for accurate measurement of small displacements.   This is done by a micrometer which can be used at will to push the carriage by small, but known, amounts.   The probe is shielded from the slot by means of

Fig. 5.11. A coaxial standing-wave detector.   (*Courtesy of General Radio Company.*)

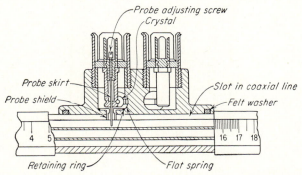

Fig. 5.12. Details of the probe and detector arrangement for standing-wave detector shown in Fig. 5.11.   (*Courtesy of General Radio Company.*)

the skirt as shown in Fig. 5.12.   The crystal detector is located near the probe, and an adjustable tuning stub is provided to resonate the reactance of the crystal circuit.

  b. The Parallel-plate Coaxial Standing-wave Detector. Some of the principal difficulties in the construction of the coaxial standing-wave detectors result from the contradictory requirements of a slot narrow enough to avoid disturbing the natural fields in the line and wide enough so that the probe-to-slot capacity can be accurately maintained without requiring impractical tolerances on the construction of the entire mechanism. The following change in the geometry of the coaxial line solves this problem.[1] The cross section of the coaxial line can be transformed into a parallel-plate (paraplate) geometry in which there occurs a wide natural slot. It can be shown that the fields and potential lines of the

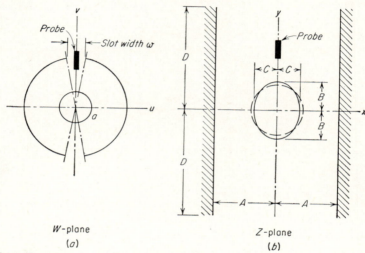

W-plane
(a)

Z-plane
(b)

FIG. 5.13. Transformation of coaxial line to the parallel-plate line. (a) A section of coaxial line in the W plane; (b) section of the parallel-plate line in the Z plane. The transformation results in an elliptical innerconductor which may be approximated by the circular one shown. (*Adopted by permission from A New Type of Slotted Line Section, by W. B. Wholey and W. N. Eldred, Proc. IRE, vol. 38, no. 3, March, 1950.*)

coaxial line can be conformally transformed into the rectangular cross section shown in Fig. 5.13 if the transformation

$$W = \tan Z \qquad (5.11)$$

is used. W and Z are complex variables $u + jv$ and $x + jy$, in which the circular and rectangular geometries are shown, respectively. The transformed fields are indicated in Fig. 5.14. These fields decrease rapidly with distance in the y direction. The infinite planes resulting from the conformal transformation can, therefore, be terminated a short distance away from the inner conductor. Terminating of the infinite

[1] See J. R. Woodyard, Ultra-high Frequency Apparatus, U.S. Patent 2,496,837 (1950); E. L. Ginzton, Ultra-high Frequency Transmission Line System, U.S. Patent 2,534,437 (1950); W. B. Wholey and W. N. Eldred, A New Type of Slotted Line Section, *Proc. IRE*, vol. 38, p. 244, March, 1950.

planes in the paraplate geometry is equivalent to providing two diametrically opposite slots in the coaxial line. The width of the equivalent slot is related to the height and separation of the plates as follows:

$$w = \frac{4}{\sinh\left(\pi D/2A\right)} \tag{5.12}$$

where w is the width of the slot in the coaxial line expressed in radians, and D and A are as shown in Fig. 5.13. Thus, as a result of the conformal transformation, a wide slot is provided automatically. As the height of the plates in the paraplate geometry is increased, the width of the "slot" remains the same, i.e., the plates are parallel. In terms of

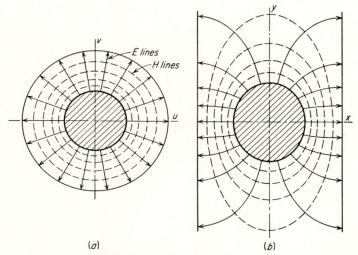

FIG. 5.14. Approximate field distributions in the coaxial and parallel-plate lines.

the coaxial equivalent, however, the electrical width of the slot can be made arbitrarily small by making the plates of the paraplate line sufficiently high. The following typical case emphasizes this. In one model, the quantity D/A was chosen to equal 5.6, resulting in a coaxial slot of 0.0012 radian. For a coaxial line 1 in. in diameter, this corresponds to a slot width of 0.0006 in.

When used as a standing-wave detector, the paraplate line must be joined to the normal coaxial line. The impedance of the paraplate and coaxial lines can be made equal by proper choice of paraplate line dimensions; but, since the field configurations are different, an abrupt junction of the two lines would result in strong reflections at the joint, due to the presence of the discontinuity capacity. Figure 5.15 shows a satisfactory method of joining the two lines. A groove in the inner conductor introduces a small inductive discontinuity in the region of the capacity discontinuity. It is possible to consider the two discontinuities as a pi filter. By proper choice of the dimensions of the groove, the characteristic impedance of the filter can be made equal to the impedance of the two lines. If properly done, the effect of the discontinuity can be eliminated. One 1-in. standing-wave detector tested was found to have about 10 per cent reflection at 3,000 Mc prior to installation of the filter section and

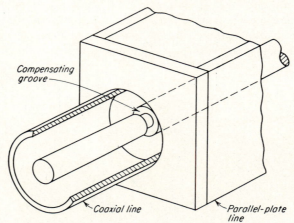

FIG. 5.15. The junction between coaxial and paraplate line.

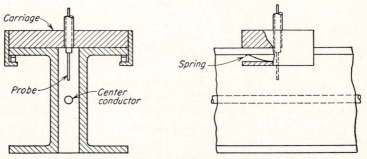

FIG. 5.16. A suitable probe mechanism for parallel-plate standing-wave detector.

no measurable reflection afterward. The cutoff frequency of the filter was estimated to be in the vicinity of 30,000 Mc, far beyond the useful frequency limit of the 1-in. line. The useful frequency range of the resultant standing-wave detector was found to be about 500 to 7,500 Mc.

The probe mechanism in the paraplate line can be of any conventional design. If the probe carriage and the ways of the bed (as shown in Fig. 5.16) are lapped flat, the good electrical contact is achieved under the pressure of light springs; the large areas of the slot region provide the return path for the probe current to the sides of the paraplate line without further refinements. Figure 5.17 shows a photograph of a paraplate standing-wave detector.

The probe itself is located in the electric field, which decreases exponentially with distance from the center conductor. If a mechanism were to be provided for changing the probe penetration, the motion of the probe would introduce known attenuation and would make it possible to measure the relative fields in terms of the probe penetration. By adjusting the probe height for constant output reading, a decibel scale, attached to the probe, could be read eliminating the response law of the detecting device from calculations. Although this added probe complexity is not often used, it can provide linear large range "volume" control.

Fig. 5.17. Coaxial standing-wave detector employing parallel-plate slotted section. (*Courtesy of Hewlett-Packard Company.*)

c. Waveguide Standing-wave Detectors. In general design, the waveguide standing-wave detector differs but slightly from the coaxial devices. Since the waveguides are often used for frequencies above those which are met with coaxial lines, the dimensions are smaller and the tolerance problem is more serious. Greater attention must be paid to the various practical problems, such as probe penetration, slot width, slot-end reflections, etc.

A successful rectangular waveguide design is illustrated in Fig. 5.18. A unique feature of this design is the provision for accepting slotted sections of various standard waveguides so that only one probe supporting mechanism needs to be purchased. Special size waveguides can be fabricated to fit the standard carriage.

Fabrication of the waveguide standing-wave detector is appreciably simpler than of the coaxial equivalent, since it does not have an inner conductor with the attendant supporting and sagging problems, although the translational symmetry must still be preserved for the remaining parts. In the particular design illustrated, the waveguide is accurately machined from annealed cast aluminum (although electroforming methods could have been used). One wide surface is precision machined parallel to the inside surface of the waveguide to insure that carriage and probe assembly, in traveling in fixed relationship with respect to this surface, maintain constant capacity and probe penetration. The probe mechanism is carried along two cylindrical rods, being held in a plane

Fig. 5.18. Waveguide standing-wave detector featuring replaceable slotted sections. A dial indicator permits accurate measurement of small displacements. (*Courtesy of Hewlett-Packard Company.*)

parallel to the axis of the waveguide. One of the rods guides the carriage by means of two bearings, providing constraint against four degrees of freedom of motion. The second rod, with one bearing, prevents rotation of the carriage about the first rod. Thus, five constraints are provided, allowing only translation along the axis of the guide. This design, although not kinematic, illustrates good practice and provides precision without using complicated and heavy parts.

The carriage is separated from the slotted section by a narrow gap.

The probe currents return to the waveguide through the capacity between the carriage and the waveguide. It is, therefore, important that no unwanted resonances occur between this capacity and any of the external parts. Two possible ways to insure good performance are shown in Fig. 5.7. The first uses the familiar resonant trap to provide a low impedance at the outer conductor of the probe; as long as the operating frequency is reasonably close to the design frequency of the resonant trap, the probe current is independent of external disturbances. In the second method, the gap between the carriage and the slotted section forms a section of radial transmission line, one side of which is made of some highly lossy material, such as powdered iron. This construction introduces significant loss in the probe line, but the resultant circuit becomes insensitive to the operating frequency and provides effective isolation from external disturbances. The design shown in Fig. 5.18 uses the latter method.

5.4. Signal Sources. The characteristics of oscillators suitable for laboratory signal sources were discussed in Chap. 1. As a source of power for impedance measurements, the specific requirements for the signal source principally depend upon *what* is being measured and *how*. For example, the primary requirement in the measurement of the impedance of a highly resonant system (such as a narrowband filter or a high-Q cavity) is good frequency stability; the power level is not important as long as the detecting system is sufficiently sensitive. On the other hand, the measurement of the r-f impedance of a crystal mixer of a superheterodyne receiver must be done at a power level which corresponds to typical receiver signals. Therefore, the power output must be very low and the required frequency stability depends upon the bandwidth of the i-f amplifier. Thus, each particular situation needs to be examined carefully before the equipment is selected.

In many applications, it is necessary to isolate the oscillator from the effect of the external circuit, including the equipment under test. This may be desirable if one wishes to examine the characteristics of a device as a function of frequency. The variation of frequency can cause interaction between the load and the oscillator which can happen, for example, in the measurement of the properties of a resonant cavity as a function of frequency. Impedances which vary rapidly with frequency can cause the oscillator to jump frequency or otherwise become unstable. The oscillator can be decoupled by inserting some type of isolation device between it and the load. A number of satisfactory isolators are described in Sec. 1.10. A klystron amplifier is an ideal buffer, but its use entails tuning additional resonant cavities and the need for additional power supplied. The simplest form of an isolation device is a resistive attenuating pad. A 10-db pad, for example, reduces reflections from the load by a minimum of 20 db before they reach the oscillator. Therefore, the incident power upon the load is nearly independent of the load conditions and the oscillator is effectively decoupled from the load variations. The ferrite isolator described in Sec. 1.10c has the advantage that isolation can be attained without introducing appreciable forward loss.

Modulation of the signal generator permits simplification of the detecting equipment and increases its sensitivity. Simple sinusoidal modulation is impractical since the frequency of most microwave oscillators depends upon the applied potentials (and, to some extent, the current). Therefore, to obtain amplitude modulation with little incidental frequency modulation, it is almost always necessary to employ square-wave modulation. This permits the oscillations to occur at constant potentials and be turned off completely during one-half cycle. The use of square-wave modulation does not require the detecting system to reproduce all the frequency components of the detected signal. It is usual practice to reduce the bandwidth of the detecting amplifier to respond only to the fundamental component of the modulation frequency.

In square-wave modulation, the following considerations are of importance:

1. The voltage during the "on" part of the cycle must be sufficiently constant to limit frequency modulation during the pulse to the desired value.

2. For the same reason, the transition period from "off" to "on," i.e., the switching transit, must be as short as possible.

These requirements determine the quality of the square-wave generator and help to specify the coupling system between the square-wave generator and the oscillator. Figure 1.52 shows a representative reflex klystron source with a typical modulator circuit power supply, and indicates the manner in which the circuits can be coupled together. The choice of circuit parameters for the coupling system depends upon the modulation sensitivity of the klystron and upon the frequency stability requirements of the particular experiment.

The signal source may also be modulated by means of auxiliary devices as described in Sec. 1.11. The oscillator can be followed by a klystron amplifier, permitting amplitude modulation with negligible reaction upon the oscillator. The master-oscillator power-amplifier systems are convenient if, for instance, measurements are to be made at a fixed frequency. Absorption modulation provides an alternate way to produce amplitude modulation. Crystal rectifiers, for example, can be used as variable resistors across the output transmission line by applying modulation voltages in series with the crystals. This method is not particularly satisfactory because the power-handling capacity of crystal rectifiers is limited. Successful modulation of the absorption type can also be attained by making use of the Faraday rotation as described in Sec. 1.11.

The absorption methods have the advantage that they permit the signal generator to be operated at constant potentials, thus minimizing the possibility of undesirable frequency modulation and reducing the complexity of power supplies to the ultimate. Modulating circuits are less complex because simple sinusoidal voltages can be used instead of the strictly square-wave signals required with oscillator modulation. The use of crystal modulators limits the power output to the value corresponding to the safe power-handling capacity of crystal rectifiers; however, the modulation frequencies can be very high. In contrast, ferrite modulators are capable of providing a much higher output, but are inconvenient except at the low audio-frequencies.

In many applications special precautions must be used to maintain the needed frequency stability. Excellent performance can be attained with free-running oscillators of the klystron type if they are operated from batteries to provide constant potentials and are isolated from vibration and temperature fluctuations. Immersing the oscillator tube in an oil bath provides liquid cooling and simultaneously eliminates the vibration encountered with forced air cooling. With these precautions, short-time stability of one part in 10^8 or 10^9 can be attained. Stability of one part in 10^4 or 10^5 can be achieved for minutes or even hours at a time.

Better long-time stability can be obtained by stabilizing the oscillator by means of external cavities. A number of stabilization systems have been described in the literature. These systems are necessarily complicated and are not often needed in ordinary applications. For further details, see Sec. 1.13.

5.5. Detectors and Indicators. The general properties of the detecting elements suitable for rectification of the probe currents were discussed in Chap. 2. The specific requirements of the detecting and indicating systems in impedance measurements are discussed in this section.

The sensitivity of the detecting system should be kept as high as possible in order to minimize the various possible errors caused by the probe and slot problems. Therefore, crystal rectifiers are often used instead of the more reliable bolometers. Since crystal characteristics are often found to change, especially if they are exposed to large changes in temperature or to excessive signals, it is necessary to determine the response law of the crystal rectifier in the expected signal range just prior to use. Preferably, this should be done with the amplifier and indicator circuit to be used in the actual measurements. Several additional precautions which were mentioned in Sec. 2.3 should be observed if the expected signals are likely to result in operation *beyond* the region of square-law response. Specifically, the adjustment of the r-f tuning mechanism can result in a change of the r-f source impedance as seen by the rectifier, and consequently, in a change in the response law. In this case, adjustments of the crystal tuning systems should not be made after the crystal is calibrated. Methods of calibrating detectors are described in Sec. 2.10.

The response law of the bolometer-type hot-wire detectors can be assumed to be square-law if the r-f power level is low compared to d-c biasing power. If calibration of the bolometer and indicator detecting system against the standing-wave pattern of a shorted transmission line shows a variation from exact square-law response, some apparatus difficulty must exist somewhere in the equipment.

In the measurement of high standing-wave ratios, the range of signals encountered is very large. For this reason, the indicating instrument should be preceded by a suitable attenuator, providing 60 or 80 db of attenuation. An attenuator with 10-db steps permits readings to be taken above half-scale, where the accuracy is less affected by the possible drift of the instrument and scale errors. It is sometimes convenient to provide a series of variable attenuator pads equipped with finer divisions, such as 10-, 1-, and 0.1-db steps. Availability of such attenuators permits the output to be kept constant, eliminating the errors due to the nonlinearity in the indicating amplifier.

The detecting system may produce erroneous indication if it is operated in the vicinity of strong fields such as those often encountered in the vicinity of high-power pulsed equipment. Signals can be picked up in the interconnecting cables at microwave frequencies and find their way to the rectifier crystal; upon rectification, they can return to the indicator in the form of audio and d-c pickup. It is sometimes necessary to install filters between the crystal rectifier and the amplifier system in order to prevent these effects.

5.6. Techniques in Standing-wave Detector Measurements. This section is concerned with the description of typical standing-wave detector apparatus and its adjustment prior to actual use. It also discusses recommended methods for obtaining data in the most accurate manner.

a. Typical Apparatus. The main components of the apparatus needed for making impedance measurements consist of the signal source, cables or waveguides for connecting the source to the standing-wave detector, the impedance-measuring device, and its detecting and indicating means. These individual pieces of apparatus have been mentioned; their assembly is obvious. In addition, several small auxiliary pieces should be available. These include an artificial termination, a short circuit of known length, and a movable short circuit with a scale. The artificial termination, providing a nearly perfect match to the main transmission line, is useful for checking the accuracy of the equipment. The fixed and movable short circuits are needed to establish certain reference planes and to aid in calibrating the effect of the transmission-line junctions.

The Z_0 termination can be a short piece of transmission line (identical in cross section to the geometry and dimensions of the standing-wave detector section) partially filled with some absorbing material. Proper proportioning of the absorber results in perfect absorption of incident power, making the section artificially equivalent to an infinite length of the transmission line. Waveguide terminations are usually made from a section of a waveguide with a tapered resistive card placed in the region of strong electric field. The usual coaxial-line termination is made from powdered iron molded or machined to an empirically determined shape.

   b. Oscillator Adjustment. To adjust and check the equipment prior to its use in impedance measurements, the following procedure, or its equivalent, should always be used.

   The oscillator should be adjusted for the desired power output and allowed to stabilize. First it should be adjusted for continuous output and tuned for maximum power. If it is to be modulated by square waves, the d-c voltage should be varied to determine the oscillation limits of the desired mode and its immediate neighbors. The square-wave modulating voltages should be applied cautiously to ensure that the combination of modulation and d-c voltages provides optimum performance at the peak of the square-wave voltage cycle; the opposite half cycle should be outside of oscillation limit of the mode in question. Careless adjustment can easily lead to operation at two different points in the same voltage mode or in two different modes, resulting in a simultaneous output at two or more frequencies. If sufficiently important, the output can be inspected by a high-Q wavemeter to insure single frequency operation.

   c. Standing-wave Detector Adjustments. First, the standing-wave detector should be terminated with a Z_0 termination. The response pattern in the slotted section should be obtained over the entire length of travel. If the termination is not perfect, a variation in the detected voltage will be observed, but in the perfect standing-wave detector, the maxima and minima should repeat closely in magnitude. If the standing-wave detector is not perfect, small variations in reading will be observed and should be noted. The final calculated impedance will be in error by an amount which can be estimated from the fractional deviation of one maximum from another. In observing the standing-wave pattern with a nearly perfect termination, one should find a perfectly smooth response as the carriage is moved; there should be no major irregularities of any kind. Near the ends of the slot the response may become significantly different from the ideal. These regions should be noted and avoided in actual measurements.

   Second, the Z_0 termination should be replaced by a short circuit, and the standing-wave pattern examined again. The voltage minima should be nearly zero in magnitude; i.e., the output at the voltage minimum points should be below the noise level of the detecting system. The presence of any substantial signal at the voltage minimum indicates the presence of unwanted frequencies and suggests a closer examination of the behavior of the oscillator.[1] It is possible that the presence of attenuation in the transmission line will cause the reflected wave to be measurably smaller than the incident wave, causing finite minima. This unusual situation should be fully understood by the operator (see Sec. 5.7d).

Third, the probe adjustments should be examined carefully. The probe depth should not exceed the minimum required for adequate sensitivity; the magnitude of the errors resulting from finite probe conductance was discussed in Sec. 5.2. Maximum permissible probe penetration should be determined on the basis of expected accuracy. Tuning of the probe tuner for maximum output eliminates the errors due to the probe susceptance. If the probe penetration is not excessive, the standing-wave pattern of the shorted line will be regular with the maxima and minima repeating at quarter-wavelength intervals.

Fourth, with the probe penetration adjusted, the standing-wave pattern should be examined again with a terminated line, with particular attention paid to any small irregularities in the response pattern. If these are found, it may be necessary to detune the probe, for the reasons given in Sec. 5.2c.

Finally, in order to establish response law of the detecting system, it should be calibrated by shorting the transmission line and observing the standing-wave pattern as discussed in Sec. 2.10. For measurements of moderately low standing-wave ratios, the detecting system can be calibrated by the abbreviated method. If the expected standing-wave ratios are higher than 3 or 4, the entire response curve of the detecting system should be checked.

When the output transmission line is shorted at a known location, a series of voltage zeros will exist in the slotted section. The location of these should be recorded; any one can be used as a "reference point" in impedance measurements. The measurement of the unknown impedance in the slotted section, when referred to the "reference" point, is equivalent to referring the measurement to the known location of the short circuit. The spacing of the voltage zeros is also important, as these determine the transmission-line wavelength. This value should be used in calculations, as it automatically avoids ambiguities due to the presence of the slot. However, this wavelength may not be the same as the wavelength in the undisturbed transmission line. Thus, if the impedance

[1] Harmonics of the oscillator frequency can be generated if monitor crystal rectifiers are tightly coupled to the main transmission line. Power monitors, if used, should be either lightly coupled, or connected to the line through a filter such as a resonant cavity (a wavemeter).

measurements are to be transformed from one point to another along the unslotted transmission line, some other method must be used to determine the transmission-line wavelength; the movable shorting plunger is useful for this purpose. If connected to the slotted section, the distance the plunger is moved to produce two successive minima establishes the undisturbed guided wavelength.

In adjusting the standing-wave detector one should always bear in mind the particular experiment that is to be performed. If the standing-wave ratios are low, particular care in most of the adjustments is not essential. The depth of the probe penetration is not very important because high sensitivity is not required; neither is the distortion of the standing-wave pattern serious because the impedances shunted by the probe are roughly constant. On the other hand, if high standing-wave ratios are to be measured, the large variation in voltages requires high sensitivity (as the voltages at the nodes become very small) and an accurate knowledge of the response law. In order to produce greater sensitivity, the probe penetration may need to be increased, which introduces the possibility of substantial error in the measurement of the voltage maxima. Furthermore, if the load is an adjustable highly resonant impedance, its effect upon the oscillator may be very important. For example, if the standing-wave detector is inspected and adjusted with a Z_0 termination but is replaced by a high-Q circuit, the oscillator may change its behavior completely. To avoid this an isolation pad must be inserted between the oscillator and the standing-wave detector and the adjustments are carried out with the isolator padding in place. Simple attenuating padding reduces the over-all sensitivity and requires the penetration of the probe to be increased; however, this exaggerates the probe errors. An obvious solution is to use an oscillator with a high power output. If sufficiently high power is unavailable, one must exercise greater care in using the equipment because various unforeseen difficulties may arise. No matter how much experience one has had with the use of these instruments, a new measurement always demands care and patience.

The accurate measurement of impedances nearly equal to Z_0 is complicated by the presence of residual reflections which are due to the abrupt termination of the slot, imperfections in the transmission-line connectors, and mechanical irregularities in the construction of the standing-wave detector. Fortunately, the presence of mechanical irregularities can be made unimportant by devising techniques in which the measurement of relative voltage is not necessary. For example, the impedance discontinuity due to a connector can be measured by the nodal-shift techniques; these are described in Sec. 5.8. The effect of residual reflections can be taken into account by calibration as described in Sec. 5.7c.

d. Measurement of Low Standing-wave Ratios. If the standing-wave ratios are below 2 or 3, the VSWR can be obtained from direct readings of the output meter by taking the ratio of observed voltage maximum and minimum. The volume control or the attenuator should be adjusted so that the maximum is read at near full scale. This increases the accuracy and minimizes the errors due to the mis-set voltage zero. If the detecting element is a galvanometer, its zero may drift; this should be checked periodically. If the VSWR is greater than 2 or 3, the voltage minimum becomes too small for accurate reading; direct ratios of scale readings should not be used.

e. Measurement of Medium Standing-wave Ratios. The indicating device should be preceded by a calibrated attenuator permitting the sensitivity to be changed in steps of 10 db. All readings, maxima and minima, can be read above the half-scale of the indicating meter by adjusting the attenuator. The standing-wave ratio can be computed from the values of maxima and minima, taking into account the change in sensitivity due to the different attenuator settings.

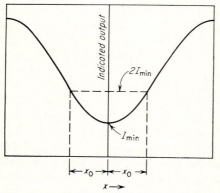

f. Measurement of High Standing-wave Ratios. If the VSWR is high, above approximately 10, the accuracy of the calibration of the indicator and the associated attenuators becomes excessively important. An alternative method, known as the *double minimum,* can be used to

Fig. 5.19. The double-minimum method of measuring high VSWR.

measure the high VSWR by merely observing the shape of the standing-wave pattern near the voltage minimum. An additional advantage of the method is the reduction of errors due to probe loading because it is always located in the region of low impedance.

To apply this method, accurate measurements of small displacements of the probe carriage are made as it is moved in the vicinity of the voltage minimum. This can be done best by attaching a small micrometer dial indicator to the probe carriage, as shown in Fig. 5.18.

The procedure consists of first finding the value of the voltage minimum. Next, the two positions are found at which the output is twice the minimum value, as indicated in Fig. 5.19. If the detector response is square-law, the standing-wave ratio is given by

$$r = \frac{V_{\max}}{V_{\min}} = \frac{\lambda_t}{2\pi x_0} \qquad (5.13)$$

where x_0 is the displacement shown in Fig. 5.19, and λ_t is the transmission-line wavelength. It is advisable to adjust the input attenuator so that the minimum occurs at midpoint and twice minimum at full scale on the indicator.

Deviation of the detector response from square law requires Eq. (5.13) to be altered. If the response-law exponent n is written as

$$n = 2(1 + \delta) \tag{5.14}$$

with $\delta \ll 1$, the VSWR will be given by[1]

$$r = \frac{\lambda_t}{2\pi x_0} (1 - 0.693\delta) \tag{5.15}$$

[1] Equations (5.13) and (5.15) are obtained as follows: Referring to Fig. 5.20, let $\overline{OB}$, $\overline{OC}$, and $\overline{BC}$ represent the incident, reflected, and total voltage, respectively. Angle θ represents the angle between the incident and reflected waves:

$$\theta = 2\beta x = \frac{4\pi x}{\lambda_t}$$

where x represents the position of the probe with respect to the voltage minimum. For simplicity, let $V_i = 1$. The total voltage $V_t = V_i - V_r = 1 - V_r$. From Fig. 5.20, assuming that $(V_i - V_r) \ll 1$, and θ small,

$$V_t = \overline{BC} = (\overline{AB^2} + \overline{AC^2})^{1/2} = (V_{\min}^2 + \theta^2)^{1/2}$$

where $V_{\min}$ is the minimum voltage obtained when $\theta = 0$. Let I be the indicated current, and as in Eq. (2.18), $I = kV^n$, with $n \approx 2$. Writing $n = 2(1 + \delta)$, the observed current is

$$I = k(V_{\min}^2 + \theta^2)^{1+\delta} \tag{5.16}$$

This has the general appearance shown in Fig. 5.19 as x (i.e., the position of the probe) is varied. Let θ_0 be the position at which I is twice its minimum value. That is,

$$I_{\min} = kV_{\min}^{2(1+\delta)}$$
$$2I_{\min} = k(V_{\min}^2 + \theta_0^2)^{1+\delta}$$
$$2kV_{\min}^{2(1+\delta)} = k(V_{\min}^2 + \theta_0^2)^{1+\delta}$$

Hence, $V_{\min} = \theta_0(2^{1/(1+\delta)} - 1)^{-1/2}$ (5.17)

The standing-wave ratio r is

$$r = \frac{V_{\max}}{V_{\min}} \approx \frac{2}{V_{\min}} \tag{5.18}$$

$$= \frac{2}{\theta_0} (2^{1/(1+\delta)} - 1)^{1/2}$$

or $\quad r = \dfrac{2}{\theta_0} F$ (5.19)

where $\quad F = (2^{1/(1+\delta)} - 1)^{1/2}$ (5.20)

But, since $\theta_0 = 2\beta x_0 = 2\dfrac{2\pi}{\lambda_t} x_0$,

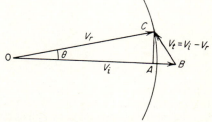

Fig. 5.20. Vector relations used in deriving the double-minimum formulas.

$$r = \frac{\lambda_t}{2\pi x_0} F \tag{5.21}$$

If $n = 2$ ($\delta = 0$), Eq. (5.21) reduces to the familiar expression given in Eq.

Thus, the knowledge of the detector response law is still important but only over a narrow range of signals.

The above formulas are applicable if the VSWR is very high. Table 5.3 shows the error in VSWR vs. r when using Eq. (5.13). The values in the table were computed with the aid of Eq. (5.22).

g. Alternate Methods of Measuring VSWR. There are several additional methods for measuring VSWR. Two are relatively simple, powerful, and accurate.

It is possible to operate the probe crystal detector as a frequency converter by introducing into the crystal a large voltage from a microwave local oscillator (LO) whose frequency is different from the signal frequency by some convenient low frequency. An i-f amplifier is used to measure the output from the crystal. If the signal voltage is much weaker than the LO voltage, the detected output is strictly proportional to the r-f signal voltage. Thus, the crystal operates as a linear detector as discussed in Sec. 2.4. By means of this arrangement, VSWR of 1,000 and higher can be accurately measured.

Another method requires the use of an accurate microwave attenuator between the signal source and the standing-wave detector. The attenu-

---

(5.13). If $\delta \ll 1$, this leads to Eq. (5.15). The correction factor F is given for a range of values of n in Table 5.2.

TABLE 5.2. CORRECTION FACTOR F

Detector response law, n	Correction factor F
1.5	1.23
1.6	1.17
1.7	1.12
1.8	1.08
1.9	1.04
2.0	1.00
2.1	0.965
2.2	0.935
2.4	0.882
2.5	0.855

The above analysis was carried out with the restriction $1 - V_r \ll 1$. Removing this restriction, but assuming square-law response, the following relation between the position of double minimum and standing-wave ratio r is obtained:

$$\theta_0 = \cos^{-1}\left(2 - \frac{r^2 + 1}{r^2 - 1}\right) \tag{5.22a}$$

$$r = \sqrt{\frac{2}{1 - \cos\theta_0} + 1} \tag{5.22b}$$

Comparing Eq. (5.22a) with Eq. (5.19), (with $F = 1$), leads to Table 5.3.

ator is adjusted to keep the crystal current equal at V_{max} and V_{min}. In this case, the response law of the crystal is not important; the values of V_{max} and V_{min} are obtained from the attenuator calibration.

h. Location of the Voltage Minimum. The phase of the standing-wave pattern can be determined by locating the position of the voltage minimum or maximum. The location of the voltage minimum is usually the more accurate because it is less disturbed by probe loading.

TABLE 5.3. ERROR IN VSWR VS. r WHEN USING EQ. (5.13)

True VSWR r	Error in r, %
2	23
3	10
5	4.5
7.5	1.9
10	0.5

The position of the minimum is hard to determine precisely because it is broad (especially in the case of low standing-wave ratios). The position of the minimum can be located more accurately by averaging two positions of equal indicator readings on either side of the minimum. It is common practice to find the position of the minimum and then to select two points approximately twice the minimum in magnitude. To realize the greatest precision, points of equal response should be selected from

$$\frac{I}{I_{min}} = \left(\frac{2r^2}{r^2 + 1}\right)^{\frac{1}{2}} \tag{5.23}$$

In this expression, r is the standing-wave ratio, I_{min} is the response (of a square-law detector) at the voltage minimum, and I is the value of the equal-response point at which the error in the determination of the nodal position is minimum. Equation (5.23) is plotted in Fig. 5.21.

In precision measurements, it is good practice to take several sets of readings at various heights of the response curve and to plot their average position as a function of the signal level. This procedure eliminates the possibility of errors due to power changes which may take place during a single set of readings. In this manner, it is also possible to detect asymmetry in the response curve which can be caused by probe loading. The scatter of points in this plot indicates the accuracy of the measurements and the shoulder of the curve determines the region beyond which asymmetry causes the average to be incorrect.

5.7. Errors in Standing-wave Detector Impedance Measurements. The various possible sources of error in the measurement of impedance by means of the standing-wave detector have been discussed in the previous sections. The following material describes experimental procedures which make it possible to eliminate or reduce some of the errors and which permit one to estimate the magnitude of residual and unavoidable errors.

It is presumed that the various equipment adjustments have been carried out as described in Sec. 5.6; in particular, that the various sources of difficulties due to the improper adjustment of the oscillator are eliminated; that the detector response law is known; and that the distortion due to the presence of the probe is minimized. This group of adjustments is under the control of the operator. There are two additional classes of errors which may limit the accuracy of the results.

The first depends upon the residual mechanical imperfections in the construction of the standing-wave detector, causing the indicated voltage readings to be different from their true values, either in a systematic or

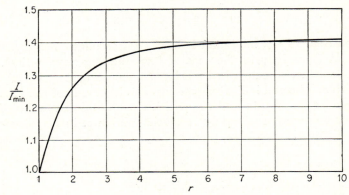

FIG. 5.21. Value of equal-response points for minimum error in location of voltage minimum as a function of the voltage standing-wave ratio. (*Adopted by permission from Evaluation of Coaxial Slotted Line Impedance Measurement, by H. E. Sorrows, W. E. Ryan, and R. C. Ellenwood, Proc. IRE, vol. 39, no. 2, February, 1951.*)

random manner. These residual errors in the measurement of the relative voltage determine the accuracy to which both the magnitude and the phase of the standing-wave pattern can be measured.

The second class of errors results from the constructional difficulties of a different kind. These include the reflections at the end of the slot in the standing-wave detector, the presence of supporting beads at the end of the transmission line, other unavoidable obstructions, and the connectors. When the standing-wave detector is used to measure the impedance, the *observed* phenomenon in the slotted region is due to the combined reflections from the load and intermediate irregularities. Fortunately, it is relatively easy to calibrate the apparatus to take into account the effect of the irregularities of this class and to correct the experimental data. They become a source of error only if the operator does not recognize their importance.

a. *Structural Defects.*[1]   The presence of residual imperfections in the slotted sections can be recognized by carefully examining the voltage distribution in a nearly terminated transmission line.   If a termination is connected to the end of a standing-wave detector and extensive data recorded and plotted, the voltage distribution along the slotted section will indicate the extent of both the irregular variations due to local imperfections and systematic variations due to the lack of translational symmetry in the slotted section.   Typical data for a coaxial standing-wave detector is shown in Fig. 5.22.   If a best fit to the laboratory data is obtained by drawing a smooth sinusoid, the deviations of experimentally determined points from the sinusoid will indicate the magnitude of the

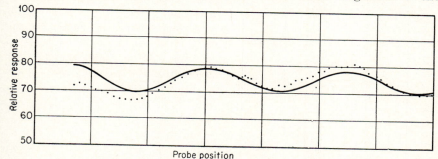

Fig. 5.22. A standing-wave pattern obtained with an imperfect standing-wave detector.   Points represent the measured response, and the solid line indicates the estimated voltage distribution.

probable error.   Merely to estimate this difference is sufficient for most applications although more elaborate methods can be used.

The estimated maximum fractional error in relative voltage readings can be converted easily into the maximum probable error in a measurement of standing-wave ratio and nodal position.   The region over which the true standing-wave pattern can be shifted because of errors in relative voltage readings is shown in Fig. 5.23.   This indicates that both standing-wave ratio and the nodal position are affected by the residual voltage errors.   Let ϵ be the possible fractional error in the measurement of the voltage in the slotted section due to unavoidable structural defects. The standing-wave ratio r:

$$r = \frac{\text{voltage maximum}}{\text{voltage minimum}}$$

is in error because both the maximum and the minimum are improperly

[1] See H. E. Sorrows, W. E. Ryan, and R. C. Ellenwood, Evaluation of Coaxial Slotted Line Impedance Measurements, *Proc. IRE*, vol. 39, no. 2, p. 163, February, 1951.   The material pertaining to errors due to mechanical imperfections is based upon this paper.

measured. The true values of voltage V_{max} and V_{min} appear modified by $1 \pm \epsilon$. Hence, the limiting values of r', the apparent VSWR, is

$$\frac{V_{max}(1 - \epsilon)}{V_{min}(1 + \epsilon)} \leqq r' \geqq \frac{V_{max}(1 + \epsilon)}{V_{min}(1 - \epsilon)} \tag{5.24}$$

or, for $\epsilon \ll 1$,

$$r(1 - 2\epsilon) \leqq r' \geqq r(1 + 2\epsilon) \tag{5.25}$$

That is, the observed value of the standing-wave ratio differs from the correct value by an amount less than twice the fractional error in the measurement of the voltage in the slot.

A corresponding error in the nodal position results if the position of the voltage node is found by averaging the two equal-response positions. For small values of ϵ and for small errors in the nodal position $\delta\psi$, the latter is given by

$$\delta\psi \simeq \frac{2r\epsilon}{r^2 - 1} \tag{5.26}$$

The error in the nodal position is minimized if equal response voltages are selected according to the relation

$$V = V_{min}\left[\frac{2r^2(1 + \epsilon^2)}{r^2 + 1}\right]^{1/2} \tag{5.27}$$

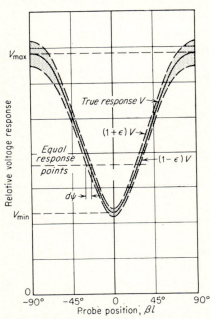

FIG. 5.23. Effect of fractional error ϵ on the standing-wave pattern. The shaded region shows possible values of detected response. (*Adopted by permission from Evaluation of Coaxial Slotted Line Impedance Measurement, by H. E. Sorrows, W. E. Ryan, and R. C. Ellenwood, Proc. IRE, vol. 39, no. 2, February, 1951.*)

Equation (5.27) is shown plotted in Fig. 5.21 for small values of ϵ. The possible error in the nodal position for this special case is plotted in Fig. 5.24 for several values of ϵ.

These errors can be reduced only by improving the mechanical features of the standing-wave detector.

b. Slot and Discontinuity Effects: Residual VSWR. As previously stated, the slotted part of the standing-wave detector can be separated from the load terminals by a length of line containing a number of discontinuities. If the standing-wave detector were terminated in a perfect Z_0 termination, these discontinuities would cause a reflected wave, and the measurement of the resultant standing waves would incorrectly indicate the reflection at the load.   The magnitude of this reflection, expressed as a standing-wave ratio, is called the *residual VSWR*.   The random errors and the effect of the discontinuities are not related.

In many measurements the presence of residual VSWR is not significant since its magnitude is not likely to be large.   However, in precision measurements of impedance the magnitude of this uncertainty needs to be known and corrected for, if necessary.

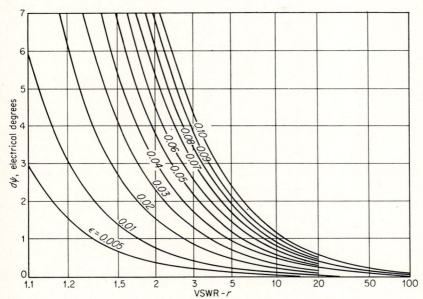

FIG. 5.24. Maximum error in location of nodal position as determined from the equal-response points as a function of fractional error ϵ and standing-wave ratio r.   (*Adopted by permission from Evaluation of Coaxial Slotted Line Impedance Measurement, by H. E. Sorrows, W. E. Ryan, and R. C. Ellenwood, Proc. IRE, vol. 39, no. 2, February, 1951.*)

As will be shown in Sec. 5.8, it is possible to represent a discontinuity (or a group of discontinuities) by an ideal transformer.   If this transformation ratio is determined, the data obtained in the slotted section can be transformed to the load terminals by multiplying the measured impedance by the transformation ratio.   In principle, the transformation ratio is determined by measuring the residual VSWR with a perfect termination.   However, since perfect terminations are difficult to obtain, other methods must be devised to determine the magnitude and phase of the residual VSWR.   These will be described in the following section.

c. Correction of SWD Data for Residual VSWR.   It is possible to find two sets of reference planes, one near the load terminals and one in the slotted section, such that the impedance at one is an arithmetic multiple

of the other.   The transformation ratio and the location of the two reference planes can be found by conducting certain calibration experiments.
The calibration procedure assumes that the region between the slotted
section and the load terminals is lossless.   The standing-wave detector
is terminated in a movable short circuit shown in Fig. 5.25.   The *calibration curve* is obtained by carrying out the nodal-shift experiment.
Specifically, the location of a voltage zero in the standing-wave detector
is noted which corresponds to a particular location of the short.   These

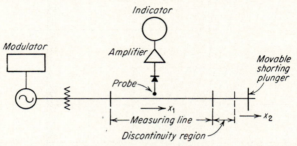

FIG. 5.25. Arrangement of the equipment needed for the nodal-shift experiment.

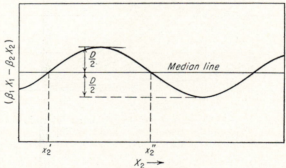

FIG. 5.26. Typical nodal-shift curve obtained with the apparatus shown in Fig. 5.25.
The ordinate represents the electrical distance between a voltage node in the standing-
wave detector and the position of the short circuit.   The abscissa is the location of
the short circuit.

data are taken for a number of positions of the movable short, resulting
in the nodal-shift curve shown in Fig. 5.26.   The intersection of the
resultant sinusoid with the median line determines the two reference
planes; the magnitude of the sinusoid is related to the transformation
constant.   Further details of this method are given in Sec. 5.8.

It is sometimes desirable to correct the VSWR and phase data as
obtained in the slotted section by making use of the calibration curve
described above.   This can be done as is described in the literature.[1]

[1] A. A. Oliner, The Calibration of the Slotted Section for Precision Microwave
Measurements, *Rev. Sci. Instr.*, vol. 25, no. 1, pp. 13–20, January, 1954.

d. Effect of Attenuation. Normal attenuation in the standing-wave detector produces only negligible errors. However, if the load is removed by a considerable distance from the standing-wave detector, the resultant loss in the transmission line may need to be taken into account. The standing-wave ratio of the load is higher than the apparent value as determined by the standing-wave detector. The standing-wave ratio at the load can be computed from

$$r = \coth\left[\tanh^{-1}\left(\frac{1}{r_m}\right) - \alpha l\right] \tag{5.28}$$

where r_m is the measured standing-wave ratio, l is a transmission-line length, α is the loss in nepers per unit length. Equation (5.28) is shown plotted in Fig. 5.27.[1,2,3]

The attenuation constant α can be found for the usual types of transmission lines in the standard references, or it can be measured by methods discussed in Chap. 11.[4]

It is also possible to consider the length of transmission line and all other apparatus separating the standing-wave detector and the load as a four-terminal network, the properties of which can be determined as discussed in Sec. 6.5. For example, the load can be replaced by a moving short circuit and the input impedance measured for a number of positions of the short. The data can be analyzed as discussed in Sec. 6.5 resulting, for instance, in the scattering coefficients of the network; the knowledge of these permits the impedance measurement in the standing-wave detector to be transformed into the impedance at the load. This transformation can be accomplished with the aid of the bilinear transformation given by Eq. (6.23) or by one of several graphical techniques.[5]

5.8. Precision Measurement of Small Reflections. In many practical problems, transmission lines of different characteristics need to be joined by a suitable transition section. An example of a simple transition is a supporting bead in a uniform coaxial line; a more complicated example is the probe transition from a coaxial line to a waveguide. In some cases,

[1] See F. E. Terman and J. M. Pettit, "Electronic Measurements," pp. 148–149, McGraw-Hill Book Company, Inc., New York, 1952.

[2] G. Glinski, The Solution of Transmission-line Problem in the Case of Attenuating Transmission Line, *Trans. AIEE,* vol. 65, pp. 46–49, February, 1946.

[3] E. N. Phillips, W. G. Sterns, and N. J. Gramara, "High Frequency Measuring Techniques Using Transmission Lines," p. 22, John Francis Rider, Publisher, Inc., New York, 1947.

[4] For example, Index of R-F Transmission Lines and Fittings, Armed Services Electro Standards Agency, Fort Monmouth, N.J.

[5] J. E. Storer, L. S. Sheingold, and S. Stein, A Simple Graphical Analysis of Two-port Waveguide Junction, *IRE,* p. 1006, August, 1953; G. A. Deschamps, A Simple Graphical Analysis of a Two-port Waveguide Junction, *IRE,* vol. 42, p. 859, May, 1954.

the transition from one type of line to another is simple and can be understood from the known geometry and elementary considerations. Frequently, however, practical structures are too complex to be analyzed simply and are subject only to experimental evaluation.

This section describes methods by which arbitrary discontinuities, especially small ones, can be evaluated easily and accurately.

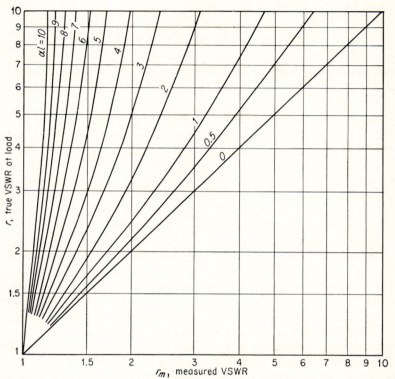

Fig. 5.27. A graph of Eq. (5.28) showing the effect of attenuation on measured standing-wave ratio. r is the true standing-wave ratio of a load impedance; r_m is the measured VSWR due to intervening loss of αl db.

The most general situation is pictured in Fig. 5.28. Two different transmission lines are joined together through an arbitrary four-terminal box, called the *coupling network*. It is assumed that this network is lossless, but otherwise no restrictions are placed upon its characteristics.

The results of an experimental study of the coupling network can be presented in several forms. A complete evaluation of the structure may lead, for example, to an equivalent circuit in the form of a T network, with three independent constants. A related process states the results in the form of a scattering matrix, consisting of a certain set of reflection coefficients.   Another convenient representation of the coupling network is based upon the application of the *transformer theorem*,[1] resulting in the determination of a set of reference planes and a certain VSWR.   This last description is the most common; in essence, it predicts the impedance that would be seen in line I if line II were terminated in its own characteristic impedance.

In principle, reflections due to the presence of the coupling network can be measured by terminating one of the lines in its own characteristic impedance, and measuring the deviation from Z_0 in the other line with a conventional standing-wave detector.   This procedure is satisfactory for evaluating the effects of the discontinuities when the latter correspond to impedance changes of a few per cent or more.   However, when these

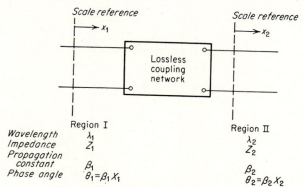

FIG. 5.28. A general lossless network.

changes become smaller than the residual errors in the standing-wave detector, direct impedance measurements are not helpful.

The standing-wave phenomena can be used to measure small reflections in another way.   If the output of the lossless network is shorted with a movable plunger, a perfect standing-wave pattern will exist in the input line.   The phase of the input standing-wave pattern depends upon the position of the shorting plunger and the nature of the discontinuity. By measuring the location of the voltage zeros in the input line for various positions of the shorting plunger, it is possible to determine accurately the nature of the discontinuity.

The voltage zero in the input line can be located in a number of ways. Perhaps the simplest method is to find the zeros by means of the moving probe of the conventional standing-wave detector.   Alternatively, a sec-

[1] The transformer theorem states that *for any lossless four-terminal network with input and output waveguides, an input and output reference plane can be found at which the input impedance differs from the output impedance only by a real multiplying constant.*   Proof of this important theorem is given in the text.

ond shorting plunger can be placed at the location of the input voltage zero which is equivalent to the formation of a resonant cavity between the two plungers. The *length* of this cavity depends upon the positions of the two plungers. The resonance in the cavity can be detected by adjusting the position of one of the plungers. These two methods are electrically equivalent, but require different equipment.

Since neither of these measurements depends upon the measurement of the relative intensity of the fields in the transmission line, the usual sources of error are absent. The location of a voltage zero with a standing-wave detector is not appreciably affected by the probe errors or by the small irregularities in the construction of the slotted section. The measurement accuracy depends upon the accuracy of the location of the voltage zero; this, in turn, depends upon the residual losses in the system and the mechanical precision in measuring small displacements of the probe (or the short). The first method which utilizes the standing-wave detector is known as the *nodal-shift* technique or the *tangent method*, described independently by Feenberg[1] and Weissfloch.[2] The second variation, known as the *cavity method*, was described by Pickering.[3]

a. The Nodal-shift Method. The following experiment is performed to determine the reflection in line I caused by the coupling system with line II matched. Referring to Fig. 5.28, if region II is terminated with a movable shorting plunger, standing waves will appear as indicated in Fig. 5.29. Region I is equipped with a standing-wave detector to find the location of the voltage node.[4] The electrical distances θ_1 and θ_2 are measured with respect to any convenient reference plane; if the transmission lines are identical, it suffices to measure the physical distances. The difference, $\theta_1 - \theta_2$, is computed for the various positions of the shorting plunger and plotted as a function of θ_2 (or x_2), as shown in Fig. 5.26. If the coupling network is a smooth continuation from line I to line II, the distance between the probe and the short remains constant (equal to an integral multiple of the half-wavelength). In general, however, the

[1] E. Feenberg, The Relation between Nodal Positions and Standing Wave Ratio in a Composite Transmission System, Sperry Gyroscope Co. Rept. 5220-120, June 5, 1943; E. Feenberg, The Relation between Nodal Positions and Standing-wave Ratio in a Composite Transmission System, *J. Appl. Phys.*, vol. 17, no. 6, pp. 530–532, June, 1946.

[2] A. Weissfloch, Ein Transformationssatz Verlustose Vierpole und Sein Anwendung auf die Experimentelle Untersuchung van Dezimeter—und Zentimeterwellen-Schaltungen, *Hochfrequenz und Electroakustik*, vol. 60, no. 3, pp. 67–73, September, 1942.

[3] W. H. Pickering, O. W. Hagelberger, C. V. Ming, and S. C. Snowden, A New Method for the Precision Measurement of Waveguide Discontinuities, *NDRC Div. 14 Rept.* 317, October, 1944.

[4] Preferably, the average of equal-response points.

resultant curve appears as shown; displacement D allows the determination of the magnitude of the reflection from the network *if region II were matched;* and the position x_2' of the short at which the curve crosses the median line, together with corresponding location of the node x_1', determines the phase of the reflection. D, x_2', and x_1' are the three constants which describe the coupling network. The theoretical description of the method is as follows:

It is assumed that the transmission lines and the discontinuity region are lossless and that one mode in each region propagates without attenuation. Inside the coupling network the geometrical discontinuities can excite other modes. These higher-order waves are attenuated rapidly away from the discontinuity. The following equations are applicable only when the fields are measured at a sufficient distance from the discontinuities of the network.

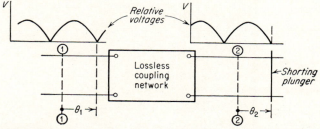

FIG. 5.29. Distribution of electric field on the two sides of the coupling network due to the shorting plunger in region II.

A general four-terminal circuit theorem states that input and output impedances, Z_{in} and Z_{out}, respectively, of a linear, passive network can be related through a linear fractional function of impedance,

$$Z_{\text{in}} = \frac{A Z_{\text{out}} + B}{C Z_{\text{out}} + D} \qquad (5.29)$$

The problem does not change if arbitrary lengths of transmission line are included inside the coupling network. It is convenient to include just enough line length on each side to reduce the complexity of the mathematical manipulations. This approach also leads to a simple interpretation of the action of the coupling network. The terminals of the coupling network are selected as follows:

1. Referring to Fig. 5.30a, suppose the transmission line in region II is terminated in its own Z_0. In general, standing waves will exist in region I. The position of the voltage maximum in region I defines the position of the *terminals* 1-1. The resultant VSWR in region I is r. If Z_1 is the characteristic impedance of region I, then

$$Z_{\text{in}} = r Z_1 \qquad (5.30)$$

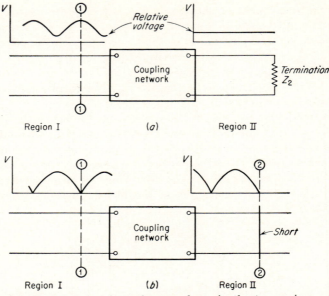

FIG. 5.30. Procedure for choosing reference planes in the two regions. In (a) the network is perfectly terminated; in (b) region II is shorted.

2. Suppose region II is shorted. The voltage node will appear somewhere in region I, as shown in Fig. 5.30b. The short is moved until the voltage zero appears at terminals 1-1, i.e., $Z_{in} = 0$. Define this position of the short in region II as *terminals* 2-2.

Under the conditions 1, Eq. (5.29) becomes

$$rZ_1 = \frac{AZ_2 + B}{CZ_2 + D} \tag{5.31}$$

where Z_1 and Z_2 are the characteristic impedances of region I and II, respectively. Condition 2 states that $Z_{out} = 0$ and $Z_{in} = 0$; hence, $B/D = 0$. Therefore, $B = 0$. But in a lossless network, constants of Eq. (5.29) A and D are real and B and C are imaginary.[1] Hence, since rZ_1 and Z_2 are real, Eq. (5.31) requires that $C = 0$. Thus, for the par-

---

[1] $D = \infty$ is impossible. If it were, Z_{in} would be zero for any value of Z_{out}. The statement regarding the constants A, B, C, and D can be proven as follows: Let $Z_{out} = jX$; for a lossless network, Z_{in} must be a *pure reactance*. Assuming that A and D are real and B and C imaginary causes the numerator of Eq. (5.29) to be always imaginary and the denominator always real for any value of X. This satisfies the requirement that Z_{in} should be purely reactive. If A or D had imaginary components and B or C real components then, for an arbitrary value of X, Z_{in} would have a real component, thus violating the initial condition. Alternatively, making A and D imaginary and B and C real is equivalent to the above, which can be seen by multiplying the numerator and denominator of Eq. (5.29) by j.

ticular choice of network terminals, $A/D = rZ_1/Z_2$, and Eq. (5.29) becomes

$$Z_{in} = r\left(\frac{Z_1}{Z_2}\right)Z_{out} \qquad (5.32)$$

or

$$\frac{Z_{in}}{Z_1} = r\left(\frac{Z_{out}}{Z_2}\right) \qquad (5.33)$$

which proves the *transformer theorem* stated previously.

Equation (5.32) predicts the most general dependence that impedance Z_{in} can have upon the load impedance Z_{out} with the terminals of the coupling network chosen as defined above. The constant r is the VSWR measured in region I with region II terminated in its own characteristic impedance; it is, therefore, a measure of the discontinuity introduced by the coupling network.

To determine the parameters of the coupling network, the nodal-shift experiment is performed in analogy to the short-circuit open-circuit technique used in the conventional network practice. Referring to Fig. 5.29, suppose a shorting plunger is placed at a distance x_2 to the right of terminals 2-2. The impedance Z_{out} is

$$Z_{out} = jZ_2 \tan \beta_2 x_2 \qquad (5.34)$$

As indicated in Fig. 5.29, this creates a voltage node to the right of terminals 1-1. Therefore, the impedance Z_{in} can be represented by

$$Z_{in} = jZ_1 \tan \beta_1 x_1 \qquad (5.35)$$

Combining Eqs. (5.34) and (5.35) with Eq. (5.32),

$$\tan \beta_1 x_1 = r \tan \beta_2 x_2 \qquad (5.36)$$

Equation (5.36) relates the position of the shorting plunger and the observed voltage zeros in region I as a function of the reflection produced by the coupling network. If positions of the voltage zeros in region I are measured as a function of the position of the shorting plunger x_2, the resultant curve will contain information which can be used to compute the value of r. The form of Eq. (5.36) leads to the name—the *tangent method*. However, the experimental data can be analyzed more accurately by taking the difference $\beta_1 x_1 - \beta_2 x_2$ and plotting it vs. x_2 as shown in Fig. 5.26. The width of the curve D determines the reflection coefficient Γ:*

* These results are obtained as follows: The quantity measured by the nodal-shift method is

$$\beta_1 x_1 - \beta_2 x_2 = \tan^{-1}(r \tan \beta_2 x_2) - \beta_2 x_2 \qquad (5.37)$$

The points of maxima and minima are obtained by differentiating Eq. (5.37) with respect to $\beta_2 x_2$. Setting the differential to zero, it is found that the maxima and

$$|\Gamma| = \sin \frac{D}{2} \tag{5.42}$$

or the VSWR due to the coupling network

$$r = \frac{1 + \sin (D/2)}{1 - \sin (D/2)} \tag{5.43}$$

The terminals 1-1 and 2-2 can be found from the experimental data as follows: The median line is drawn through the curve as indicated in

---

minima occur at

$$\beta_2 x_2 = \pm \tan^{-1} \frac{1}{\sqrt{r}} \tag{5.38}$$

The corresponding values of $\beta_1 x_1$ are found by substituting this into Eq. (5.36):

$$\beta_1 x_1 = \pm \tan^{-1} \sqrt{r} \tag{5.39}$$

Therefore, the values of $\beta_1 x_1 - \beta_2 x_2$ at maxima and minima are

$$(\beta_1 x_1 - \beta_2 x_2)_{\substack{\max \\ \min}} = \pm \tan^{-1} \tfrac{1}{2} \left(\sqrt{r} - \frac{1}{\sqrt{r}} \right) \tag{5.40}$$

Displacement D in Figs. 5.26 and 5.31 is determined from Eq. (5.40) as

$$D = 2 \tan^{-1} \tfrac{1}{2} \left(\sqrt{r} - \frac{1}{\sqrt{r}} \right) \tag{5.41}$$

Solving this equation for r leads to Eqs. (5.42) and (5.43).

The reference terminals can be obtained as follows: The median line drawn through the experimental data corresponds to $\beta_1 x_1 - \beta_2 x_2 = 0, \pi, 2\pi, \ldots, 2\pi n$, where n is an integer (n could be determined by a length measurement in the laboratory if it were needed).

According to the formulation of the problem, a short placed at terminals 2-2 corresponds to a short at terminals 1-1; i.e., when $\beta_2 x_2 = 0, 2\pi$, etc., the voltage node in region I is located at terminals 1-1. Thus, with the shorting plunger placed at the terminals 2-2, $\beta_1 x_1 = 0, 2\pi$, etc. Therefore, in the laboratory experiment, in order to find terminals of the coupling network, it is necessary to establish the position of the short which causes $\beta_1 x_1 - \beta_2 x_2 = 0$. The value of $\beta_2 x_2$ at which this happens is readily located from the graph of $\beta_1 x_2 - \beta_2 x_2$ vs. $\beta_2 x_2$, as the places where the curve crosses the median line. The values of $x_2 \pm n\lambda_2/2$ determine the terminals 2-2. The corresponding positions of the voltage node x_1' in region I determine the terminals 1-1.

Actually, from Eq. (5.37), or from the corresponding graphs, it can be observed that there are three situations which cause $\beta_1 x_1 - \beta_2 x_2$ to become zero. These are:

1. $r = 1$; this is a triviality, corresponding to a reflectionless coupling network.

2. $\beta_2 x_2 = 0, 2\pi$, etc.; this corresponds to the case just discussed. It can be identified in the following way: By observation, it can be seen that if $\beta_2 x_2 = 0$, the quantity $\beta_1 x_1 - \beta_2 x_2$ passes from low values to high values (i.e., crosses the median line with a positive slope).

3. $\beta_2 x_2 = \pi/2, 3\pi/2$, etc.; it can be shown that this situation corresponds to the curve crossing the median line as the quantity $(\beta_1 x_1 - \beta_2 x_2)$ goes from high values through zero to lower values (i.e., with negative slope).

These results are summarized in Table 5.4.

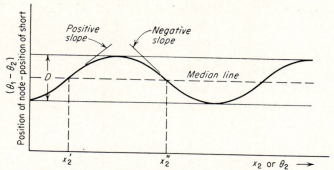

FIG. 5.31. Identification of coupling-network terminals; see Table 5.4.

Fig. 5.26. The experimental curve crosses the median line at certain values of x_2; for these values of x_2, corresponding values of x_1 can be found either from the data or by actually setting the shorting plunger at x_2 and accurately locating the corresponding position of x_1. The resultant data can be interpreted with the aid of Table 5.4 and Fig. 5.31.

TABLE 5.4. SUMMARY OF THE PROCEDURE FOR THE ANALYSIS OF THE NODAL-SHIFT DATA*.

Curve passes the median line with slope m

1. Positive slope: $m = r - 1$.	1. Negative slope: $m = 1/r - 1$.
2. Locate point x_2'.	2. Locate point x_2'.
3. x_2' is the position of terminals 2-2 ($\pm n\lambda_2/2$).	3. x_2'' is displaced from terminals 2-2 by $\lambda_2/4$.
4. From laboratory data determine voltage node in region I corresponding to shorting plunger at x_2'. Call its position x_1'.	4. From laboratory data determine voltage node in region I corresponding to shorting plunger at x_2''. Call its position x_1''.
5. Terminals 1-1 of the coupling network are at x_1'.	5. Terminals 1-1 of the coupling network are displaced from x_1'' by $\lambda_1/4$.
6. At terminals 1-1, the impedance with region II terminated is rZ_1.	6. At x_1'' the impedance with region II terminated is Z_1/r.
7. $r = \dfrac{1 + \sin(D/2)}{1 - \sin(D/2)}$, or $r = 1 + m$.	7. $r = \dfrac{1 + \sin(D/2)}{1 - \sin(D/2)}$, or $r = \dfrac{1}{1 + m}$.

* Symbols refer to Fig. 5.31.

The nodal-shift technique is most useful for the measurement of small reflections. Large reflections cause the accuracy to become poor; there is no special reason to use the nodal-shift technique as the conventional methods of measuring impedance become adequate.[1] The lower limit in

---

[1] It may be desirable to employ the nodal-shift technique even if the reflection is large. For instance, in measuring the discontinuity produced by the junction of two dissimilar lines, this method obviates the need for a perfect termination. In this

the measurement of discontinuities is determined principally by the accuracy to which the voltage node can be located. As stated above, this depends upon the residual losses in the system and the technique used in the measurement of small displacements of the probe.

In addition, the accuracy of this method is affected by the residual frequency modulation of the signal source, the presence of harmonics, and frequency drift; these should be minimized by the usual procedures. Also, the voltage minima may become broad due to resonance between the coupling network and the moving plunger. As long as the reflections under study are not too large, this effect is not serious and can be alleviated by finding the position of the minimum by averaging the positions of equal response.

The median line drawn through the experimental data should have zero slope. The presence of a finite slope indicates that the transmission-line wavelength on one or both sides of the coupling network has not been correctly determined. To obtain the best results, the transmission-line wavelength should be determined directly by measuring the distance between successive minima under operating conditions.

With moderate care in execution at a wavelength of 10 cm, it is possible to determine reflection coefficients of about 0.1 per cent, or standing-wave ratios in the vicinity of 1.001.

The nodal-shift technique is also useful in the study of certain characteristics of periodically loaded waveguides such as are encountered in the microwave linear electron accelerator and in certain high-power traveling-wave tubes. For example, the method is useful in determining the reflection at the transition between a uniform waveguide and a periodically loaded waveguide. Also, the propagating characteristics of periodically loaded waveguides can be obtained by conducting experiments essentially

---

case, the following alternate procedure may be found helpful: Place the shorting plunger at four successive places, $\lambda_t/8$ apart; call these x_2', x_2'', x_2''' and x_2''''. Locate the corresponding minima on the input end and plot the points x_1', x_1'', x_1''', x_1'''' along the periphery of the Smith chart. Join points x_1' to x_1''', and x_1'' to x_1'''' by circles orthogonal to the periphery of the Smith chart. (This may be done in one of the several ways described in Sec. 6.5b; viz., using another transparent Smith chart as an overlay, find a circle of constant reactance which joins the two points.) The intersection of the two circles obtained determines the reflection coefficient of the discontinuity. For proof of the method, see Chap. 6.

It is not necessary to place the shorting plungers $\lambda_t/8$ apart. Graphical geometrical construction, based upon the interpretation of the scattering matrix of an arbitrary junction, has been devised to permit the use of three arbitrarily selected shorting plunger positions. For description of this procedure, see F. L. Wentworth and D. R. Barthel, A Simplified Calibration of Two-port Transmission Line Devices, *Trans. IRE*, vol. MTT-4, no. 3, pp. 173–175, July, 1956.

equivalent to the nodal-shift procedures.   These and related techniques can be found described in the literature.[1]

b. The Cavity Method.   A variation of the nodal-shift technique consists of determining the voltage zero in region I by replacing the voltage probe with a movable shorting plunger; the equipment required for this experiment is indicated in Fig. 5.32.   The space between the two shorting plungers becomes a resonant cavity which can be excited by providing an input coupling loop as shown.   A detector can be introduced by means of a coupling loop at the second shorting plunger or some other equivalent place.   The shorting plungers must be designed carefully for the transmission line in question.   Various types of plungers can be used; because of its lower loss the noncontacting resonant-trap type is generally best.

The equipment is used as follows: For each of a number of locations of the shorting plunger in region II, the shorting plunger in region I is

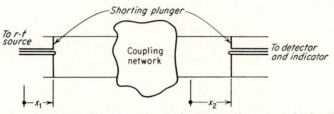

FIG. 5.32. Essential components for the study of coupling networks by the cavity method.   Plunger positions, x_1 and x_2, are measured with respect to arbitrary positions but in the same direction.

adjusted to a place indicating cavity resonance.   The position data are obtained in the cavity method by considering the position of the shorting plunger in region II as the independent variable, and the position of the shorting plunger in region I as if it were the moving probe.   The resultant data is plotted and interpreted as in the nodal-shift method.

The cavity method and the nodal-shift technique are nearly identical in their applicability, the choice between them being mostly a matter of convenience and available apparatus.   However, in the cavity method the discontinuity in question is a part of a uniform transmission line, and the indicated result is the correct value for the structure under study.

[1] E. T. Jaynes, The Concept and Measurement of Impedance in Periodically Loaded Wave Guides, *J. Appl. Phys.*, vol. 23, no. 10, pp. 1077–1084, October, 1952; R. L. Kyhl, The Use of Non-Euclidean Geometry in Measurements of Periodically Loaded Transmission Lines, *Trans. IRE*, vol. MTT-4, no. 4, pp. 111–115, April, 1956; E. J. Nalos, Measurement of Circuit Impedance of Periodically Loaded Structures by Frequency Perturbation, *Proc. IRE*, vol. 42, no. 10, pp. 1508–1511, October, 1954.

In the slotted-section technique, on the other hand, the direct use of the data leads to the final answer in terms of the impedance *referred* to the *slotted section*. Since the slotted section and the network under study may be separated by a number of discontinuities, the answer may require correction in the manner described in Sec. 5.7c, i.e., by conducting a separate nodal-shift experiment to separate out the transformation due to the intermediate elements. These corrections are not required in the use of the cavity technique if the equipment is arranged without intermediate discontinuities as indicated in Fig. 5.32.

As in the nodal-shift technique, the plungers must be sufficiently far from the discontinuities of the network to insure that they do not interfere with the fringing fields of the discontinuity.

c. The Sliding-termination Method. As stated previously, the direct method of measuring small reflections due to the presence of a coupling network is difficult for two reasons. The first and the most important

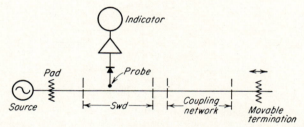

FIG. 5.33. Arrangement of equipment for the sliding-termination method.

is the difficulty of measuring small changes in the relative voltage in the slotted section accurately. The second reason is less basic. If perfect terminations are not available, the direct method cannot be used even if the standing-wave detector measurements were perfect since a reflection from an imperfect termination reaching the standing-wave detector cannot be distinguished from those caused by the coupling network. However, there is a variation of the direct procedure which allows the separation of the reflections due to the coupling network and the termination by making it possible to move the termination continuously over a distance of at least one-half wavelength.

The input impedances to the coupling network are measured with the standing-wave detector indicated in Fig. 5.33. As the sliding termination is moved, at certain positions of the termination the reflections from the discontinuity and termination will add; a quarter-wavelength further, the reflections subtract. By measuring the maximum and minimum standing-wave ratios, it is possible to deduce the magnitude of the reflection from the coupling network and the sliding termination.

Referring to Fig. 5.34, the locus of impedances measured in the slotted section forms a circle as indicated. If $\mathcal{R}_1$ and $\mathcal{R}_2$ are the minimum and maximum values of the resistances observed, the VSWR of the discontinuity r will be given by

$$r = \sqrt{\frac{\mathcal{R}_1}{Z_0} \frac{\mathcal{R}_2}{Z_0}} \tag{5.44}$$

and the standing-wave ratio r_0 of the sliding termination will be given by

$$r_0 = \sqrt{\frac{\mathcal{R}_2}{\mathcal{R}_1}} \tag{5.45}$$

The above equation could be written in terms of the standing-wave ratios; however, this could lead to ambiguity because the reflection from the sliding termination can be either smaller or larger than the reflection from the discontinuity under test.

The phase of the reflection can be determined in the following manner: If the original impedance data are taken in the slotted section with respect to some arbitrary reference point, the circular impedance locus will lie in some part of the Smith chart as shown in Fig. 5.34. This circle can be rotated about the center of the Smith chart through an angle 2ψ until it becomes symmetrical about the real axis. The angular distance ψ is subtracted from the original arbitrary reference plane to establish a new reference plane

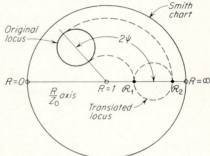

FIG. 5.34. The impedance loci on the Smith chart obtained in the use of the sliding-termination method.

in the slotted section. The geometric mean of the maximum and minimum resistance points of this new circle corresponds to the resistance that would be seen at the *new reference* plane if the sliding termination were replaced by a *perfect termination*. The location of this reference plane can be interpreted as the phase of the reflection in the same sense as in Sec. 5.8a.*

5.9. Resonance-curve Method of Impedance Measurements (Chipman Method). The standing-wave phenomena can be used to determine two-terminal impedances in still another manner. The method is related to

---

* These results can be obtained as follows: If the sliding termination were replaced by a perfect termination a standing-wave ratio r would exist in the slotted section; it is of interest to determine its value. According to the transformer theorem, two reference planes exist, on either side of the discontinuity, at which the impedances are related by the standing-wave ratio. As the imperfect sliding termination is moved,

the conventional slotted section technique but requires neither the slot nor the use of a moving probe. The use of a standing-wave detector results in errors in the measurement of relative voltage due to the slot and probe errors. The extreme accuracy required in construction invariably leads to expensive and delicate mechanisms. Most of the difficulties in the fabrication of the standing-wave detector can be avoided by means of a different arrangement shown in Fig. 5.35. The load is connected to a uniform section of transmission line. Near the load a fixed probe, loosely coupled, introduces the signal into the transmission line and a shorting plunger which carries a detector is placed on the opposite end. A coupling loop, a crystal detector, and a conventional indicator-amplifier correspond to the equipment usually used in the conventional standing-wave detector measurements.

The motion of the sliding short produces periodic variation in the detector output with maxima and minima corresponding to those of the conventional standing-wave detector. If the sliding short were perfectly reflecting, the resultant data could be interpreted in a manner identical to

---

the impedance at the output reference plane will vary continuously; the locus of points lying on the circle is characterized by the standing-wave ratio r_0 of the sliding termination. The extreme values of the impedances available at the output reference planes are

$$R_1 = \frac{Z_0}{r_0} \qquad \text{and} \qquad R_2 = r_0 Z_0 \qquad (R_1 R_2 = Z_0{}^2)$$

The corresponding input impedances $\mathcal{R}_1$ and $\mathcal{R}_2$ are

$$\begin{aligned} \mathcal{R}_1 &= r R_1 \\ \mathcal{R}_2 &= r R_2 \end{aligned} \qquad\qquad (5.46)$$

The resistances $\mathcal{R}_1$ and $\mathcal{R}_2$ can be determined by direct impedance measurements in the slotted section. Since the output impedance locus is a circle, the input impedances must lie on a circle also. The product of the last two equations leads to Eq. (5.44); the ratio to Eq. (5.45). The phase information is obtained directly from the Smith chart.

An alternative proof of this method, in a generalized form, has been given by A. C. Macpherson and D. M. Kerns, A New Technique for the Measurement of Microwave Standing-wave Ratios, *Proc. IRE*, vol. 44, no. 8, pp. 1024–1030, August, 1956. They show that the equipment described above may be modified by connecting the generator, the detector, and the movable ("phasable") load by a T junction. Variation in position of the movable load results in variation in the detector current which can be interpreted to provide the magnitude and phase of the movable load. The use of the equipment in this manner does not require the standing-wave detector and avoids the probe and slot errors inherent in the standing-wave measurements. The method is capable of providing excellent accuracy in the measurement of the unknown impedance provided that the unknown impedance can be moved electrically with respect to the T junction without introducing variable reflections due to the phase-shifting element. The paper cited shows that a sliding trombone is sufficient for this purpose if it is constructed carefully.

that of the standing-wave detector data. If the moving short is not perfectly reflecting, the data must be interpreted somewhat differently. This method of measuring impedances is generally referred to as the *resonance-curve method* or the *Chipman method*.[1]

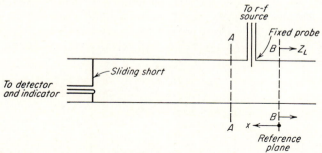

FIG. 5.35. The essential elements required for the Chipman method. A sliding short, carrying the detector, moves through the uniform transmission line. The unknown load is located at the reference plane, *B-B*.

The Chipman method can be understood as follows: Referring to Fig. 5.35, the region to the right of section *A-A* can be replaced by an equivalent load resistance R_0 and a source of voltage E by applying Thévenin's theorem, resulting in the equivalent circuit shown in Fig. 5.36.

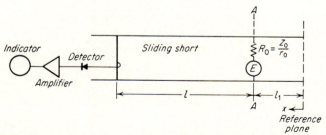

FIG. 5.36. The equivalent circuit of the Chipman method. The impedance at *A-A* represents the effect of the generator and the load to the right of line *A-A* in Fig. 5.35.

To the left of *A-A* the transmission line (ideally) can develop either a short circuit or an open circuit at *A-A*. The detector at the sliding short makes it possible to measure the relative values of the r-f current at *A-A* in the two cases. If the sliding short is displaced from section *A-A* by some multiple of half-wavelength, the short is equivalent to being at sec-

[1] R. A. Chipman, A Resonance-curve Method for Absolute Measurement of Impedance at Frequencies of the Order of 300 Mc, *J. Appl. Phys.*, vol. 10, no. 1, pp. 27–38, January, 1939; A. S. Meier and W. P. Summers, Measured Impedance of Vertical Antennas over Finite Ground Planes, *Proc. IRE*, vol. 37, no. 6, pp. 609–616, June, 1949.

tion A-A, and the r-f current measurement by the detector is a direct measurement of the relative magnitude of the short-circuit current. If the sliding short is displaced from this position, the resultant current at the detector can be related simply to the current at the generator.

Let r_0 be the true VSWR of the load under test, and r be the VSWR of the sliding short. Also, let I_{max} and I_{min} be the maximum and minimum values of the r-f current at the r-f terminals of the detector. The ratio $\rho_0 = I_{max}/I_{min}$ is the *observed* standing-wave ratio. It can be shown that[1]

$$\rho_0 = \frac{I_{max}}{I_{min}} = \frac{1 + rr_0}{r + r_0} \qquad (5.47)$$

or, if written in terms of reflection coefficients,

$$\rho_0 = \frac{1 + |\Gamma|\,|\Gamma_0|}{1 - |\Gamma|\,|\Gamma_0|} \qquad (5.48)$$

where Γ_0 is the reflection coefficient of the load, and Γ is the reflection coefficient of the shorting plunger. If $r \gg r_0$, Eqs. (5.47) and (5.48) reduce to the familiar expressions found in the analysis of standing-wave detector data:

$$\rho_0 = r_0 \qquad (5.49)$$

and

$$r_0 = \frac{1 + |\Gamma_0|}{1 - |\Gamma_0|} \qquad (5.50)$$

The standing-wave ratio r of the sliding short circuit can be determined by replacing the load by a short circuit. An accurate measurement of the VSWR of the short circuit is not important if it is sufficiently higher than the load VSWR. However, if the two values are comparable, the accuracy in the determination of the losses in the shorting plunger becomes important. This implies that the Chipman method is most

---

[1] These results can be obtained as follows: Referring to Fig. 5.36, consider the impedances presented to the left of section A-A. If r is the standing-wave ratio presented by the sliding short, the maximum and minimum resistances are equal to rZ_0 and Z_0/r, respectively. The current flowing at A-A from the generator E in the two cases is

$$I'_{min} = \frac{E}{Z_0}\frac{1}{1/r_0 + r}$$

$$I'_{max} = \frac{E}{Z_0}\frac{1}{1/r_0 + 1/r}$$

in which the primes denote the current at terminals A-A. The current measured at the detector terminals is related to these values. The maximum current I_{max} is proportional to I'_{max}, since it is measured when the sliding short is at A-A (or removed from A-A by some multiple of half-wavelength). The current I_{min} will exist when the detector terminals are removed from A-A by one-quarter wavelength; therefore, $I_{min} = rI'_{min}$. The ratio of I_{max} to I_{min} leads to Eq. (5.47).

accurate for low values of the VSWR and becomes progressively poorer as the load VSWR approaches the value of the moving short.

The phase of the load impedance can be determined as follows. Referring to Fig. 5.36, it can be seen that the detector current is a *maximum* when the distance l is some multiple of the half-wavelength. Therefore, the location of a current maximum $I_{\max}$ is equivalent to the location of terminals A-A at which the load may be represented by a resistance Z_0/r_0. The load impedance Z_L is obtained with the aid of the transmission-line equations or the Smith chart by transforming (Z_0/r) through the angle βl_1.

The determination of high standing-wave ratios may be as difficult as it is in the conventional standing-wave detector method because of the difficulty of measuring two quantities substantially different in magnitude. High standing-wave ratios can be measured, however, by determining the shape of the current distribution curve near its maximum.

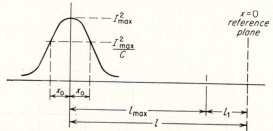

FIG. 5.37. The equal-response-point procedure for measuring high standing wave ratios with the Chipman method.

The observed standing-wave ratio ρ_0 can be computed in the manner closely analogous to the double-minimum method discussed in Sec. 5.6f. Referring to Fig. 5.37, if two equal-response points are found, lower in magnitude than the maximum by a factor of C (assuming a square-law crystal), the observed standing-wave ratio ρ_0 is given by

$$\rho_0 = \sqrt{\frac{2(C-1)}{1-\cos 2\beta x_0} + 1} \tag{5.51}$$

For standing-wave ratios higher than 10 and $C = 2$, Eq. (5.51) reduces to

$$\rho_0 = \frac{\lambda_t}{2\pi x_0} \tag{5.52}$$

The remarks made in Sec. 5.6f pertaining to the measurement of high standing-wave ratios are applicable in this case as well.

The position of the detector and r-f excitation can be exchanged without causing any difference in the results or their interpretation. The exact arrangement of the apparatus is a matter of convenience.

In use, the Chipman method requires equally careful adjustment of the detector and signal generator coupling to the transmission line. In using the standing-wave detector method, errors can be introduced because of the probe loading. Similar errors are encountered in the Chipman method due to the detector losses; these errors can be minimized in the same manner in both cases. The Chipman method also requires the *r-f source impedance* to be small compared to the load resistance referred to terminals *A-A* in Fig. 5.36. The presence of a finite source impedance causes errors in a manner which is obvious from the examination of the equivalent circuit shown in Fig. 5.36.

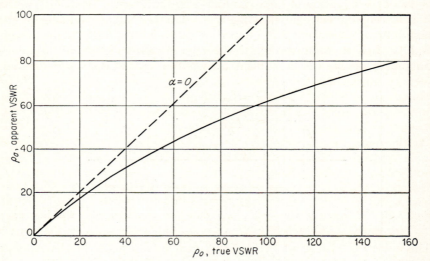

FIG. 5.38. The effect of attenuation in the measuring line in the Chipman method. ρ_0 is the true standing-wave ratio, ρ_a the observed value. The solid curve is plotted for $\alpha l = 0.006$, a typical value for $\lambda = 10$ cm, $l = 20$ cm. (*Data from A. S. Meier and W. P. Summers, Measured Impedance of Vertical Antennas over Finite Ground Planes, Proc. IRE, vol. 37, no. 6, pp. 609–616, June, 1949.*)

It has been assumed in this discussion that the transmission line between the load and the sliding short is lossless; however, if the standing-wave ratio being measured is high, the attenuation cannot be neglected. The correction for finite attenuation can be made simply. If l is the distance between the load terminals and a particular current maximum, and α is the attenuation constant of the line nepers per unit length, the observed value of standing-wave ratio ρ_a can be corrected to give the true current ratio ρ_0 from

$$\rho_0 = \frac{\rho_a - \alpha l}{1 - \rho_a \alpha l} \tag{5.53}$$

The effect of attenuation in a typical case is shown in Fig. 5.38.

Whereas in the Chipman method close machining tolerances in the transmission line proper are not essential, the sliding-short must make an excellent and constant contact to the transmission line. Considerable difficulty can be experienced in the fabrication of a suitable moving short. The residual losses in the sliding short must be measured each time and taken into account in computation.

The use of the conventional standing-wave detectors requires the probe to be weakly coupled to the slotted section, but the generator can be relatively tightly coupled without causing serious difficulties. In the Chipman method, on the other hand, both the generator and detector must be loosely coupled. This implies that the Chipman method requires considerably greater r-f power than the slotted-section technique and this limits its usefulness.

5.10. Bridge Methods of Impedance Measurements. In the low-frequency region, the conventional method of measuring impedance consists of comparing the unknown against a standard impedance. Two things are essential to make this comparison: an impedance standard and a bridge circuit to which the standard and the unknown can be connected to indicate the equality between the standard and the unknown. At the lower radio frequencies both the impedance standards and suitable bridges can be devised easily. It becomes more difficult to devise impedance standards and bridge circuits as the frequency increases. Several bridge techniques have been tried at microwave frequencies. Examples of the most successful are described below. Some of these have been successful over a limited frequency range and others as comparison devices enabling a rapid measurement of impedance on a relative basis.

The reader should be aware of the advantages of bridge techniques. To obtain bridge balance two independent adjustments are required matching the absolute value of the impedance and its phase angle against those of the standard. In practical bridge circuits, the two adjustments are largely independent and make possible rapid balancing of the bridge. The value of the impedance is found directly from the bridge calibration and no further manipulation of data is required as is necessary with the standing-wave detector. The measurement accuracy depends principally upon the accuracy of the standard and the precision in the construction of the bridge circuit; it is independent of the detector response law.

At microwave frequencies a resistance standard of unity magnitude (normalized to the impedance of the transmission line) can be provided easily by fabricating artificial terminations and checking their accuracy by conventional standing-wave detector measurements (especially by the methods described in Sec. 5.8c). However, variable resistance standards at microwave frequencies are not available. Pure reactance standards can be provided by utilizing sections of uniform transmission lines.

A standard of complex impedance in the form of $1 + jx$ can be made by connecting a variable shorting stub in parallel (or in series) with a Z_0 termination. A T junction of this type is not as simple as it may appear at first but involves a separate determination of the two parameters of the junction. The two parameters are usually represented by a reactance shunting the termination and an ideal transformer with a turn ratio $n{:}1$ connecting the movable short to the main transmission line as shown in Fig. 5.39. Both the shunting reactance and the turn ratio of the transformer are frequency dependent. This knowledge is required if the impedance at terminals a-a is to be interpreted simply in terms of the geometrical configuration. These circuit constants can be determined easily by several methods, all of which involve the use of impedance measurements with a standing-wave detector. Thus, the reactive component of the impedance standard is related to the length of the shorting stub but is also strongly affected by the operating frequency.

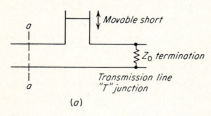

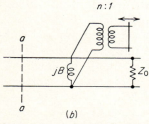

FIG. 5.39. A method of providing a microwave impedance standard. (a) A transmission-line T junction terminated with its characteristic impedance and a movable short in the two arms; (b) its equivalent circuit. The values B and n vary with frequency.

Many structures are described in the literature which behave as bridge circuits at microwave frequencies.[1] The simplest have four arms and closely resemble the hybrid junction. These four-arm circuits act as bridges in the sense that if the impedances connected to two arms are identical, there is zero transmission of power between the remaining two arms. If variable resistance and reactance standards were available at microwave frequencies, those circuits would be useful as true bridges. Since variable impedance standards are unavailable, the four-arm junctions are useful only for comparing the unknown against some simple impedance such as a Z_0 termination. There are more complicated microwave structures, such as six-arm junctions which more closely correspond to the Wheatstone bridge circuit. Examples of such bridge circuits are described in greater detail below.

[1] W. A. Tyrrell, Hybrid Circuits for Microwaves, *Proc. IRE*, Vol. 35, no. 11, pp. 1294–1307, November, 1947; C. G. Montgomery, R. H. Dickey, and E. M. Purcell (eds.), "Principles of Microwave Circuits," chap. 12, McGraw-Hill Book Company, Inc., New York, 1948.

a. Magic-T Bridge. Two microwave hybrid junctions are shown in Fig. 5.40. These are the waveguide junction, known as the *side-outlet T* or sometimes as a *magic T*, and the coaxial junction of four transmission lines, called the *ring*. The properties of such hybrid junctions are well known and are described in the literature.[1]

Referring to the magic T, if a wave enters arm 4, the symmetry of the junction assures that a wave splits evenly between arms 1 and 2. Examination of the fields of the junction shows that this set of waves cannot excite arm 3. Thus, if a generator is connected to arm 4 and the detector to arm 3, there is no transmission of power to the detector as long as arms 1 and 2 are identically terminated. If an impedance standard is connected to arm 1, the bridge is balanced if the unknown connected to arm 2 is equal to the standard connected to arm 1. However, since it is difficult to make the impedance standard variable, the usefulness of this bridge is restricted to those applications where it is merely necessary to detect any deviation of the unknown from the standard. This comparison can be made quantitative if the magic T is completely matched. The attenuation from the generator to the detector can be related simply to VSWR at arm 2, with arm 1 matched. If a matched bolometer is connected to arm 3 and a known power is introduced into

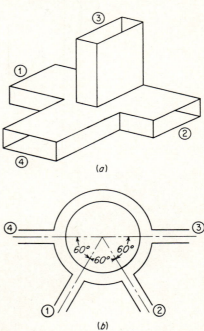

Fig. 5.40. Examples of hybrid structures suitable for impedance measurements. (*a*) A waveguide magic-T structure; (*b*) ring transmission line with four arms connected in series. The length of the ring is made 1½ wavelengths long.

arm 4, the bolometer power can be made to indicate VSWR directly. Such an arrangement permits a rapid examination of the components. Various modifications of this scheme can be devised to allow the measurement of the VSWR over a band of frequencies. For example, if several frequencies are simultaneously introduced into arm 4 and modulated at different audio-frequencies, the bolometer output from arm 3 can be fed to several tuned audio amplifiers to measure VSWR at a number of frequencies simultaneously.

[1] For example, see Montgomery et al. (eds.), "Principles of Microwave Circuits."

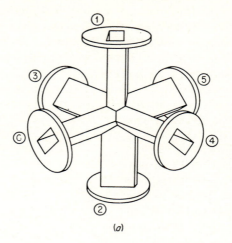

(a)

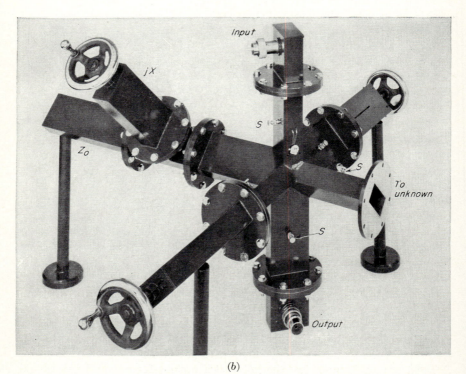

(b)

FIG. 5.41. (a) Symmetrical six-arm waveguide junction.   (b) Photograph showing the use of a symmetrical waveguide junction as a microwave equivalent of the Wheatstone bridge.   Note screws S in each arm for compensation of the junction fringing reactance.

b. Wheatstone-bridge Circuits.[1] A six-arm junction is shown in Fig.
5.41a. This junction behaves as a Wheatstone bridge in the sense that
no transmission takes place from arm 1 to arm 2 if the following relation
exists between the impedance connected to the remaining four arms.

$$Z_3 Z_4 = Z_5 Z_6 \tag{5.54}$$

or

$$Z_3 = \frac{Z_5}{Z_4} Z_6 \tag{5.55}$$

Thus, if the impedance Z_6 is made in the form of $1 + jx$ and Z_5 and Z_4
are variable reactances, a balance can be attained for an arbitrary value
of the unknown impedance Z_3. The balance can be obtained because
the phase angle of standard impedance $1 + jx$ can be adjusted to equal
the phase angle of the unknown; the ratio of the reactances at arms 4

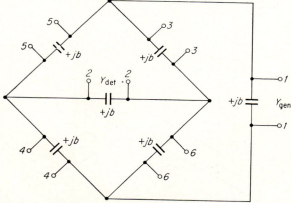

FIG. 5.42. An equivalent circuit of the six-arm waveguide bridge.

and 5 becomes a multiplying factor, adjusting the magnitude of the right-
hand side of Eq. (5.55) to equal the magnitude of the unknown impedance Z_3. A photograph of a complete bridge arrangement is shown in
Fig. 5.41b.

The exact equivalent circuit of the six-arm waveguide bridge is shown
in Fig. 5.42. Due to the fringing fields at the center of the junction a
shunting reactance exists across each one of the bridge arms. As in the
case of the simpler T junction shown in Fig. 5.39, the value of this
reactance is strongly frequency dependent. Furthermore, due to asym-
metries in the construction, the actual values of the shunting reactances
are not precisely equal. As a result, the bridge circuit must be calibrated as a function of frequency to determine the values of the shunting reactance; in reducing the impedance data, the presence of these

[1] M. Chodorow, E. L. Ginzton, and F. Kane, A Microwave Impedance Bridge,
Proc. IRE, vol. 37, no. 9, p. 634, June, 1949.

reactances must be taken into account. For these reasons, the apparent simplicity of the bridge circuit is spoiled. It is possible to resonate the fringing reactances in a number of ways, one of which is shown in Fig. 5.41*b* in the form of properly located inductive posts (screws); this greatly simplifies the use of the bridge. Once the necessary calibration has been made, the six-arm bridge provides the value of the unknown in terms of physical lengths only. This eliminates the many sources of errors ordinarily encountered in VSWR measurements, such as the uncertainty in the detector response-law, etc.

c. Pseudo-bridge Circuits. Two of the many arrangements which permit the measurement of impedance in a manner closely resembling the bridge method are described below.

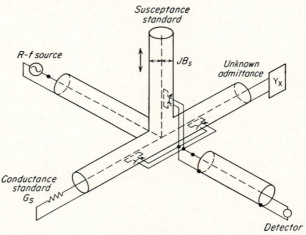

FIG. 5.43. A schematic diagram showing the principal elements of the Thurston admittance comparator.

Figure 5.43[1] shows a null instrument devised by Thurston in which four coaxial lines are combined in a T junction. The first arm is terminated in a conductance standard, the second in a susceptance standard, and the third is connected to the unknown admittance. A signal source is connected to the three arms in parallel, making the current in each arm at the junction proportional to the admittance of the arm. By providing electrostatically shielded adjustable coupling loops, the three currents can be sampled and combined together; a detector connected to the loops indicates the resultant voltage. When the loops are properly

[1] W. R. Thurston, A Direct-reading Impedance Measuring Instrument for the Uhf Range, *General Radio Experimenter*, vol. 24, no. 12, May, 1950; R. A. Soderman, Improved Accuracy and Convenience with Type 1602-B Admittance Meter in VHF and UHF Bands, *General Radio Experimenter*, vol. 28, no. 3, August, 1953.

oriented, the combined voltage becomes zero. The conductances and susceptance of the load can be presented in terms of the rotation of the coupling loops next to the conductance and susceptance standards, respectively. The calibration of the conductance and susceptance dials can be made to be independent of frequency by always adjusting the length of the susceptance arm to be $\lambda_t/8$ so that the susceptance at the junction is always unity.

The simple picture of the operation of this device is valid at low frequencies. It is assumed that the current in the transmission line adjacent to the center of the coupling loop on each branch line is equal to the generator voltage multiplied by the arm admittance. At high frequencies this assumption is not justified. The coupling loops must be some distance from the junction to avoid interaction with each other and also with the fringing fields of the junction. The short length of transmission line between the common junction point and the center of each pickup loop is equivalent to connecting the arm to the junction through a series inductance. The voltage drop through this unavoidable inductance depends upon the magnitude of the current and, therefore, upon the magnitude of the unknown admittance. This effect can be compensated partially by making the series inductance a part of a π-matching filter; the compensating devices cannot be perfect, and in practice it is found that the Thurston bridge is not accurate above 1,500 Mc. For lower frequencies, however, this simple device is convenient, direct reading, and not subject to errors of the standing-wave detector type.

Another comparison technique, originated by Byrne,[1] is illustrated in Fig. 5.44. Power from the signal source is fed to the unknown through a coaxial line. The impedance is determined by sampling the magnetic and electric fields at the point near the load by introducing inductive and capacitive probes into the main coaxial line. The voltage induced in the inductive probe is proportional to the current flowing by the sampling point; the voltage induced in the capacitive probe is proportional to the voltage at this point. The determination of the ratio of these induced voltages provides a measure of the impedance at the sampling point. The comparison of the phase angle between these voltages determines the phase of the unknown.

In one successful model, the probe-to-line couplings are adjustable by gang controls. By adjusting the two voltages for equality, the magnitude of the impedance is determined directly in units of impedance from the calibration of the ganging control. Both the magnitude and phase

[1] J. F. Byrne, A Null Method for the Determination of Impedance in the 100–400 Mc Range, *Proc. Natl. Electronic Conf.*, vol. 3, pp. 603–614, 1947; A. Fong, Direct Measurement of Impedance in the 50–500 Mc Range, *Hewlett-Packard J.*, vol. 1, no. 8, April, 1950.

angle of the two voltages can be compared by connecting the two probes to a common slotted section as illustrated. If the voltages from the two probes are equal in magnitude, a voltage null will exist in the slotted section. The position of the null is determined by the phase angle of the two voltages, i.e., of the unknown. In operation, the probe ganging control and the probe in the slotted section are moved, one at a time, until the null is observed. The operation of the Byrne bridge is analogous to bridge techniques in the sense that a comparison of voltages produces a null.

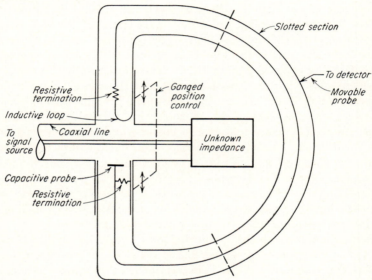

FIG. 5.44. Schematic diagram of the Byrne impedance bridge. The capacitive and inductive pickup elements are mechanically ganged together.

For proper operation, the slotted section should be matched in both directions. The two resistors shown in Fig. 5.44 indicate the manner in which this can be done. Since good terminations are difficult to obtain over a large frequency band (especially at the higher end of the microwave region) the Byrne bridge is usually found to be inaccurate above 700 Mc. Below this frequency it is convenient and accurate.

5.11. Reflectometers. The traveling-wave phenomena in transmission lines may be studied by several other means besides the standing-wave detector. Another way to investigate the characteristics of the termination is to measure directly the reflected wave produced by the discontinuity. Two directional couplers (or a single bidirectional coupler) can be arranged to indicate the magnitude of the incident and reflected waves. If directional couplers were electrically perfect, the indicated magnitude of the reflected and incident waves would be a direct measure of the magnitude of the reflection coefficient.   Ideally, and nearly so in practice, this provides a simple way of measuring reflections.   A suitable arrangement of components of such a *reflectometer* is shown in Fig. 5.45. A signal generator is connected to the equipment through an isolation pad, preferably matched in both directions.   Two directional couplers follow with the load attached as shown.   Two detectors with an accurately known response law are required—barretters are the best for this

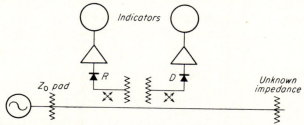

FIG. 5.45. The use of directional couplers in a microwave reflectometer.   *D* and *R* represent directional couplers, indicating incident and reflected waves, respectively.

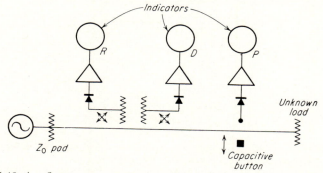

FIG. 5.46. A reflectometer with an additional probe for phase measurement.

purpose; the indicators can be ordinary meters, amplifiers, etc.   In operation, a short circuit is placed at the load terminals and the gain of the two indicator channels adjusted to make the output of the two detectors equal.   Replacing the short circuit by the unknown impedance changes the magnitude of the reflected signal; the magnitude of the incident wave may or may not change, depending upon the care used in matching of the isolation pad.   The ratio of the two indicated readings is a direct measure of the reflection coefficient of the unknown.

Using the directional couplers in the manner described cannot give any information about the relative phase of the two traveling waves.   However, there are a number of techniques which, with relative ease, can provide this information.   One possible method is illustrated in Fig. 5.46.

In addition to the directional couplers, a fixed probe is provided at some convenient point along the transmission line. This probe leads to a detector-amplifier identical to those used with the directional couplers. The location of the probe can be called the *phase reference plane*. In the same plane is a removable button which can introduce a capacitative discontinuity at will. The probe detector sensitivity is adjusted to equal that of the incident wave channel by providing a matched termination and adjusting the probe sensitivity control. With the unknown placed at the load terminals, three readings are obtained, i.e., of the two directional couplers and the probe. The use of the three voltage readings can be understood by reference to Fig. 5.47 where V_i, V_r, and V_p are the

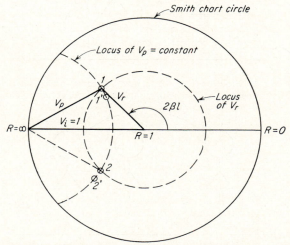

FIG. 5.47. The vector diagram illustrating the use of the auxiliary probe voltage to determine the phase angle of the unknown impedance.

incident, reflected, and probe voltages, respectively. For convenience, the magnitude of the incident voltage is taken as equal to unity. The measured value of V_r determines the size of the circle corresponding to the existing reflection without specifying the phase. The measurement of the probe voltage V_p removes the uncertainty. The intersection of the two dashed curves in Fig. 5.47 determines the phase of the reflected wave at the position of the probe. Actually, two intersections of the two circles are possible. By inserting a known discontinuity, such as a capacity button at the auxiliary probe, both the probe and reflected voltages will change. If the admittance form of a Smith chart is used, points 1 and 2 would change into points 1' and 2'. The corresponding changes in the probe and reflected voltages can easily be distinguished from each other, determining unambiguously the sign of the angle.

Analysis of the vector diagram shown in Fig. 5.47 leads to the relation between the measured voltages and the phase angle between the reflected and incident waves. This is

$$\cos 2\beta l = \frac{V_p{}^2 - V_r{}^2 - 1}{2V_r} \tag{5.56}$$

in which $2\beta l$ is the electrical angle as shown. Therefore, l is the distance between the phase reference plane and the location of the voltage minimum of the existing standing-wave pattern.

The use of reflectometers can lead to a number of errors due to imperfect equipment. These faults are of the following kind:

1. Imperfect directivity in the reverse coupler. Due to electrical or mechanical imperfections, the reverse detector will contain a small signal proportional to the incident wave.

2. The incident wave causes a signal in the reverse coupler which should be absorbed by the termination in the reverse coupler. Because of the imperfect termination a reflection occurs, causing a signal to arrive at the reverse detector.

3. A reflected wave in the main line causes a wave in the forward coupler which should be absorbed in its termination. Due to the imperfect termination a reflection occurs, thus affecting the magnitude of the forward indication.

These errors can be significant, especially when measuring small reflections. The imperfect directivity of the coupler is the most serious source of error; long-slot or multihole directional couplers appear best for this application, although they tend to be long electrically and inconvenient at the lower frequencies. The errors of the type mentioned can be minimized by carefully selecting quality components; the residual error signals can be canceled by the addition of an artificial reflection between the load and the reverse coupler. The procedures for reducing the observable errors by compensation are described in detail in the literature.[1] The use of reflectometers is substantially simplified by employing ratio meters to compute the value of the reflection coefficient.[2]

5.12. Multiple-probe Method. The standing-wave pattern in a transmission line can be determined by a system of fixed probes.[3] It can be

[1] See, for example, J. K. Hunton and N. L. Pappas, The H-P Microwave Reflectometers, *Hewlett-Packard J.*, vol. 6, nos. 1–2, September–October, 1954; C. G. Montgomery (ed.), "Techniques of Microwave Measurement," chap. 14; B. Parzen, Impedance Measurements with Directional Couplers and Supplementary Voltage Probe, *Proc. IRE*, vol. 37, no. 10, pp. 1208–1211, October, 1949.

[2] Hunton and Pappas, *op. cit.*

[3] Unpublished Naval Research Laboratory memorandum by C. H. Taylor, September, 1945.

shown that a measurement of relative voltage at a minimum of three points along the transmission line is required to establish the magnitude and position of the standing waves. If four equally spaced probes are used (preferably, but not necessarily, one-eighth wavelength apart) the resultant voltage readings can be easily interpreted to derive the unknown impedance from certain contours on the Smith chart.

The advantage of the four-fixed-probe method is the simplicity of the apparatus, relatively high accuracy, and ease of operation. Since no moving parts are involved, there is no problem of wear and poor contacts. In practice, a single detector can be moved from probe to probe; a faster and more satisfactory method requires the use of four matched permanently installed detectors. It is necessary to insure that each of the probes does not introduce any of the probe-loading errors described in Sec. 5.6c. Preferably the detectors should be of the barretter type and should have square-law response for best accuracy. Since four probes are used, four times as much power is required to operate the device as would be required with a moving probe.

This method involves graphical interpretation of the data. The analysis is particularly simple when the spacing between the probes is one-eighth wavelength and becomes somewhat more difficult as the spacing is changed due to a change in operating wavelength. However, it is possible to prepare charts for each operating frequency.

The multiple-probe method can be understood as follows: If an observer moves along the transmission line, from the generator to the load, the phase of the incident and reflected waves will change; the important parameter is their relative phase. The magnitude of the observed voltage can be obtained as the sum of the incident and reflected waves. The observer may choose to regard either the incident or reflected waves as the reference. The first leads to the conventional reflection-coefficient diagram shown in Fig. 5.48a, and the second to Fig. 5.48b; in either case, the same answer is obtained. The first is more logical if the point of observation is fixed and the load is moved. The second is more logical if the point of observation is moved with respect to a fixed load. Figure 5.48b demonstrates that, for a given terminating impedance, a vector drawn from the periphery of the Smith chart to any point is proportional to the voltage across the line at that point.

The four probes, one-eighth wavelength apart along the transmission line, result in four points in the Smith chart at 90° intervals. The ratio of the voltages from these probes taken in pairs can be used to determine the parameters which locate the unknown impedance. A parametric chart can be constructed for a series of constant voltage ratios between the alternate probes. This chart, when superimposed on the Smith chart, can be used to read the impedance of the point in question with reference to the location of the probes. The exact meaning of this procedure becomes clearer when the construction of the chart is completed.

A parametric chart for any probe spacing can be constructed as follows: Select one of the reference points on the periphery of the Smith chart (corresponding to the location of one of the probes) and draw an arc with the point as the center. Then increase the radius of the arc by some desired fixed number and draw another arc from another point on the Smith chart periphery (corresponding to the position of the alternate probe). The two intersections of the two arcs determine two particular points on the curve of constant voltage ratio of the magnitude selected. Additional points on the same curve may be obtained by choosing additional radii, differing in size but in the same ratio as the first pair. This procedure results in a series of points which can be connected to form a

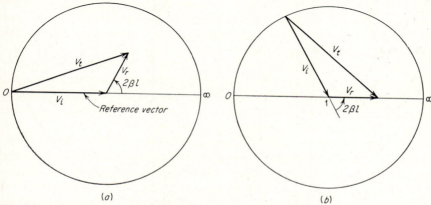

FIG. 5.48. Vector diagrams showing the relation of incident and reflected voltages. (a) The incident voltage as the reference; (b) the reflected wave as the reference.

smooth curve for the particular ratio between the two probes considered. This procedure is repeated again for another selected voltage ratio until a family of curves is obtained from which any desired voltage ratio can be determined. The number of such plotted ratios is determined by the accuracy necessary in the final data. The above procedure is repeated for the second set of alternate probes. A chart plotted for the special case of one-eighth wavelength probe spacing is shown in Fig. 5.49.

The four probes may be adjusted for equal sensitivity by placing a matched termination at the end of the line and adjusting the reading to the same value. Alternatively, if a well padded generator is available, a short circuit can be moved with respect to the load terminals until a maximum is obtained at each probe; the sensitivity of each probe is adjusted for the same reading. When the unknown is placed at the end of the transmission line, the four sets of readings are obtained and the

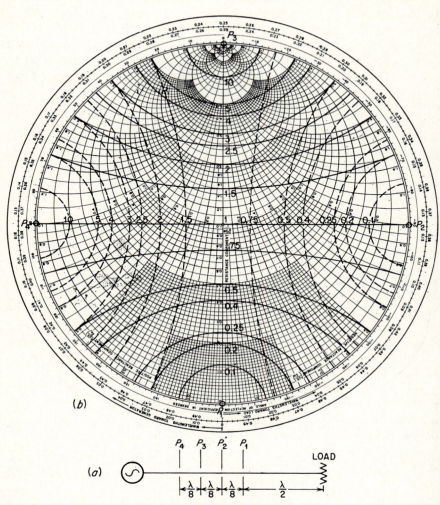

Fig. 5.49. A parametric chart for determination of impedance by the four-probe method. (a) The arrangement of the signal source, the load, and the four probes. The ratio of voltages read by the third probe to the first is shown in (b) by solid contours. The ratio of the fourth probe voltage to the second is shown as dashed. The values of the ratios are indicated on the curves. The parametric overlay is superimposed over the Smith chart so that probe P_1 may be used as the reference plane; i.e., impedance values determined from the Smith chart as shown correspond to the impedance at P_1.

ratios located on the previously prepared chart.   The impedance is then
determined from the Smith chart overlay.[1]

The four-probe method can be used over a range of frequencies by
constructing additional charts for each frequency of interest.   The usefulness of the method can be increased by the expedient of using voltage-
ratio meters.

5.13. Low-level Impedance Measurements.   It is sometimes necessary
to measure the r-f impedance of a device at extremely low power levels.
An example is the measurement of the input impedance of a receiver
which cannot be carried out with the standard slotted-line technique
because of the power level required for the probe detector.   The power
in the slotted section must be much higher than the power absorbed by
the probe in order to limit the probe errors; unless the power level in the
slotted section is of the order of 10^{-4} watt or greater, there will be insufficient signal to operate the indicator amplifier, especially when high
standing-wave ratios are being measured.   However, this may be too
high for proper operation of the receiver.   Interchanging the signal
generator and the indicator-amplifier connections to the slotted line substantially reduces the power level at which impedance measurements can
be made.   This arrangement is illustrated in Fig. 5.50.   Application of
the reciprocity theorem shows that, as long as the probe coupling is weak
enough to prevent the probe impedance from varying with the probe
position, the measurement of the standing-wave ratio and position of the
minima may be made in the conventional manner.

If a crystal under test is matched to the main transmission line, the
power required for satisfactory detection need not exceed 10^{-6} watt.   If
a converter-type receiver is used in place of the conventional square-law
detector, the measurements can be made at a level as low as 10^{-12} watt.
In this arrangement two receiver input impedances can be measured
simultaneously if they are connected at the opposite ends of the single
slotted line; as the probe is moved along the line, the variation in output
of one receiver is a measure of the input impedance of the second.[2]

5.14. Dynamic Presentation of Impedance Data.   It is often necessary
to make extensive experimental studies of the behavior of microwave
structures.   In some cases it is merely necessary to measure the variation
in impedance vs. frequency for some particular device; the various methods described above involving manipulations, observations, computations,
and final plotting of results are not particularly difficult or too time-consuming.   However, there are applications in which it is necessary to vary

---

[1] Referring to Fig. 5.49, the voltage at P_1 is used as the reference, resulting in ratios
of voltages of P_3 to P_1.   A voltage zero at P_1 would correspond to zero impedance at
P_1; hence, the Smith chart is oriented with its origin $(0,0)$ at P_1.

[2] Private communication to the author by E. T. Jaynes.

some parameter or parameters and to observe the resultant changes as a function of frequency. In impedance matching, for example, a given change may improve the matching at one frequency, but make it worse elsewhere. This makes it desirable to observe visually the impedance of a given structure as a function of frequency. A number of schemes have been devised which permit automatic presentation of impedance information, either on the face of an oscilloscope, or by scribing the results on a suitable chart. Most of the methods of measuring impedance described above can be modified to allow a rapid recording of data. A variety of

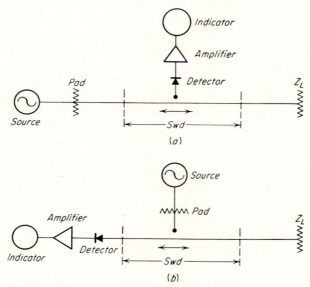

Fig. 5.50. Use of standing-wave detector apparatus for measurement of impedances at low level. The ordinary arrangement shown in (a) is rearranged for this purpose as shown in (b).

electrical and mechanical means are known; some of these are described to indicate a few of the possible approaches to the problem.

In some applications it is sufficient to present the absolute magnitude of the reflection coefficient or the standing-wave ratio. In others, the phase information is also essential, requiring the actual impedance to be plotted; it is often convenient to plot the data on the reflection plane.

Perhaps the simplest way to obtain impedance data dynamically is to use a mechanical reciprocating action to drive the carriage of a standing-wave detector back and forth. Alternatively, the slotted section can be built in a form of a partial circle and the probe can be rotated in the circular slot. The relative voltage as an audio signal can be displayed on an oscilloscope.

The reciprocating motion of the probe can be avoided by sweeping the standing-wave pattern by a fixed probe. This can be done by interposing between the load and the fixed probe a length of line whose electrical length can be varied rapidly. In waveguide transmission systems, the variation of electrical length can be accomplished easily by a number of expedients. One possibility is to provide two long slots in the wide faces of the rectangular waveguide to allow rapid mechanical squeezing of the waveguide; this changes the wavelength and, consequently, the electrical length of the intervening region. The guided wavelength can be also changed by rapidly moving a slab of dielectric material in the transverse direction of the waveguide.

In these schemes only the manual movement of the probe is eliminated. There is no simple way to transfer the impedance information to the impedance plane as a function of frequency.

The reflectometers described in Sec. 5.11 utilizing high directivity broadband directional couplers provide a means for rapid observation of the absolute magnitude of the reflection coefficient as a function of frequency. Usually, the variation of the frequency of signal source results in changes in amplitude so that a measurement of reflected signal is not sufficient to determine the magnitude of the reflection coefficient. However, using a ratio meter to determine the ratio of the magnitudes of the reflected and the incident signals avoids this difficulty. The reflectometer method is simple, convenient, and accurate for relatively low values of the reflection coefficient. In one application, the reflection coefficient was found to be determined to an accuracy of about 4 per cent over a band of frequencies of about 20 per cent.[1]

In using the reflectometer it is possible to determine the phase of the reflection coefficient by comparing the phase of the reflected and incident waves. An arrangement using three microwave mixers has been described which allows the comparison of phases to be accomplished at a constant frequency. The phase and magnitude are measured separately and the resultant vector value of the reflection coefficient is plotted automatically on a turntable.[2]

Another method which used four probes to obtain the necessary information, described by Samuel, is illustrated in Fig. 5.51.[3] These probes are used in pairs, each pair being spaced by a quarter-wavelength and the pairs being separated by one-eighth wavelength. Each probe is connected to a crystal rectifier which is presumed to be an accurate square-

---

[1] Hunton and Pappas, *op. cit.*

[2] D. D. King, "Measurements at Centimeter Wavelength," pp. 242–243, D. Van Nostrand Company, Inc., Princeton, N.J., 1952.

[3] A. L. Samuel, An Oscilloscope Method of Presenting Impedances on the Reflection-Coefficient Plane, *Proc. IRE*, vol. 35, no. 11, pp. 1279–1283, November, 1947.

law detector. The two crystals from one pair of probes are connected to a balanced circuit so that the difference in their outputs can be impressed on the one set of oscilloscope deflection plates. The difference from the second set of probes is similarly provided at the opposite deflection plates. If the frequency of the oscillator is varied but the amplitude is kept constant, the oscilloscope spot will describe the impedance variation in the

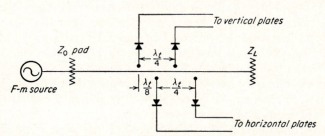

FIG. 5.51. Schematic representation of the four-probe method for presenting impedance information dynamically.

reflection coefficient plane. The center of the reflection coefficient plane can be determined by replacing the load with a short circuit.[1]

As can be seen from the theory, there are several inherent difficulties in the use of the four-probe method. Since the probes are separated by

[1] The principle of operation of the Samuel plotter can be demonstrated simply. If the incident wave, reflected wave, and the phase angle between them are V_i, V_r, and θ, respectively, then at some specific angular frequency ω the output from one of the crystals is

$$[V_i \cos \omega t + V_r \cos (\omega t + \theta)]^2 = V_i{}^2/2 + V_r{}^2/2 + V_i V_r \cos \theta + \text{r-f terms} \quad (5.57)$$

The output current from the second crystal of the pair is given by

$$\left[V_i \cos \left(\omega t + \frac{\pi}{2} \right) + V_r \cos \left(\omega t + \theta - \frac{\pi}{2} \right) \right]^2$$
$$= V_i{}^2/2 + V_r{}^2/2 - V_i V_r \cos \theta + \text{r-f terms} \quad (5.58)$$

The difference between these two crystals is introduced to the oscilloscope; the r-f terms disappear by filtering, leaving the difference

$$V_{p1} - V_{p2} = k V_i V_r \cos \theta \quad (5.59)$$

Similarly, the difference between the remaining probes can be formed and is given by

$$V_{p3} - V_{p4} = k V_i V_r \sin \theta \quad (5.60)$$

Thus, if the incident magnitude is constant, the position of the spot on the oscilloscope is given by the coordinates x and y,

$$x = V_r \cos \theta$$
$$y = V_r \sin \theta \quad (5.61)$$

If the frequency of the source is varied over a narrow range, the oscilloscope spot will trace the value of V_r in magnitude and phase in the reflection plane.

a fixed distance, they cannot be used in a manner indicated over a large frequency interval.   There are also a number of practical difficulties. Aside from the usual care to avoid distortion of the standing-wave pattern due to the presence of the probes, special attention must be paid to the detecting system; the response law of each detector must be identical, and the detector mounts must be sufficiently broadband so that their outputs remain constant over the frequency band used.   It is also difficult to maintain the signal generator output sufficiently constant over a large frequency interval.   In spite of these difficulties, in one model tested, Samuel reports an accuracy of the order of 5 per cent over about a 5 per cent frequency band at 3 cm.   Other more complicated sampling arrangements which are capable of improving the possibilities of this system are described in the reference cited.   Also, other promising sampling systems have been devised.[1]

Another type of automatic indicator capable of presenting the magnitude of phase and impedance at a number of closely spaced frequencies is described by Riblet.[2]   The fields in a waveguide are sampled by means of an ingeniously devised wave sampler.   The wave sampler is a form of the waveguide coupler with two output terminals.   At these terminals voltages are developed which are identical to the voltages that would be developed by two uncoupled probes placed in the waveguide one-quarter wavelength apart.   However, the wave sampler is able to provide these voltages in such a way that the equivalent probe separation is one-quarter wavelength regardless of frequency.   Upon detection with square-law detectors, the two voltages derived from the wave sampler become proportional to $V_i^2 + V_r^2 + 2V_iV_r \cos \theta$ and $V_i^2 + V_r^2 - 2V_iV_r \cos \theta$. These two voltages are introduced into a ratio meter, the output of which is connected to the vertical plates of the oscilloscope.   The horizontal plates of the oscilloscope are supplied by a voltage which is proportional to the frequency of the variable-frequency signal source.   The wave sampler and the load are separated by a long length of line; if the frequency of the signal source is varied by substantial amounts, the propagation constant in the transmission line changes.   As a result, the standing-wave pattern moves back and forth by the wave sampler in accordance with frequency variation of the signal source.   At a series of frequencies the angle θ becomes 0 and π.   Therefore, the ratio meter output produces alternatively the values

$$\left(\frac{V_i + V_r}{V_i - V_r}\right)^2 \quad \text{and} \quad \left(\frac{V_i - V_r}{V_i + V_r}\right)^2$$

[1] S. Cohn, Impedance Measurement by Means of a Broadband Circular-polarization Coupler, *Proc. IRE*, vol. 42, no. 10, pp. 1554–1558, October, 1954.

[2] H. J. Riblet, A Swept Frequency 3-cm Impedance Indicator, *Proc. IRE*, vol. 36, no. 12, pp. 1493–1499, December, 1948.

For a 3-ft separation between the load and the wave sampler at 3 cm, these values are obtained once for every 1 per cent change in wavelength. These values can be recognized as the square of the standing-wave ratio and its reciprocal, respectively.   Therefore, the pattern presented on the oscilloscope represents the true values of the standing-wave ratio at a series of wavelengths.   The points of maximum response are the wavelengths at which the impedance at the wave sampler is a pure resistance. Since the wavelengths at which this happens can be measured, the known length of transmission line between the wave sampler and the load enables one to determine the phase as well as the magnitude of the terminating impedance at the specific wavelengths.   Although the evaluation of the phase angle is not obtained automatically, the impedance variation can be detected over an appreciable bandwidth quickly.

The performance of the Riblet impedance indicator is roughly comparable to the device described by Samuel in its accuracy, but has been demonstrated to cover a wider frequency range.   An accurate way of using the equipment is to tune the oscillator slowly across the frequency interval and to record the maxima and minima values of the output together with the frequencies at which they occur.   The device can be calibrated by replacing the unknown load by a termination.   More rapid observations are obtained by mechanical sweeping of the oscillator.

Still another form of an impedance recorder uses the reflectometer principle together with a specially designed phase discriminator.   A ratio meter determines the absolute magnitude of the reflection coefficient; a servo-driven phase discriminator derives the phase information.   The result can be presented as an ink graph on a Smith Chart.   In one model tested, good accuracy could be obtained over the frequency range of 8,400 to 9,900 mc.*

* W. F. Gabriel, An Automatic Impedance Recorder for X-band, *Proc. IRE*, vol. 42, no. 9, pp. 1410–1412, September, 1954.

CHAPTER 6

REPRESENTATION AND MEASUREMENT OF MICROWAVE CIRCUITS

6.1. Introduction. It is convenient to think of microwave-transmission systems as being composed of sections of uniform transmission lines joined together through coupling networks or transducers. It is assumed that the reader has an adequate understanding of the behavior of uniform transmission lines; therefore, this chapter is concerned with those topics which are helpful in understanding the propagation of electromagnetic waves through regions of geometrical discontinuity at which the normal transmission line theory does not apply. Examples of simple coupling networks are common waveguide components, such as bends or twists; a more complicated network is the junction of several transmission lines; still more complicated structures include cavity filters, attenuators, mode changers, antennas, mixers, etc. It is often useful to describe the characteristic behavior of such networks in terms of equivalent circuits; by establishing proper correspondence between the actual microwave device and its equivalent circuit, it is possible to predict the behavior of the micro-

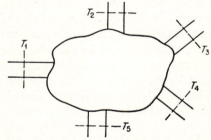

Fig. 6.1. The general N-terminal microwave circuit. Reference planes T_n must be located within uniform transmission lines.

wave network by conventional circuit analysis. The equivalent circuit representation is also helpful in understanding intuitively the microwave network and leads to systematic design, study, and testing.

The representation of microwave circuits by equivalent circuits is based upon the concept of the normalized voltage and current discussed in Chap. 4. With the aid of these, the electromagnetic-field quantities can be described in terms of equivalent voltage and current. The appearance of the general microwave structure is shown in Fig. 6.1, where the transmission lines are assumed to be uniform. A number of reference planes, T_1, T_2, . . . , T_n sufficiently far from the regions of geometrical

313

discontinuity are selected arbitrarily; the higher-order modes present in the vicinity of these discontinuities attenuate rapidly with distance so that their only effect is to determine the boundary conditions at the discontinuity. The incident and reflected waves in each branch can propagate only in the dominant mode of transmission of the particular branch. At the selected reference planes, the microwave circuit can be described by appropriate sets of normalized voltages and currents which formally correspond to the ordinary voltages and currents of an arbitrary electrical network. Thus, the field analysis of the microwave network can proceed in exact analogy to the development of the circuit theory. With the aid of Kirchhoff's law and the principle of superposition, many familiar expressions can be derived, including the important network expressions relating the voltage-current sets at the input and output terminals. Thus, the multiterminal microwave circuit within the boundaries defined by the reference planes can be readily studied by the conventional circuit theory.

In deriving the equivalent circuit, it is necessary to establish a set of convenient terminals or reference planes on all sides of the discontinuity region. The intervening region and the sections of uniform transmission lines within the boundaries delineated by the plane selected can be called the *microwave circuit*. The process of selection of the terminal planes is one of the distinguishing features of the microwave circuit analysis. At low frequencies, the location of the circuit terminals is self-evident; however, at microwave frequencies, the arbitrary choice of reference planes determines the physical appearance of the equivalent circuit and the magnitude of the circuit parameters. Although the selection of the reference planes is arbitrary, there is usually a logical choice for a particular set, either because this simplifies the mathematical manipulations or because of some other obvious uniqueness.[1]

Microwave circuits, as well as their low-frequency equivalents, may involve any number of terminals. A complete description of N-pair terminal network requires $N(N + 1)$ constants. The study of a complex multiterminal network can be reduced to the analysis of a four-terminal network by terminating all but two terminal-pairs in known impedances. A complete description of the network requires the measurement of input-output relations as many times as there are pairs of terminals. By this procedure, the analysis of the multiterminal network is straightforward, although in practice it may prove to be difficult. For simplicity, the following material is restricted almost exclusively to the study of the four-terminal structures.

[1] The inclusion of an arbitrary length of uniform transmission line with the microwave circuit is equivalent to cascading two microwave circuits—the circuit proper, and another, consisting of a length of transmission line.

The microwave circuit can be represented in several ways: as in the low-frequency network theory, numerous forms of equivalent circuits can be found. The T, π, lattice, ladder, and other networks can be used to describe the behavior of an arbitrary four-terminal network; which of these, if any, it is logical to use depends upon the physical configuration of the microwave circuit. In general, the four-terminal network can be represented by specifying three independent complex constants. In using the T network the three constants can be written in the form of the three impedances indicated in Fig. 6.3. Alternatively, the three constants can be written in terms of the *reflection* or *scattering* coefficients which are determined by considering the reflection of traveling waves incident upon the network from both directions. The scattering representation is a different mathematical description of the terminal impedance conditions. To determine either the impedance or scattering coefficients it is necessary to measure the input impedance of the network for three independent conditions at the output.

Another method of finding the equivalent circuit is based upon the analysis of the circle diagram which results from the input impedance measurement when the output terminals are terminated in a movable short circuit. It can be shown that an arbitrary lossy network can be represented in two parts, one a resistive network and the other a lossless four-terminal network. Both of the networks can be specified from the characteristics of the circle diagram, leading to the so-called *canonical* network which describes the behavior of the network with a minimum number of parameters.

Another method of representation is based upon the experimental procedure just described and may be regarded as a generalization of the nodal-shift experiment described in Chap. 5. The previous discussion of the method was restricted to the study of lossless networks, but it can be extended to include the more general case. The coefficients appearing in the tangent expression can be used to describe the characteristics of the network; this procedure is especially useful for the study of lossless networks, because it leads to a particularly simple set of constants, i.e., a set of uniquely defined reference planes and an ideal transformer.

The various methods of representation of a given microwave circuit are merely different ways of examining the same physical structure. All of the representations are related to each other through straightforward mathematical equations and can be converted from one to the other as necessary. The choice of the particular representation depends upon the particular problem, the familiarity of the individual with the methods of analysis, and the proposed application.

The presence of symmetry in a given structure can lead to substantial

simplification of the equivalent circuit. Often a simple and logical interpretation results from the proper choice of the reference planes. The
symmetry conditions can be used in the derivation of the equivalent
circuit by employing standing-wave field solutions in the region of the
discontinuity. These methods permit the fringing fields in the vicinity
of the discontinuity to be taken into account and result in equivalent
circuits which closely correspond to the low-frequency analogues of the
physical structure. For example, the symmetry methods predict qualitatively the division of power between the branches of waveguide T junction by showing that its equivalent circuit is a T junction, modified as
indicated in Fig. 5.39.

In approaching an experimental study of a microwave structure, it is of
paramount importance to know the number of circuit constants required
for a complete description of the particular circuit. This knowledge
determines the number of independent experiments which must be performed. Also, the arrangement of the components in an equivalent
circuit is helpful in selecting the proper types of experiments. The symmetry considerations make it possible to predict both the nature of the
equivalent circuit and the number of independent circuit parameters
needed for its complete description.[1] The study of the dominant fields
far from the discontinuity region cannot predict the values of the circuit
constants. The stored energy represented by the fringing fields associated with the physical discontinuities is determined by the details of the
boundary conditions at the discontinuity. In order to compute the circuit constants, it is necessary to know the actual field distribution
throughout the microwave network. In nearly all practical cases, mathematical solutions of the boundary value problem are too complicated to
be attempted. It is, therefore, necessary to evaluate the circuit constants by purely experimental procedures.

Thus, the equivalent circuit of a microwave network can be obtained
in one of two ways. In the first, an arbitrary equivalent circuit is
selected, such as a T or a π; appropriate experiments are conducted from
which the circuit parameters can be computed resulting in either the
circuit parameters or the scattering coefficients. In the second approach
the physical characteristics of the circuit are first examined with the
principal emphasis on the symmetry properties of the structure. The
result is an equivalent circuit which differs from its low-frequency
counterpart because of the presence of the fringing reactances at the
various discontinuities. The experimental evaluation of the parameters
of the equivalent circuit are carried out in a manner suggested by its form.

The equivalent circuit concepts have numerous practical applications.

---

[1] J. C. Slater, "Microwave Electronics," chaps. 6 and 7, D. Van Nostrand Company,
Inc., Princeton, N.J., 1950.

For example, the insertion loss of a four-terminal microwave device (such as a section of r-f cable) can be determined by finding the scattering coefficients of the network. Although the procedures used in the measurement of the attenuation of a section of radio-frequency cable can be understood with the aid of simpler concepts, the more general analysis puts the specialized technique into its proper perspective as a part of the method of measuring the entire set of circuit parameters; this results in the simultaneous determination of the loss, impedance of the cable, and the reflection at its terminals. Another example showing the usefulness of equivalent circuit is the explanation of the behavior of the waveguide T junction. This demonstrates that it is possible to transmit power around a corner through a properly constructed junction without reflection; and that reflectionless transmission is impossible if the tuning stub at the corner of the T is not symmetrical with respect to the transmission arms of the junction. In general, the equivalent circuit concepts are useful because they predict the behavior of microwave circuits in terms of easily understood phenomena. These procedures allow one to group microwave components together in the design of complex structures as if one were grouping ordinary circuit constants. The design of microwave circuits can become as simple as it is at low frequencies if the equivalent circuit of the individual components is known and if it is remembered that the equivalent circuits are valid only at the special reference planes.

In the following sections of this chapter the various methods of representation are described, together with a summary of the mathematical relations which interconnect the more important forms; the natural experimental techniques in arriving at the various representations are also given together with a number of methods for analyzing the data. The reader is referred to the numerous references in the literature for further study of these topics.[1-8]

6.2. Some Possible Methods of Representation. Among the possible methods of representing microwave circuits are the following:

a. T and π Networks. Since Maxwell's equations are linear and because the reciprocity theorem applies to the electromagnetic field under the

[1] S. A. Schelkunoff, "Electromagnetic Waves," chap. 12, D. Van Nostrand Company, Inc., Princeton, N.J., 1943.

[2] C. G. Montgomery, R. H. Dickey, and E. M. Purcell, "Principles of Microwave Circuits," McGraw-Hill Book Company, Inc., New York, 1948. This is the most comprehensive treatment of the subject.

[3] "The Representation, Measurement, and Calculation of Equivalent Circuits for Waveguide Discontinuities with Application to Rectangular Slots," Polytechnic Institute of Brooklyn Microwave Research Institute, 1949. Useful reference in connection with representation and measurement of microwave circuits.

[4] L. B. Felsen, Measurement of Impedance and Other Equivalent Representation,

usual restrictions, the discontinuity region described at two arbitrarily chosen reference planes (as illustrated in Fig. 6.2) can be described in terms of the usual voltage-current relations:

$$V_1 = Z_{11}I_1 + Z_{12}I_2$$
$$V_2 = Z_{12}I_1 + Z_{22}I_2$$

$$(6.1)$$

These voltage-current relationships contain constants which have the units of impedance but do not in themselves correspond to any particular part of the circuit. However, application of Kirchhoff mesh rules to the

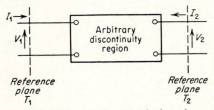

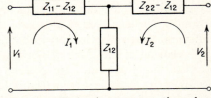

FIG. 6.2. Voltage-current relations in an arbitrary four-terminal network.

FIG. 6.3. T-circuit representation of an arbitrary circuit.

T network shown in Fig. 6.3 verifies that this arrangement corresponds to the network equations given by Eq. (6.1). Thus, the T network shown can be used to represent an arbitrary four-terminal network contained between reference planes T_1 and T_2.*

The parameters of the T network can be determined in several ways. Since there are three independent constants, at least three independent

chap. 6, in M. Wind and H. Rapaport (eds.), "Handbook of Microwave Measurements" *Polytechnic Institute of Brooklyn Microwave Research Institute Rept.* R-352-53, PIB-286, 1954.

[5] A. Weissfloch, Circle Geometric Four-terminal Network Theory; Its Significance as a Circuit Theory at Microwaves, *Hochfrequenztechnik und Elektroakustik*, pp. 100–123, April, 1943.

[6] L. B. Felsen and A. A. Oliner, Determination of Equivalent Circuit Parameters for Dissipative Microwave Structures, *Proc. IRE*, vol. 42, no. 2, pp. 477–483, 1954.

[7] G. A. Deschamps, Determination of Reflection Coefficients and Insertion Loss of a Wave-guide Junction, *J. Appl. Phys.*, vol. 24, no. 8, pp. 1046–1050, August, 1953.

[8] J. E. Storer, L. S. Sheingold, and S. Stein, A Simple Graphical Analysis of a Two-port Waveguide Junction, *Proc. IRE*, vol. 41, no. 8, pp. 1004–1013, August, 1953; also F. L. Wentworth and D. R. Barthel, A Simplified Calibration of Two-port Transmission Line Devices, *Trans. IRE*, vol. MTT-4, no. 3, pp. 173–175, July, 1956.

* The justification for the above procedure is straightforward. Following the procedure described in Sec. 4.7, a set of traveling waves propagating along the input transmission line can be expressed in terms of the normalized voltage and current. In response to this set, there is a traveling-wave set propagating in the output waveguide; a reflected wave set also exists on the input side because of the possible presence of a discontinuity. The total normalized voltage and current on the input side consists of the sum of the reflected and incident waves. The ratio of total voltage to

measurements of input impedance are needed.   The output line at plane T_2 can be terminated in zero, infinity, and some other known impedance. Measurement of corresponding values of impedance at T_1 allows evaluation of the equivalent circuit parameters.   This procedure is discussed more fully in Sec. 6.3.

  b. Scattering-coefficient Representation.   An analysis of the behavior of the microwave circuits shown in Figs. 6.1 and 6.2 by considering the traveling waves at the selected reference planes results in the use of reflection or *scattering* coefficients.

  The electromagnetic fields at each of the terminal planes can be written in terms of the normalized voltage and current.   Following the notation introduced in Chap. 4, the transverse electric and magnetic fields can be written as follows:

$$E_t^i(x,y) = V_1^i F_1(x,y)$$
$$H_t^i(x,y) = I_1^i F_1(x,y) \qquad (6.2)$$

The function F_1 is normalized; therefore, the coefficients V_1 and I_1 are interpreted as voltage and current.   The subscript 1 indicates that the dominant mode is being considered; the superscript i indicates that this set represents the incident wave.   Similarly, the reflected wave set indicated by the superscript r is

$$E_t^r(x,y) = V_1^i F_1(x,y)$$
$$H_t^r(x,y) = -I_1^i F_1(x,y) \qquad (6.3)$$

The total voltage and current are the sum of the incident and reflected waves.   If M_1 represents the wave admittance for the dominant mode, the total voltages and currents become

$$V_1 = V_1^i + V_1^r$$
$$I_1 = M_1(V_1^i - V_1^r)$$
since $\qquad\qquad I_1^i = M_1 V_1^i \qquad (6.4)$

In these equations the electric and magnetic fields are vector quantities and are a function of time.   The coefficients V and I are, therefore, complex quantities.   For simplicity, the voltage coefficients can be written as

$$a = V_1^i \qquad \text{and} \qquad b = V_1^r \qquad (6.5)$$

total current on the input side depends upon the characteristics of the network. The proportionality factor Z_{11} is called the impedance coefficient of the input side. In general, the voltage at any terminal is due to the superposition of the voltages imposed upon the circuit at all of its terminals.   This procedure is carried out in a manner analogous to the ordinary circuit theory; however, since normalized voltages and currents are used, the result is applicable to waveguide structures of an arbitrary character.

The total voltage and current become

$$V_1 = a + b$$
$$I_1 = M_1(a - b) \tag{6.6}$$

The incident and reflected waves can be written for each of the arms of the microwave circuit in this form. The incident wave propagating toward the circuit in the nth arm is called a_n. The corresponding "reflected" wave in the nth arm is called b_{mn}; the first subscript refers to the number of the arm in which the signal is observed and the second to the number of the arm where the signal is introduced. In general, in response to the illumination of the microwave circuit at the nth arm, reflected signals will propagate *away* from the circuit in all of the arms. These waves are known as *partial reflected* waves since the illumination is due to one arm only. Thus, b_{21} refers to the wave flowing away from the junction in the second arm when a generator is connected to the first arm. The partial reflected waves b_{mn} are proportional to the signals which create them. The complete set of partial reflected waves is

$$b_{11} = S_{11}a_1$$
$$b_{21} = S_{21}a_1$$
$$\cdot$$
$$\cdot \tag{6.7}$$
$$\cdot$$
$$b_{n1} = S_{n1}a_1$$

in which a_1 is the magnitude of the signal in arm number one. Similarly, if the signal is present in the second arm, the partial waves due to this source are

$$b_{12} = S_{12}a_2$$
$$b_{22} = S_{22}a_2$$
$$\cdot$$
$$\cdot \tag{6.8}$$
$$\cdot$$
$$B_{N2} = S_{N2}a_2$$

In general, if excited by the mth arm, these are

$$b_{1m} = S_{1m}a_m$$
$$\cdot$$
$$\cdot \tag{6.9}$$
$$\cdot$$
$$b_{Nm} = S_{Nm}a_m$$

The constants which relate the incident and reflected waves, S_{Nm}, are called *scattering coefficients*. It can be shown that in the case of transmission lines filled with ordinary substances, reciprocity conditions require that $S_{nm} = S_{mn}$.

The total signal reflected from the microwave circuit is obtained by summing the partial waves in the particular arm. Thus,

$$b_1 = \sum_{m=1}^{m=N} b_{1m}$$

$$\cdot$$
$$\cdot \tag{6.10}$$
$$\cdot$$

$$b_N = \sum_{m=1}^{m=N} b_{Nm}$$

For the four-terminal case ($N = 2$), Eq. (6.10) becomes

$$b_1 = b_{11} + b_{12}$$
$$b_2 = b_{21} + b_{22} \tag{6.11}$$

Making use of Eq. (6.9), these become

$$b_1 = S_{11}a_1 + S_{12}a_2$$
$$b_2 = S_{12}a_1 + S_{22}a_2 \tag{6.12}$$

The scattering equations, Eqs. (6.12), correspond closely to the impedance relations given by Eq. (6.1) and provide an alternate method of describing the characteristics of the four-terminal network. Determination of the scattering coefficients, S_{11}, S_{12}, and S_{22}, is sufficient to completely specify the characteristics of the four-terminal network.

The scattering coefficients have a simple meaning. If $a_2 = 0$, there is no incident signal upon the circuit from arm 2. This corresponds to matching arm 2 in its characteristic impedance. S_{11}, therefore, corresponds to the reflection due to the network under these conditions. Similarly, S_{22} determines the reflection as seen from arm 2 if arm 1 is matched in its characteristic impedance. The coefficient S_{12} determines the insertion loss of the network, including both the dissipation and reflection losses. The simple interpretation of the scattering coefficients also suggests experimental methods for their measurement.

Since reflection coefficients are complex quantities, the scattering coefficients are complex likewise. Although their magnitudes are independent of the selection of the reference planes, the phase angle depends upon their location.

c. The Tangent (Transformer) Method. The experimental study of four-terminal networks often consists of measuring the input impedances corresponding to a series of reactances at the output terminals provided by a movable short circuit. The resultant information can be evaluated in various ways, leading to either an equivalent circuit or the scattering representation. The experimental data obtained in this manner have certain characteristics which uniquely specify the four-terminal network; this also can be used as a basis of representation.

The simplest point of departure is to recall the theory of the nodal shift experiment discussed in Sec. 5.8. In a lossless network, the relation between the position of a voltage node on one side of the network and the position of a short circuit on the other is given by Eq. (5.36), repeated below:

$$\tan \beta_1 x_1 = r \tan \beta_2 x_2 \qquad (6.13)$$

If the origins of x_1 and x_2 are selected as discussed in Sec. 5.8 at x_1' and x_2', respectively, Eq. (6.13) becomes

$$\tan \beta_1 (x_1 - x_1') = r \tan \beta_2 (x_2 - x_2') \qquad (6.14)$$

This tangent expression leads to the nodal-shift curves whose geometrical properties can be used to identify the parameters of the network. The location of the two reference planes, i.e., values of x_1' and x_2', taken together with the standing-wave ratio r or the distance D serve to completely specify the characteristics of the network, so that the network becomes equivalent to an ideal transformer.

In principle, the tangent method can be extended to encompass dissipative networks as well. Equation (6.14) is applicable to lossy networks if x_1', x_2', and r are allowed to assume a more general meaning. It can be shown that in the presence of loss x_1' becomes a complex quantity. The real part of x_1' has the usual meaning and specifies the location of the reference plane at which the voltage minimum is found in the input waveguide. The imaginary part of x_1' is determined by the standing-wave ratio in the input waveguide. The coefficients x_2' and r may become complex also, so that none of the quantities in the tangent expression can be so simply identified with the physical quantities as is possible in the lossless case. Nevertheless, it is possible to find the complex parameters which will predict the experimental results analogous to the nodal-shift method when inserted into Eq. (6.14). This can be done as follows:

If the nodal-shift experiment described in Sec. 5.8 is carried out, the impedances provided at the output terminals of the network are given by

$$\frac{Z_{\text{out}}}{Z_2} = j \tan \beta_2 x_2 \qquad (6.15)$$

On the input side a standing-wave ratio r will be observed with a voltage minimum at the distance x_r to the right of an arbitrarily selected reference plane. The impedance at the voltage minimum is given by

$$Z_L = \frac{1}{r} \qquad (6.16)$$

The input impedance Z_{in} at this reference plane is, therefore,

$$\frac{Z_{in}}{Z_1} = \frac{1/r + j \tan \beta x_r}{1 + j(1/r) \tan \beta x_r} \tag{6.17}$$

where Z_1 is the characteristic impedance of the input guide. Equation (6.17) is recognized as the trigonometric equality of the tangent of a sum of two angles. Therefore, it can be written as

$$\frac{Z_{in}}{Z_1} = j \tan \beta(x_r + jx_i) \tag{6.18}$$

where $x_i = (1/2\pi) \tanh^{-1}(1/r)$. In order to describe the network by means of this approach, it is necessary to obtain a set of values of x_r, x_i, and r.

The experimental procedure for evaluating these constants consists of determining x_r and x_i as a function of the position of the short circuit x_2. These values must be obtained with respect to arbitrary reference planes, because there is no way to obtain the location of the reference planes directly such as using the median line in the lossless case. A trial set of r, x_1', and x_2' can be assumed and substituted into Eq. (6.14) to see if the resultant values of x_r and x_i correspond to the measured set. This trial procedure is not practical because r, x_1', and x_2' may all be complex; it is desirable to obtain the initial trial set of constants in some other way. A simpler procedure is to determine the scattering coefficients and use them to calculate the tangent parameters to find the approximate location of the reference planes, leading to the first approximation of x_r and x_i. Repeating the process of approximation eventually gives the values of x_r and x_i which, taken together with r, satisfy Eq. (6.14) to the limit of experimental accuracy.

The tangent approach to the analysis of networks with dissipation is cumbersome. In practice, therefore, it is generally restricted to dissipationless circuits, in which it provides a simple method of recording and cataloguing the characteristics of networks without additional analysis or calculations.

d. Canonical Networks. The nodal-shift or tangent method represents a powerful technique for the experimental study of four-terminal networks. Although formally applicable to both lossless and lossy networks, the direct interpretation of the nodal-shift data is simple only in the former case. However, there exists a graphical interpretation of the nodal-shift experiment which enables one to describe the nodal-shift results in terms of an equivalent circuit. The method, first introduced by Weissfloch,[1] was improved by Felsen and Oliner.[2] This results in

[1] Weissfloch, *op. cit.*

[2] Felsen and Oliner, *op. cit.*

an equivalent circuit which has a simple physical meaning. The experimental determination of the network constants can be made with good accuracy because the final circuit parameters are obtained after averaging of the laboratory data.

The general four-terminal dissipating network can be separated into lossy and lossless parts. The parameters of the dissipative part can be obtained directly from the plot of the input impedance on the Smith chart; this automatically establishes a logical reference plane. The remaining part of the circuit can be represented as a four-terminal lossless network whose parameters can be interpreted easily by means of a graphical procedure. The final circuit representation, termed the

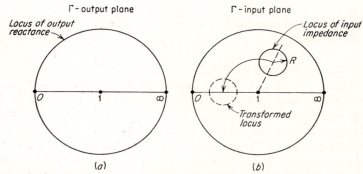

FIG. 6.4. Input-output impedance loci used in deriving the canonical circuit. A four-terminal network is terminated in the lossless movable short circuit and the resultant impedances are measured at the input terminals. (a) The locus of impedances at the output terminals; (b) the locus of input impedance. The small solid circle represents the impedance seen at some arbitrary input terminals; transformation of the locus to the dotted position determines the input reference plane.

canonical circuit by Felsen and Oliner, represents the observed experimental behavior of the network with a minimum number of elements.

If the network is terminated in a movable short circuit, the locus of the reactances at the output terminals is the periphery circle of the Smith Chart shown in Fig. 6.4a. The corresponding measured input impedances fall on a circle shown in Fig. 6.4b. If the impedances were to be measured with respect to an arbitrary reference plane, the circle would lie in some position as shown in Fig. 6.4b. However, the reference plane can be shifted to transform the observed locus to that shown in dotted form. The particular reference plane which makes the observed circle symmetrical about the resistance axis is used to define the reference plane on the input side.

The details of the transformed circle are shown in Fig. 6.5a, and an equivalent circuit representing the behavior of the network in Fig. 6.5b.

It can be shown that the equivalent circuit has the proper characteristics to represent the observed behavior of the input impedance.   The choice of the input reference plane, in the manner described, and the resistances R_s and R_p specify the dissipative part of the circuit.   The parameters X_p, transformer ratio n, and the choice of the output reference plane form the three additional parameters to make a set of six needed to specify completely the four-terminal network.   The output reference plane T_2 is chosen as that position of the short circuit which causes the input impedance to be equal to R_s.   The resistances R_s and R_p, completely specified by the diameter of the input impedance circle and its radial position, are independent of the choice of the reference plane T_1; for this reason, they are often referred to as *distance-invariant* parameters.

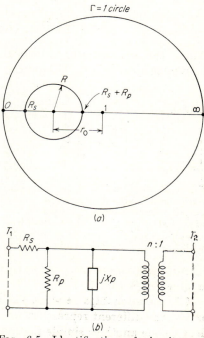

Although the canonical method provides a simple way to interpret the laboratory data and represent the characteristics of the network, it also has certain undesirable features.   The characteristic elements of the canonical network shown in Fig. 6.5b are unsymmetrical, although the physical structure may be inherently symmetrical about some geometrical plane.   The existence of physical symmetry in the structure suggests that the canonical structure can be altered so that the resultant electrical circuit becomes symmetrical with respect to

FIG. 6.5. Identification of circuit constants in the canonical representation. (a) The cardinal points in the impedance locus; (b) the canonical equivalent circuit.

the two sets of terminals.   There are situations in which the symmetrical representation of a symmetrical physical structure is more desirable than the equally valid asymmetric circuit.

An electrical circuit of the canonical form can be made symmetrical by shifting the reference plane T_2 to a new position T_2' so its physical position is symmetrical with respect to plane T_1 about the symmetry plane of the structure.   The physical shift of the reference plane T_2 to T_2' can be represented by adding a series reactance to the canonical circuit as shown in Fig. 6.6.   By equating the open-circuit impedances as seen from both sets of terminals, it can be shown that the new canonical network is symmetrical if

$$X' = - \frac{R_s R_p}{X'_p} \tag{6.19}$$

$$\frac{1}{n'^2} = 1 + \frac{R_s}{R_p} - \frac{X'}{X'_p} \tag{6.20}$$

The physical shift of the reference plane from T_2 to T'_2 is given by

$$\tan \beta l = \left(\frac{1}{n^2} - \frac{R_s}{R_p} - 1 \right) X_p \tag{6.21}$$

Thus, the symmetrical canonical network can be obtained from the unsymmetrical one by computing the new circuit constants from these relations. Alternatively, the lossy section of the circuit can be obtained as before, together with the input reference plane T_1; the output reference plane T_2 is then chosen by symmetry, and the remaining circuit constants derived directly.

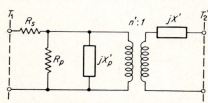

Fig. 6.6. Modification of the canonical representation by displacement of the output reference plane. Proper choice of the latter for a physically symmetrical network leads to electrical symmetry with respect to the new terminal planes.

The simple interpretation of circuit elements in the equivalent network, in either the symmetrical or unsymmetrical form, suggests numerous ways to obtain the required circuit parameters from laboratory data. An example of this procedure is given in Sec. 6.5.

6.3. Relationships between Various Representations. As stated previously, the different representations of the microwave circuits are equivalent to one another; simple mathematical relations can be found to interconnect them. The following are among the most useful.

a. T Network and Scattering Representation. The elements of the T network shown in Fig. 6.3 can be related to the scattering coefficients as follows: From the second half of Eq. (6.12) it is found that

$$\frac{a_2}{a_1} = \frac{S_{12}}{b_2/a_2 - S_{22}} \tag{6.22}$$

Define $\Gamma_{in} = b_1/a_1$ and $\Gamma_{out} = a_2/b_2$. Using the first half of Eq. (6.12), Eq. (6.22), and these definitions,

$$\Gamma_{in} = S_{11} - \frac{S_{12}^2}{S_{22} - 1/\Gamma_{out}} \tag{6.23}$$

Similarly, from Eq. (6.1) and Fig. 6.2 (with $Z_{in} = V_1/I_1$, $Z_{out} = -V_2/I_2$,

$Z_{in}/Z_1 = Z'_{in}$, $Z_{out}/Z_2 = Z'_{out}$),

$$\frac{V_1}{I_1} = Z_{11} + Z_{12}\frac{V_2}{I_1}$$

Hence,

$$Z_{in} = Z_{11} - \frac{Z_{12}{}^2}{Z_{out} + Z_{22}} \tag{6.24}$$

or

$$Z_{in} = \frac{Z_{11}Z_{out} + (Z_{11}Z_{22} - Z_{12}{}^2)}{Z_{out} + Z_{22}} \tag{6.25}$$

Also, if $Z_{in}/Z_1 = Z'_{in}$, and $Z_{out}/Z_2 = Z'_{out}$,

$$Z'_{in} = \frac{1 + \Gamma_{in}}{1 - \Gamma_{in}}$$

$$Z'_{out} = \frac{1 + \Gamma_{out}}{1 - \Gamma_{out}} \tag{6.26}$$

or

$$\Gamma_{in} = \frac{Z'_{in} - 1}{Z'_{in} + 1}$$

$$\Gamma_{out} = \frac{Z'_{out} - 1}{Z'_{out} + 1} \tag{6.27}$$

Combining Eqs. (6.23) and (6.27) and solving for Z'_{in} in terms of Z'_{out}, a complicated expression results having the form of Eq. (6.25). By a comparison with Eq. (6.25), the coefficients Z_{11}, Z_{22}, and Z_{12} are found to be

$$Z_{11} = \frac{1 + S_{11} - S_{22} - S_{11}S_{22} + S_{12}{}^2}{1 - S_{11} - S_{22} + S_{11}S_{22} - S_{12}{}^2} \tag{6.28}$$

$$Z_{22} = \frac{1 - S_{12} + S_{22} - S_{11}S_{22} + S_{12}{}^2}{1 - S_{11} - S_{22} + S_{11}S_{22} - S_{12}{}^2} \tag{6.29}$$

$$\frac{Z_{12}}{\sqrt{Z_1 Z_2}} = \frac{2S_{12}}{1 - S_{11} - S_{22} + S_{11}S_{22} - S_{12}{}^2} \tag{6.30}$$

$$Z_{11}Z_{22} - Z_{12}{}^2 = \frac{1 + S_{11} + S_{22} + S_{11}S_{22} - S_{12}{}^2}{1 - S_{11} - S_{22} + S_{11}S_{22} - S_{12}{}^2} \tag{6.31}$$

The set of Eqs. (6.28) to (6.31) allows the conversion of scattering coefficients into the generalized T network shown in Eq. (6.3); this procedure can be carried out also in terms of the π circuit. These equations can be inverted to provide the scattering coefficient from the T circuit constants.

b. *T Network and Tangent Relationship.* For the special case of the lossless network a simple relationship exists between the tangent and the T circuit parameters. Expression (6.14) contains the three parameters of a lossless network, i.e., x'_1, x'_2, and r. These can be related to the T circuit constants of Fig. 6.3. Using trigonometric identities, Eq. (6.14) can be written as

$$\frac{\tan \beta_1 x_1 - \tan \beta x_1'}{1 + \tan \beta_1 x_1 \tan \beta x_1'} = r \frac{\tan \beta x_2 - \tan \beta x_2'}{1 + \tan \beta x_2 \tan \beta x_2'} \quad (6.32)$$

Let $a = \tan \beta x_1'$ and $b = \tan \beta x_2'$. Equation (6.32) can then be written as

$$(b - ar) \tan \beta_1 x_1 \tan \beta_2 x_2 + (1 + abr) \tan \beta_1 x_1 - (ab + r) \tan \beta_2 x_2$$
$$- (a - br) = 0 \quad (6.33)$$

If Eq. (6.25) is expanded, there results

$$\frac{Z_{in}}{Z_1} \frac{Z_{out}}{Z_2} + \frac{Z_{22}}{Z_2} \frac{Z_{in}}{Z_1} - \frac{Z_{11}}{Z_1} \frac{Z_{out}}{Z_2} - \frac{Z_{11}}{Z_1} \frac{Z_{22}}{Z_2} - \frac{Z_{12}{}^2}{Z_1 Z_2} = 0 \quad (6.34)$$

From the theory of the nodal-shift experiment, the input and output impedances are given by Eqs. (5.34) and (5.35). These are

$$\begin{aligned} Z_{in} &= jZ_1 \tan \beta_1 x_1 \\ Z_{out} &= jZ_2 \tan \beta_2 x_2 \end{aligned} \quad (6.35)$$

With the aid of these, Eq. (6.33) may be rewritten as

$$(b - ar) \frac{Z_{in}}{Z_1} \frac{Z_{out}}{Z_2} - (1 + abr) \frac{Z_{in}}{jZ_1} + (ab + r) \frac{Z_{out}}{jZ_2} + (a - br) = 0 \quad (6.36)$$

or

$$\frac{Z_{in}}{Z_1} \frac{Z_{out}}{Z_2} + j \frac{1 + abr}{b - ar} \frac{Z_{in}}{Z_1} - j \frac{ab + r}{b - ar} \frac{Z_{out}}{Z_2} + \frac{a - br}{b - ar} = 0 \quad (6.37)$$

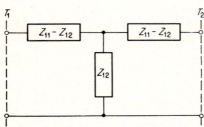

FIG. 6.7. Symmetrical T circuit derived from symmetric canonical representation.

Comparing Eqs. (6.34) and (6.37), it is found that

$$\frac{Z_{11}}{Z_1} = j \frac{r + ab}{ar - b} \quad (6.38)$$

$$\frac{Z_{22}}{Z_2} = j \frac{abr + 1}{ar - b} \quad (6.39)$$

$$\frac{Z_{11}}{Z_1} \frac{Z_{22}}{Z_2} - \frac{Z_{12}{}^2}{Z_1 Z_2} = \frac{a - br}{ar - b} \quad (6.40)$$

Equations (6.38), (6.39), and (6.40) can be inverted to provide tangent expression constants in terms of T circuit parameters.

c. *T Circuit and Canonical Relationship.* The equivalence between the symmetric canonical circuit and the symmetric T network can be obtained by comparing the short-circuit and open-circuit impedances of Figs. 6.6 and 6.7, including the symmetry conditions given by Eqs. (6.19) and (6.20). The resultant expressions relating the two networks are given by

$$Z_{11} = R_s + \frac{X_p'^2 R_p}{R^2 + X_p'^2} + j \frac{R_p{}^2 X_p'^2}{R_p{}^2 + X_p'^2} \tag{6.41}$$

$$Z_{12} = \frac{1}{n'} \left(\frac{R_p X_p'^2}{R_p{}^2 + X_p'^2} + j \frac{R_p{}^2 X_p'}{R_p{}^2 + X_p'^2} \right) \tag{6.42}$$

6.4. Symmetry Considerations. *Far-field Standing-wave Solutions.* It has been shown by Slater[1] that symmetry considerations are sufficient to establish certain general characteristics of a microwave structure. This method is based upon the fact that the general solution for the electromagnetic fields existing in a structure can be built up by superimposing two independent standing-wave solutions, one of which can be symmetric and the other antisymmetric about the symmetry plane. If the frequency of operation allows the propagation of the dominant mode only, then the field far away from the plane of symmetry will consist of only the dominant fields. A study of these far-field solutions easily leads to an understanding of the general behavior of microwave structures.

By this method it is possible to obtain the equivalent circuit of the microwave structure and tell how many independent parameters are required to specify completely the behavior of the device. Such general considerations do not allow the determination of the *values* of the circuit parameters in the equivalent circuit because this analysis does not consider detailed boundary conditions. Actual circuit parameters can be determined by an experimental procedure.

Since the symmetry arguments do not consider the details of the physical structure, it can be concluded that the equivalent circuit of any two structures possessing the same degree of symmetry must contain the same number of parameters. Further consideration of symmetry arguments permits one to predict the power flow from one branch of microwave circuit to another. Finally, the concept of *reference planes* introduced in the previous discussion shows how various microwave structures can be connected in series or in parallel. The symmetry arguments further emphasize their importance and prove that equivalent circuits can be especially simple at specific reference planes.

The importance of the symmetry arguments can be emphasized by an example of their usefulness. It may be desired to join two resistive loads in parallel and to require that the power division between them be equal. Symmetry arguments show that *any* microwave circuit can be used to accomplish this if the two loads are symmetrically disposed with respect to the input branch. An asymmetry in the connecting structure introduces an impedance transformer in one of the branches, causing unequal division of power.

[1] J. C. Slater, "Microwave Electronics," pp. 112–116, D. Van Nostrand Company, Inc., Princeton, N.J., 1950.

The symmetry methods can be illustrated by the behavior of an obstruction in the transmission line such as the iris in a waveguide, shown in Fig. 6.8. For simplicity, it is assumed that the structure consists of two identical rectangular waveguides joined at the plane of symmetry. The symmetry arguments are not based upon this detailed picture, but are equally applicable to any symmetrical transmission system having two outputs. This analysis will not determine the magnitude of the parameters of the circuit but will predict the fact that a simple discontinuity can be represented by a single constant, i.e., a simple shunting reactance across the transmission line at the location of the discontinuity.

Two standing-wave solutions of Maxwell's equations can be found which can be combined to produce any arbitrary field in the vicinity of

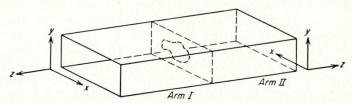

FIG. 6.8. Example of a symmetrical microwave circuit. A metal plane of infinitesimal thickness forms a partial obstruction, called an iris. The coordinate axes are used in the analysis of the structure.

the obstacle. When examined far from the obstacle, one of these solutions will have the form of a sine wave and the other the form of a cosine wave. If the electric field of two waves traveling in opposite directions is superimposed by addition, it can be shown that the axial variation of the electric field $V(z)$ and the axial current $i(z)$ can be written in normalized form (leaving out time factors for convenience) as

$$
\begin{aligned}
V(z) &= \cos \beta z \\
Z_0 i(z) &= -j \sin \beta z
\end{aligned}
\tag{6.43}
$$

This is called the *symmetric* solution because $V(z)$ has a cosine dependance upon the z coordinate. If the superposition of the traveling waves is obtained by taking the difference between them, the normalized voltage and current expressions become

$$
\begin{aligned}
V(z) &= \sin \beta z \\
Z_0 i(z) &= j \cos \beta z
\end{aligned}
\tag{6.44}
$$

This set is called the *antisymmetric* solution.

Using these symmetric and antisymmetric solutions, a general solution is found which takes into account the presence of the iris located at the origin, at $z = 0$. It is convenient to consider separately the coordinate systems in each of the two waveguides as shown in Fig. 6.8; i.e., the z coordinate is positive in the direction away from the iris in both waveguides.   In this system, positive power flow corresponds to power flowing out of the junction; an impedance connected to the waveguide as seen from the obstacle is a positive impedance; a generator connected to the waveguide is considered as a negative resistance.   In the following notation, the first subscript will refer to the number of the waveguide shown in Fig. 6.8.   The second subscript refers to the type of solution being utilized, with I standing for the antisymmetric and II for the symmetric.

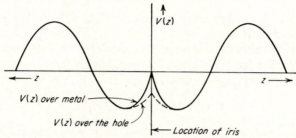

FIG. 6.9. Distribution of the electric field in the symmetric solution in the waveguide containing an iris.

Consider first the antisymmetric solution.   The field in arm 1 is of the type shown in Eq. (6.44) and is described by

$$V_{11} = \sin \beta z$$
$$Z_0 i_{11} = j \cos \beta z \qquad (6.45)$$

In arm 2 the fields are described by

$$V_{21} = -\sin \beta z$$
$$Z_0 i_{21} = -j \cos \beta z \qquad (6.46)$$

The reversal in the sign in Eq. (6.46) is due to the notation adopted. That is, since z is positive in both directions away from the iris, a negative sign in Eq. (6.46) is needed to describe the continuity of the sine functions through the origin.

The solutions described by Eqs. (6.45) and (6.46) are not affected by the presence of the metallic iris at the origin, as long as it is infinitely thin because the tangential component of the electric field is zero on the plane $z = 0$.   Thus, the antisymmetric solution is satisfied irrespective of the size or shape of the hole in the iris.

The symmetric solution is more complicated.   Figure 6.9 shows a possible form of symmetric solution.   Far from the origin, the fields are symmetric; at $z = 0$, however, the field must disappear at the surface of the iris but remain finite in the opening of the iris.   The generality of the symmetric solution can be satisfied by assuming a phase shift in the dominant wave. The boundary conditions are satisfied by excitation of the higher-order modes which combine with the dominant mode to make the tangential component of the electric field zero over the surface of the iris. The higher-order modes are attenuated rapidly with distance and are not considered if the equations apply to the fields far from the iris. The condition in Fig. 6.9 can be described by

$$V_{1\text{II}} = V_{2\text{II}} = \cos \beta(z - z_0)$$
$$Z_0 i_{1\text{II}} = Z_0 i_{2\text{II}} = -j \cos \beta(z - z_0) \tag{6.47}$$

The quantity z_0 is an arbitrary distance which adjusts the phase angle of the symmetric solution.

The general solution for a waveguide containing the iris can be obtained by superposing the two solutions with suitable arbitrary constants. For example, the total voltage in arm 1 $V_1(z)$ is

$$V_1(z) = C_\text{I} V_\text{II} + C_\text{II} V_\text{III} \tag{6.48}$$

where C_I and C_II are arbitrary constants. The complete fields in arms 1 and 2 are given by the set:

$$\begin{aligned}
V_1(z) &= C_\text{I} \sin \beta z + C_\text{II} \cos \beta(z - z_0) \\
V_2(z) &= -C_\text{I} \sin \beta z + C_\text{II} \cos \beta(z - z_0) \\
Z_0 i_1(z) &= C_\text{I} j \cos \beta z - C_\text{II} j \sin \beta(z - z_0) \\
Z_0 i_2(z) &= -C_\text{I} j \cos \beta z - C_\text{II} j \sin \beta(z - z_0)
\end{aligned} \tag{6.49}$$

These equations are written for any value of z. If a *reference plane* is selected one-half wavelength from the iris, the sine functions become zero and cosine functions become ± 1. This allows considerable simplification of Eqs. (6.49). This choice of the reference plane is convenient for analysis and is also important conceptually. Using this value of z, Eqs. (6.49) become

$$V_1 = C_\text{II} \cos \beta \left(\frac{\lambda_t}{2} - z_0 \right)$$

$$V_2 = C_\text{II} \cos \beta \left(\frac{\lambda_t}{2} - z_0 \right)$$

$$Z_0 i_1 = -C_\text{I} j - C_\text{II} j \sin \beta \left(\frac{\lambda_t}{2} - z_0 \right)$$

$$Z_0 i_2 = C_\text{I} j - C_\text{II} j \sin \beta \left(\frac{\lambda_t}{2} - z_0 \right)$$

$$\tag{6.50}$$

Adding the last two equations, the sum of the two currents is obtained:

$$(i_1 + i_2)Z_0 = -2C_\text{II} \sin \beta z_0 \tag{6.51}$$

Dividing Eq. (6.51) by V_1 or V_2 ($V_1 = V_2$),

$$\frac{i_1}{V_1} + \frac{i_2}{V_2} = -\frac{2C_{II}j \sin \beta z_0}{V_1 Z_0} \qquad (6.52)$$

which leads to

$$\frac{i_1}{V_1} + \frac{i_2}{V_2} = \frac{2j}{Z_0} \tan \beta z_0 \qquad (6.53)$$

or

$$Y_1 + Y_2 = -jb_0 \qquad (6.54)$$

where

$$Z_0 \frac{i_1}{V_1} = Y_1$$

$$Z_0 \frac{i_2}{V_2} = Y_2$$

$$2 \tan \beta z_0 = -b_0$$

Y_1 and Y_2 are the normalized admittances as seen from the iris. Hence, the admittance looking into the arm 1 is $-Y_1 = Y_2 + jb_0$; that is, the admittance looking into the waveguide from one side is equal to the load connected to the second side in parallel with the susceptance jb_0.

The magnitude of the susceptance can be obtained only by full consideration of the boundary problem, a question beyond the purpose of the present discussion. The simplest way to determine the magnitude of b_0 is to terminate the output in an open circuit, i.e., $Y_2 = 0$. The location of the voltage node in arm 1 determines the magnitude of b_0; for greater accuracy the nodal shift experiment can be performed.

The equivalent circuit of the waveguide containing an infinitely thin iris is a transmission line shunted by a susceptance. The reference planes at which the susceptance is located happen to be located $n\lambda_t/2$ away from the iris, where n is some integer. Hence, it is possible to think of the susceptance as if it were physically located at the iris itself. Consider, however, a more complicated structure, such as a right-angle bend in the waveguide. The formal analysis can proceed as before. It should be possible to write the symmetric and antisymmetric solutions in terms of the dominant mode (applicable at a sufficiently large distance from the origin); the derived set of equations would be identical to Eqs. (6.49). They could be simplified also, but it would not be possible to arbitrarily select the reference plane at $\lambda_t/2$ from the bend. This is because the antisymmetric set does not automatically satisfy the boundary conditions in the vicinity of the corner. An antisymmetric solution exists as before, but it must contain a phase constant for reasons similar to those requiring the symmetric solution to contain a phase constant in the previous case. To simplify the set of equations for the bend, select a *location* in waveguides 1 and 2 at which the antisymmetric solution vanishes; the resultant equations are identical in form to those written for the iris.

The final conclusion is that the corner can be also represented by a shunt susceptance, but the reference planes at which this circuit is valid must be determined experimentally.

Consider further a waveguide bend consisting of two adjacent 45° bends, often called a *mitered* bend. If the two bends are separated by $\lambda_t/4$, the ensemble is nearly reflectionless. It may seem that the symmetry arguments should apply to the whole structure and that the bend could be represented by a single discontinuity reactance. It is almost obvious, however, that this is not correct. Each of the two 45° bends creates a discontinuity reactance, and the combination becomes a π circuit, being reflectionless because the two discontinuities are separated by $\lambda_t/4$.

Similarly, if the thickness of the iris is appreciable compared to the guided wavelength, it can no longer be represented by a simple reactive discontinuity. To understand the behavior of a thick iris, the junction of two dissimilar waveguides at each surface of the iris must be considered, and the distance between the two faces taken into account later.[1]

Symmetry considerations can be applied to more complicated structures such as the waveguide T, the Y junction, the junction of a coaxial line to the waveguide, the magic T, etc. It is desirable to find the equivalent circuits for these to determine the division of power flow between the various arms of the structure if any or all are excited. The approach to these problems consists of finding symmetric and antisymmetric standing-wave-field solutions about the symmetry plane in all of the branches. To obtain the generalized field in each arm, two independent standing-wave solutions are needed. Thus, a three-arm junction requires six sets of fields; this set may be reduced to a smaller number depending upon the degree of symmetry. The solution to a complicated problem can be simplified by first recognizing that a set of reference planes can be found at which some of the fields become zero. The remaining fields are then written specifically for this set of reference planes. For further discussion of this method, the reader is referred to the literature.

6.5. Measurement and Analysis of Data. Useful procedures for laboratory determination of the equivalent circuits and their parameters are apparent from the formulation of the several methods of representation. Some of the available techniques are discussed below; many other procedures can be devised as well.

a. The Three-point Method. Since the four-terminal network can be described by three complex constants, three independent laboratory determinations are required for the complete description of the network. In analogy to the low-frequency practice, the equivalent circuit of a four-

---

[1] J. R. Whinnery and H. W. Jamieson, Equivalent Circuits for Discontinuities in Transmission Lines, *Proc. IRE*, vol. 32, pp. 98–114, February, 1944.

terminal network can be obtained by measuring the input impedance of the network when it is terminated with three known impedances. For convenience, these can be a short circuit, an open circuit, and a reflectionless load.

To determine the parameters of the equivalent circuit shown in Fig. 6.3, impedance-measuring equipment is provided to measure the input impedance at the selected input terminals of the microwave circuit. The required open-circuit and short-circuit conditions can be obtained by a sliding short circuit at the output terminal. Moving the short circuit through a distance of one-quarter guided wavelength with respect to the selected output reference plane provides the short-circuit and open-circuit conditions. The short circuit is replaced by a matched load to provide the third known impedance.

If Z_1 and Z_2 are the input and output characteristic impedances, respectively, the normalized input and output impedances can be abbreviated as follows:

$$Z'_{in} = Z_{in}/Z_1$$
$$Z'_{out} = Z_{out}/Z_2 \tag{6.55}$$

and, with reference to Fig. 6.3,

$$Z'_{11} = Z_{11}/Z_1$$
$$Z'_{22} = Z_{22}/Z_2$$
$$Z'_{12} = \frac{Z_{12}}{\sqrt{Z_1 Z_2}} \tag{6.56}$$

The input impedances corresponding to the three known output impedances are measured; let the following symbols represent these conditions:

Output impedance Z'_{out}	Input impedance Z'_{in}
$Z'_{out} = 0$	Z'_{sc}
$Z'_{out} = \infty$	Z'_{oc}
$Z'_{out} = 1$	Z'_0

where the first column gives the impedance conditions at the output side and the corresponding input quantities measured in the laboratory are indicated in the second column. It can be shown that the circuit parameters of Fig. 6.3 can be determined from the following relations:

$$Z'_{11} = Z'_{oc}$$
$$Z'_{22} = \frac{Z'_{oc} - Z'_0}{Z'_0 - Z'_{sc}}$$
$$Z'^2_{12} = \frac{(Z'_{oc} - Z'_0)(Z'_{oc} - Z'_{sc})}{Z'_0 - Z'_{sc}} \tag{6.57}$$

If both the network and reference planes are physically symmetrical, the above equations become

$$Z'_{11} = Z'_{22} = Z'_{oc}$$
$$Z_{12}{}^2 = Z'_{oc}(Z'_{oc} - Z'_{sc}) \tag{6.58}$$

The scattering coefficients can be determined similarly. If the three output impedances cause the reflection coefficients to be $\Gamma_{01} = -1$, $\Gamma_{02} = +1$, and $\Gamma_{03} = 0$, and the corresponding measured input reflection coefficients are called Γ_{sc}, Γ_{oc}, and Γ_0, the scattering coefficients are determined as follows:

$$S_{11} = \Gamma_0$$
$$S_{22} = \frac{2\Gamma_0 - \Gamma_{sc} - \Gamma_{oc}}{\Gamma_{sc} - \Gamma_{oc}} \tag{6.59}$$
$$S_{11}S_{22} - S_{12}{}^2 = \frac{\Gamma_0(\Gamma_{oc} + \Gamma_{sc}) - 2\Gamma_{sc}\Gamma_{oc}}{\Gamma_{sc} - \Gamma_{oc}}$$

If the network and reference planes are physically symmetrical, these equations become

$$S_{11} = S_{22} = \frac{\Gamma_{oc} + \Gamma_{sc}}{2 + \Gamma_{oc} - \Gamma_{sc}}$$
$$S_{11}S_{22} - S_{12}{}^2 = \frac{2\Gamma_{oc}\Gamma_{sc} - \Gamma_{oc} + \Gamma_{sc}}{2 + \Gamma_{oc} - \Gamma_{sc}} \tag{6.60}$$

The determination of either the equivalent circuit parameters or of the scattering coefficients by the three-point method requires minimum laboratory effort. As a result, an error in any single measurement causes errors in all of the calculated parameters. For this reason, it is usually desirable to accumulate more laboratory information than is required for the three-point method.

Additional data can be obtained and used in sets to compute independent values of the desired quantities. This procedure is tedious and does not indicate a direct method for averaging the final result, should a significant discrepancy be observed because of errors in the data. A more systematic approach to using additional data is obviously desirable.

b. Graphical Determination of the Scattering Coefficients. A number of useful methods have been devised which permit accurate determination of the scattering coefficients by using graphical procedures. These methods are based upon the graphical interpretation of the fractional bilinear transformation relating the output and input impedances of the four-terminal network. The laboratory procedure used in this method is reminiscent of the nodal-shift experiment described in Chap. 5; a shorting plunger terminates the output terminals of the unknown network and the corresponding input impedances are measured on the input side. In fact, the following discussion can be interpreted as the generalized theory of the nodal-shift experiment; however, because of the presence of losses in an arbitrary network, it is necessary to use a more complicated graphical procedure for the interpretation of the data. This method is powerful, equally useful for lossless and lossy networks, and can be extended to certain classes of nonuniform transmission lines, such as periodically loaded waveguides.[1]

The experimental procedure consists of placing the sliding short circuit at the output terminals and moving it through a series of points separated by some even fraction of a guided wavelength, such as $\frac{1}{16}$. In principle, only three points, arbitrarily spaced, are required; for greater convenience and accuracy, and to explain the method, it is more convenient to use the spacing stated. In practice, the amount of data needed depends upon the accuracy desired in the final result. The input impedances corresponding to each of the short-circuit positions are measured and plotted on the reflection coefficient plane, resulting in the familiar circle. (The data may be plotted on a Smith chart for convenience, although the Smith chart coordinate system is not used in the interpretation of the method.) By means of simple graphical procedures the scattering coefficients of the network can be determined.[2]

One particular advantage of this method is that its accuracy can be increased by merely taking more laboratory data, i.e., by using smaller intervals between consecutive short-circuit plunger positions. The graphical procedure employed to interpret the data indicates the presence of systematic or random errors and averages the accumulated information directly.

The method is based upon the fundamental properties of the linear fractional transformation; those of importance to this method are the following: If the reflection coefficients at the input and output terminals of the network are plotted in reflection planes, a circular locus in one plane will be transformed into a circular locus in the other. The transformations are conformal, i.e., the angles between intersecting lines are preserved upon transformation. Using these principles, the method can be explained as follows: Referring to Fig. 6.2, the position of the short circuit is measured with respect to some desirable reference plane T_2. The magnitude of the reflection coefficient due to the short circuit is unity but varies in phase with its displacement from the reference plane. The reflectances corresponding to a set of points $\lambda_t/16$ apart are shown as points w_1, w_2, w_3, . . . , w_8 in Fig. 6.10a. The input impedances corresponding to each position of the short circuit are measured on the input

[1] E. T. Jaynes, Concept and Measurement of Impedance in Periodically Loaded Waveguides, *J. Appl. Phys.*, vol. 23, pp. 1077–1084, October, 1952.

[2] Deschamps, *op. cit.* This reference forms the principal basis of the following material. Other relevant material is also found in Storer et al., *op. cit.*

side with respect to some desirable reference plane T_1. Although the
origin of the coordinate can be arbitrary on both sides, for convenience

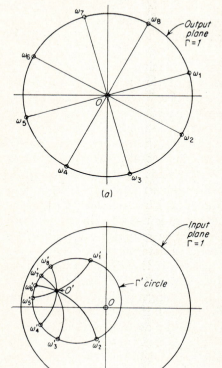

(a)

(b)

FIG. 6.10. Input-output relations in the
reflection plane for an arbitrary four-
terminal network. (a) Eight reflectances resulting from the displacement
of a shorting plunger by one-sixteenth
wavelength. The diameters shown intersect at the point O, which corresponds to zero reflection. (b) The
general form of the transformed locus
in the input reflection plane. The
transformed point O' is called the
iconocenter.

it is assumed that the distance increases in the direction away from
the network on each side of the network. Using the properties of the
bilinear transformation, it is plain
that the periphery of Fig. 6.10a transforms into a circle in the input reflection plane as shown in Fig. 6.10b.
The reflectances $w_1, \ldots , w_8$, located on the periphery circle Γ, transform into the periphery of the new
circle Γ' where the distribution of
transformed points $w'_1, \ldots , w'_8$ becomes uneven as shown. The diam-
eters of the unit circle Γ in Fig. 6.10a
become circles upon transformation,
but must remain orthogonal to the
new circle Γ'. The orthogonal intersection of the diameters in Fig. 6.10a
at point O must remain orthogonal
in Fig. 6.10b at some other point O'.
The intersection of the transformed
diameters, O', is called the iconocenter
and is useful in the determination
of the scattering coefficients of the
network.[1]

The interpretation of this procedure begins with the plotting of the
laboratory data which consist of the
measured points, $w'_1, \ldots , w'_8$ on
the reflection plane. The circle Γ' is
drawn through the measured points,
establishing the center C. The iconocenter is then determined in one of
several ways. Remembering that
the diameters, namely, $w_3 - w_7$, must
transform into circles orthogonal to
Γ', the construction shown in Fig. 6.11 can be used to draw the transformed diameters (circles) connecting the points $w'_3 - w'_7$. Referring to

[1] The point O' is the transformation, or image, of point O; hence the name is iconocenter, after εἰκών, the Greek word for image.

Fig. 6.11, tangents to the circle Γ' can be drawn at points w_3' and w_7', intersecting at the point a; with a as the center, an arc can be drawn connecting points w_3' to w_7'; this is the required transform. Similarly, another arc can be constructed between points w_5' to w_1' with point b as the center. The intersection of the two arcs is the iconocenter O'. This procedure can be repeated, using as many of the diameters as are available. Random or systematic errors become apparent as the various arcs determine a polygon whose center can be estimated accurately.

Alternatively, the iconocenter can be obtained by placing the Smith chart paper (assumed to be transparent) on which the construction is

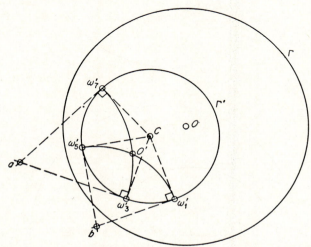

FIG. 6.11. Graphical determination of the iconocenter from experimental data.

being made over another Smith chart. It will be noted that the Smith chart contains two sets of coordinate circles orthogonal to each other. By finding a constant-resistance circle on the Smith chart equal in size to Γ', the graph can be rotated so that a reactance circle on the Smith chart connects the opposite points, w_3' to w_7'; this circle can then be drawn on the graph paper. Similarly, other points can be connected by mere rotation of the graph paper with respect to the Smith chart, keeping the Γ' circle superimposed over the proper Smith chart circle.

Another construction is shown in Fig. 6.12 to locate the iconocenter. The chords $w_1' - w_5'$, $w_2' - w_6'$, etc., have a common cross-over point $\bar{O}$; using the construction shown, the iconocenter can be located easily as the intersection of lines $\bar{O}C$ and LK.*

* The proof of this is given by Deschamps, *op. cit.*

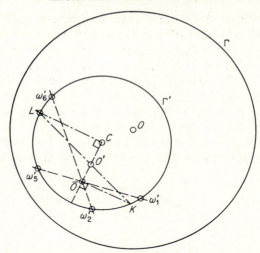

FIG. 6.12. Alternate graphical method of locating the iconocenter.

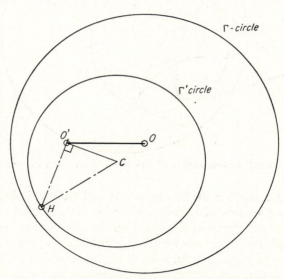

FIG. 6.13. Graphical construction needed for the determination of the scattering coefficients.   The radius of Γ' circle is R.

The scattering coefficients of the network can be determined as follows: Point O in Fig. 6.10a corresponds to the output of the network being matched; therefore, the transformed point O' corresponds to the reflection on the input side when the output is matched.   Hence, the distance OO' in Fig. 6.10b corresponds to the value of the scattering coefficient S_{11}.

From the geometrical considerations the scattering coefficients can be determined from Fig. 6.13 as follows:[1]

$$|S_{11}| = OO' \tag{6.61}$$

$$|S_{22}| = \frac{CO'}{R} \tag{6.62}$$

$$|S_{12}| = \frac{O'H}{R^{1/2}} \tag{6.63}$$

or

$$|S_{12}|^2 = R(1 - |S_{22}|^2) \tag{6.64}$$

The use of a lossless sliding short circuit is not required for the determination of S_{11}, but is merely a matter of convenience. This can be seen by considering the locus of reflectances due to moving of a partially absorbing termination; this is a circle concentric with the periphery of

---

[1] Deschamps, *op. cit.*; Storer et al., *op. cit.*

The absolute value and the phase angles of the scattering coefficients can be determined in the following manner: Referring to Fig. 6.14, assume that the reference planes T_1' and T_2' are selected so that the scattering coefficients S_{11} and S_{22} are real.

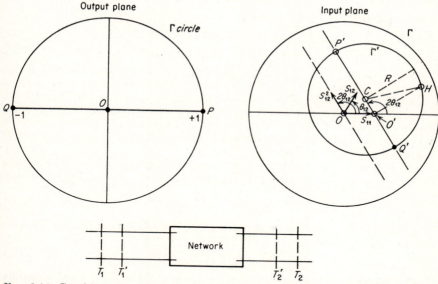

Fig. 6.14. Graphical construction used in derivation of relations connecting experimental data to the magnitude and phase of scattering coefficients. For the purpose of the proof, the input and output reference planes, T_1' and T_2', are selected to make S_{11} and S_{22} real.

Let points P and Q correspond to the output reflectances of $+1$ and -1, respectively. Upon transformation to the input plane, they will lie at P' and Q'. A straight line passing through points P' and Q' also passes through the iconocenter O' and the center of the circle Γ' point C; this is proved by noting the consequences of the bilinear

circle Γ in Fig. 6.10a; transformation of its diameters leads to the determination of iconocenter O' as before. The determination of S_{12} and S_{22}, however, requires the use of a *lossless* short circuit as the radius of Γ' appears in Eqs. (6.62) and (6.63).

The phase angles of the scattering coefficients can be determined in several ways. When it is known that the phase angles are needed before the laboratory data is taken, special points can be selected experimentally which will simplify the problem. This is done, as explained in the footnote above, by selecting the reference planes T_1' and T_2' in a manner which makes the scattering coefficients S_{11} and S_{22} real. On the input side this occurs when the Γ' circle is rotated about point O so that the iconocenter O' falls on the positive real axis as indicated in Fig. 6.15. The position of the output reference plane T_2' causes S_{22} to be real when the position of the short circuit is chosen so that its image falls at point P' in Fig.

---

transformation. The explicit relation connecting the input and output planes is given by Eq. (6.23):

$$\Gamma_{in} = S_{11} + S_{12}{}^2/[(1/\Gamma_{out}) - S_{22}] \tag{6.65}$$

For the points P and Q this becomes

For P': $$\Gamma_{in} = S_{11} + S_{12}{}^2/(1 - S_{22}) \tag{6.66}$$

For Q': $$\Gamma_{in} = S_{11} - S_{12}{}^2/(1 + S_{22}) \tag{6.67}$$

In the last two equations, the denominator of the last term is real because S_{22} is real by the choice of plane T_2'. Therefore, the last terms in these equations have the phase angle of $S_{12}{}^2$. Therefore, the vectors corresponding to these terms, $O'P'$ and $O'Q'$, when plotted as shown in Fig. 6.14 must lie on the same straight line. This straight line must meet the Γ' circle at right angles. The only straight line within a circle which meets its periphery at right angles is its diameter; hence, the line $P' - Q'$ passes through the center of the circle C.

The diameter of the circle Γ' can be obtained from the sum $(\overline{O'P'} + \overline{O'Q'})$ which is obtained by adding the last terms of Eqs. (6.66) and (6.67). The radius of the circle is

$$R = S_{12}{}^2/(1 - S_{22}{}^2) \tag{6.68}$$

The distance $\overline{O'C}$, needed for other construction, is obtained by taking the difference $(O'P' - R)$. It is equal to

$$\overline{O'C} = S_{22} S_{12}{}^2/(1 - S_{22}{}^2) \tag{6.69}$$

Taking the ratio of Eqs. (6.69) and (6.68) leads to Eq. (6.62). Combining Eqs. (6.68), (6.62), and from the right triangle $CO'H$, S_{12} is determined as given by Eq. (6.63).

The line $P'Q'$ is parallel to the vector $S_{12}{}^2$. Therefore, the phase angle θ_{12} is obtained immediately. The phase angles θ_{11} and θ_{22} of the scattering coefficients S_{11} and S_{22}, respectively, are zero at the reference planes T_1' and T_2'. If the reference plane T_1' is displaced to some position T_1, the circle Γ' will be rotated by some angle θ_{11} as shown in Fig. 6.15, i.e., an angle between the chosen reference P and the vector OO'. This angle is the phase angle of the scattering coefficient S_{11}.

6.15 at the continuation of the line from $O'C$. This can be proven by examining Fig. 6.14; the reference plane T_2' corresponds to the point P ($S_{22} = +1$) which transforms into P' on the line $P'CO'$. The laboratory determination of these reference planes is straightforward.

If, however, it is impossible or inconvenient to determine experimentally the reference planes T_1' and T_2', the phase of the scattering coefficients can be obtained as follows: The Γ' circle is plotted as shown in Fig. 6.16 where the cardinal points are retained. Point P on the Γ circle represents any one of the w_n's for which data were obtained. Point P' on Γ' is its image. Because point P is assumed to be different from the

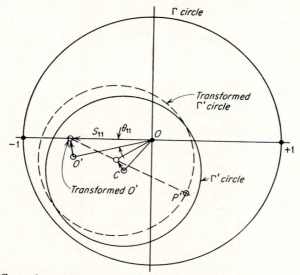

FIG. 6.15. Effect of transforming the input reference plane through an angle θ_{11}.

reference plane T_2' (where S_{22} is real), the image P' will lie at some point as shown and not on the extension of $O'C$. If a straight line $P'O'K$ is drawn to locate K, and the line from K to P'' passing through C, the phase angles of the scattering coefficient are found from Fig. 6.16. Specifically,

$$\theta_{22} = \arg S_{22} = (O'C, CP'') \tag{6.70}$$
$$\theta_{12} = \arg S_{12} = \tfrac{1}{2}(OP, CP'') \tag{6.71}$$

The angles given by these expressions must be taken between the directed segments of vectors as shown. Changing either the sense of one of these vectors or their order would lead to an erroneous result.[1]

c. Canonical Networks. The canonical networks described in Sec. 6.2d can be obtained from the laboratory data in the manner which is clear

[1] Construction used in Fig. 6.16 is proven by Deschamps, *op. cit.*

from the formulation of the method. A movable short circuit is connected to the output terminals of the network; the short circuit is moved through a series of points, preferably spaced by some even fraction of a wavelength, and the corresponding input impedances are plotted on a reflection plane, using the Smith chart for convenience. The best-fit circle is drawn through the measured points. The radius of the resultant circle is measured and normalized with respect to the radius of the periphery of the Smith chart. At the beginning of this procedure, no logical place for establishing the reference planes exists; as a result, the plotted circle would be located at some arbitrary position, as shown in Fig. 6.4b.

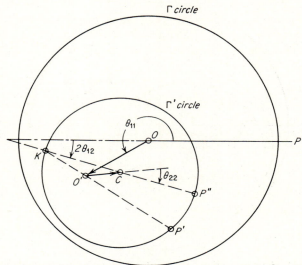

FIG. 6.16. Graphical determination of the phase angles of the scattering coefficients. The angles are measured between directed vectors as indicated.

The analysis of the data must provide, in the general case, six constants for the network. These are: the location of the input reference plane, the location of the output reference plane, and R_s, R_p, X_p, and n. If the structure is symmetrical, the number of required constants is reduced.

The location of the reference plane T_1 on the input side is obtained by rotating the input impedance circle until its center is located on the real axis, as shown in Fig. 6.5a. The output reference plane T_2 is found by identifying that location of the short circuit which causes the input locus to provide the point R_s. If the data are plotted on a Smith chart, the intersection of the circle with the real axis provides the points R_s and $R_s + R_p$. If the data are plotted on the reflection plane, R_s and R_p may be determined with the aid of Fig. 6.5a as follows:

$$R_s = \frac{1 - (r_0 + R)}{1 + (r_0 + R)} \tag{6.72}$$

$$R_p = \frac{4R}{(1 + r_0)^2 - R^2} \tag{6.73}$$

Reactance X_p is found by placing the short-circuiting plunger one-quarter wavelength from reference plane T_2. In Fig. 6.5b this is equivalent to placing an infinite impedance across X_p. Since R_s and R_p are known, the measurement of the input impedance determines X_p. The transformer ratio n can be found by determining that position of the short-circuiting plunger which causes the input impedance circle to pass through the point $R_s + R_p$. Here the impedance presented by the transformer must equal $-X_p$. If this occurs at the distance $x_2 + \lambda_g/4$ with respect to terminals T_2, the transformer ratio n may be computed from the formula

$$n^2 = x_p/Z_2 \tan \beta_2 x_2 \tag{6.74}$$

where Z_2 is the characteristic impedance and β_2 the propagation constant of the output line, X_p is the circuit constant previously determined, and x_2 is the displacement of the short circuit with respect to the terminals $T_2 + \lambda_g/4$.

Other equivalent procedures can be devised as will be obvious to the interested reader. Symmetry considerations can change the form of the canonical network, resulting in the modification of the procedures needed to evaluate the circuit constants.

CHAPTER 7

MEASUREMENT OF WAVELENGTH

7.1. Introduction. The measurement of the wavelength or the frequency is one of the primary requirements in most microwave problems. It might be thought that the measurements of the wavelength or of the frequency are equivalent because one can be converted into the other, according to the relation

$$\lambda_0 = \frac{c}{f} \tag{7.1}$$

where λ_0 is the free-space wavelength, f is the frequency, and c the velocity of light. This relation is assumed to be equally applicable at microwave frequencies as in all parts of the electromagnetic spectrum. Hence, if f is measured, the wavelength λ_0 can be determined, and conversely. It should be noted, however, that the measurements of wavelength and frequency are basically different; the first depends upon the measurement of length and the second upon the measurement of time. The measurement of frequency is more meaningful because under steady-state conditions the frequency of electromagnetic waves is the same in all parts of a given system. The wavelength, on the other hand, depends upon the particular field configuration as determined by the geometrical factors of the system and its dimensions. In those parts of the system where propagation occurs in transmission lines of simple geometry, the wavelength can be measured easily by making use of the standing-wave phenomena. The knowledge of geometry, dimensions, and the measured transmission-line wavelength allows the free-space wavelength to be determined with ease and (relatively) good accuracy. Because this method is convenient, wavelength measurement is as useful in the microwave frequency region as its counterpart at the lower radio frequencies.

Because the velocity of light is known only to an accuracy of 1 part in 10^5, the conversion of wavelength into frequency is not as accurate as some applications require.[1] Therefore, for best accuracy, it is preferable

[1] The presently accepted value of the velocity of light as obtained by Michelson and revised by Birge and others is equal to $299,772 \pm 10$ km/sec. However, the more recent determinations at microwave frequencies lead one to believe that this value is low. The value of $299,793.0 \pm 0.3$ km/sec is more consistent with these experiments.

346

to measure and state the frequency directly without depending on conversion of frequency into wavelength; the direct frequency-measurement methods are discussed in Chap. 8.   However, in those microwave applications where the utmost accuracy is not important, wavemeter techniques are universally used because of the convenience, speed, and cost of equipment.

At the lower radio frequencies resonant-circuit wavemeters are constructed using a coil and a condenser connected so that circulating currents can be detected by means of a suitable rectifying device.   It is presumed that this coil-condenser combination has a single resonant frequency which can be computed from the known values of the inductance and the capacitance.   If necessary, this computed calibration can be checked against a series of frequencies obtained from a *frequency* standard.

At microwave frequencies the resonant system takes the form of a cavity resonator.   In principle, the resonant wavelength of a cavity can be computed from its dimensions, just as the inductance and the capacitance of the coil-condenser combination can be calculated from dimensions and geometrical factors.   There are four characteristic properties of a cavity that are of importance in considering the value of a particular cavity for wavemeter applications.   These are the resonant wavelength, the selectivity factor Q_0, mode interference, and the methods of tuning.

The resonant wavelength of a cavity can be determined in two ways. It can be calculated from the known dimensions by finding a solution of Maxwell's equations for the particular geometry.   Alternatively, the cavity can be calibrated against a generator whose frequency has been established by other means; methods of calibration against frequency standards are discussed in Chap. 8.

A high selectivity factor Q_0 is desirable because it determines the width of the resonance curve which, in turn, determines the accuracy to which the wavemeter can be adjusted and read.

The question of mode interference pertains to the proximity of the main resonant frequency to other possible modes of oscillation and is governed by the size of the cavity in relation to the wavelength.   It is well known that a given cavity has an infinite number of resonant frequencies.   At best, it must be decided which particular mode of the infinite set is being excited by the operating frequency; at worst, the resonant frequencies may be so close together that it becomes impossible to distinguish one resonant frequency from another.[1]

The fourth characteristic relates to mechanical design and the resultant

---

[1] These phenomena can occur with low-frequency wavemeters.   However, in the case of lumped circuits, the higher-order resonances occur at very high frequencies and are not of general interest.   Their frequencies cannot be determined from the L and C values.

convenience in the adjustment and operation.   The mechanical features are extremely important in the design of a practical wavemeter.   Some satisfactory solutions are discussed at the end of the chapter.

A number of methods can be used to determine the resonant wavelength of a cavity wavemeter.   Calibrating the cavity against an auxiliary standard is obvious and will not be discussed as this is a matter of checking the predicted calibration.   For convenience the wavemeters can be grouped into three types:

1. Cavities which correspond to sections of uniform transmission lines
2. Simple geometrical shapes, such as rectangular boxes, spheres, spheroids, etc.
3. Irregular shapes, such as the reentrant cavities used in the klystron

The resonant wavelength for the first of these can be determined by computing the transmission-line wavelength λ_t.   If a certain field configuration is excited in a transmission line, standing waves can be produced by providing a total reflection; this produces voltage nodes spaced half-wavelengths apart.   The simplest wavemeter contains a single half-wavelength of the standing-wave pattern, bounded by reflecting planes perpendicular to the axis of the waveguide.   If the cutoff wavelength of a given mode is λ_c, the distance between two consecutive nodes in the standing-wave pattern is $L = \lambda_t/2$, the free-space wavelength λ_0 of the source can be found from

$$\lambda_0 = \frac{2L}{\sqrt{1 + (2L/\lambda_c)^2}} \tag{7.2}$$

If there are N half-wavelengths between the reflecting planes,[1] this becomes

$$\lambda_0 = \frac{2l}{N} \frac{1}{\sqrt{1 + (2L/N\lambda_c)^2}} \tag{7.3}$$

Wavemeters using resonant sections of transmission lines are ideal for measuring wavelength.   Simple geometrical structures, such as round waveguides, are easily constructed and fitted with reflecting plungers. It is possible to produce favored conditions for the excitation of some specific mode by properly placing the input and output coupling probes. With the transverse dimensions of the waveguide and the field configuration known, the cutoff wavelength can be determined.   Motion of the

[1] Resonance occurs when $L = N\lambda_t/2$.   Using Eq. (4.35),

$$L = \frac{N\lambda_0}{2} \frac{1}{\sqrt{1 - (\lambda_0/\lambda_c)^2}}$$

which leads to Eq. (7.3).

reflecting plunger indicates resonance much the same way as adjusting the condenser does in the low-frequency wavemeter.

For cavities of simple geometrical shapes, such as a sphere, solutions of Maxwell's equations can be found and the resonant frequencies can be determined. Such cavities are seldom useful as wavemeters because it is difficult to provide mechanical tuning, but they can be used as accurate fixed standards.

Irregular shapes, such as klystron cavities, are also useful in wavemeter application; however, the resonant frequency cannot be determined as easily as in simple sections of transmission lines. Moreover, for reasons discussed below, their Q values are relatively low.

In considering the usefulness of a cavity wavemeter, it is important to understand the dependence of the selectivity factor Q_0 upon the geometrical proportions of the cavity: A general insight into this question can be obtained by first disregarding completely any practical consideration such as physical size, construction difficulties, etc. Even in this case, there are fundamental factors which limit the highest obtainable Q_0. This can be demonstrated as follows: According to the usual definition,

$$Q_0 = 2\pi \frac{\text{energy stored}}{\text{energy lost per cycle}} \tag{7.4}$$

$$= 2\left(\frac{\lambda_0}{\delta}\right) \frac{\int\int\int H^2\, d\tau}{\lambda_0 \int\int H^2 |d\sigma|} \tag{7.5}$$

where H = magnetic field

  $d\tau$ = an element of volume in the cavity

  $d\sigma$ = an element of its surface

  δ = skin depth, given in gaussian units by

$$\delta = \sqrt{\frac{\rho}{2\pi\omega}} \tag{7.6}$$

where ρ is the resistivity of the cavity material.[1]   At a given wavelength the dimensionless quantity λ_0/δ has the maximum value determined by the best conductivity available. For copper at $\lambda_0 = 10$ cm (at room temperature) $\lambda_0/\delta = 83{,}200$. Equation (7.5) shows that Q_0 depends upon the ratio of the two integrals. Intuitively, it can be seen that the highest possible Q_0 results in those cavities in which large current concentrations have been avoided. Thus, the magnetic field in a high-Q wavemeter will change only slowly from point to point. It is apparent that many resonator shapes exist in which there are large variations in the magnetic field but these indicate a poor design and the following remarks are not applicable to them. A qualitative analysis of the problem can be obtained by neglecting spatial variation in the magnetic field

[1] For clarification of units used in Eq. (7.6), see Sec. B.4.

H; with this restriction it is apparent that the ratio of integrals in Eq. (7.5) is, in essence, the ratio of volume-to-surface of the cavity. Irregular shapes, such as coaxial quarter-wavelength cavities, have low values of volume-to-surface ratio; simple nonreentrant shapes, such as sections of uniform waveguides, have relatively high volume-to-surface ratios. Hence, a sphere would be expected to have the highest Q_0 for a given size. This argument leads to the conclusion that for a given wavelength Q_0 is proportional to the cavity dimensions.[1]

However, cavity wavemeters cannot be made arbitrarily large for two reasons. First is a matter of convenience; at $\lambda_0 = 10$ cm, if the cavity is made too many wavelengths in size, the weight and bulk become prohibitive for laboratory use. Secondly, the fundamental question of mode interference limits the maximum attainable size and, consequently, the highest Q_0.

The basic difficulty due to mode interference can be examined by applying a formula which predicts the permissible number of vibrations in a given *hohlraum* of volume V. This formula states that the number N of possible modes with a wavelength greater than λ_0 is given by[2]

$$N = \frac{8\pi}{3} \frac{V}{\lambda_0{}^3} \tag{7.8}$$

This formula is applicable if all dimensions of the volume are large compared to λ_0; for qualitative purposes, it can be used disregarding this qualification. This relation can be used to compute the number of possible modes lying within the wavelength interval $d\lambda_0$. Differentiating Eq. (7.8),

$$dN = 8\pi \frac{V}{\lambda_0{}^3} \frac{d\lambda_0}{\lambda_0} \tag{7.9}$$

This relation can be applied to a cavity consisting of a cube with side

---

[1] The qualitative argument can be verified by computing Q_0 for some geometry in which the fields are known exactly. For example, for a sphere with a radius a, Q_0 is given by

$$Q_0 = k \frac{a}{\lambda_0} \frac{\lambda_0}{\delta} \tag{7.7}$$

if $a \gg \lambda_0$. The constant k is nearly equal to unity. For the dominant mode, $k = 0.725$. Thus, Q_0 is proportional to a.

[2] A consideration of the number of degrees of freedom in an enclosure, or hohlraum, leads to the well-known Lord Rayleigh formula. See, for example, F. K. Richtmyer and E. H. Kennard, "Introduction to Modern Physics," pp. 184–189, McGraw-Hill Book Company, Inc., New York, 1942.

Formulas more specifically applicable to cavity resonators are given by I. G. Wilson, C. W. Schramm, and J. P. Kinzer, High-Q Resonant Cavities for Microwave Testing, a chapter in "Radar Systems and Components," D. Van Nostrand Company, Inc., Princeton, N.J., 1949.

dimensions $2a$, for which $\lambda_0 = 2\sqrt{2}\, a$. Substituting this into Eq. (7.9),

$$dN = 8\pi \left(\frac{2a}{\lambda_0}\right)^3 \frac{\Delta\lambda_0}{\lambda_0} \tag{7.10}$$

The number of modes per unit wavelength interval increases very rapidly with the size of the cavity. Increasing Q_0 by increasing its size eventually introduces so many modes of oscillation that it becomes impossible to distinguish one mode from another. If the side of a cubical 10-cm cavity resonator is 40 wavelengths long, the cavity is continuously resonant, i.e., some one mode is always excited.[1]

Thus, it can be concluded that to obtain the highest Q_0 the cavity should be made as large as possible without introducing spurious modes. In order to be more quantitative, it is necessary to examine the relation between the resonant frequency of the cavity and its size for all possible modes; this can be done by plotting the *mode chart* for the specific cavity as discussed in Sec. 7.3. Not all of the possible interfering modes will cause difficulty in practice; it is often possible to arrange the input and output coupling systems so that undesirable modes are not excited. Slots which remove certain classes of modes without affecting the desired one can sometimes be provided in the cavity walls. Alternatively, small objects, such as resistance wires, can be introduced into the cavity which provide substantial damping for the interfering modes without disturbing the desired mode. The details of this method of mode suppression require the knowledge of the field configuration of all possible modes within the frequency interval of interest.

A practical cavity wavemeter consists of a resonant cavity, an input line coupled to a loop, an iris, or a probe, and a detector element similarly coupled to indicate resonance. To maintain the cavity Q near its natural value, the coupling between the cavity and the detector and input lines must be sufficiently weak. In the absence of the disturbing effects of the coupling elements, the cavity can resonate in any one of the possible *normal* modes. The complete set of the normal modes can be calculated from the solution of the wave equation, Eqs. (4.24) and (4.25). When the frequencies of the normal modes are tabulated in the order of increasing frequency, the lowest frequency of the set is called the *dominant* mode. In the direction of increasing frequency, the higher modes occur closer and closer together and the field configurations increase in complexity. Only the first few modes, in the immediate proximity of the dominant mode, are of particular interest in the wavemeter application. In con-

---

[1] Continuously resonant cavities, sometimes called *echo* boxes, are useful in testing radar systems. Because of its high Q, the echo box can be used to provide test signals in the absence of real targets by providing a long "ringing" signal after initial excitation by the transmitter pulse.

trast to the low-frequency wavemeters, the higher order modes in the cavity wavemeter may become important, as mentioned in Sec. 7.1.   The tuning range of a microwave wavemeter is usually quite small because of the possible difficulties due to mode interference.

The presence of high-order modes also modifies the simple single-mode concept of resonance, as will be mentioned below.   The presence of the coupling systems between the cavity and the transmission lines further alters the normal mode frequencies.   However, in the typical well-designed wavemeter these effects are not particularly important, and with care can be made completely negligible.   Under favorable circumstances, the computed set of frequencies based upon unperturbed normal modes is useful for direct calibration of the wavemeter.

The normal mode frequencies for a given cavity can be obtained simply for those cavities in which the wave equation is separable.   The process of determining the normal mode frequencies for a particular cavity will be discussed more fully in Sec. 7.3.   The following material pertains to the general behavior of microwave cavities from the viewpoint of the equivalent circuit concept; these may be used qualitatively to explain the effect of excitation of the higher order modes and of the coupling systems.

7.2. Equivalent Circuit of the Cavity Wavemeter. If a microwave cavity is coupled to the transmission line by some arbitrary method, the

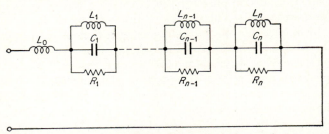

Fig. 7.1. Equivalent circuit representing the input impedance of a resonant cavity as seen in a coupled transmission line.

input impedance can be described accurately as shown in Fig. 7.1 provided the cavity losses are not too large.[1]   The resonant frequencies of the circuits shown correspond to the resonant frequencies of the normal modes.   The values of the circuit elements depend upon the strength of the coupling between the transmission line and the cavity and upon the particular choice of reference plane at which the input impedance is measured.

[1] R. Beringer, Resonant Cavities as Microwave Circuit Elements, chap. 7 in C. G. Montgomery, R. H. Dicke, and E. M. Purcell (eds.), "Principles of Microwave Circuits," vol. 8, Massachusetts Institute of Technology Radiation Laboratory Series, McGraw-Hill Book Company, Inc., New York, 1948.

If the resonant frequencies are not too close together, the behavior of the cavity at some particular resonant frequency can be obtained by representing remaining resonance circuits by the lumped parameters shown in Fig. 7.2.   In a typical situation the series resistance R', representing the losses in off-resonance modes, is very low and usually can be neglected.   The equivalent circuit can be simplified further by selecting a special reference plane in the transmission line.   The special position of the voltage node in the input line which is found when the cavity is tuned far from resonance is usually called the *detuned-short* position.   At this particular reference plane, the cavity can be represented

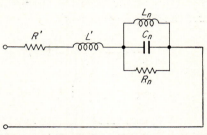

FIG. 7.2. Equivalent circuit representing the input impedance of a resonant cavity near one of the normal modes.

by a simple-shunt resonant circuit indicated in Fig. 7.3a.   At a distance of $\lambda_t/4$ from the detuned-short position, the cavity appears as the series resonant circuit shown in Fig. 7.3b.

The equivalent circuit of a cavity with two coupling systems is shown in Fig. 7.4.   The resonant condition of a particular mode can be represented by a single resonant circuit.   The generator connected to the

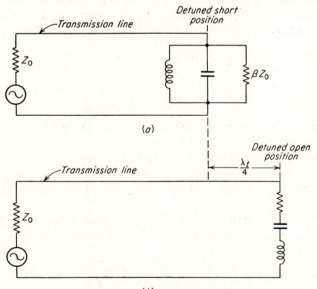

FIG. 7.3. Equivalent circuit representation of a resonant cavity at special reference planes (a) at the detuned short position, (b) at the detuned open position.

cavity by an arbitrary lossless coupling network can be represented by an ideal transformer. Similarly, the load resistance R_L can be considered coupled through another ideal transformer. The exact method of coupling to the cavity is generally unimportant; the ideal transformers represent in symbolic form the change in impedance level between the cavity and the coupling transmission lines.[1]

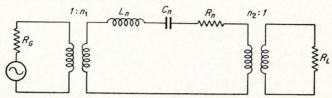

FIG. 7.4. Equivalent circuit of a resonant cavity coupled to a generator and a load. The coupling mechanism is represented by means of ideal transformers.

The degree of coupling between the cavity and the transmission lines is usually specified by introducing two additional definitions of Q factors. The Q of the entire system, including all sources of energy loss, is defined as the *loaded* Q or Q_L. The relation between the unloaded Q, Q_0, and the loaded Q is given by

$$Q_0 = (1 + \beta)Q_L \tag{7.11}$$

in which the constant β is called the coupling parameter, whose meaning is discussed more fully in Chap. 9. Another useful parameter, the *external* Q, can be defined as

$$Q_{ext} = \frac{Q_0}{\beta} \tag{7.12}$$

Combining,

$$\frac{1}{Q_L} = \frac{1}{Q_0} + \frac{1}{Q_{ext}} \tag{7.13}$$

In defining Q_0 the losses are due to internal cavity losses, whereas in Q_{ext} they are due to external load only.[2]

7.3. Mode Charts for Cavity Wavemeters. For cavities using sections of uniform transmission lines analytical and graphical relations between the cavity proportions, size, and frequency can be obtained in the following way.

For any uniform transmission line the relation between the cutoff wavelength, free-space wavelength, and guided wavelength is given by Eq. (4.33):

$$\left(\frac{2\pi}{\lambda_c}\right)^2 = \left(\frac{2\pi}{\lambda_0}\right)^2 - \left(\frac{2\pi}{\lambda_t}\right)^2 \tag{7.14}$$

[1] These statements can be proved by the transformer theorem.

[2] These relations are obtained as follows: Referring to Fig. 7.3a, suppose the resistance of the circuit at resonance is βZ_0, where Z_0 is the characteristic impedance of the

The most useful geometry for wavemeter application is the cylindrical waveguide. The cutoff wavelength for $TE_{m,n}$ and $TM_{m,n}$ waves is given by the following formulas,

$TE_{m,n}$:
$$\lambda_c = \frac{2\pi a}{u'_{m,n}} \qquad (7.15)$$

$TM_{m,n}$:
$$\lambda_c = \frac{2\pi a}{u_{m,n}} \qquad (7.16)$$

The constant $u'_{m,n}$ is the mth root of the equation $J'_m(u) = 0$; the constant $u_{m,n}$ is the mth root of the equation $J_m(u) = 0$; a is the radius of the waveguide. Some of the lower values of $u_{m,n}$ and $u'_{m,n}$ are given in Table 7.1.[1]

For convenience, the symbol $u_{m,n}$ refers to roots of either the $TE_{m,n}$ or the $TM_{m,n}$ modes.

If L is the length of a cavity, diameter $D = 2a$, and c is the velocity of light, Eq. (7.14) can be written as

$$(fD)^2 = \left(\frac{cu_{m,n}}{\pi}\right)^2 + \left(\frac{cN}{2}\right)^2 \left(\frac{D}{L}\right)^2 \qquad (7.17)$$

where N is the number of half-wavelengths contained in the distance L.

---

transmission line. Let the transmission line to the left of the circuit be terminated by Z_0. From the ordinary circuit theory, the shunt impedance R_0 of the resonant circuit and its Q_0 are related by

$$R_0 = \omega L Q_0$$

In the absence of external loading the unloaded Q would be

$$Q_0 = \frac{\beta Z_0}{\omega L}$$

In the presence of the coupled resistance Z_0, Q_L can be obtained by taking into account the parallel resistance due to the circuit losses and external Z_0. Q_L is

$$Q_L = \frac{1}{\omega L} \frac{1}{1/Z_0 + 1/\beta Z_0}$$

$$\frac{1}{Q_L} = \frac{\omega L}{\beta Z_0} + \frac{\omega L}{Z_0}$$

$$= \frac{1}{Q_0} + \frac{1}{Q_{ext}}$$

where
$$Q_{ext} = \frac{Z_0}{\omega L}$$

or
$$Q_{ext} = \frac{Q_0}{\beta}$$

[1] The values of the roots of Bessel functions for the first 180 modes in a circular cylindrical resonator are given in Wilson et al., *op. cit.*, p. 919. The cutoff wavelengths for the first 183 modes are given in Appendix A.

It should be noted that the boundary conditions for TE_{0mn} and TM_{1mn} nodes can be satisfied simultaneously, which results in an important class of *degenerate* modes, sometimes referred to as *companion* modes. This degeneracy is important in the design of some wavemeters and is discussed in Sec. 7.4.

The graph of this equation, called the *mode chart,* shows the dependence of the resonant frequency of each mode upon the length and diameter of the cavity. A mode chart for a cylindrical wavemeter is shown in Fig. 7.5. For $D/L = 0$, a number of frequencies are obtained corresponding

TABLE 7.1. ROOTS OF BESSEL FUNCTION
$$J'_m(u) = 0 \quad \text{and} \quad J_m(u) = 0$$

TE modes		TM modes	
$TE_{m,n}$	$u'_{m,n}$	$TM_{m,n}$	$u_{m,n}$
TE_{01}	3.83171	TM_{01}	2.40483
TE_{02}	7.01559	TM_{02}	5.52008
TE_{03}	10.17343	TM_{03}	8.65373
TE_{11}	1.84118	TM_{11}	3.83171
TE_{12}	5.33144	TM_{12}	7.01559
TE_{13}	8.53632	TM_{13}	10.17343
TE_{21}	3.05424	TM_{21}	5.13562
TE_{22}	6.70613	TM_{22}	8.41724
TE_{23}	9.96947	TM_{23}	11.6198

to the cutoff frequencies of the various possible modes. From each of these points on the ordinate axis an infinite set of straight lines originate which correspond to all possible values of N. A particular mode of oscillation in the cavity can be identified by adding a *third* subscript to the conventional notation to indicate the number of half-wavelength loops contained in the cavity.

Mode charts are useful in designing and using wavemeters. In using the conventional wavemeter tuned by length adjustment, it is convenient to refer to the mode chart to predict the modes of oscillation which may occur within the given displacement of the tuning plunger; this can assure the operator that extraneous frequencies are not accidently being mistaken for the expected result. In designing a wavemeter for a particular frequency range, the chart predicts those frequencies which must be suppressed to avoid ambiguities. If TE_{011} mode were to be employed, the solid rectangle shown in Fig. 7.5 indicates the frequency range which can be obtained without interference from the unwanted modes. Corresponding length displacement, required to provide this particular frequency coverage, is the base of the rectangle. A larger frequency coverage is indicated by the dashed rectangle but this permits several extraneous modes to interfere with the interpretation of the results. A mode which crosses the tuning curve of the main mode is called a *crossing* mode; a mode which crosses the rectangle without crossing the main tuning curve is called an *interfering* mode.

In designing a wavemeter, one first chooses the mode which seems to be most desirable, principally on the basis of the desired Q. By visual inspection of the mode chart, it is possible to select that region which has least number of crossing or interfering modes. In practice the effect of the extraneous modes can be minimized by proper orientation of the

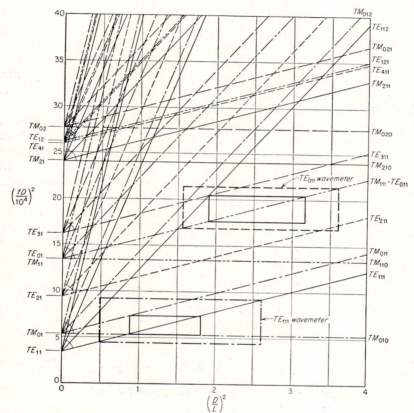

FIG. 7.5. Mode chart for a cylindrical resonant cavity. In this chart, f is in megacycles, D and L are diameter and length of the cavity respectively, in centimeters. The mode types are identified in accordance with the waveguide nomenclature and are indicated at the left side of the diagram. The rectangles indicate the operating range of the wavemeters described in the text.

coupling elements, or they can be suppressed sometimes as in the TE_{011} wavemeter described in Sec. 7.4.

7.4. Typical Wavemeters. The several types of cavity wavemeters which have been found useful can be divided into three groups: low Q, medium Q, and high Q. At a wavelength of 10 cm, typical Q values may be 1,000, 10,000, and 50,000 respectively. From the general remarks in Sec. 7.1 the physical size is the principal difference between the various types, as this factor plays the predominant role in determining the Q value.

Simple coaxial wavemeters can be used to provide low values of Q. Because of their small size, a large class of unwanted modes are automatically excluded, permitting a substantial tuning range to be obtained in one instrument. Higher values of Q necessitate larger cavities. For example, a cavity operating in TE_{111} mode may have a Q_L of 15,000 at 10 cm. The tuning range of this mode may be made about 20 per cent without danger of extraneous modes, and up to 50 per cent if moderate interference can be tolerated. Higher Q values can be obtained by using larger cavities operating in the TE_{011} mode. This results in a number of unwanted modes, some of which can be suppressed easily.

Table 7.2 summarizes the pertinent information for the three types of wavemeters mentioned. This table lists characteristics obtained from theoretical calculations as well as for the practical wavemeters discussed in the remaining parts of this section. The practical tuning range of the wavemeters listed is restricted by available plunger motion in the coaxial wavemeter and by the mode interference in the other two cases.

The quantity of interest in some applications is the frequency of the signal; in this case the calculated resonant frequency of the cavity is usually not sufficiently accurate and the calibration is particularly important. The absolute frequency may not be important in other applications, but frequency changes must be determined accurately. In this case, incremental frequency calibration can be obtained theoretically by differentiating the tuning curve of a particular mode.[1]

In practice, the high-Q wavemeters are difficult to use unless the frequency is known approximately. In the process of searching a given band it is relatively easy to miss the unknown signal. When starting an experiment, it is usually easier to find the unknown frequency with a

---

[1] The incremental tuning can be determined by differentiating Eq. (7.17) with respect to L (letting $N = 1$):

$$\frac{df}{dL} = -\frac{1}{4}\frac{c^2}{fL^3}$$

which can be written as

$$\frac{df}{f} = -\left(\frac{c}{2fL}\right)^2 \frac{dL}{L}$$

$$= -\left(\frac{\lambda}{2L}\right)^2 \frac{dL}{L}$$

or

$$df = -\frac{\lambda c}{4L^3}\, dL$$

Thus, at a given frequency, the fractional frequency change is proportional to the fractional length change; the constant of proportionality depends upon the mode type through the variable L.

low-Q wavemeter first and later determine the frequency more accurately with a high-Q device. The use of two wavemeters of radically different proportions also ensures that the spurious mode has not been mistaken accidently for the main response.

All wavemeters have several common features irrespective of their size or the particular modes being used. Provisions must be made for coupling the signal into the cavity and for detecting the resonance phenomena; these elements are described below with specific examples of the low-, medium-, and high-Q wavemeters given later.

TABLE 7.2. CHARACTERISTICS OF 10-CM CAVITY WAVEMETERS

Type	Q		Tuning range	
	Theoretical Q_0	Usual Q_L	Mode free	Practical
Coaxial $\lambda/4$ (Sec. 7.4b)................	5,000	2,000	3:1	1.32:1
TE$_{111}$ cylindrical cavity (Sec. 7.4c)......	30,000	15,000	1.2:1	1.5:1
TE$_{011}$ cylindrical cavity (Sec. 7.4d)......	60,000	40,000	1.075:1	1.13:1

a. Methods of Coupling and Loading Errors. The two ways that cavity wavemeters can be used to measure the frequency in a transmission system are commonly called the *transmission* and *reaction* methods and are shown schematically in Fig. 7.6.

In the transmission system the detector is separated from the r-f source by the cavity wavemeter so that power transmission through the cavity is possible at its resonant frequency only. In use, the wavemeter is adjusted until the detected signal reaches its maximum value; if the coupling between the generator and the detector were sufficiently weak, the frequency of the signal would correspond to the calculated normal-mode frequency of the cavity. In practice, theoretical calculations cannot be relied on completely and calibration is needed to take into account the residual effects of the coupling and mechanical imperfections.

In the reaction method the detecting element is placed between the r-f source and the cavity. The detected signal is present irrespective of the tuning of the wavemeter, but if the wavemeter is tuned to resonance the impedance coupled into the system changes rapidly near resonance and produces a reaction upon the detected signal. The frequency of greatest reaction upon the detected signal is taken as the frequency of the signal.

A cavity wavemeter intended for transmission service can be used as a reaction wavemeter as well. A wavemeter intended for reaction use may not have the second output and cannot be used directly as a transmission device. However, a standing-wave detector can be placed between the generator and the cavity, and the probe located at the detuned short position where its response will correspond to the output of the transmission-type system. This can be seen from Fig. 7.3a and the accompanying discussion; the probe placed at the detuned short position measures the voltage across the equivalent shunt-resonant circuit.

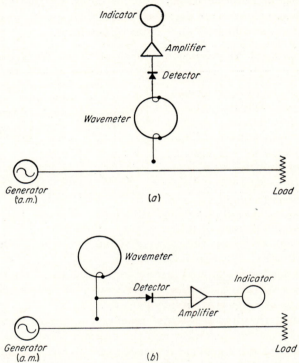

FIG. 7.6. Schematic representation showing the connection of a resonant cavity wavemeter to the equipment under test. In (a) the cavity is used as a transmission device and in (b) as a reaction device.

Transmission-line couplings of different kinds are indicated in Fig. 7.7; Figs. 7.7a and b show magnetic and electrostatic coupling by a loop and probe, respectively; Fig. 7.7c shows coupling to a cavity by an iris. The orientation of the coupling elements and their position in the cavity depend upon the particular mode being used. If interfering modes are possible within the tuning range of the cavity, the coupling elements can usually be placed to favor the excitation of the desired mode.

It can be demonstrated that both the transmission and reaction systems produce indications which are in error slightly if the generator or the load impedances are not matched; the extent of the error depends upon the degree of mismatch and the unloaded Q of the cavity. If the cavity has been designed specifically as a wavemeter, i.e., with the coupling weak between it and the input and output lines, the resultant error is a small but not a negligible fraction of the cavity bandwidth.[1]

b. Coaxial Wavemeter. Operating in the TEM mode the coaxial cavity wavemeter shown in Fig. 7.8 is a small and convenient device for applications where wide-range tuning and only moderate accuracy are desired.[2] It is most useful at frequencies up to 10,000 Mc. Small manufacturing tolerances and a low Q generally limit the usefulness at higher frequencies.

The particular design illustrated uses a cavity one quarter-wavelength long which is made adjustable in length by moving the inner conductor with an ordinary micrometer. The r-f contact between the inner conductor and the cavity is made by capacity traps as shown;

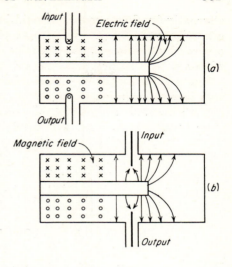

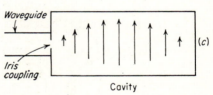

Fig. 7.7. Three methods of coupling the cavity wavemeters to the transmission line. (*a* and *b*) The magnetic and electric coupling, respectively, to a coaxial cavity; (*c*) an iris coupling between a waveguide and a cavity.

[1] The details of the errors caused by the generator and load mismatches upon the measurement accuracy are discussed by R. Beringer, chap. 5, pp. 309–318, in C. G. Montgomery (ed.), "Technique of Microwave Measurements," McGraw-Hill Book Company, Inc., New York, 1947. It is shown, for example, that the difference between the frequency of maximum transmission with matched generator and load impedances as contrasted to the measured frequency with generator and load impedances, VSWR of r_1 and r_2 respectively, is

$$\delta = \pm \frac{\omega_0}{4Q_0} \left[\beta_1 \left(r_1 - \frac{1}{r_1} \right) + \beta_2 \left(r_2 - \frac{1}{r_2} \right) \right] \tag{7.18}$$

in which β_1 and β_2 are the coupling parameters between the cavity and the transmission lines as given in Eq. (7.12). For a cavity at 10,000 Mc, with $Q_0 = 24,000$, $\beta_1 = \beta_2 = 0.5$, the bandwidth of the response curve is about 0.8 Mc/sec. If $r_1 = r_2 = 1.1$, the error may be as much as 0.02 Mc/sec. If $r_1 = r_2 = 2$, the error can be as much as 0.2 Mc/sec.

[2] E. L. Ginzton and F. L. Salisbury, Ultra-high-frequency Wavemeter, U.S. Patent 2,503,256, April, 1950. Similar devices are manufactured by Sperry Gyroscope Co., New York.

alternatively, finger contacts could have been used, but they are found generally more lossy. The "open-circuit" end of the coaxial line is covered by a metallic plate sufficiently far removed from the inner conductor so that its presence does not affect the calibration.

The principal mode of a coaxial line has an infinite cut-off wavelength and, hence, according to Eq. (7.14), the free-space wavelength is equal to the measured transmission-line wavelength. If L is the length of the inner conductor, $\lambda_t = 4L$. This relation is not strictly accurate for the

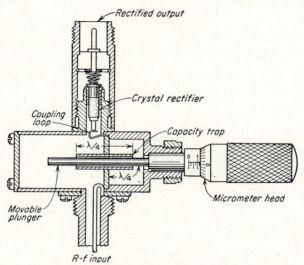

FIG. 7-8. Low-Q wide-range coaxial wavemeter.

quarter-wavelength cavity because of the fringing capacity at the end of the inner conductor. This fact, combined with other irregularities in the design shown (such as the capacity bypass sleeve), makes it necessary to calibrate this wavemeter against some frequency standard. However, the measured wavelength is found to be proportional to the length of the inner conductor as predicted by the idealized theory.

The method used to couple the input and output transmission lines is shown in Fig. 7.8. In this case the output contains a built-in crystal detector holder and a bypass condenser and no additional r-f parts are needed.

The mode chart for this wavemeter can be obtained in the usual way. At higher frequencies, the one-quarter-wavelength structure can become resonant in the $\frac{3}{4}\lambda$, $\frac{5}{4}\lambda$, etc., modes. The length of the inner conductor is given approximately by

$$L = \frac{\lambda_t}{4} (2N - 1) \qquad (7.19)$$

where $N = 1, 2, 3, \ldots$. Higher order modes, either TE or TM, can also be excited in the coaxial resonator. The lowest order mode of this set is the TE mode, analogous to the TE_{10} mode in the rectangular waveguide. The cutoff wavelength for this mode occurs when the average circumference is approximately equal to the wavelength. In general, the cut-off wavelength for the TE set is approximately given by[1]

$$\lambda_c \cong \frac{2\pi}{n} \left(\frac{a + b}{2} \right) \tag{7.20}$$

where $n = 1, 2, 3, \ldots$, and the inner and outer radii are a and b, respectively. Using these relations, together with Eq. (7.14), a mode chart for a coaxial wavemeter can be constructed.

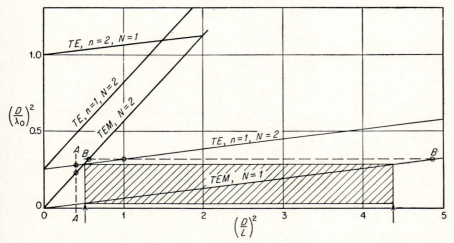

FIG. 7.9. Mode chart for the coaxial wavemeter shown in Fig. 7.8. The chart is plotted for $b = 1$ cm, $b/a = 3.6$, where b and a are outer and inner radii, respectively. $D = 2b$, and L is the length of the cavity in centimeters. The cross-hatched region corresponds to mode-free operation occurring between $L = 2.9$ cm and $L = 0.95$ cm, shown by arrows along the abscissa [$(D/L)^2 = 0.5$ and 4.4, respectively].

A mode chart for a wavemeter designed to operate in the vicinity of 10 cm with $b = 1$ cm, and $b/a = 3.6$ is shown in Fig. 7.9. In the range of L of 0.95 to 2.9 cm, there are no crossing modes, which results in a mode-free tuning range of 3.8 to 11.6 cm. If L is made larger than 2.9 cm to permit operation at longer wavelengths, spurious resonances would become possible at the shorter wavelengths as indicated by circles along line AA. Similarly, for smaller values of L than 0.95 cm to allow operation at shorter wavelengths, spurious modes would be observed at the higher frequencies as indicated along line BB. Therefore, when wave-

[1] See also Fig. A.11.

meters of this type are used for exploratory purposes, the approximate wavelength already known should be checked in some other way.

The unloaded Q of the coaxial cavity wavemeter is given by

$$Q_0 = \frac{\lambda_0}{\delta} \frac{b}{\lambda_0} \frac{2 \ln (b/a)}{1 + b/a} \tag{7.21}$$

This expression has a maximum value at $b/a = 3.59$.   The maximum value of Q_0 is

$$Q_0 = 0.557 \frac{\lambda_0}{\delta} \frac{b}{\lambda_0} \tag{7.22}$$

For silver, $\lambda_0/\delta = 89,000$ at $\lambda_0 = 10$ cm; for the dimensions of the wavemeter discussed, the theoretical value of Q_0 should be about 5,000.   Actually, the loaded Q of the wavemeter is found to be about 2,000 because

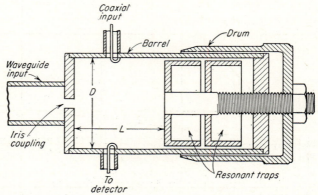

FIG. 7.10. Typical medium-Q cavity wavemeter employing the TE_{111} mode; two alternate input systems are shown.   The drum and the barrel can be engraved as a micrometer to indicate tuning plunger displacement.   The useful range of this wavemeter (shown for $D = 8.12$ cm and L variable from 5.05 to 11.75 cm) is indicated by the dash-dot rectangle in Fig. 7.5.

of imperfections in plating, losses in the choke joint, and loading due to coupling.

An ordinary coaxial standing-wave detector can be used for wavemeter purposes by terminating it in a short circuit which produces nearly perfect standing waves.   By means of the moving probe, the separation between successive minima can be determined.   The accuracy is nearly equivalent to that obtained with the one quarter-wavelength cavity.

c. TE_{111}-mode Wavemeter.   A wavemeter intended to provide higher accuracy than is possible with the coaxial cavity is shown in Fig. 7.10. It uses the TE_{111}-cylindrical waveguide mode which results in the loaded Q of about 15,000.   The increase in Q_L is due to the larger volume, but this also requires the tuning range to be decreased to restrict the effect of interfering modes. The wavemeter shown in Fig. 7.10 is capable of operation between 8.00 and 11.65 cm.

The length adjustment of the cavity is made by moving the end plunger, which is connected electrically to the walls of the cylinder by resonant choke joints as shown; over the limited frequency range of interest, these prove to be satisfactory. The input and output circuits can be coupled to the cavity by means of either the iris or loop coupling.

Often the TE_{111} mode of operation is selected because it is the dominant mode of the waveguide and permits the largest tuning range without interfering modes. An examination of Fig. 7.5, which makes this more apparent, indicates the region of useful operation. It can be seen that TM_{010} appears as a crossing mode; however, because it does not tune with the plunger adjustment, it is readily recognizable and usually does not cause any difficulty. The TM_{011} and TE_{112} appear as interfering modes; the former is not too important, as its excitation is automatically minimized by proper orientation of the coupling loops for TE_{111} mode; the TE_{112} mode can be excited and is not readily differentiated from TE_{111} mode.

If the cavity is slightly elliptical, the TE_{11} mode splits, producing two TE_{11} modes appropriate to the two axes of the ellipse. Under some conditions of the orientation of the axis of the ellipse with respect to the coupling elements, both of the split modes can be excited and observed. The separation of these modes depends upon the degree of ellipticity and can easily become large enough to be troublesome. The split mode is observed as a double peak (or, in the extreme case of considerable ellipticity, as two separate peaks some distance apart) which tune together.

The unloaded Q of TE_{111} cavity is given by

$$Q_0 = \frac{\lambda_0}{\delta} \frac{L}{\lambda_0} \frac{\left[(u'_{n,m})^2 + \left(\frac{\pi D}{2L} \right)^2 \right] \left[1 - \left(\frac{n}{u'_{m,n}} \right)^2 \right]}{\left[\frac{2L}{D} (u'_{m,n})^2 + \frac{\pi^2}{2} \left(\frac{D}{L} \right)^2 + \frac{D(L-D)}{2L^2} \left(\frac{\pi n}{u'_{m,n}} \right)^2 \right]} \quad (7.23)$$

This expression has a flat maximum at $D/L = 1.5$. For this shape, Q_0 becomes

$$Q_0 = 0.275 \frac{\lambda_0}{\delta} \quad (7.24)$$

For a silver-plated cavity at 10 cm, this produces a theoretical Q_0 of about 32,000. For practical conditions of plating and including usual loading losses, the value of Q_L of about 15,000 is typical.

d. *TE$_{011}$-mode Wavemeter.* A wavemeter with a higher Q than of those described in the two preceding sections is shown in Fig. 7.11 and uses the TE_{011} mode. The cavity tuning is obtained by varying the length of the cylinder by moving the tuning plate as illustrated.   It has a small tuning range, 10.3 to 11.2 cm.

In contrast to the TE_{111} wavemeter, the tuning plate does not need to contact the cylinder wall electrically.   Since the current flow in the TE_{011} mode is everywhere circumferential, there is no current flow between the cylinder and the plate; hence no electrical contact is required and the gap between the plate and the cylinder has no effect.   The presence of

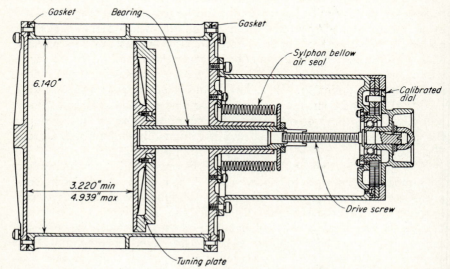

FIG. 7.11. Main elements of a TE_{011} wavemeter. The input and output coupling systems are not shown. The gaskets and the bellows are used to prevent changes in pressure and humidity from affecting the calibration. (*Adopted by permission from "Technique of Microwave Measurements," edited by C. G. Montgomery. Copyright, 1947. McGraw-Hill Book Company, Inc., New York.*)

the gap is helpful in eliminating or reducing the possibility of mode interference.   All modes (except the $TE_{0,n,l}$ type) have currents tending to cross the gap; this causes their fields to excite the chamber beyond the tuning plate where absorbing material can be placed if needed.   The presence of the gap and this damping effectively removes the interfering modes from the tuning region.   The Q of the desired TE_{0111} mode is much higher than of the modes of the interfering set so that a coupling coefficient chosen to provide proper coupling for the desired mode becomes very small for the extraneous modes.   As a result, the magnitude of response to TE_{011} mode is much greater than to the unwanted modes.

The fact that the TM_{111} mode is a companion of the TE_{011} mode and that they are simultaneously resonant was mentioned in Sec. 7.3.   The TM_{111} mode, strongly perturbed by the presence of the gap, has a relatively low Q. Since the current distribution in the walls of the cavity is different, the TE_{011} mode can be preferentially excited by suitable disposition of the coupling elements. Any asymmetry in the construction of the cavity, such as tilting of the tuning plate, will partially excite the TM_{111} mode which establishes a cross coupling between the two modes and transfers the energy from the high-Q mode to the lower-Q mode. Consequently, high machining precision is necessary in constructing the TE_{011}-type wavemeters. In some wavemeters, adjustments are provided at the factory to set the endplate experimentally for minimum reduction in Q.

The tuning range of this wavemeter is shown by the dashed rectangle in Fig. 7.5 which is appreciably larger than the mode-free region; the TE_{311}, TE_{112}, TE_{211}, and TM_{012} are within the tuning range. Although these are suppressed in the manner indicated, weak responses can be detected.

The wavemeter shown is hermetically sealed with rubber gaskets and a sylphon bellows to minimize the effect of humidity and temperature changes upon its calibration. The tuning screw mechanism is directly calibrated in frequency. The coupling system consists of two loops; the output loop is connected to a built-in crystal detector and a d-c meter.

The Q of this wavemeter is substantially higher than those described previously. The theoretical Q for this mode can be computed from:

$$Q_0 = 0.610 \left(\frac{\lambda_0}{\delta}\right) \sqrt{1 + \left(0.410 \frac{D}{L}\right)^2} \frac{1 + 0.168(D/L)^2}{1 + 0.168(D/L)^3} \qquad (7.25)$$

This function has a maximum at $D/L = 1$, where

$$Q_0 = 0.66 \left(\frac{\lambda_0}{\delta}\right) \qquad (7.26)$$

For a silver surface at 10 cm, the theoretical Q_0 is about 59,000. The loaded Q for the wavemeter described is in the neighborhood of 40,000.

A photograph of TE_{011} 3-cm wavemeter is shown in Fig. 7.12.

7.5. Precision Comparison of Resonant Cavities. It is often necessary to measure wavelength to a precision which exceeds the accuracy corresponding to the bandwidth of $1/Q_0$. For example, the measurement of small wavelength differences is often important in the calibration of wavemeters. It is also sometimes necessary to measure accurately the change in resonant frequency of a cavity due to the presence of a small perturbing object such as in the R_0/Q_0 measurements described in Chap. 10. Various techniques can be devised to detect small changes in resonant wavelength that provide the ultimate in accuracy. Two useful methods are described below.

A precise comparison of a cavity under study against a tunable calibrated wavemeter can be made with the equipment shown in Fig. 7.13. The two cavities are connected to a frequency-modulated signal generator to allow dynamic observation of the transmission response curves of

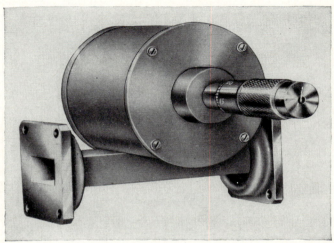

FIG. 7.12. Photograph of a 3-cm TE_{011} wavemeter.   (*Courtesy of Polytechnic Research and Development Co., Inc., Brooklyn, New York.*)

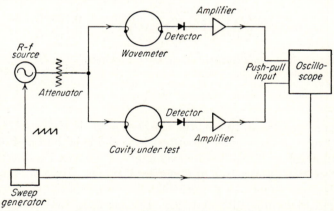

FIG. 7.13. Schematic representation of components needed for accurate comparison of resonant frequencies of two cavities.   The amplified detected output from the two cavities is combined at the oscilloscope (or at an earlier stage) to present the difference signal between the two channels.

both cavities.   The transmission curves are displayed on an oscilloscope in phase opposition, which can be done by connecting the two detectors in phase opposition.   Some typical oscilloscope patterns obtained with this arrangement are shown in Fig. 7.14.   In Fig. 7.14a, the resonant frequencies are different from each other by an amount somewhat greater than their respective bandwidths; in Fig. 7.14b, the resonant frequencies of the two cavities are nearly equal but the inequality still may be detected easily by observing that two branches of the curve are unsymmetrical; in Fig. 7.14c, the frequency of the two cavities is exactly the same. This method is particularly accurate when the two values of Q

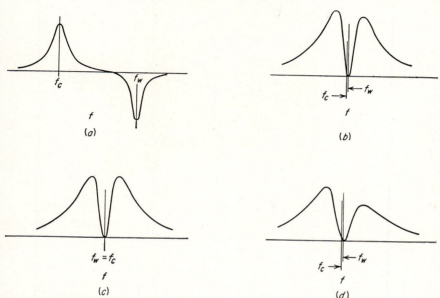

FIG. 7.14. Oscilloscope patterns obtained in precision comparison of resonant frequencies of cavity resonators. f_w and f_c indicate resonant frequencies of the wavemeter and the cavity under test, respectively. The pattern when the resonant frequencies are (a) substantially different, (b) nearly equal, and (c) exactly equal. In (a), (b), and (c), $Q_w = 2Q_c$. In (d) f_w is nearly equal to f_c, with Q values also being nearly equal. (By permission from R. L. Sproull and E. L. Linder, Resonant Cavity Measurements, Proc. IRE, vol. 34, p. 305, May, 1946.)

are nearly equal. If the detected outputs are adjusted to be equal, their difference results in a complete cancellation of the signal. That a small departure from equality between the two resonant frequencies is readily observable is shown in Fig. 7.14d, which is plotted for 0.01δ. With $Q_0 = 10,000$, this corresponds to a detection accuracy of 1 part per million.[1]

Another precision method uses the symmetry of the transmission resonance curve. If the signal source is sine-wave frequency-modulated with the frequency swing approximating the bandwidth of the cavity, the

[1] For further details, see R. L. Sproull and E. L. Linder, Resonant Cavity Measurements, Proc. IRE, vol. 34, p. 305, May, 1946.

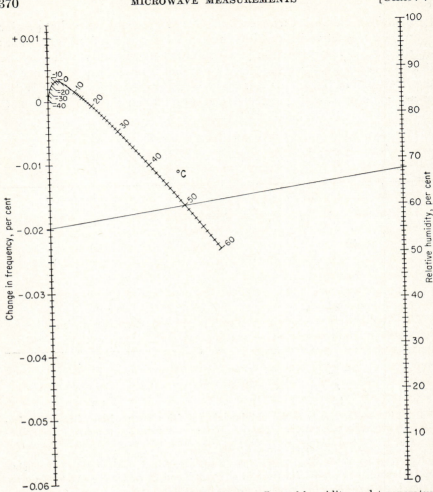

Fig. 7.15. Adams nomograph for predicting the effect of humidity and temperature on the resonant frequency of a cavity resonator. The chart is normalized to conditions at 25°C and 60 per cent relative humidity. The correction obtained from the nomograph is to be added to the frequency read by an unsealed cavity wavemeter. Further corrections must be applied if the wavemeter is used at the high altitudes. (*Adopted by permission from "Technique of Microwave Measurements," edited by C. G. Montgomery. Copyright, 1947. McGraw-Hill Book Company, Inc., New York.*)

detected output from the cavity will contain only the second harmonic of the modulation frequency *provided* the cavity is precisely tuned to the carrier frequency. Small deviations from the exact resonance can be detected by observing the presence of the fundamental in the detected output by a sensitive audio amplifier sufficiently selective to respond only to the modulation frequency. It is found that detuning from resonance by 0.01δ is easily detectable. Providing the reading accuracy of the wavemeter scale is sufficiently accurate, this procedure results in a measurement accuracy of about one part per million.

7.6. Effect of Temperature and Humidity upon Cavity Calibration. The resonant frequency of the cavity wavemeter can change due to thermal expansion of its parts and variation in the dielectric constant of the air caused by temperature and humidity fluctuations.

The first of these depends upon the temperature coefficient of expansion of the cavity materials and the details of its construction. It is relatively simple to prevent the thermal expansion from affecting the resonant frequency by making cavity parts from materials with different coefficients of expansion.

The second cause results in the change in cavity resonant frequency if it is exposed to the air. A chart prepared to correct wavemeter readings is shown in Fig. 7.15. It can be seen that warm, humid conditions produce the largest departure from the correct frequency and a change of 1 part in 10,000 is not uncommon. By attaching to the wavemeter a chamber containing a drying agent the accuracy of the readings can be improved considerably.

7.7. Application of Optical Methods. At the short end of the microwave region, particularly at the millimeter wavelengths, the dimensions of the cavity wavemeter become inconveniently small, which increases the mechanical tolerance requirements in manufacture—sometimes beyond practical limits. In addition, the selectivity factor Q also decreases with frequency for the reasons discussed in Sec. 7.1. It is, therefore, desirable to establish the standing-wave interference pattern in space without confining the radiation within the inconveniently small microwave transmission-line components. This can readily be done by utilizing the techniques familiar in geometrical optics, where length and wavelength measurements are commonly made by means of interferometers. Several devices representing microwave equivalents of the optical interferometers have been devised for the shorter wavelengths, both for the measurement of the wavelength and for the determination of dielectric constants of certain materials.[1]

---

[1] For further discussion of optical methods and their application to microwave practice, the reader is referred to the following references: W. Culshaw, The Michelson Interferometer at Millimeter Wavelengths, *Proc. Phys. Soc. (London)*, sec. B, vol. 63, no. 1, pp. 939–954, 1950; K. D. Froome, Investigation of a New Form of Microwave Interferometer for Determining the Velocity of Electromagnetic Waves, *Proc. Roy. Soc. (London)*, sec. A, vol. 233, pp. 195–215, 1954; B. A. Lengyel, A Michelson-type Interferometer for Microwave Measurements, *Proc. IRE*, vol. 37, pp. 1242–1244, November, 1949; W. Culshaw, The Fabret-Perot Interferometer at Millimeter Wavelengths, *Proc. Phys. Soc. (London)*, sec. B, vol. 66, pt. VII, pp. 597–608, July, 1953; C. L. Andrews, Microwave Optics, *Am. J. Phys.*, vol. 14, pp. 379–382, November–

Many of the principles of geometrical optics can be applied directly to microwave measurements. The analogy cannot be exact, because of the different order of the dimensions of the apparatus when compared to the wavelength. In microwave analogues of optical instruments, the transmitting and receiving elements consist of devices such as horns, lenses, and gratings, whose apertures must remain practical in terms of

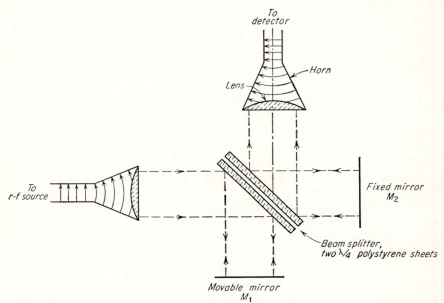

FIG. 7.16. Interferometric measurement of the wavelength by the Michelson interferometer adopted for use at the millimeter wavelengths.

the laboratory dimensions. Even at the shortest wavelengths, the apertures are only moderately large when measured in wavelengths. Hence, it is impractical to avoid divergent beams and the phase fronts cannot be considered plane as they are in the optical case. The problems of diffraction must be considered carefully, and, in fact, form the principal objection to a more universal use of the optical methods.

Two examples of microwave interferometers are shown in Figs. 7.16 and 7.17; these are the microwave equivalents of the Michelson and Fabret-Perot interferometers, respectively.[1] In Fig. 7.16, a microwave source supplies power into a waveguide which gradually expands to

December, 1946; A. B. Pippard, Wave Guide Interferometers as Differential Wave Meters, *J. Sci. Instr.*, vol. 26, no. 9, pp. 296–298, September, 1949; R. J. Coates, A Grating Spectrometer for Millimeter Waves, *Rev. Sci. Instr.*, vol. 19, no. 9, pp. 586–590, September, 1948.

[1] Culshaw, *op. cit.*, 1950.

become an electromagnetic horn; the aperture is made as large as is practicable.   In order to reduce the divergence of the radiated beam, the horn is fitted with a suitable lens which tends to transform the divergent beam into a parallel one with a plane phase front.   A similarly constructed receiving horn is connected to a detecting element.   In a true Michelson interferometer, a half-silvered mirror is used to split the beam; in the microwave case the beam splitters can be made of dielectric sheets covered with scattering objects, such as regularly spaced pieces of metal, gratings using wires, slots, etc.   An improved beam splitter is shown in Fig. 7.16.   It consists of two $\lambda/4$-thick dielectric plates separated from each other by an air gap which is adjusted by trial to give a

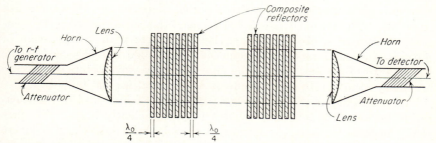

Fig. 7-17. Fabret-Perot interferometer for use at the millimeter wavelengths.   Separation between the composite reflectors (or mirrors) is 100 to 200 wavelengths.   Reflection coefficient of each mirror is about 0.995.

reflection coefficient of 50 per cent at the required 45° incidence angle. The mirrors $M1$ and $M2$ are made of some reflecting material such as copper or silver-plating deposited on a flat metallic surface.   One of the mirrors is left fixed while the other is mounted on a movable carriage with a provision for measuring the displacement accurately.

An examination of the Michelson interferometer shows that the signals arrive at the receiver horn from two sources, the relative phases of which are determined by the position of the mirror $M1$.   The variation of detected current with the motion of the mirror results in the standing-wave phenomena which are similar to those occurring in the shorted transmission line.   If the Michelson interferometer is symmetrical so that the two signals are of the same strength, the standing-wave pattern would produce complete cancellation at the nodes.   However, the equivalent standing-wave ratio is not infinite because of diffraction and scattering effects.   The wavelength can be measured simply by observing the displacement of the mirror between successive minima.   The accuracy of these measurements can be improved by conventional techniques used in VSWR measurements; the distance between several successive minima can be measured and averaged; the location of each minimum can be determined more accurately by the use of the double-minimum method.

The microwave equivalent of the Fabret-Perot interferometer is shown in Fig. 7.17.[1] The optical version of this instrument consists of a source and an "eyepiece" separated by two mirrors between which multiple reflections are made to occur. In the illustration shown, the mirrors are replaced by a series of dielectric sheets, each one quarter-wavelength thick separated by a quarter-wavelength. The composite reflector system built up of quarter-wavelength plates of low-loss material acts as a nearly perfect reflector. The region between the two composite reflectors corresponds to the interior region of a cavity resonator where multiple reflections also occur. A resonance phenomenon is observed at the receiving horn as it is moved through a series of positions spaced by half-wavelength intervals. The received signals behave as if the region between the composite reflectors consisted of a cavity resonator; with a separation of mirrors of about 1 meter, an apparent Q of 60,000 was observed at the wavelength of 0.8 cm. As in the case of cavity wavemeters, it may be necessary to take into account effects of temperature and humidity.

The possibility of diffraction and scattering effects requires the separation between the reflecting mirrors to be sufficiently large.[2] In spite of the large dimensions, the apparatus must be held rigidly and accurate adjustments provided for the various parts. Because of these complications, optical methods are not useful except at very short wavelengths where normal microwave techniques become impractical.

[1] Culshaw, *op. cit.*, 1953.

[2] It is also possible to use interferometers within the region of strong diffraction and to apply corrections for the effects observed. See Froome, *op. cit.*

CHAPTER 8

MEASUREMENT OF FREQUENCY

8.1. Introduction. The measurement of wavelength as discussed in Chap. 7 presents the simplest and most convenient method of determining frequency. Wavelength methods, however, depend upon the calibration of devices whose frequency is affected by temperature, humidity, time, and mechanical inaccuracies. It is seldom possible to obtain an accuracy better than 1 part in 10^4; if better accuracy is required, it is necessary to measure the frequency directly.

As at the lower frequencies, microwave applications often require great accuracy. In some cases it is necessary to specify the frequency very accurately because a given system may operate only at or near the specified frequency, as in the case of the linear electron accelerator. Sometimes precise relative frequency measurements are needed to study instantaneous frequency stability of a communications system which may be of greater importance than the long-time average frequency. In addition, the shortage of frequency spectrum makes it increasingly necessary to be more accurate in assigning frequencies to the various classes of microwave transmission; this further emphasizes the need for accurate frequency standards and measurements.

Contrasted with other microwave techniques, the measurement of microwave frequencies is an extension of the conventional low-frequency practice. The knowledge of the low-frequency techniques is helpful in understanding and using the microwave methods. Most of the following material is concerned with methods which can be used to establish the standard frequencies throughout the microwave spectrum and with the details of the comparison of the unknown against one of the standard frequencies. This process results in the beat frequency between the unknown and the standard, reducing the problem to that of measuring a low radio frequency. The conventional methods of frequency measurement are discussed in the literature.[1]

[1] See, for example, F. E. Terman and J. M. Pettit, "Electronic Measurements," chap. 5, McGraw-Hill Book Company, Inc., New York, 1952; also J. E. Thwaites and F. J. M. Laver, The Technique of Frequency Measurements, and Its Application to Telecommunications, *J. IEE*, vol. 89, pt. III, p. 139, September, 1942.

The present standard of frequency is based upon the astronomical observation of the period of rotation of the earth. In the United States the procedure of standardizing radio frequencies against astronomical observations is carried out at the National Bureau of Standards in Washington, D.C. The national primary frequency standard is obtained by comparing a group of eight 100-kc crystal oscillators against each other and against the time established by the U.S. Naval Observatory. The comparison is made by dividing 100-kc signals down to 1,000 cycles in order to drive a synchronous clock. The time indicated by the synchronous clock can be compared over short and long periods of time against astronomical time. A 100-kc oscillator standardized by this procedure is used as a master oscillator to provide the signal for radio station WWV at Washington, D.C., which transmits radio signals at 5, 10, 15, and 20 Mc.* The resultant transmitted frequencies are known to be accurate to about 1 part in 10^8. The corrections to each daily transmission frequency are obtained by observing the oscillator frequency over 100-day intervals and using this information by extrapolation to adjust future transmitted frequencies. *Daily* and *short* time fluctuations of the transmitted signal are much better than the mean frequency, and are believed to be in the order of 1 or 2 parts in 10^9 and 1 or 2 parts in 10^{10}, respectively. The accuracy of 1 part in 10^8 seems to represent the best accuracy that can be obtained in terms of time derived from the period of the earth's rotation over a period of 100 days. At present longer averaging periods cannot be used to improve the accuracy because 100-kc standard oscillators are not sufficiently stable and also because certain fluctuations exist in the period of the mean solar day.[1]

* Standard Frequencies and Time Signals WWV and WWVH, *Natl. Bur. Standards Circ.* LC 1,009, U.S. Dept. of Commerce, National Bureau of Standards, Washington 25, D.C.; also, F. D. Lewis, Frequency and Time Standards, *Proc. IRE*, vol. 43, p. 1046, September, 1955. This paper describes current methods in establishing the astronomical time, as well as the various frequency standards in use today. A list of the standard-frequency broadcast stations is included. A description of the signals available from the radio stations WWV and WWVH, their characteristics, radio propagation forecasts, accuracy, and regions of reliable reception and lists of foreign standard-frequency stations are given in the paper Standard Frequencies and Time Signals WWV and WWVH, *Proc. IRE*, vol. 44, no. 10, pp. 1470–1473, October, 1956.

[1] The period of the rotation of the earth is believed to change in several ways. A number of irregular changes in the rotation of the earth have occurred during the last 100 years. In 1870, for example, the earth's rate of rotation was fast by about 1.6 sec for the year compared with the average rotation of the earth over longer periods. Smaller random variations occur in periods shorter than one year. Some of these changes seem to be related to the irregular displacement of the earth's poles (by distances of as much as 30 ft). In addition to these effects, the earth's rotation is gradually slowing down because of the tidal friction in the shallow seas. The length of one day seems to have seasonal periodicity because of the effect of atmospheric circulation.

It is possible to establish a laboratory standard to an accuracy in 1 part in 10^8 by receiving radio signals from WWV.[1] However, certain precautions must be observed because the received frequency can be substantially changed due to the Doppler shift caused by the changing height of the ionosphere layers, which is known to have made the received frequency differ from the correct values by several parts in 10^7 or even greater during ionospheric storms. Averaging a number of determinations obtained during the noon or midnight periods makes it possible to obtain the precision stated above.

TABLE 8.1. STANDARD-FREQUENCY STATIONS OUTSIDE THE UNITED STATES*

Station call letters	Location	Transmitted signals	
		Carrier frequency, Mc	Modulation, cycles
LOL............	Buenos Aires, Argentina	2.5, 5, 10, 15, 20, 25	1, 440, 1,000
ZUO............	Johannesburg, South Africa	5	1
ZLFS............	Lower Hutt, New Zealand	2.5	
....	Moscow, USSR	10, 15	1
MSF............	Rugby, England	2.5, 5, 10	1, 1,000
JJY............	Tokyo, Japan	2.5, 5, 10, 15	1, 1,000
IBF............	Torino, Italy	5	1, 440, 1,000
....	Uccle, Belgium	2.5	

* From Standard Frequencies and Time Signals WWV and WWVH, *Proc. IRE*, vol. 44, no. 10, pp. 1470–1473, October, 1956.

Recently, an appreciable effort has been expended trying to develop frequency standards based upon the molecular absorption spectrum. The spectral lines of a molecule, such as ammonia, can be expected to remain more constant than the periods of solar systems which are subject to various gross mechanical changes. Although none of the molecular methods proposed to date to establish an *atomic clock* has yet been perfected, several seem to be very promising. It is believed that eventually accuracies of 1 part in 10^{10} can be obtained.[2]

The maximum change in the length of one day appears to be in the vicinity of 1 part in 60 million. See D. Brouwer, A Study of the Changes in the Rate of Rotation of the Earth, *Astron. J.*, vol. 57, no. 5, pp. 125–146, September, 1952.

[1] Table 8.1 lists the radio stations which transmit standard frequencies in addition to WWV in Washington, D.C., and WWVH in the Territory of Hawaii.

[2] The first serious effort to use molecular resonance for frequency and time standards was made at the National Bureau of Standards in 1948. For a description of the first atomic clock see H. Lyons, The Atomic Clock and Atomic Standard of Frequency and Time, *Natl. Bur. Standards Tech. News Bull.*, vol. 33, pp. 17–24, February, 1949; see also a review article by H. Lyons, Atomic Clocks, *Sci. American*, vol. 196, no. 2, pp. 71–82, February, 1957.

8.2. Standards of Frequency. Not all microwave applications have the stringent accuracy requirements implied in the previous discussion. Various frequency standards can be devised to meet the several degrees of stability and accuracy. Examples of some of these are described below.

Frequency standards can be considered either primary or secondary; a distinction which is not necessarily concerned with the stability of the oscillators themselves. A primary standard is one whose frequency is regularly compared to astronomical observations; a secondary standard is one whose frequency is compared, as necessary, against a primary standard. Thus, an oscillator can be extremely stable, but the fact that its mean frequency is not controlled by astronomical time classifies it as a secondary standard.

a. Primary Standards of Frequency. Contemporary primary frequency standards use stable quartz-crystal oscillators operating in the vicinity of 100 kc which are commonly known as *quartz clocks.* These are carefully designed so that their frequency and amplitude are nearly independent of tube characteristics, voltages, and temperature. Quartz clocks can be made to provide a frequency stability over short periods of time of 1 or 2 parts in 10^{10}; over a period of months the frequency can be made to stay within 1 or 2 parts in 10^8. By means of pulse counters, fractional frequency generators, synchronized or locked oscillators, or multivibrators, the 100-kc frequency is reduced to 1,000 cycles to operate a synchronous clock. The time maintained by this clock is periodically compared against astronomical observations by radio or wire transmission from an observatory. The frequency of the 100-kc oscillator is regularly adjusted so that the mean clock time corresponds to the astronomical time.[1]

To establish a standard frequency in the vicinity of the unknown, the 100-kc frequency can be increased by means of frequency multipliers into the region of the unknown signal. In addition, closely spaced harmonic series can be generated (for example, by multivibrators) so that a standard frequency close to the unknown becomes available. Specific applications of these techniques to microwave methods are discussed in Secs. 8.3 and 8.4.

b. Secondary Standards of Frequency. Secondary standards of frequency are carefully constructed quartz oscillators without provisions for comparison with astronomical observations. As stated in Sec. 8.2,

---

[1] For further discussion of this topic see J. M. Shaull, Adjustment of High-precision Frequency and Time Standards, *Proc. IRE*, vol. 38, no. 1, pp. 6–15, January, 1950; also, W. A. Marrison, The Evolution of the Quartz Crystal Clock, *Bell System Tech. J.*, vol. 27, p. 510, July, 1948; C. F. Booth, The Evolution of Frequency Control, *Proc. IEE*, vol. 98, pt. III, p. 1, January, 1951; L. Essen, Frequency Standardization, *Proc. IEE*, vol. 98, pt. II, p. 154, April, 1951; H. M. Smith, Determination of Time and Frequency, *Proc. IEE*, vol. 98, pt. II, p. 143, April, 1951; Lewis, *op. cit.*

it is possible to compare a secondary standard against WWV to produce a stability of 1 part in 10^8 if desired. In many practical situations a temperature-controlled quartz oscillator operating at 1 or 5 Mc is sufficiently accurate.

c. *Molecular Spectral Lines as Frequency Standards.* Molecular absorption lines, molecular emission lines, and certain atomic transitions can be used as frequency standards. Since the atomic and molecular systems consist of a small number of fundamental particles, the frequencies resulting from their interaction are not likely to be affected by gross physical changes. For instance, the microwave spectral lines of an ammonia molecule or a cesium atom should remain constant unless the particular particles are unexpectedly disturbed. The study of molecular spectroscopy has shown that some of the transition lines have a very small bandwidth and are suitable for controlling the frequency of electronic oscillators to an accuracy equal to or better than the present quartz clock.[1]

The atomic clock constructed at the National Bureau of Standards used the 3,3 absorption line of ammonia which occurs at the frequency of 23,870.13 Mc.* The absorption line was detected in a section of $\frac{1}{2}$- by $\frac{1}{4}$-in. 30-ft-long waveguide filled with the ammonia gas at low pressure (viz., 10 μ of mercury) to minimize collision broadening of the line. When used as a transmission device, this waveguide cell exhibited a substantial absorption at the transition or "resonant" frequency; the absorption resembled a resonance curve and had a selectivity corresponding to a Q of about 70,000. The signal generator consisted of a 100-kc quartz crystal oscillator and a chain of multipliers and modulators to provide a frequency in the vicinity of the absorption line. The 100-kc frequency was adjusted by an automatic frequency control mechanism so that the final microwave signal corresponded to the frequency of maximum absorption. In early trials the atomic clock showed a frequency stability of about 5 parts in 10^8 over a period of several days.

Stable frequencies can be obtained also by using an emission line in the molecular spectrum; this process is analogous to the emission of light from an excited atom and is capable of producing microwave power directly. The first device of this type, called a *molecular oscillator* or

---

[1] The use of spectral lines as frequency standards is discussed in the following articles: C. H. Townes, Atomic Clocks and Frequency Stabilization on Microwave Spectral Lines, *J. Appl. Phys.*, vol. 22, no. 11, pp. 1365–1372, November, 1951; H. Lyons, Spectral Lines as Frequency Standards, *Ann. N.Y. Acad. Sci.*, vol. 55, art. 5, pp. 831–871, November, 1952 (the same report is published by the National Bureau of Standards as *Natl. Bur. Standards Rept.* 1848, Aug. 8, 1952); H. Lyons, *op. cit.*, 1957.

* Lyons, *op. cit.*, 1952; the improved version of the National Bureau of Standards clock was described by B. F. Husten, Improved N.B.S. Ammonia Clock, *Proc. IRE*, vol. 39, p. 208, 1951 (a summary). The term 3,3 refers to spectroscopic transition numbers where the quantum numbers J and K are both equal to 3.

maser, demonstrated the usefulness of the principle using the 3,3 inversion line of ammonia.[1]   The main elements of the maser are illustrated in Fig. 8.1.   Molecules of ammonia diffuse from a container at room temperature into an evacuated region through a series of small tubes to form a molecular beam.   The beam passes between four cylindrical rods, electrically connected to establish a quadrupolar cylindrical electrostatic field; about 40,000 volts d-c are required between the electrodes.   It can

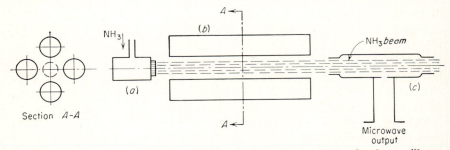

FIG. 8.1. Schematic diagram showing the main elements of a molecular oscillator. (*a*) A box from which the ammonia gas diffuses through the tubular holes; (*b*) the focusing elements whose cross section is shown at left; (*c*) the microwave cavity.   The vacuum enclosure is not shown.

be shown that the focusing system exerts an inward focusing force upon the molecules which are in the upper inversion levels and an outward or defocusing force upon those in the lower states.   Thus, the ammonia molecules emerging from the focusing element are principally in the upper states.   As the molecules enter the microwave cavity, transitions to a lower level occur which results in the radiation of microwave power into the cavity.   The produced signal can be observed at the output waveguide.

The maser can be regarded as equivalent to an electronic oscillator in which the feedback is provided by the electromagnetic field in the cavity which acts upon the dipole moments of the molecules and causes *induced* (stimulated) radiation from the molecules.   As in ordinary oscillators, it is necessary that the available ammonia current be sufficiently high; specifically, for a given ammonia current the cavity Q must be high

[1] J. P. Gordon, H. J. Zeigler, and C. H. Townes, Molecular Microwave Oscillator and New Hyper-fine Structure in the Microwave Spectrum of NH_3, *Phys. Rev.*, vol. 95, no. 1, pp. 282–284, July 1, 1954; N. G. Bassov and A. M. Prokhorov, The Theory of the Molecular Generator and Power Amplifier, *Proc. Acad. Sci. (USSR)*, vol. 101, no. 1, p. 47, 1955; W. Lamb, The Theory of the Microwave Molecular Oscillator, unpublished notes, Stanford University, 1955; J. C. Helmer, Maser Oscillators, *Microwave Laboratory Tech. Rept.* 327, Stanford University, September, 1956.   The term *maser*, due to Gordon et al., means *microwave amplification by stimulated emission of radiation*.

enough so that the power produced by molecular radiation exceeds the power lost in the cavity and external load.   An analysis of the oscillating system must take into account the energy introduced into the cavity by individual molecules, each of which must be considered separately.   The results are obtained by considering the phenomenon on a statistical quantum-mechanical basis.   That the cavity has only a secondary effect upon the oscillation frequency is indicated by both the theory and experiments.   A frequency stability in the order of 1 part in 10^{10} can be attained.

Frequency standards based upon the molecular or atomic transitions promise to provide new standards in frequency stability and may make it possible to eliminate the rotational period of the earth as the principal time standard.   The precision of atomic clocks may become high enough to allow the measurement of the length of the mean sidereal year in the same way that the present quartz clocks are used to measure the period of rotation of the earth.   Thus, it is possible that the atomic clocks together with astronomical observation of the sidereal year, which astronomers believe to be considerably more stable than the period of the rotation of the earth, will enable a new system of time and frequency standards to be established.

It is also possible to use microwave absorption lines as calibration markers throughout the microwave region.   For instance, the ground vibrational state of the molecule OCS has 24 absorption frequencies between 20 and 30 kMc; these frequencies, now known to within 2 parts in 10^6, have excellent stability and are not affected by the external circumstances, such as mishandling by the operator.   With time, microwave spectroscopic research is establishing an ever increasing number of known frequencies throughout the upper portion of the microwave-frequency region with an ever increasing accuracy.   Reference to a specific molecular absorption line furnishes an unambiguous identification of a given signal to great precision, even though the frequency is not yet accurately known.

d. Cavity Resonators as Frequency Standards.   Secondary frequency standards can be made in the form of carefully constructed resonant cavities.   Despite the various difficulties in maintaining sufficiently stable calibration they can be useful in certain applications because of their simplicity.

If a resonant cavity is to be used as a frequency standard, its construction must minimize the effect of temperature, humidity, and loading conditions upon its calibration.   The effects of temperature can be minimized by either careful temperature compensation of the cavity itself or by the provision of temperature control of the entire cavity. Humidity effects can be eliminated by evacuating the cavity.   The loading effects can be made negligible by using sufficiently weak coupling to external circuits. Thus, by proper attention to the details governing the frequency stability, the accuracy of the measurement will be determined primarily by the cavity selectivity, that is, Q_0.

Frequency-standard cavities can be constructed using invar or quartz with the interior suitably electroplated; alternatively, the cavity can be made of solid quartz and electroplated externally.[1]

8.3. Microwave-frequency Standards. The direct method of measuring the frequency of an unknown microwave signal consists of providing a standard frequency so close to the unknown that the beat difference between the two can be measured by conventional low-frequency practice. To measure an unknown signal in any part of the microwave region, a series of closely spaced standard frequencies are needed; these must be derived from a low-frequency standard-frequency generator. The choice between the various possible methods of deriving the microwave standard-frequency sequence from the low-frequency source depends upon the intended use of the microwave-frequency standard. In some cases it may be desired to provide the standard-frequencies sequence over a substantial fraction of the microwave region to permit the measurement of any unknown frequency in the interval. In other applications the signal may be approximately known so that only a single standard frequency is needed.

The various types of frequency standards also differ in the type of elements used to multiply the frequency into the microwave-frequency region. Triodes, klystrons, traveling-wave tubes, and other vacuum-tube devices used as frequency multipliers generate a substantial amount of power which may be convenient in certain applications. Crystal rectifiers can also be used as harmonic generators, especially to produce high-order harmonics, such as one hundredth, but because of their limited power-handling capacity the resultant power output is very small and sensitive detection systems are necessary. High-order multiplication produces closely spaced standard frequencies which may be an advantage or a disadvantage. At times it may be difficult to distinguish one harmonic from another, but in the following discussion it is assumed that sufficiently accurate wavemeters or other means are available to identify the harmonic number by an approximate measurement of the unknown frequency.

Three examples of microwave-frequency standards are described which illustrate some of the possible arrangements.

---

[1] For further discussion of the use of resonant cavities as secondary frequency standards, see L. B. Young, chap. 6, pp. 375–392, in C. G. Montgomery (ed.), "Technique of Microwave Measurements," McGraw-Hill Book Company, Inc., New York, 1947.

a. *Standard-frequency-sequence Generator.* An example of a microwave-frequency standard capable of providing a closely spaced standard-frequency sequence is shown in Fig. 8.2.[1] A 5-Mc crystal oscillator is used as a secondary frequency standard; a radio receiver compares the oscillator against WWV. This oscillator can be replaced by a sequence of frequency multipliers originating from a 100-kc oscillator, or by any other desirable arrangement depending upon the precision required. The subsequent frequency-multiplier stages are ordinary radio vacuum tubes and provide a source of approximately 300 Mc. The choice of multiplication

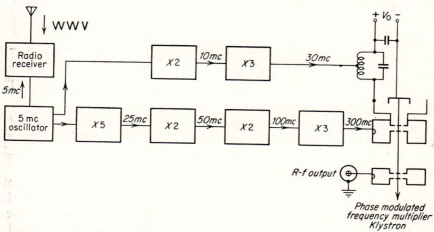

Fig. 8.2. Microwave-frequency standard employing phase modulation of the frequency-multiplier klystron.

factors in the different stages is not important, and other arrangements would be equally satisfactory. The stopping point in this chain could be higher than 300 Mc; however, a large multiplication factor in the final stage is desirable because the resultant spacing between successive harmonics becomes small. In Fig. 8.2 the frequency-multiplier klystron generates 10th, 11th, and 12th harmonics and produces 3,000, 3,300, 3,600 Mc, respectively. Other harmonics could be obtained if the tuning range of the output cavity of the klystron were sufficient.

The spacing between these standard frequencies can be reduced by providing sidebands around each harmonic by modulating the frequency-multiplier klystron. Phase modulation, described in Sec. 1.5*i*, is particularly useful as a number of sidebands can be derived simultaneously with

---

[1] A. E. Harrison, Frequency Standards in the Microwave Region, unpublished report of the Sperry Gyroscope Company, May 22, 1945; an improved version is described by R. E. Wall and A. E. Harrison, A Method of Forming a Broad-band Microwave Frequency Spectrum, *Trans. IRE*, PGMTT, vol. MTT-3, no. 1, pp. 4–10, January, 1955.

sinusoidal modulation. A 30-Mc signal is introduced in series with the accelerating voltage of the frequency-multiplier klystron, resulting in a number of sidebands separated by 30 Mc. Figure 8.3 shows a part of the spectrum and the location of the standard signals made available by this arrangement. Since the catcher cavity of the klystron can have a Q in the order of 1,000, its bandwidth in this frequency range is about 3 Mc; hence, the klystron output consists of a single frequency selected from the set shown in Fig. 8.3. The solid lines correspond to the harmonic carrier frequencies and the dotted lines to the phase-modulation

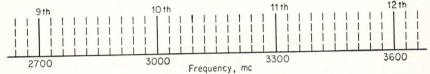

FIG. 8.3. Portion of the frequency spectrum available from the frequency standard shown in Fig. 8.2. Solid lines represent harmonics of the 300-Mc carrier, the dotted lines represent 30-Mc phase-modulation sidebands.

sidebands. An approximate calibration of the output cavity permits adjustment to the expected frequency and the output signal is optimized after it is detected. The fractional accuracy of the output signal is equal to the fractional accuracy of the crystal oscillator.

The advantages of this method lie in the relatively high-power output and the simplicity with which the standard frequencies can be made available. Limitation of the method is due to the small number of successive harmonics because of the narrow tuning range of the available klystrons and the relative complexity of the equipment.[1]

b. Crystal Rectifiers as Harmonic Generators. Another method that can be used to derive microwave standard frequencies from a low-frequency standard makes use of the high-harmonic content in the output of a crystal detector when it is used to rectify a radio-frequency current. If sufficiently sensitive indicators are available, harmonics as high as the 50th or 100th are useful. Conventional crystal rectifiers can be used for applications up to 30 kMc; for higher frequencies, it is usually more efficient to modify or build the crystals as described in Sec. 1.15.[2]

[1] Special forms of frequency multipliers employing the traveling-wave tube can be made to overcome the difficulties encountered with the klystron frequency multiplier. A severed helix traveling-wave tube employing a nondispersive input helix can provide bunching over a frequency range of 10 to 1. The output helix, preferably highly dispersive and voltage tuned, can be used to derive the desired harmonic. Multiplication factors as high as 40 have been observed at a power level of a few milliwatts. Further details can be found in the literature. See D. J. Bates and E. L. Ginzton, A Traveling-wave Frequency Multiplier, submitted to *Proc. IRE*, March, 1957.

[2] The 15th or 16th harmonic of the 25-kMc fundamental has been used to provide harmonic frequencies as high as 391 kMc. See C. A. Burras and W. Gordy, Submillimeter Wave Spectroscopy, *Phys. Rev.*, vol. 93, no. 4, pp. 897–898, Feb. 15, 1954.

When the crystal is used for the generation of harmonic frequencies, it is usually mounted in a holder similar to those described in Chap. 2 for microwave converter applications. A low-frequency signal, such as 100 Mc, is introduced into the crystal through the i-f terminals and the microwave signals derived at the r-f terminals of the converter. Other arrangements, suitable for use as frequency multipliers, are also shown in Sec. 1.15. The conversion loss has been found to be approximately inversely proportional to the harmonic number.

A transmission-type wavemeter can be used at the output terminals of the converter to simplify the identification of the harmonic order.[1]

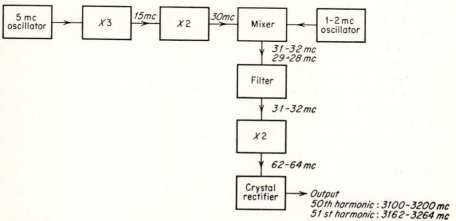

Fig. 8.4. Variable-frequency microwave standard employing crystal rectifiers to generate high-order harmonics.

c. *Variable-frequency Standard.* It is sometimes convenient to be able to continuously vary the output frequency of a frequency standard in order to obtain smooth interpolation over a wide frequency range. One such application is the additive frequency method of measurement described in Sec. 8.4c.

One example of the variable-frequency standard, employing a crystal harmonic multiplier, is shown in Fig. 8.4. A 5-Mc quartz oscillator is followed by a chain of frequency multipliers which produce 30 Mc. This is mixed with a signal from a variable oscillator tunable from 1 to 2 Mc. After mixing, the upper sideband is selected, providing a source of variable frequency from 31 to 32 Mc, which can be multiplied further. A frequency doubler increases the frequency to 62 to 64 Mc. This can be

---

[1] A typical arrangement using crystal rectifiers is described in B. F. Hasten and H. Lyons, Microwave Frequency Measurements and Standards, *Trans. AIEE*, vol. 67, p. 436, 1948.

introduced into a crystal rectifier; in the case illustrated, the 50th harmonic of the input signal provides a continuous coverage of 3,100 to 3,200 Mc. Neighboring harmonics provide overlapping frequency coverage as the variable-frequency oscillator is tuned.

8.4. Methods of Frequency Measurement. The methods of comparing the frequency of an unknown signal against a standard depend upon the available equipment and the precision required. There are three principal methods which are useful in the laboratory and many variations. The first is the *direct measurement* of the difference frequency between the unknown and the nearest standard frequency; since the difference frequency can be made to lie in the region of zero to a few megacycles, the measurement of microwave frequencies is reduced to the measurement of low radio frequencies. The second is known as an *interpolation method*. A special interpolation or transfer oscillator is used to zero beat against two consecutive standard frequencies which bracket the unknown, thus calibrating the oscillator tuning scale. When the unknown signal is heterodyned against the interpolation oscillator, its position on the tuning scale provides the measurement of the unknown by interpolation. The third, called the *additive method*, uses a variable-frequency standard, similar to the one described in Sec. 8.3c, which is adjusted to provide a zero beat (or a beat of some known frequency) against the unknown; the calibration of the variable standard determines the unknown frequency. These methods are described more fully below.

a. Direct Measurement. The direct measurement of the frequency difference between the signal and the standard frequency is a straightforward procedure.[1] Consider, for example, the use of the standard-frequency-sequence generator described in Sec. 8.3a. The standard-frequency generator can be used as the local oscillator in the mixer circuit and the unknown as the signal; the resultant beat frequency can always be made to lie between 0 and 15 Mc. The measurement of the beat frequency in this range is simple because accuracy is relatively unimportant. For instance, to obtain an accuracy of 1 part in 10^6 at 3,000 Mc requires the measurement of the beat frequency to 3 kc. If the beat frequency happens to be 3 Mc, the measurement of the beat frequency to 1 part in 1,000 is needed. Generally, a well calibrated radio

---

[1] The following references are concerned with the measurement of low radio frequencies obtained in beating the unknown microwave signal against a frequency standard. These techniques are also important in the determination of the frequency of the interpolation or transfer oscillator (described in Sec. 8.4b). J. K. Clapp, Calibration of Equipment in the Low and Medium Frequency Ranges, in Small Steps of Frequency, *General Radio Experimenter*, vol. 18, no. 5, October, 1943; J. K. Clapp, Continuous Interpolation Methods, *General Radio Experimenter*, vol. 18, no. 8, January, 1944; J. K. Clapp, Continuous Interpolation Methods, *General Radio Experimenter*, vol. 18, no. 9, February, 1944.

communications receiver is sufficient to attain accuracies approaching this value.

A simple low-frequency standard with a moderate accuracy, such as 1 part in 10^5, is a convenient addition in the laboratory. It can be used to calibrate the radio receiver used for the measurement of the beat frequency at the time of measurement. The frequency standard should be arranged to produce harmonics of 1 Mc up to 10 or 20 Mc and provide standard-frequency sequences spaced 100 kc, 10 kc, and 1 kc apart. It can be checked against WWV with the aid of the radio receiver.

The standard-frequency generator, when used as the local oscillator, does not need to operate at the frequency of the unknown but can be

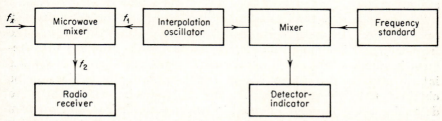

FIG. 8.5. Block diagram of the equipment needed for the interpolation method of frequency measurement.

harmonically related. For example, in measuring the frequency of the unknown in the vicinity of 3,000 Mc the frequency standard can be at 1,500, 1,000, 750 Mc, etc. The mixer will form the beat frequency between the harmonic of the local oscillator and the unknown. In measuring frequencies in the vicinity of 3,000 Mc, the frequency standard can operate successfully at 100 Mc, thus eliminating the need for the microwave portion of the frequency standard.

b. Interpolation Method. The interpolation method can best be explained by referring to the typical equipment illustrated in Fig. 8.5. A calibrated oscillator, called the *interpolation* or *transfer oscillator*, operating in some convenient intermediate-frequency region, such as 100 to 200 Mc, supplies a local oscillator signal to a microwave mixer. Suppose the unknown frequency f_x happens to be in the vicinity of 3,000 Mc. If the interpolation oscillator is adjusted to 150 Mc, its 20th harmonic will beat against the unknown, producing a beat frequency in the radio receiver which can operate at any convenient low frequency, such as 1 Mc. The unknown frequency f_x is equal to

$$f_x = nf_1 \pm f_2 \qquad\qquad (8.1)$$

where f_1 is the frequency of the interpolation oscillator, n is the order of the harmonic, and f_2 is the frequency detected by the receiver. The plus or minus sign appears in Eq. (8.1) because the local oscillator signal can be either below or above the unknown. If the interpolation oscillator is tuned from the low to high frequencies, two closely spaced beat frequency signals are observed in the receiver; the first beat occurs when the local oscillator is below the unknown; the second, when it is above the unknown. Therefore, the plus sign in Eq. (8.1) corresponds to the lower of the two beats.

The frequency f_2 can be read from the calibrated scale of the receiver; since the fractional accuracy does not need to be great, only moderate calibration accuracy is required. The calibration of the receiver can be checked against the known frequencies of the local radio stations or by any other convenient method, such as the one mentioned in Sec. 8.4a.

The frequency of the interpolation oscillator f_1 can be determined in several ways. In the true interpolation method, shown in Fig. 8.5, the frequency f_1 is introduced into a mixer which is also supplied with frequencies from a frequency standard. A beat frequency between the interpolation oscillator and two or more standard frequencies can be obtained and detected. After making the preliminary adjustment to determine the frequency f_1 needed to produce the desired beat between the unknown and the interpolation oscillator, the interpolation oscillator scale reading corresponding to f_1 is carefully noted. The interpolation oscillator is then compared against the standard-frequency sequence using the two closest standard frequencies on either side of f_1. This establishes an accurate calibration of the interpolation oscillator scale and by interpolation permits accurate determination of f_1.

Alternatively, the frequency of the interpolation oscillator f_1 can be found by using high-speed frequency counters or scalers. This is done by connecting a high-speed conventional scaler-counter to the interpolation oscillator and allowing it to count the number of cycles for some convenient length of time, such as one-tenth or one second. The counting-time interval must be carefully controlled by a suitable frequency and time standard. The accuracy of measurement of f_1 is determined by the number of cycles counted during the counting period. Therefore, the accuracy is improved with longer counting intervals. Commercial instruments are available for making these measurements quickly to an accuracy of 1 part in 10^6.* The interpolation system permits the frequency standard to operate at low radio frequencies. For example, in the case illustrated in Fig. 8.5, a frequency near 3,000 Mc can be measured by using the interpolation oscillator in the vicinity of 150 Mc. This frequency (f_1) can be determined by using a standard-frequency-sequence generator operating in the 10-to-20-Mc region. Thus, this method

* See D. Hartke, A Simple Precision System for Measuring CW and Pulsed Frequencies up to 12,400 Mc, *Hewlett-Packard J.*, vol. 6, no. 12, August, 1955.

enables one to measure microwave frequencies using low-frequency standards and an additional single piece of equipment, the interpolation oscillator. Similarly, only moderately high-speed counters are needed to measure f_1. The frequency of the variable interpolation oscillator can be heterodyned to a convenient counting frequency, such as 0 to 10 Mc, with the aid of an additional precision fixed-frequency oscillator operating close to the frequency of the interpolation oscillator.

c. Additive-frequency Method. The variable-frequency standard described in Sec. 8.3c is used in the additive-frequency method. The name of the method is derived from the fact that the variable frequency is obtained by adding a low variable frequency to a relatively high stable frequency.

In using the variable-frequency standard, the unknown and the variable-standard frequencies are mixed in a microwave converter to produce a beat frequency. The beat signal can be adjusted to produce a zero beat frequency or the more convenient low radio frequency such as 1 Mc. The unknown frequency is determined from the calibration of the variable standard and the beat frequency (being careful to observe whether the variable standard is above or below the unknown).

8.5. Heterodyne Frequency Meter. The frequency of the unknown signal can be measured with moderate accuracy by an instrument called the heterodyne frequency meter. It consists of the following components: a carefully constructed variable oscillator, calibrated directly in terms of frequency; a mixer using a crystal rectifier; and an audio amplifier. The frequency of the unknown is determined from the calibration of the oscillator when it is zero-beat against the unknown, as indicated by the audio signal observed by the operator with earphones or a meter.

Typically, heterodyne frequency meters have a calibration accuracy of 0.1 per cent. Some heterodyne frequency meters also contain quartz-crystal oscillators which can be used for the calibration of the variable oscillator when desirable. A heterodyne frequency meter, when equipped with an internal calibrating oscillator, can be used to produce standard-frequency sequences in the low radio-frequency region for the calibration of radio receivers, and also for interpolation between known sets of frequencies.

A simple heterodyne frequency meter requires input signal power several orders of magnitude smaller than the power needed to operate a conventional wavemeter. This is due to the linear action of the super-heterodyne or converter detector. The accuracies of the frequency meter and the ordinary wavemeters are comparable but that of the former can often be made considerably greater by the appropriate use of the internal or external quartz-crystal calibrators as mentioned above.

The oscillator of a typical heterodyne frequency meter can operate at some intermediate frequency range such as 100 to 200 Mc.   The microwave signals can be detected by using the harmonics of the oscillator which are produced in the internal detector of the meter.   Harmonics up to the twentieth can be used conveniently and reliably.[1]

The elements of a representative heterodyne frequency meter, intended for use between 10 to 3,000 Mc, are shown in Fig. 8.6.   The variablefrequency oscillator, tuning from 100 to 200 Mc, is coupled to a crystal

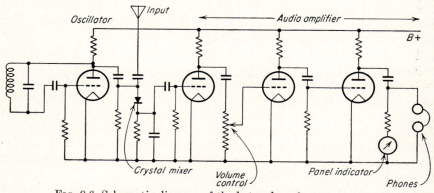

FIG. 8.6. Schematic diagram of the heterodyne frequency meter.

rectifier detector.   The beat frequency is introduced into the audio amplifier, the output of which is available at either a panel meter or at terminals for use with head phones.   The meter is used when the frequency is not sufficiently stable to produce steady, audible beat notes or the beat note is below an audible rate.   The quartz-crystal oscillator can be connected to the input terminals for calibration.   A 1-Mc quartz oscillator may be used to control a chain of multivibrators to generate low-frequency sequences.   The 1-Mc crystal oscillator can be checked against WWV with the aid of a radio receiver.[2]

[1] One commercial model of a heterodyne frequency meter is described by E. Karplus, A Heterodyne Frequency Meter for 10 to 3,000 Megacycles, *General Radio Experimenter*, vol. 20, nos. 2 and 3, July and August, 1945.

[2] Details of operation of a heterodyne frequency meter can be found in an instruction book for the General Radio type 720-A heterodyne frequency meter.   Several useful techniques of wide applicability are described.

CHAPTER 9

RESONANT-CAVITY CHARACTERISTICS: MEASUREMENT OF Q

9.1. Introduction. At the low radio frequencies, the simple resonant circuit can be specified completely by stating the circuit parameters in terms of L, C, R_s as shown in Fig. 9.1. The equivalent description of the microwave resonant circuit cannot be so explicit because, as in the waveguide, the ordinary concept of voltage and current does not play its usual role. To define the circuit parameters in any microwave problem, it is necessary to select the set of field quantities that are of importance in the given application. Using these, the microwave circuit can be described in a manner that closely resembles low-frequency circuit practice. However, the microwave equivalent circuit concept is complicated by the relatively close spacing of the resonant frequencies of the microwave cavity. In most practical situations the cavities are used at sufficiently low frequencies that only one mode is excited at a time, thus making it possible to represent the energy stored in the fields of some particular mode by the energy stored in the lumped parameters of the equivalent circuit shown in Fig. 7.1. In the remaining material, it is assumed that this equivalent circuit accurately describes the observed physical phenomenon.[1]

A consideration of the low-frequency analogue clarifies the meaning of the equivalent circuit parameters. The three parameters shown in Fig. 9.1 can be related to the three universally useful relations:

$$\omega_0{}^2 = \frac{1}{LC}$$

$$Q_0 = \frac{\omega_0 L}{R_s}$$

$$R_0 = \omega_0 L Q_0$$

$$= \frac{(\omega_0 L)^2}{R_s}$$

(9.1)

[1] R. Beringer, chap. 7, in C. G. Montgomery, R. H. Dicke, and E. M. Purcell (eds.), "Principles of Microwave Circuits," vol. 8, Massachusetts Institute of Technology Radiation Laboratory Series, McGraw-Hill Book Company, Inc., New York, 1948.

The three quantities defined by these relations can be measured experimentally to provide the three relations needed to compute the three circuit parameters. If ω_0, Q_0, and R_0 are measured, the circuit parameters can be found by solving Eq. (9.1), resulting in

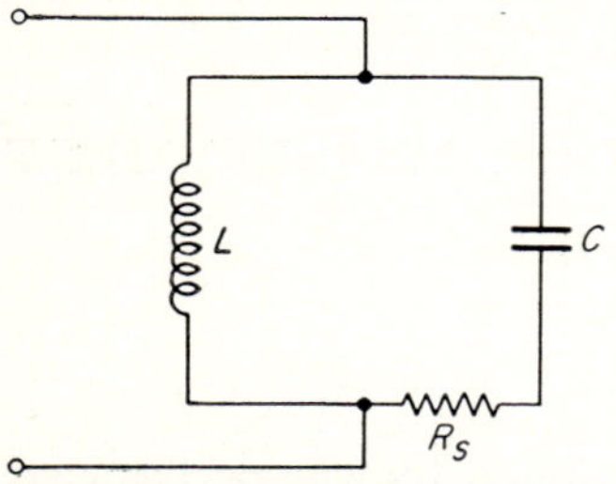

FIG. 9.1. Low-frequency resonance circuit.

$$L = \frac{R_0}{\omega_0 Q_0}$$

$$C = \frac{Q_0}{\omega_0 R_0} \qquad (9.2)$$

$$R_s = \frac{R_0}{Q_0{}^2}$$

This procedure indicates how the three microwave circuit parameters can be evaluated from the experimental study of the resonant circuit as a whole.

The study of the microwave resonant cavity differs from that of the low-frequency circuit in two respects: first, the equivalent-circuit parameters must be established separately for each mode under consideration; and second, the quantity R_0, called the shunt resistance, is not uniquely defined due to the ambiguity in the meaning of the voltage and current. For convenience, R_0 can be defined as

$$R_0 = \frac{(\int \mathbf{E} \, dl)^2}{2(\text{power dissipated})} = \frac{(\int \mathbf{E} \, dl)^2}{2W} \qquad (9.3)$$

where $\mathbf{E}$ is the peak electric field along the path of integration between some two points in the cavity and W is the power dissipated in the cavity.[1] For a few simple geometrical shapes the quantities ω_0, Q_0, and R_0 can be computed from the geometrical factors and the conductivity of the cavity walls. However, for most useful cavity shapes, mathematical computation is too difficult to be practical, and these quantities must be determined directly by experiment. Furthermore, both R_0 and Q_0 depend upon the particular sources of loss in the cavity and can be found only by experiment.

The knowledge of ω_0, Q_0, and R_0 is necessary and sufficient for the

[1] The choice of the definition of the shunt impedance on the basis of the power-voltage quantities is arbitrary. The impedance could also be defined on the basis of the voltage-current or current-power ratios, etc. As in the case of transmission-line problems, it can be shown that these definitions lead to different numerical results for the impedance, being the same only in special cases. The choice of the proper definition for a given problem depends upon the specific application. The particular definition stated above is useful in the class of problems in which one wishes to know the *axial electric field* in the cavity for a given *power dissipated* in the cavity. Specification of these quantities leads to a particular definition of impedance. It is useful in applications involving the interaction of electrons with the electric field in the cavity.

complete description of the resonant cavity in a given mode; in practice, these experimentally determined quantities form the set of cavity characteristics which are descriptive and sufficient for most applications. If necessary, the equivalent circuit parameters shown in Fig. 9.1 can be computed with the aid of Eq. (9.2).

In Chap. 7 experimental procedures for the determination of the resonant frequency of the cavity are discussed in connection with the measurement of wavelength. The experimental techniques used to measure Q_0 are discussed in this chapter and those to determine R_0 in Chap. 10.

a. *Equivalent Circuits; Definitions of Q_0, Q_L, Q_{ext}, and Coupling Coefficient β.* A microwave cavity can be coupled to one, two, or more transmission lines. The cavity characteristics can be studied experimentally by measuring the self-impedance at one pair of input terminals, or by measuring the transfer of power from one set of terminals to another; the unused terminals, in either case, can be terminated in some known impedance. The complete description of the cavity characteristics and the effect of the coupled transmission lines can be evaluated by performing as many independent experiments as there are coupled transmission lines. By this process, the study of a cavity with multiple sets of input terminals can be reduced to the study of a system with only one or two sets of terminals.

The equivalent circuit of a cavity with two inputs is shown in Fig. 9.2. The coupling between the cavity and the transmission lines is symbolically represented by an iris which indicates some arbitrary method of exciting the cavity fields; it can be shown that the actual form of the coupling mechanism does not effect the equivalent circuit. The cavity resonance in a particular mode is represented by the parameters L, C, and R_s. Two alternate forms of the equivalent circuit representing the coupling between the circuit and the transmission lines are shown in Fig. 9.2b and c; in the first, the coupling is represented by ideal transformers and in the second, by mutual inductances. In general, the coupling between the cavity and the transmission lines contains both resistive and reactive components; for example, a coupling loop has both self-inductance and resistive loss. Irrespective of the details of the coupling mechanism, the inductances L_1 and L_2 represent the self-inductances of the coupling elements which are due to the fringing field caused by the geometrical discontinuity at the junction of the transmission line and the cavity. These equivalent circuits can be simplified for analysis by referring the impedances of the three circuit loops to a single one, as indicated in Fig. 9.2d and e.

The characteristic behavior of the complete system can be studied in several ways. The simplest is to observe the variation in the power delivered to the load as the frequency of the signal source is varied or

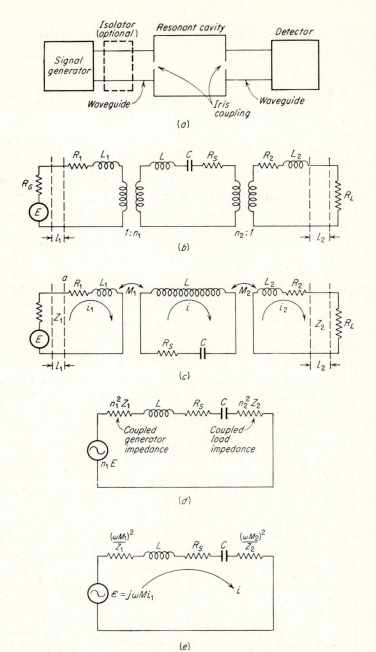

Fig. 9.2. Resonant cavity connected between a signal generator and a detector. (a) Symbolic representation using iris coupling to the waveguides; (b) the equivalent circuit using ideal transformers; (c) the equivalent circuit using mutual inductances; (d and e) the equivalent circuits referred to the middle loop, neglecting self-impedances of each side and assuming $R_G = Z_1$ and $R_L = Z_2$.

the cavity is tuned.   In either case, the familiar resonance phenomenon
occurs, causing the power output at
resonance to differ substantially from
the detuned condition.   The exact
behavior of the system depends upon
the characteristics of the cavity and
the degree of coupling between the
cavity and the transmission lines.

Sometimes it is desired to measure
the cavity parameters and the coefficients of coupling between the cavity
and the transmission lines; sometimes it is merely desired to determine
the unloaded cavity parameters, i.e.,
the characteristics of the cavity if it
were not perturbed by the presence
of the coupled transmission lines.
For this purpose, it is convenient to
measure the degree of coupling
between the cavity and the transmission lines by specifying Q_0, Q_L, and
Q_{ext}, the unloaded, the loaded, and
the external Q values, respectively,
as defined in Chap. 7.   These definitions are important because applications occur in which the effective
coupling is of primary importance
and also because in any given
measurement the effect of residual
coupling must be known if the meaning of the measurements is to be
properly interpreted.

For convenience, the definitions of
the Q values given in Chap. 7 are
repeated below.   Consider a cavity
coupled to a signal source whose
internal impedance is equal to the
characteristic impedance of the transmission line as indicated in Fig. 9.3a.
The equivalent circuit of the cavity
and the transmission line is shown in

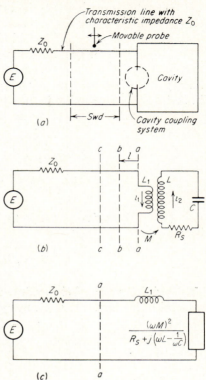

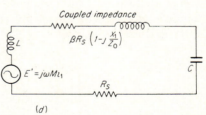

Fig. 9.3. Cavity coupled to a signal
generator through a standing-wave
detector.   (a) The cavity-coupling system schematically; (b) the equivalent
circuit; (c) the equivalent circuit with
the impedances referred to the primary;
(d) the equivalent circuit with the
impedances referred to the secondary.

Fig. 9.3b, where the terminals of the coupling system (or network) are
presumed to be located at some arbitrary position a-a near the cavity. L_1

represents the self-inductance of the coupling mechanism and M the mutual inductance between it and the cavity inductance L. The resistive losses in the coupling network are neglected (the effect of dissipation in the coupling network is included in the analysis given in Sec. 9.4). This circuit can be simplified further as shown in Fig. 9.3c and d; in the first, the cavity is shown as a coupled impedance in series with the primary; in the second, the primary is represented as a coupled impedance in series with the cavity parameters. The impedance coupled in series with the cavity parameters due to a matched generator is given by

$$Z = \frac{(\omega M)^2}{Z_0 + j\omega L_1} \tag{9.4}$$

$$= \frac{(\omega M)^2}{Z_0[1 + (\omega L_1/Z_0)^2]}\left(1 - j\frac{\omega L_1}{Z_0}\right) \tag{9.5}$$

Using definitions given by Eqs. (9.11) and (9.12), and $X_1 = \omega L_1$, Eq. (9.5) becomes

$$Z = \beta R_s\left(1 - \frac{jX_1}{Z_0}\right) \tag{9.6}$$

The *loaded* Q value of the system is defined as the ratio of total reactance to total series loss. It is given by

$$Q_L = \frac{\omega L - \beta R_s X_1/Z_0}{R_s(1 + \beta)} \tag{9.7}$$

$$= \frac{\omega L}{R_s}\frac{1 - (\beta R_s/Z_0)(X_1/\omega L)}{1 + \beta} \tag{9.8}$$

The second term in the numerator of Eq. (9.8), representing the ratio of coupled reactance to the cavity reactance, is usually small compared to unity and can be neglected. Equation (9.8) then becomes

$$Q_L = \frac{Q_0}{1 + \beta} \tag{9.9}$$

where

$$Q_0 = \frac{\omega L}{R_s} \tag{9.10}$$

$$\beta = \frac{(\omega M)^2}{Z_0 R_s}\frac{1}{1 + (X_1/Z_0)^2} \tag{9.11}$$

$$= \beta_1\frac{1}{1 + (X_1/Z_0)^2} \tag{9.12}$$

where $\beta_1 = (\omega M)^2/Z_0 R_s$ is the ratio of the coupled resistance to the cavity resistance R_s. When $\beta_1 = 1$, the coupled resistance and cavity losses are equal, and the cavity is said to be *critically* coupled. When $\beta_1 < 1$, the cavity is said to be *undercoupled;* when $\beta_1 > 1$, the cavity is called *overcoupled.* Under most circumstances, the second term in Eq. (9.12) is nearly equal to unity and $\beta \approx \beta_1$. Thus, at critical coupling $Q_L \approx Q_0/2$.

Equation (9.9) can be written as

$$\frac{1}{Q_L} = \frac{1}{Q_0} + \frac{\beta}{Q_0} \tag{9.13}$$

or

$$\frac{1}{Q_L} = \frac{1}{Q_0} + \frac{1}{Q_{ext}} \tag{9.14}$$

where

$$Q_{ext} = \frac{Q_0}{\beta} \tag{9.15}$$

or

$$\beta = \frac{Q_0}{Q_{ext}} \tag{9.16}$$

b. Q Circles. The solution of many problems involving resonant cavities can be simplified by considering, either graphically or analytically, the cavity input impedance in the complex impedance plane.

The impedance at the terminals of the coupling network *a-a* in Fig. 9.3*b* is equal to

$$Z_{aa} = jX_1 + \frac{(\omega M)^2}{R_s + j(\omega L - 1/\omega C)} \tag{9.17}$$

or

$$\frac{Z_{aa}}{Z_0} = j\frac{X_1}{Z_0} + \frac{\beta_1}{1 + j(\omega L/R_s)[1 - (\omega_0/\omega)^2]} \tag{9.18}$$

where $\omega_0^2 = 1/LC$. For cavities with high Q_0, $\omega \approx \omega_0$. Equation (9.18) can then be written as

$$\frac{Z_{aa}}{Z_0} = j\frac{X_1}{Z_0} + \frac{\beta_1}{1 + j2Q_0\delta} \tag{9.19}$$

where

$$\delta = \frac{\omega - \omega_0}{\omega} \tag{9.20}$$

The quantity δ is called the *frequency-tuning parameter*. For high-Q systems, δ can be considered to be the variable, irrespective of whether the frequency of the signal ω or the resonant frequency of the cavity ω_0 is changed.

Consider a plot of Eq. (9.19) in the rectangular impedance plane. The second term of this equation corresponds to an equation of a circle, representing the impedance of a shunt resonance circuit with a resonant impedance $\beta_1 Z_0$. The effect of the self-reactance of the coupling system, as expressed by the first term in Eq. (9.19) is to displace the circle along the imaginary axis, as indicated in Fig. 9.4*a*.

The analysis and interpretation of certain experiments can be aided by choosing special reference planes along the transmission line at which the term representing the self-reactance of the coupling system disappears. This happens at a series of singular locations, half a wavelength apart, which are called the *detuned-short* positions. At frequencies far off resonance, the second term in Eq. (9.19) vanishes, leaving the self-reactance of the coupling system as the terminating load. This reactive termination produces a complete reflection of the incident signal and results in a series of voltage nodes which can be found by means of the standing-wave detector.

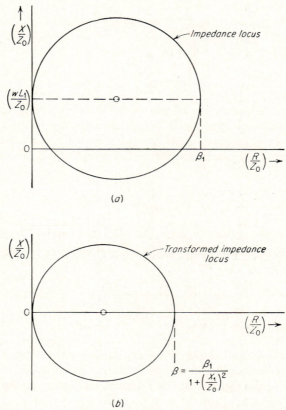

FIG. 9.4. Input impedance of the resonant cavity. (a) The impedance referred to some arbitrary position near the cavity; (b) the impedance locus referred to the detuned short position.

The impedance at the detuned short position, looking toward the cavity, is especially simple, having the form of a simple resonant shunt circuit. This can be demonstrated analytically as follows: Let the terminals b-b be selected at a distance l away from the terminals a-a.*

---

* The arbitrary choice of the original terminals at a-a determines the effective value of the coupling reactance L_1. In practice, the exact location of the terminals a-a is of no concern because all of the quantities can be referred directly to the unambiguous location of the detuned short.

Using Eq. (4.64), the cavity impedance at a-a can be transformed to the terminals b-b.* Therefore,

$$\frac{Z_{bb}}{Z_0} = \frac{Z_{aa} + jZ_0 \tan \beta l}{Z_0 + jZ_{aa} \tan \beta l} \tag{9.21}$$

The location of the terminals b-b can be chosen so that the impedance at terminals b-b becomes zero when the cavity is detuned.

With the cavity detuned, $Z_{aa} = jX_1$. Hence, $Z_{bb} = 0$ when

$$\tan \beta l = - \frac{X_1}{Z_0} \tag{9.22}$$

or

$$\beta l = - \tan^{-1} \left(\frac{X_1}{Z_0} \right) \tag{9.23}$$

Combining Eqs. (9.19), (9.21), and (9.23), the impedance at the detuned short position for any value of δ becomes

$$\frac{Z_{bb}}{Z_0} = \frac{\beta}{1 + j2Q_0(\delta - \delta_0)} \tag{9.24}$$

where

$$\delta_0 = \frac{\beta}{2Q_0} \left(\frac{X_1}{Z_0} \right) \tag{9.25}$$

Equation (9.24) represents the impedance of a parallel resonant circuit with a resonant impedance βZ_0; a graph of this location in the impedance plane is shown in Fig. 9.4b. A comparison of Eqs. (9.19) and (9.24) shows that the diameter of the resultant transformed circle is different from the one that corresponds to the impedance at a-a. Also, the resonant frequency of the circuit described by Eq. (9.24) no longer occurs at the natural resonant frequency of the cavity but is altered by the amount given by Eq. (9.25). However, these changes are not especially significant and can be taken into account in the interpretation of the results.

The shunt representation can be transformed into a series representation if the reference plane is chosen $\lambda_t/4$ away from the detuned-short position. This position can be termed the *detuned-open* position. Transforming Eq. (9.24) through $\lambda_t/4$ with the aid of Eq. (4.64) leads to

$$\frac{Z_{cc}}{Z_0} = \frac{1}{\beta} [1 + j2Q_0(\delta - \delta_0)] \tag{9.26}$$

This is an equation of a series resonant circuit; the impedance at resonance is Z_0/β. Both the shunt and series representations are indicated in Fig. 9.5.

* Unfortunately, the symbol β has two different meanings in the following equations. When used in the expression $\tan \beta l$ it represents the *propagation constant* in the transmission line; when β is used alone, the meaning is the principal one in this chapter, i.e., the *coupling coefficient*.

c. Types of Q Measurements. The *Q* values of a resonant cavity can be determined experimentally in many ways. These can be divided into four groups:

1. Transmission method
2. Impedance measurement
3. Transient decay or the decrement method
4. Dynamic methods

In the first of these, the cavity with input and output terminals is used as a transmission device. The output signal is measured as a func-

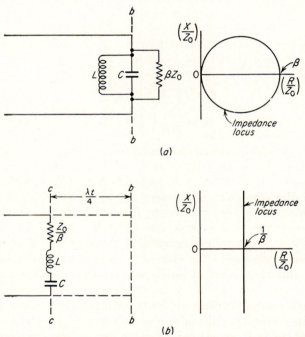

(*a*)

(*b*)

FIG. 9.5. Shunt and series representation of the resonant cavity: The equivalent impedance (*a*) at the detuned-short position, (*b*) at the detuned-open position. The corresponding loci are shown in the complex impedance plane.

tion of frequency, resulting in the conventional resonance curve from whose bandwidth the *Q* value can be computed. Although it is simple conceptually, there are practical difficulties in its application which make it necessary to pay considerable attention to several details to obtain accurate results. The use of this method is described in Sec. 9.2.

The second method, discussed in Sec. 9.3, is based upon the observation of the variation of the cavity input impedance with frequency. If the impedance of the cavity is measured as a function of frequency, the impedance locus referred to the detuned-short position will lie on a circle; if referred to the detuned-open position, the locus will lie on a straight line.   These data can be readily interpreted to provide the values of Q_0, Q_L, and Q_{ext}.   Since a circle can be defined by three points, it is necessary to make only three independent impedance measurements to describe completely the characteristics of the cavity and its coupling system.   To improve the accuracy, additional data are usually taken to detect random, systematic, or accidental errors.

The impedance data can be interpreted by one of several methods. The standing-wave ratio can be used alone without the corresponding phase data.   A plot of VSWR versus frequency contains all the necessary information; the use of this data is analogous to employing the universal resonance curve of a resonant circuit at low frequencies.   Conversely, the phase data can be used without the VSWR data.   The detailed discussion of these methods shows that sometimes one can choose between these methods in accordance with his preference.   Sometimes, however, the choice of a particular method can lead to greater accuracy.   Consider, for example, the Smith chart plot shown in Fig. 9.6 of the input impedance for three degrees of coupling.

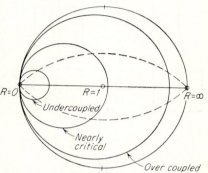

Fig. 9.6. Input impedance of a resonant cavity referred to the detuned-short position plotted in the Smith chart for three degrees of coupling.

If the cavity is nearly critically coupled, the circle passes through the real axis near the point (1,0).   In this case, both the VSWR and the phase information are equally important; the best accuracy is obtained for measuring the vector impedance at each frequency.   If, however, the cavity is weakly coupled ($\beta \ll 1$), the resultant impedance locus is a very small circle.   In this case, the phase data are not accurate because the entire circle is contained within a small range of phase angles.   However, the VSWR varies substantially with frequency and the determination of the frequency interval between certain "half-power points" results in good accuracy.   If the cavity is greatly overcoupled ($\beta \gg 1$), the resultant circle approaches the periphery of the Smith chart; the VSWR is high and does not change appreciably, but the phase angle changes rapidly and provides the needed information.

The decrement method described in Sec. 9.5, particularly applicable to high-Q cavities, uses the transient decay of the natural oscillations in the cavity.   If the cavity under study is excited by a pulsed signal, during the off period the natural fields in the cavity decay exponentially with time and the time constant of the decay determines the Q. Figure 9.7a shows the equipment necessary for this method. A pulsed-modulated oscillator provides signals of sufficient duration to establish steady-state fields in the cavity. The output signal from the cavity is detected by a sensitive detector (preferably, a superheterodyne receiver), amplified by

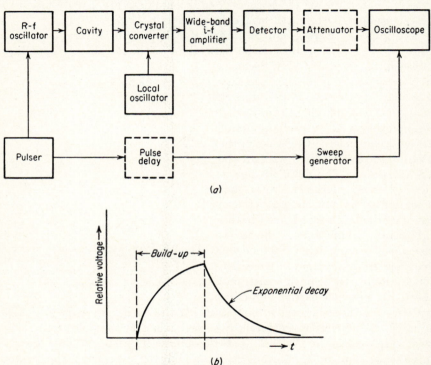

(a)

(b)

FIG. 9.7. The transient decay method of measuring the Q value. (a) The typical equipment, with dashed rectangles indicating optional equipment; (b) the transient build-up and decay observed on the oscilloscope.

a wideband amplifier, and observed by an oscilloscope whose sweep is synchronized by the pulser. The typical response is indicated in Fig. 9.7b. The time constant is measured and the results interpreted as described in Sec. 9.5.

The decrement method is especially convenient for the high-Q systems because it does not need the high degree of frequency stability required in other types of measurements. This is apparent from the fact that in other methods the frequency must be sufficiently stable during the course of a given measurement; for example, in using VSWR measurements, the frequency must be constant at least during the time needed to measure a single standing-wave ratio. The measurement of Q values in excess of 10^4 is especially simple; however, at lower values, the decay period is too short for convenient measurement.

The fourth group of methods described in Sec. 9.6 is based upon the dynamic observation of the cavity characteristics. These techniques are useful for two reasons: the frequency stability requirements of the signal

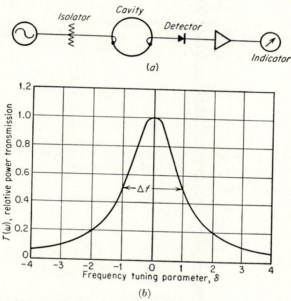

FIG. 9.8. Transmission method of measuring the Q value. (a) The equipment used; (b) the typical transmission curve.

source are reduced; and the Q values can be obtained more quickly, sometimes from a direct reading meter.

9.2. Transmission Method. The transmission method illustrated in Fig. 9.8a is the simplest phenomenological measurement of Q. A signal generator, preferably completely isolated from the load by a resistive pad or a ferrite isolator, is connected to the cavity through the input coupling system; a detector with a known response low is connected to the output coupling system. By varying the frequency of the signal generator, the transmission resonance curve shown in Fig. 9.8b can be observed from whose bandwidth the cavity Q can be determined. The resonance curve can be obtained also by tuning the cavity and keeping the frequency of the oscillator fixed. A choice between the two methods depends upon the details and ease of tuning and calibrating the apparatus under test.

The relation between the observed bandwidth of the resonance curve, the input and output coupling coefficients, Q_0, and Q_L can be obtained as follows: Assume that the load and generator impedances indicated in Fig. 9.2b are equal to the characteristic impedances of their respective lines. The losses of the coupling systems represented by R_1 and R_2 can be neglected or considered as parts of R_G and R_L, respectively. The self-inductances L_1 and L_2 can also be neglected; this approximation changes slightly the apparent resonant frequency of the system but for high-Q systems does not have other effects. With these approximations, Fig. 9.2b can be altered by referring both the primary and the tertiary loops into the middle loop, which results in the equivalent circuits shown in Fig. 9.2d and e. The loaded Q of the system is

$$Q_L = \frac{\omega_0 L}{R_s + n_1^2 Z_1 + n_2^2 Z_2} \tag{9.27}$$

or

$$Q_L = \frac{\omega_0 L}{R_s + (\omega M_1)^2/Z_1 + (\omega M)^2/Z_2} \tag{9.28}$$

where Z_1 and Z_2 represent the characteristic impedances of the input and output transmission lines, respectively. The input and output coupling coefficients are defined as

$$\beta_1 = n_1^2 \frac{Z_1}{R_s} = \frac{(\omega M_1)^2}{R_s Z_1} \tag{9.29}$$

$$\beta_2 = n_2^2 \frac{Z_2}{R_s} = \frac{(\omega M_2)^2}{R_s Z_2} \tag{9.30}$$

Using these, the relation between Q_0 and Q_L becomes

$$Q_0 = Q_L(1 + \beta_1 + \beta_2) \tag{9.31}$$

The relation between the width of the resonance curve and the cavity Q is obtained as follows: The *transmission loss* $T(\omega)$ through the cavity is defined as

$$T(\omega) = \frac{P_L}{P_0} \tag{9.32}$$

where P_L is the power delivered to a load and P_0 is the maximum power available from the generator (to a matched load). Computing P_L and P_0 for Fig. 9.2d,

$$T(\omega) = \frac{4\beta_1\beta_2}{(1 + \beta_1 + \beta_2)^2 + 4Q_0^2\delta^2} \tag{9.33}$$

where δ is the tuning parameter defined in Eq. (9.20). At resonance $\delta = 0$, and Eq. (9.33) becomes

$$T(\omega_0) = \frac{4\beta_1\beta_2}{(1 + \beta_1 + \beta_2)^2} \tag{9.34}$$

Dividing Eq. (9.33) by Eq. (9.34), and using Eq. (9.31),

$$T(\omega) = \frac{T(\omega_0)}{1 + 4Q_L{}^2\delta^2} \tag{9.35}$$

The *half-power* points of transmission occur when

$$2Q_L\delta = \pm 1 \tag{9.36}$$

or

$$2\delta = \pm \frac{1}{Q_L} \tag{9.37}$$

or

$$2\delta = \pm \frac{1 + \beta_1 + \beta_2}{Q_0} \tag{9.38}$$

The quantity Δf is known as the *half-power bandwidth* of the resonance curve and is given by

$$\frac{\Delta f}{f} = 2\delta \tag{9.39}$$

Hence,

$$Q_0 = \frac{f}{\Delta f}(1 + \beta_1 + \beta_2) \tag{9.40}$$

Thus, if the signal generator and detector impedances are both matched, the measured transmission curve shown determines Q_L. The unloaded Q can be calculated if the coupling coefficients can be measured separately. However, the greatest value of the procedure lies in finding Q_0 by reducing the coupling coefficients sufficiently. This is usually done by reducing the coupling between detector and the cavity until it is found that further reduction in coupling no longer affects the measured resonance curve. A separate experiment must also be carried out to assure that the coupling between the cavity and the signal generator is sufficiently small. Depending upon practical circumstances, these procedures can be either simple or complicated. For example, if the coupling systems consist of inductive coupling loops, adjustable by rotation or withdrawal, the coupling coefficients can be reduced readily. If the coupling is provided by means of an iris, such procedures are generally impractical.

The transmission method suffers from the fact that a single measurement of the transmission curve alone, no matter how accurately made, does not give the Q values directly. For this reason, the unambiguous procedures involving the measurement of impedance, described in Sec. 9.3, are more commonly used. However, the transmission method, if carefully executed, is capable of producing good accuracy. It should be noted that the presence of loss in the coupling systems is not important, which is not the case in the impedance methods.

9.3. The Impedance Method. As explained in Sec. 9.1b, the cavity characteristics can be determined by measuring the input impedance of a cavity as a function of frequency. The details of this method are considered in this section in several forms.

In Sec. 9.3a, procedures for determining the Q parameters are described for those conditions of coupling which permit accurate measurement of the impedance with frequency. If the coupling coefficient is very small, corresponding to the high values of Q_L, the standing-wave ratio alone can be measured, a procedure described in Sec. 9.3b. When the coupling coefficient is large compared to unity, corresponding to low values of Q_L, the phase of the input impedance becomes more meaningful and can be used independently as described in Sec. 9.3c.

The choice of the most appropriate method in a particular application is a matter of convenience, experience, and personal preference as there is no obvious division between the usefulness of the three methods mentioned. In some cases, a combination is more convenient; for example, the phase data can be used more readily if the standing-wave ratio at resonance is measured also. However, experience with the basic methods is most helpful in deciding upon the value of possible variations.

In the discussion of the basic methods the effect of loss in the coupling system is neglected; this is justified in nearly all cases. The more general case is discussed in Sec. 9.4 where this assumption is avoided.

a. Interpretation of the Impedance Data. The impedance method is used as follows. Figure 9.3 shows the cavity under study connected to a uniform transmission line through its cavity coupling system. A standing-wave detector is placed between the signal generator and the cavity to measure the input impedance. The measurement procedures are simplified if the relative tuning of the cavity and the signal generator are independent, i.e., if cavity tuning does not affect the output of the signal generator. It is particularly convenient to have the impedance of the signal source equal to Z_0.

The procedure begins with the determination of the detuned short position. The signal frequency is adjusted to the desired value and the cavity is detuned completely; this effectively terminates the transmission line in a pure reactance. The standing-wave detector is used to find a voltage node which locates the detuned short position; this location is recorded for future use (for convenience it can be marked on the standing-wave detector with a pencil). If the cavity is not tunable, the equivalent experiment can be performed by tuning the signal generator sufficiently far from the resonant frequency of the cavity. For high-Q systems, the change in frequency is not large, and the location of the detuned short determined in this manner is nearly the correct one. It is the approximate but not quite the correct value, as can be seen from Eq. (9.23). In case of doubt, it may be necessary to plot the position of the detuned short as a function of frequency and to refer further impedance measurements to a detuned short position appropriate for the particular frequency.

Next, it is necessary to determine the magnitude of the coupling coefficient, as the choice among the possible techniques depends upon its value.   The probe of the standing-wave detector is placed at the detuned short position; Figure 9.5a shows that this locates the probe across the terminals of an equivalent-shunt resonant circuit.   Tuning the cavity to produce the maximum voltage in the probe is equivalent to tuning the cavity to resonance, *provided* the source impedance is purely resistive. If this procedure is carried out correctly, the motion of the probe with respect to the detuned-short position will result in *either* a voltage maximum or voltage minimum at the detuned-short position since the cavity at resonance is a pure resistance.   If the exploration of the standing-wave pattern results in a voltage minimum, the cavity is undercoupled; if it produces a maximum, the cavity is overcoupled.   If the exploration indicates that a minimum (or a maximum) is not at the detuned-short position, some adjustment has been executed incorrectly.   Assuming that the detuned-short position is located correctly, this means that the cavity is not exactly tuned to resonance, which is most likely if the source impedance is not purely resistive.   The correct cavity tuning for resonance can be found by trial until either a minimum or a maximum occurs exactly at the detuned-short position.

The magnitude of the coupling coefficient is obtained by measuring VSWR at resonance.   Since the impedances at the voltage minimum and maximum are Z_0/r_0 and $Z_0 r_0$, respectively, where r_0 is the value of VSWR at resonance, Eq. (9.24) results in

Undercoupled case:
$$\beta = \frac{1}{r_0} \tag{9.41}$$

Overcoupled case:
$$\beta = r_0 \tag{9.42}$$

The evaluation of β locates the intersection of the impedance circle with the real axis in an impedance plot shown in Fig. 9.6.

If the coupling coefficient β is not greatly different from unity, the cavity tuning parameter δ can be changed in small increments and the impedance measured at each frequency.   Typical experimental data are shown plotted in Figs. 9.9a and 9.9b; the first shows the impedance referred to the detuned-short position, and the second, to the detuned-open position.

Referring to Eq. (9.24), at certain frequencies the imaginary part of the denominator becomes equal to ± 1.   At these values of δ, the input impedance becomes

$$\frac{Z_{bb}}{Z_0} = \frac{\beta}{1 \pm j} \tag{9.43}$$

The locus of these points (corresponding to $R = X$) for all possible values of β shown in Fig. 9.10 is a circle with the center on the periphery of the Smith chart at 90° points and passes through the two endpoints of the resistive axis. The intersection of this circle with the circle representing the graph of the impedance as a function of frequency determines

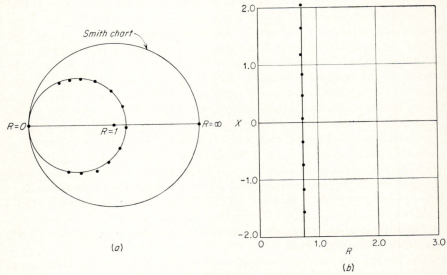

FIG. 9.9. Typical experimental data showing the variation of the input impedance of a resonant cavity with frequency. Impedance referred (a) to the detuned-short position, (b) to the detuned-open position. Data obtained for $f_0 = 3,000$ Mc, $Q_0 = 2,180$, $\beta = 1.31$.

those frequencies at which

$$2Q_0(\delta - \delta_0) = \pm 1 \tag{9.44}$$

Let these two values of δ be called δ_1 and δ_2. Hence,

$$\begin{aligned} 2Q_0(\delta_1 - \delta_0) &= 1 \\ 2Q_0(\delta_2 - \delta_0) &= -1 \end{aligned} \tag{9.45}$$

Subtracting and rearranging,

$$Q_0 = \frac{1}{\delta_1 - \delta_2} \tag{9.46}$$

or, in terms of frequency,

$$Q_0 = \frac{f_0}{f_1 - f_2} = \frac{f}{\Delta f} \tag{9.47}$$

Thus, the two frequencies at which the impedance locus passes through the points $R = X$ determine the unloaded Q value. Frequencies f_1 and f_2 are called the *half-power points*.

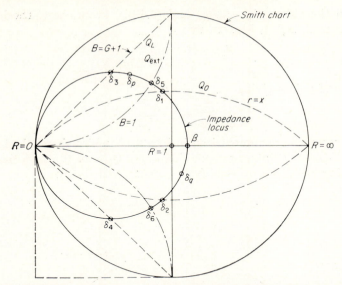

Fig. 9.10. Identification of the half-power points from the Smith chart. Q_0 locus is given by $X = R(B = G)$; Q_L by $X = R + 1$; Q_{ext} by $X = 1$.

The loaded and external Q values can be determined as follows: These are related to Q_0 through Eqs. (9.9) and (9.16). In terms of Q_L, Eq. (9.24) becomes

$$\frac{Z_{bb}}{Z_0} = \frac{\beta}{1 + j2Q_L(1 + \beta)(\delta - \delta_0)} \tag{9.48}$$

In terms of Q_{ext},

$$\frac{Z_{bb}}{Z_0} = \frac{\beta}{1 + j2Q_{ext}\beta(\delta - \delta_0)} \tag{9.49}$$

Let δ_3 and δ_4 be the tuning parameters at which

$$2Q_L(\delta - \delta_0) = \pm 1 \tag{9.50}$$

and δ_5 and δ_6 the tuning parameters at which

$$2Q_{ext}(\delta - \delta_0) = \pm 1 \tag{9.51}$$

From these it is found, in a manner analogous to the derivation of Eq. (9.47), that

$$Q_L = \frac{1}{\delta_3 - \delta_4} \tag{9.52}$$

$$Q_{ext} = \frac{1}{\delta_5 - \delta_6} \tag{9.53}$$

By using the conditions given by Eqs. (9.50) and (9.51) the values of these tuning parameters can be identified from the graph of impedance plot with the aid of Eqs. (9.48) and (9.49). From these, the locus of points determining Q_L is given by

$$\frac{Z_{bb}}{Z_0} = \frac{\beta}{1 \pm j(1 + \beta)} \tag{9.54}$$

The locus of points giving Q_{ext} is given by

$$\frac{Z_{bb}}{Z_0} = \frac{\beta}{1 \pm j\beta} \tag{9.55}$$

These remarks are summarized in Fig. 9.10, which shows the location of the half-power points corresponding to Q_0, Q_L, and Q_{ext} with the aid of the defining loci given by Eqs. (9.43), (9.54), and (9.55).

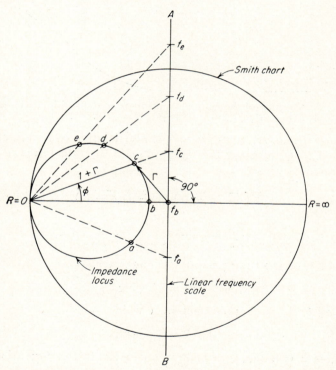

FIG. 9.11. Geometrical construction used to establish a linear frequency scale for the Q-circle impedance locus.

The distribution of the measured points along the circular locus in the Smith chart is not linear with frequency; this makes impossible the accurate determination of the frequencies corresponding to the half-power points by interpolation between the measured points. An auxiliary scale of linear frequency, helpful in avoiding this difficulty, can be established by the construction shown in Fig. 9.11. The line AB is drawn perpendicularly to the resistive axis at any convenient location. The experimental impedance points such as a, b, c, d, and e, corresponding to the frequencies f_a, f_b, f_c, f_d, and f_e, respectively, are plotted. These points are projected upon the auxiliary frequency scale as indicated.[1] Thus, the frequency of any point on the impedance locus whose frequency is not known can be found by projecting it to the frequency scale.

The Q values can be obtained also from the rectangular impedance chart shown in Fig. 9.12. The derivation of the defining loci for the three Q values is obtained as above, using Eq. (9.26) in place of Eq. (9.24). The use of the rectangular impedance chart is often advantageous because:

1. All loci are straight lines, which permits simple graphing.

2. The frequency scale along the impedance locus is linear.

3. The frequency scale along the impedance locus is independent of the position of the locus in the impedance plane.

4. The half-power points identifying the tuning parameters corresponding to Q_0, Q_L, and Q_{ext} are found at the intersection of the straight lines.

5. The change of the cavity Q, due to changes in loading, displaces the impedance locus horizontally.

It is not necessary to use the half-power points to find Q values. A knowledge of the wavelength λ_t and two impedances, measured at two arbitrary values of δ, is sufficient to provide the necessary information. Consider, for example, points δ_p and δ_q shown in Figs. 9.10 and 9.12. If the laboratory data are plotted on the Smith chart, the resistance and

---

[1] The construction used in Fig. 9.11 can be proved as follows: The reflection coefficient Γ corresponding to the impedance given by Eq. (9.24) can be computed from

$$\Gamma = \frac{Z_{bb}/Z_0 - 1}{Z_{bb}/Z_0 + 1} \tag{9.56}$$

$$= \frac{\beta - [1 + j2Q(\delta - \delta_0)]}{\beta + [1 + j2Q(\delta - \delta_0)]} \tag{9.57}$$

$$= -1 + \frac{2\beta}{\beta + 1 + j2Q(\delta - \delta_0)} \tag{9.58}$$

or

$$\Gamma + 1 = \frac{2\beta}{\beta + 1 + j2Q(\delta - \delta_0)} \tag{9.59}$$

The phase angle ϕ of the radius vector originating from the origin (O,O) in Fig. 9.11 is equal to the phase angle of the vector $(1 + \Gamma)$. Hence,

$$\phi = \arg(\Gamma + 1) \tag{9.60}$$

$$= \tan^{-1} \frac{2Q(\delta - \delta_0)}{\beta + 1} \tag{9.61}$$

Therefore, the intercept along the axis AB, being proportional to $\tan \phi$, is proportional to the frequency.

reactance components of the impedances can be obtained directly from the chart coordinates. [Alternately, they can be computed from the measured VSWR and the position of the minimum using Eq. (4.78).]

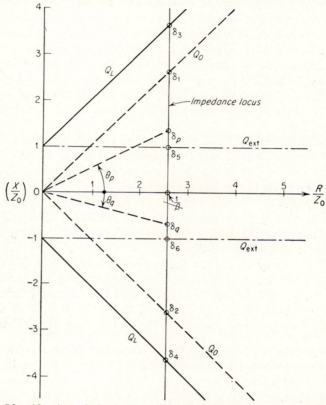

FIG. 9.12. Identification of the half-power points from the rectangular impedance chart.

If X and R are the imaginary and the real parts of the impedance given by Eq. (9.24), the ratios X/R for δ_p and δ_q are

$$\left(\frac{X}{R}\right)_q = -2Q_0(\delta_q - \delta_0)$$

$$\left(\frac{X}{R}\right)_p = -2Q_0(\delta_p - \delta_0)$$

(9.62)

Subtracting and rearranging,

$$Q_0 = \frac{1}{2} \frac{1}{\delta_p - \delta_q} \left[\left(\frac{X}{R}\right)_q - \left(\frac{X}{R}\right)_p\right]$$

(9.63)

which reduces to Eqs. (9.46) and (9.47) if $(X/R)_p = 1$, and $(X/R)_q = -1$.

If the laboratory data are plotted in the rectangular coordinates, as shown in Fig. 9.12, the quantity X/R is recognized as the angle θ of the radius vector to a point on the impedance locus. Thus, if $\tan \theta_p = (X/R)_p$, $\tan \theta_q = (X/R)_q$, using Eq. (9.62),

$$Q_0 = \frac{1}{2} \frac{1}{\delta_p - \delta_q} (\tan \theta_p - \tan \theta_q) \tag{9.64}$$

$$= \frac{1}{2} \frac{f_0}{f_1 - f_2} (\tan \theta_p - \tan \theta_q) \tag{9.65}$$

When $X = \pm R$, $\theta = \pm 45°$, which again reduces to Eq. (9.47).

To summarize, this method is used as follows: The detuned-short position is found, the cavity tuned to resonance, and the value of the coupling coefficient β measured by finding the VSWR r_0 at resonance. Additional measurements of VSWR and phase are then made at two other frequencies (which are also measured), and at as many other frequencies as are considered necessary for accuracy. Referring the measured impedances to the detuned-short position, the impedance locus is plotted together with the construction lines necessary to identify the half-power points, as shown in Fig. 9.10. The intersection of the impedance locus with the construction lines identifies the three half-power points whose frequencies can be found from the auxiliary linear-frequency scale and the construction shown in Fig. 9.11. Alternatively, the measured impedance can be referred to the detuned-open position and the VSWR and phase information transformed into data suitable for plotting in the rectangular impedance chart. The experimental points will lie along a straight line perpendicular to the resistive axis; the intersection of this locus with the construction lines shown in Fig. 9.12 locates the ordinates which correspond to the three half-power points. Since the vertical scale is linear in frequency, the ordinate intervals can be transformed into the units of frequency using the scale calibration provided by the experimental points.[1]

b. *The Standing-wave Ratio Method.* The method for interpreting the impedance data, described in the preceding section, is the most accurate of the three discussed in this section. However, it is time-consuming because it requires the measurement of phase and VSWR at each frequency as well as subsequent calculations to convert the laboratory data for plotting in the impedance plane. This can be simplified substantially by recording only the VSWR data as a function of frequency. Accuracy is not sacrificed by this simplification because a considerable quantity of data can be taken in a short time.

The experimental data required for the determination of Q values con-

---

[1] It is possible to improve the accuracy of the linear-frequency scale by arithmetically averaging the frequency intervals or by plotting the linear distance X vs. frequency and graphically finding the average slope.

sist of the plot of VSWR as a functional frequency and the value of the coupling coefficient β which is found as described in Sec. 9.3a by exploring the standing-wave pattern at the detuned-short position with the cavity tuned to resonance.   Using this information, the Q values are determined as follows:

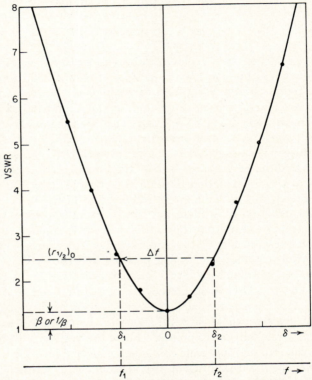

FIG. 9.13. Determination of the half-power points from the VSWR data. $r_{1/2}$ points are computed from Eqs. (9.66), (9.67), and (9.68) for Q_0, Q_L, and Q_{ext}, respectively. The curve shown represents typical data for $f_0 = 3,000$ Mc, $Q_0 = 2,180$, $\beta = 0.76$.

The variation of the input impedance of a cavity resonator referred to the detuned-short position is shown in Fig. 9.6.   It can be seen that the radius vector measured from the center of the Smith chart, corresponding to the reflection coefficient, increases continuously with the frequency-tuning parameter δ.   Figure 9.13 shows the typical variation of VSWR with frequency.   To find the Q values, it is necessary to identify the specific values of the standing-wave ratio which correspond to the half-power points.   These can be found either graphically or analytically.

The standing-wave ratios at half-power points, $(r_{1/2})_0$, $(r_{1/2})_L$, $(r_{1/2})_{ext}$, corresponding to Q_0, Q_L, and Q_{ext}, respectively, can be found graphically, using the construction shown in Fig. 9.10, which is included for clarity in Fig. 9.14.   The known value of β [see Eqs. (9.41) and (9.42)] establishes the intercept between the circular impedance locus and the resistive axis, thus permitting the circle to be drawn.   The construction lines corresponding to Q_0, Q_L, and Q_{ext} loci can be drawn which define the impedances at the three half-power points.   The VSWR corresponding to these

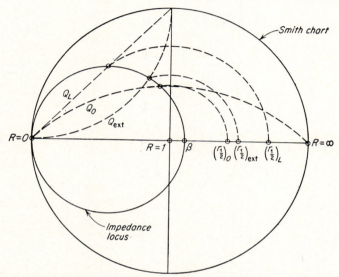

FIG. 9.14. Graphical determination of the half-power VSWR's. The experimental value of β locates the circular impedance locus; its intersection with the half-power construction lines determines the half-power VSWR values by projection to the resistive axis as indicated.

are found by drawing the dashed circular arcs, as indicated, and reading their intercept along the resistive axis.

To obtain greater accuracy, it may be desirable to find the half-power VSWR points analytically.   The input impedance at the detuned short at the frequencies given by Eqs. (9.44), (9.50), and (9.51) are given by Eqs. (9.43), (9.54), and (9.55), respectively.   The half-power values of VSWR at these frequencies can be found by substituting these impedance values into Eq. (4.70), giving

For Q_0: $$(r_{1/2})_0 = \frac{2 + \beta^2 + \sqrt{4 + \beta^4}}{2\beta} \qquad (9.66)$$

For Q_L: $$(r_{1/2})_L = \frac{1 + \beta + \beta^2 + (1 + \beta)\sqrt{1 + \beta^2}}{\beta} \qquad (9.67)$$

For Q_{ext}: $$(r_{1/2})_{ext} = \frac{1 + 2\beta^2 + \sqrt{1 + 4\beta^4}}{2\beta} \qquad (9.68)$$

The ratio of the half-power VSWR to VSWR at resonance r_0 is plotted for the three cases in Fig. 9.15. For small and large values of β, this ratio is

For $\beta \ll 1$:

$$\left(\frac{r_{1/2}}{r_0}\right)_0 = 2$$

$$\left(\frac{r_{1/2}}{r_0}\right)_L = 2 \qquad (9.69)$$

$$\left(\frac{r_{1/2}}{r_0}\right)_{ext} = 1$$

For $\beta \gg 1$:

$$\left(\frac{r_{1/2}}{r_0}\right)_0 = 1$$

$$\left(\frac{r_{1/2}}{r_0}\right)_L = 2 \qquad (9.70)$$

$$\left(\frac{r_{1/2}}{r_0}\right)_{ext} = 2$$

These relations show that for small β the VSWR at the half-power points for Q_0 and Q_L is twice the minimum value and can be measured easily. For Q_{ext}, however, the half-power VSWR becomes undistinguishable from the VSWR at resonance and cannot be used. For similar reasons, when β is large, Q_L and Q_{ext} can be found, but Q_0 cannot. If β is measured accurately, Q_L and Q_{ext} can be computed from Q_0 (and conversely) by using Eqs. (9.9) and (9.16).

The values of Q_0, Q_L, and Q_{ext} are found from the frequencies at which the half-power VSWR occur. Calling these δ_1 and δ_2, δ_3 and δ_4, δ_5 and δ_6, respectively,

$$Q_0 = \frac{1}{\delta_1 - \delta_2} = \frac{f_0}{f_1 - f_2}$$

$$Q_L = \frac{1}{\delta_3 - \delta_4} = \frac{f_0}{f_3 - f_4} \qquad (9.71)$$

$$Q_{ext} = \frac{1}{\delta_5 - \delta_6} = \frac{f_0}{f_5 - f_6}$$

In summary, the method is used as follows: The detuned-short position is found, the cavity carefully adjusted to resonance, and the standing-wave pattern explored to determine whether the cavity is over-coupled or undercoupled. The VSWR r_0 at resonance is measured and the value of the coupling coefficient β calculated, using Eqs. (9.41) and (9.42), as appropriate. From Eqs. (9.66), (9.67), and (9.68), or Fig. 9.15, the VSWR at the half-power points is obtained. From the experimental graph of the VSWR vs. frequency (such as Fig. 9.13) the frequencies corresponding to the half-power VSWR are obtained. The Q values are computed from Eqs. (9.71).

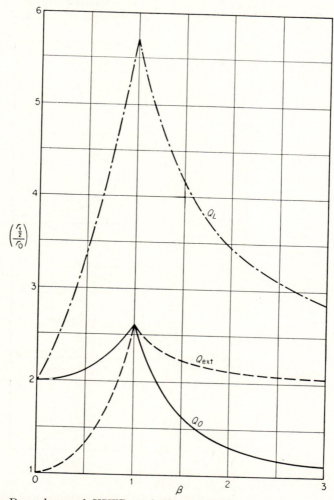

FIG. 9.15. Dependence of VSWR at half-power points upon β. $\beta = r_0$ or $1/r_0$, depending upon the degree of coupling.

c. The Phase Method. The phase method is based upon the measurement of the nodal position as a function of frequency. If $\beta \gg 1$, the standing-wave ratio is very high and difficult to measure, but the associated voltage nodes are sharp and they shift rapidly with tuning of the cavity or the source and are easily located accurately. In its basic form, the measurement of the standing-wave ratio is not needed; thus, many possible errors connected with the measurement of relative voltages, calibration of the detector-amplifier, etc., are eliminated.

The necessary laboratory data are obtained with the equipment arranged as in Fig. 9.3a. The laboratory procedure consists of tuning the cavity

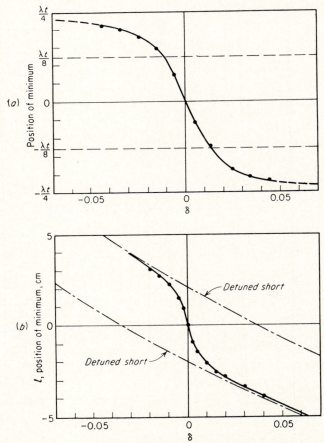

FIG. 9.16. Typical experimental data showing the displacement of the nodal position with frequency. In (a) the frequency is constant as the cavity is tuned; $f_1 = 1,360$ Mc, $Q_{ext} = 41$. In (b) the cavity tuning is constant and the frequency is varied; $f_0 = 9,100$ Mc, $Q_{ext} = 115$.

or the signal source and measuring the location of voltage nodes with respect to some arbitrary reference plane; typical data are shown in Fig. 9.16. In Fig. 9.16a, the frequency is kept constant and the cavity is tuned. Except near resonance, the transmission line appears to be shorted, producing a series of voltage nodes half a wavelength apart.

As the cavity is tuned close to resonance, the positions of the nodes change; plotting the position of one of the nodes results in the curves shown. Similar data are obtained if the cavity tuning is fixed and the signal frequency is changed. A typical curve is shown in Fig. 9.16*b*. With the cavity tuned far off resonance, the node position changes with frequency, as indicated by the dashed lines; the slope of these depends upon the distance of the measuring probe from the cavity. With the

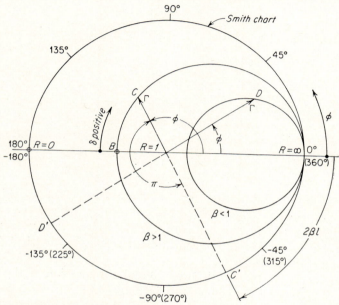

Fig. 9.17. Relation between the phase angle ϕ of the reflection coefficient Γ and the position of the voltage minimum.

cavity tuned to resonance, tuning the signal source through the resonance frequency of the cavity results in the curve shown. The data can be altered, if desired, to appear as shown in Fig. 9.16*a* by subtracting from each point a distance corresponding to the displacement of the detuned short.

In the analysis of this procedure it is convenient to use the series representation of the cavity given by Eq. (9.26). The term δ_0 is not important as it merely represents a shift along the frequency scale and is neglected for brevity. Thus, Eq. (9.26) can be written as

$$\frac{Z_{cc}}{Z_0} = \frac{1}{\beta}\left(1 + j2Q_0\delta\right) \tag{9.72}$$

Figure 9.17 shows the impedance referred to the detuned-open position plotted on the Smith chart. Points A and B show the impedance at resonance for the undercoupled and overcoupled cases, respectively. The complex reflection coefficient Γ measured at a distance l from the detuned-open position is obtained by substituting Eq. (9.72) into Eq. (4.69); thus,

$$\Gamma = \left| \frac{(Z_{cc}/Z_0) - 1}{(Z_{cc}/Z_0) + 1} \right| \underline{/\phi - 2\beta l} \tag{9.73}$$

where ϕ is the phase angle Γ at $l = 0$. For convenience, let

$$y = 2Q_0\delta \tag{9.74}$$

Substituting Eq. (9.72) into Eq. (9.73) and rationalizing, the phase angle ϕ is

$$\phi = \tan^{-1} \frac{2\beta y}{1 - \beta^2 + y^2} \tag{9.75}$$

At resonance ($y = 0$), from Fig. 9.17 or Eq. (9.75), the phase angle $\phi = 0$ and $\phi = \pi$ for the undercoupled and overcoupled cases, respectively.

The voltage minimum occurs when the phase angle of Γ is $n\pi$, or

$$\phi - 2\beta l = \pm n\pi \tag{9.76}$$

or

$$2\beta l = \phi \pm n\pi \tag{9.77}$$

with $n = 1, 3$, etc. Equation (9.77) determines the distance l between the voltage node and the detuned-open position; the phase angle ϕ is defined by the frequency through Eq. (9.75). Thus, the location of the voltage node is found from the Smith chart to be the electrical distance $2\beta l$, as indicated in Fig. 9.17.

Qualitatively, the relation between δ and the location of the voltage node can be predicted by tracing a point along the impedance locus and observing the variation in $2\beta l$. Consider the two cases illustrated in Fig. 9.17. For $\beta > 1$, at resonance, the minimum occurs at point B; as δ increases from zero to infinity, ϕ varies from π to zero. Consequently, $2\beta l$ begins at $0°$ and progresses through negative angles to $-180°$, as can be verified by tracing the motion of the point C' when C moves from B to O. When $\beta < 1$, at resonance the point A corresponds to a voltage maximum; the voltage minimum is found by adding $180°$. Tracing the point D along the impedance locus as δ increases from zero to infinity causes the point D' to begin at $-180°$, decrease toward $-90°$, and return again to $-180°$. Figure 9.18 shows the plot of $2\beta l$ vs. the tuning parameter δ obtained by calculation from Eqs. (9.77) and (9.75) for three conditions of coupling and illustrates the data that can be obtained in the laboratory.

The characteristics of the curves shown in Fig. 9.18 depend upon Q_0 and β. For computation, the cardinal points can be selected in the following manner: The resonant frequency, $\delta = 0$, can be taken as the point of antisymmetry.   Let the slope at this point be called S_0.   In the overcoupled case, let the frequencies at which the curve passes through $\pm 90°$ points be called δ_1 and δ_2.   In the undercoupled case the frequencies corresponding to the points of zero slope are called δ_3 and δ_4.   These values are identified in Fig. 9.18.

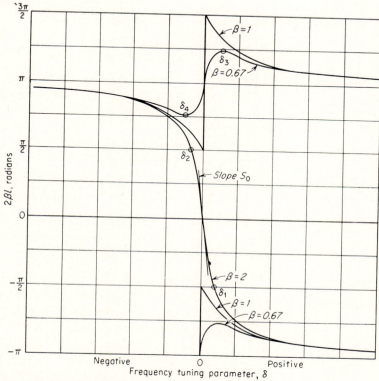

FIG. 9.18. Computed curves showing the displacement of the voltage minimum with respect to the detuned-open position.   The cardinal values of δ used in the calculation of the Q values are shown.

Analytic expressions connecting the β and Q values with $\delta_1, \ldots, \delta_4$ can be found as follows: The slope of the curves shown in Fig. 9.18 can be obtained by differentiating Eq. (9.77) with respect to δ:

$$\frac{d}{d\delta}\,(2\beta l) \;=\; \frac{d\phi}{d\delta} \;=\; 2Q_0\,\frac{d\phi}{dy} \tag{9.78}$$

Hence, differentiating Eq. (9.75) with respect to y leads to

$$\frac{d\phi}{d\delta} \;=\; 4Q_0\beta\,\frac{1 - \beta^2 + y^2}{(1 - \beta^2 + y^2)^2 + (2y\beta)^2} \tag{9.79}$$

At resonance,

$$S_0 = \frac{d\phi}{d\delta}\bigg|_{y=0} \tag{9.80}$$

$$S_0 = \frac{4Q_0\beta}{1 - \beta^2} \tag{9.81}$$

In the undercoupled case the points of zero slope are found from Eq. (9.79) by equating the numerator to zero. These occur at

$$\begin{aligned} 2Q\delta_4 &= \sqrt{1 - \beta^2} \\ 2Q\delta_3 &= -\sqrt{1 - \beta^2} \end{aligned} \tag{9.82}$$

In the overcoupled case the curve passes through the points $\pm 90°$ at which $2\beta l = \pm\pi/2$. Therefore, from Eq. (9.77), this occurs when $\phi = \pi/2$. Hence, $\tan \phi = \infty$; this occurs when the denominator in Eq. (9.75) is zero. This leads to

$$\begin{aligned} 2Q\delta_1 &= \sqrt{\beta^2 - 1} \\ 2Q\delta_2 &= -\sqrt{\beta^2 - 1} \end{aligned} \tag{9.83}$$

Equations (9.81), (9.82), and (9.83) contain the necessary information to evaluate the cavity parameters. Solving these for Q_0 and β results in

Undercoupled case $(\beta < 1)$:

$$\beta = \frac{\delta_3 S_0}{2\sqrt{(\delta_3 S_0/2)^2 + 1}} \tag{9.84}$$

$$Q_0 = \frac{1}{2\delta_3\sqrt{(\delta_3 S_0/2)^2 + 1}} \tag{9.85}$$

Overcoupled case $(\beta > 1)$:

$$\beta = \frac{S_0\delta_1}{2\sqrt{(S_0\delta_1/2)^2 - 1}} \tag{9.86}$$

$$Q_0 = \frac{1}{2\delta_1\sqrt{(S_0\delta_1/2)^2 - 1}} \tag{9.87}$$

$$Q_{ext} = \frac{Q_0}{\beta} = \frac{1}{S_0\delta_1{}^2} \tag{9.88}$$

$$Q_L = \frac{Q_0}{1 + \beta} = \frac{1}{2\delta_1[\sqrt{(S_0\delta_1/2)^2 - 1} + (S_0\delta_1/2)]} \tag{9.89}$$

If $\beta \gg 1$, from Eq. (9.81), $S_0 = 4Q_0/\beta$, or

$$Q_{ext} = \frac{S_0}{4} \tag{9.90}$$

Alternatively, combining Eqs. (9.88) and (9.90), for $\beta \gg 1$,

$$Q_{ext} = \frac{1}{2\delta_1} \tag{9.91}$$

or

$$Q_{ext} = \frac{1}{\delta_2 - \delta_1} = \frac{f_0}{f_1 - f_2} \tag{9.92}$$

Equating Eqs. (9.90) and (9.91) shows that the quantity $S_0 \delta_1$ is approximately equal to 2 for the overcoupled case. An examination of Eqs. (9.86) through (9.89) shows that the denominators contain the difference of two nearly equal numbers. For this reason, the values of β and Q_0 cannot be accurately determined by this method, although it is accurate for measuring Q_{ext}. For the undercoupled case, the method is

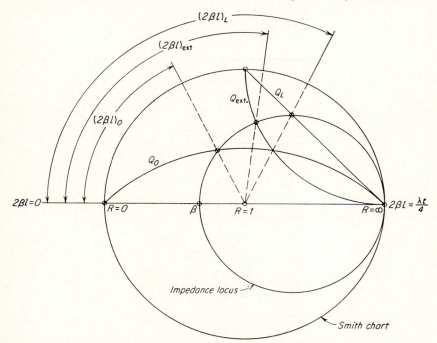

FIG. 9.19. Determination of the voltage node displacements $2\beta l$ corresponding to the half-power points for Q_0, Q_L, and Q_{ext}. The circular impedance locus is drawn through the experimental value of β.

not as useful as the VSWR method described in Sec. 9.3b, since it is difficult to find accurately the location of the minima due to their breadth at low VSWR; also, for $\beta \ll 1$, the minima do not shift sufficiently for accurate measurement.

To summarize, this method is used as follows: With the cavity tuned far from resonance, a location of a voltage node is found. As either the cavity or the signal source is tuned toward resonance, the position of the node changes. A graph showing the node position vs. the tuning parameter δ is plotted using the coordinate axes shown in Fig. 9.18. Using Eqs. (9.86) through (9.92), as appropriate, the Q values can be computed.

This method can be modified by measuring the VSWR at resonance. The displacement of the voltage node at the frequencies corresponding to the three half-power points can be found graphically from the construction lines shown in Fig. 9.10. These are repeated for convenience in Fig. 9.19, which shows the nodal displacements explicitly. The measured value of β at resonance establishes the intercept of the impedance locus with the resistive axis and permits the circle to be drawn. The intersection of the construction lines with the impedance locus determines the displacement of the voltage node at the half-power frequencies.

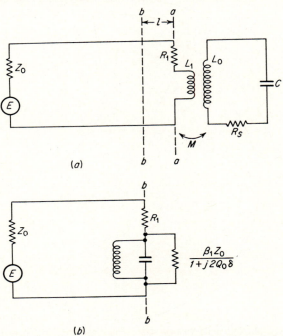

(a)

(b)

FIG. 9.20. Equivalent circuit used in the analysis of the effect of the coupling loss. (a) Equivalent circuit of the coupling system, (b) referred to the detuned-short position, b-b.

From the experiment graph of V_{min} vs. frequency, shown in Fig. 9.16, the frequencies corresponding to these displacements are found and the Q values computed using Eqs. 9.71.

9.4. Impedance Method—Effect of Coupling Loss. The three impedance methods for measuring the Q values, described in Sec. 9.3, are based upon the assumption that the cavity coupling network is lossless. In most practical cases this approximation is valid; however, if losses are present, the impedance methods presented cannot be applied directly and must be altered. For brevity, only the modification of the VSWR method is considered in detail, but the method of analysis can be extended to the remaining cases as well. It should be noted that the definitions of the loaded and external Q values are also modified by the presence of loss.[1]

Figure 9.20a is the equivalent circuit of a cavity coupled to the transmission line and corresponds to Fig. 9.3b with the addition of the series resistance R_1. It is assumed that the loss in the coupling element can be represented in this manner regardless of the actual cause of loss. The input impedance as a function of frequency results in a circular locus as

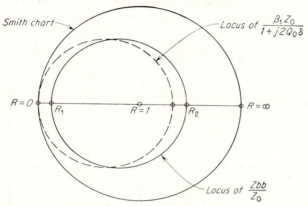

Fig. 9.21. Input impedance locus of a resonance cavity in the presence of loss in the coupling network.

shown in Fig. 9.21. The plot of VSWR vs. frequency is shown in Fig. 9.22. The characteristic feature of the two graphs is the fact that the VSWR far off resonance reaches a limiting value, r_{min}, instead of becoming infinite.

Qualitatively, the impedance information is interpreted as in the former case. Certain points on the impedance locus are found which correspond to the half-power points and the frequency interval between them defines Q_0. Due to the coupling loss, the identification of the half-power points is somewhat different from the lossless case. The desired relations between the characteristic points of the impedance locus and the frequencies corresponding to the half-power points can be obtained in the following manner:

Referring to Fig. 9.20a, the impedance at a-a is

$$\frac{Z_{aa}}{Z_0} = \frac{R_1 + jX_1}{Z_0} + \frac{\beta_1}{1 + j2Q_0\delta} \tag{9.93}$$

With the cavity tuned far off resonance, the transmission line is terminated by the self-impedance of the coupling element. As before, using

[1] L. Malter and G. R. Brewer, Microwave Q Measurements in the Presence of Series Losses, *J. Appl. Phys.*, vol. 20, no. 10, pp. 918–925, October, 1949.

the standing-wave detector, the position of a voltage minimum is found at some point b-b. In analogy to the lossless case, it is called the detuned-short position. If the self-reactance of the coupling system is sufficiently small, the impedance at the detuned-short position becomes

$$\frac{Z_{bb}}{Z_0} = \frac{R_1}{Z_0} + \frac{\beta_1}{1 + j2Q_0\delta} \tag{9.94}$$

The approximate equivalent circuit is shown in Fig. 9.20b.

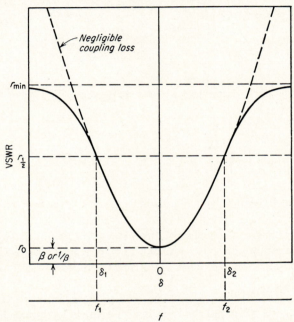

FIG. 9.22. Variation of VSWR with frequency in the presence of loss in the coupling network.

Let the two intercepts in Fig. 9.21, R_1 and R_2, be

$$\alpha = \frac{R_1}{Z_0} \tag{9.95}$$

$$\beta = \frac{R_2}{Z_0} = \beta_1 + \frac{R_1}{Z_0} = \beta_1 + \alpha \tag{9.96}$$

Also, let

$$\gamma = \frac{\alpha}{\beta} \tag{9.97}$$

In terms of these, Eq. (9.94) becomes

$$\frac{Z_{bb}}{Z_0} = \beta\left(\gamma + \frac{1 - \gamma}{1 + j2Q_0\delta}\right) \tag{9.98}$$

At the half-power frequencies, $2Q_0\delta = \pm 1$; hence,

$$\frac{Z_{bb}}{Z_0} = \frac{\beta(1 + j\gamma)}{1 + j} \tag{9.99}$$

The VSWR at these frequencies is obtained by substituting Eq. (9.99) into Eq. (4.70):

$$(r_{\frac{1}{2}})_0 = \frac{|1 + j + \beta(1 + j\gamma)| + |1 + j - \beta(1 + j\gamma)|}{|1 + j + \beta(1 + j\gamma)| - |1 + j - \beta(1 + j\gamma)|} \tag{9.100}$$

Rationalizing and simplifying,

$$(r_{\frac{1}{2}})_0 = \frac{2 + \beta^2(1 + \gamma^2) + \sqrt{4 + \beta^4(1 + \gamma^4) - 2\gamma\beta^2(4 - \gamma\beta^2)}}{2\beta(1 + \gamma)} \tag{9.101}$$

If $\gamma = 0$ ($R_1 = 0$), Eq. (9.101) reduces to Eq. (9.66). The ratio of $(r_{\frac{1}{2}})_0$ to VSWR r_0 at resonance is plotted in Fig. 9.23.

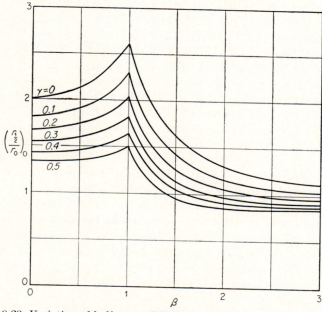

FIG. 9.23. Variation of half-power VSWR for Q_0 as a function of β and γ.

Thus, the measured values of β and α permit the determination of $(r_{\frac{1}{2}})_0$. The frequencies corresponding to these, δ_1 and δ_2 or f_1 and f_2, can be found from the experimental plot, such as is shown in Fig. 9.22. The value of Q_0 is computed from

$$Q_0 = \frac{f}{f_1 - f_2} \tag{9.102}$$

The loaded and external Q values can be derived, using the equivalent circuit shown in Fig. 9.20b. The definitions of the Q values can be obtained by considering the loss resistance R_1 to be either a part of the load or of the cavity; the choice between the two depends upon the application. Letting R_1 be a part of the load, the Q values are related by

$$Q_L = Q_0 \frac{1 + \gamma\beta}{1 + \beta} \qquad (9.103)$$

$$Q_{ext} = Q_0 \frac{1 + \gamma\beta}{\beta(1 - \gamma)} \qquad (9.104)$$

and

$$\frac{1}{Q_L} = \frac{1}{Q_0} + \frac{1}{Q_{ext}} \qquad (9.105)$$

Other definitions of Q values, derived by including the series resistance R_1 with the cavity losses, are given in the literature.[1]

In summary, the method is used as follows: The detuned-short position is found as the location of a voltage minimum with the cavity tuned far off resonance. With the cavity tuned to resonance, VSWR is found, determining β. The VSWR r is then measured as a function frequency, resulting in a graph, such as shown in Fig. 9.22. The parameter γ is computed from the knowledge of the VSWR's r_0 and r_{min}. The knowledge of β and γ permits the computation of $r_{1/2}$, and the corresponding frequencies from the experimental data. Q_0 is computed from Eq. (9.102) and Q_L and Q_{ext} from Eqs. (9.103) and (9.104). For small values of the loss parameter γ and negligible self-inductance, these formulas are accurate; when these approximations are not valid, both the definitions of the Q values and the described procedures become ambiguous.

9.5. The Decrement Method. The transient decay process may be used to determine the cavity Q as described in Sec. 9.1b.[2] The circuit shown in Fig. 9.7a represents one possible method of performing the experiment to measure the rate of decay in the high-Q cavity. The pulser, or modulator, turns the oscillator on for some convenient length of time, such as 1 μsec. It also initiates the linear sweep of the oscilloscope where the transient signal from the cavity is observed. During the build-up process, the fields in the cavity are established by means of forced oscillations induced by the oscillator. After the oscillator is turned off, the fields in the cavity decay exponentially at the natural frequency of the cavity or at a frequency altered slightly by the presence

---

[1] Malter and Brewer, *op. cit.*

[2] The observation of transient decay in a cavity is often used in testing radar system performance. The cavity is connected to the pulsed transmitter so that after the termination of the pulse the cavity fields decay exponentially. The time interval during which the signal is detectable in the receiver is a measure of the over-all sensitivity of the system. In this application, the cavity resonator is called the *echo box*.

of the coupled impedances from the oscillator and detector transmission lines. The r-f fields in the cavity are detected either by a crystal rectifier or a superheterodyne system, preferably the latter. The envelope of the decaying fields can be observed by the oscilloscope.

The essential elements are represented in the equivalent circuit shown in Fig. 9.2e, where the coupled reactances are neglected for convenience. The resistance R of the middle loop is given by

$$R = R_s + \frac{(\omega M_1)^2}{Z_1} + \frac{(\omega M_2)^2}{Z_2} \tag{9.106}$$

$$= R_s(1 + \beta_1 + \beta_2) \tag{9.107}$$

where β_1 and β_2 are the coupling coefficients. The loaded Q is given by $Q_L = \omega L/R$,

$$Q_L = Q_0 \frac{1}{1 + \beta_1 + \beta_2} \tag{9.108}$$

Referring to Fig. 9.2e, let i_0 be the magnitude of the current at the time the signal source is turned off. The decaying current is given by the expression

$$i(t) = i_0 e^{-(R/2L)t} \tag{9.109}$$

where the sinusoidal variation of the fields with time is understood. In terms of Q_L,

$$i(t) = i_0 e^{-(\omega_0/2Q_L)t} \tag{9.110}$$

If the current $i(t)$ is measured at two successive times, t_1 and t_2, the currents are

$$i(t_1) = i_0 e^{-(\omega/2Q_L)t_1} \tag{9.111}$$
$$i(t_2) = i_0 e^{-(\omega/2Q_L)t_2}$$

The ratio of these is

$$\frac{i(t_1)}{i(t_2)} = e^{-(\omega/2Q_L)(t_1-t_2)} \tag{9.112}$$

Solving for Q_L,

$$Q_L = \frac{\pi f(t_2 - t_1)}{\ln \dfrac{i(t_1)}{i(t_2)}} \tag{9.113}$$

If Δt corresponds to the interval of time during which the current changes by a factor of e, Eq. (9.113) becomes

$$Q_L = \pi f \, \Delta t \tag{9.114}$$

The quantity $f \, \Delta t$ is equal to the number of r-f cycles during the period Δt. Thus, the fields change by $1/e$ in Q_L/π cycles.

Equations (9.113) and (9.114) contain quantities which can be determined easily by experiment. If the detector is linear, the oscilloscope readings are proportional to the r-f current $i(t)$. If the response of the detector is square-law, the oscilloscope deflection is proportional to the square of the quantity given by Eq. (9.112). Since only the ratio of amplitudes are of interest, the constant of proportionality in the detecting system is not needed. The experimental procedure can be carried out in one of several ways.

If the time interval Δt is measured corresponding to a change of detected amplitude by $1/e$, it is possible to use Eq. (9.114) directly.

A second procedure uses an adjustable attenuator and a variable time delay as shown in Fig. 9.7a.[1] Under typical operating conditions, the position of the exponential decay curve on the oscilloscope, shown in Fig. 9.7b, is noted; an attenuation of A db is then introduced, causing the oscilloscope trace to shift. It can be restored to its former position by adjusting the time delay between the pulser and the oscilloscope. Q_L can be found from

$$Q_L = 4.343 \frac{\omega \, \Delta t}{A} \tag{9.115}$$

The time constant of the decay can be determined in another way by applying the pulser voltage to a series RC circuit and observing its response and the cavity decay simultaneously. By adjusting the circuit constants of the RC network the two decay curves can be made to coincide. The Q value can be determined from the RC values.

The transient decay method is useful if Q_L values are sufficiently high. For reasonable amounts of signal power and typical detector sensitivity, for $Q_L = 30,000$ the decay period can be in the order of 10 μsec, which can be measured easily and accurately. For substantially lower Q values, the time intervals are too short to be measured accurately.

As in the transmission method, the decrement method measures the loaded Q value but does not give the coupling coefficients. Therefore, to find Q_0 and Q_{ext}, it is necessary to perform additional experiments to find β_1 and β_2. To find Q_0, it is simplest to decrease the coupling until the measured Q value is no longer affected by further decreases in β.

Although the rate of decay is independent of the frequency of the signal source, the magnitude of the initial current in the circuit depends upon the frequency. As a result, the position of the decay curve on the oscilloscope will be unsteady if the signal source frequency is not constant from pulse to pulse. To obtain accurate results, it is necessary that the frequency be constant during the period of visual observation.

It is not essential to use the cavity as a transmission element. A cavity with a single input can be used as a reaction device as discussed

[1] C. G. Montgomery (ed.), "Technique of Microwave Measurements," p. 340, McGraw-Hill Book Company, Inc., New York, 1947.

in Chap. 7.   A probe placed at some convenient point between the oscillator and the cavity can be used to detect the decaying fields.   The
probe location is not critical; during the decay the cavity acts as the
source and the rest of the system as the load.   A probe placed at the
detuned-short position permits the observation of the build-up process
as if the cavity were used in the transmission system.

9.6. Dynamic Methods.   An accurate measurement of high-Q cavities
is sometimes difficult because of a residual instability of the signal source.
This is especially serious in those measurements requiring appreciable
periods of time to accumulate the necessary data, such as in the impedance method.   The decrement method, described in Sec. 9.5, avoids this

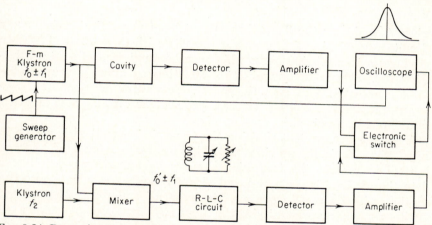

Fig. 9.24. Dynamic measurement of cavity Q by comparison of its transmission curve
against that of the low-frequency resonance circuit.

problem but the measurement of short time intervals may be difficult.
A number of methods employing dynamic presentation of the resonance
curve have been devised which allow rapid and accurate determination
of Q_L.   Three examples of these are described below.

Figure 9.24 shows an arrangement which permits the transmission resonance curve of a high-Q cavity to be compared directly against the transmission curve of a low-frequency resonance circuit.   Assuming that the
characteristics of the low-frequency circuit can be measured, the method
is straightforward and avoids many possible errors.   The two transmission curves are presented on an oscilloscope in the following manner:
A reflex klystron is frequency-modulated with a linear sweep, which is
also applied to the horizontal plates of the oscilloscope.   The frequency-
modulated signal passes through the cavity, is detected, amplified, and
introduced into the vertical plates of the oscilloscope through an electronic switch.   The low-frequency transmission curve is obtained simul-

taneously by heterodyning the microwave f-m signal to some convenient part of the radio-frequency spectrum with the aid of a fixed microwave local oscillator. The resultant f-m signal, introduced into the low-frequency circuit, is detected and amplified as in the microwave channel. This signal passes through an electronic switch which permits alternate observation of the two channels. By adjusting either the local oscillator frequency or the frequency of the resonant circuit, and also the Q of the low-frequency circuit (using a variable shunting resistor), it is possible to make the two traces coincide. The cavity Q_0 can be calculated from the relation

$$Q_0 = Q_0' \frac{f_0}{f_0'} \qquad (9.116)$$

where Q_0' and f_0' are the Q and the resonant frequency of the low-frequency circuit, respectively. For example, a cavity with $Q_0 = 10^5$ at 3,000 Mc produces a transmission curve which can be duplicated at 3 Mc with a $Q_0' = 100$. The method requires the detecting and amplifying apparatus to be identical in both channels, as well as careful calibration of the low-frequency circuit. Neither of these problems is difficult and excellent results can be obtained.[1]

A second arrangement utilizing the transmission method is shown in Fig. 9.25a. As in the previous method, a frequency-modulated klystron is used to present the transmission curve on an oscilloscope. If the detecting element is a square-law device, the half-power points observed on the oscilloscope will correspond to frequencies at which $2Q_L \delta = \pm 1$. Oscilloscope markers identifying the frequency corresponding to the half-power points can be generated in several ways, two of which are described.

A fixed-frequency microwave local oscillator is used to provide frequency f_0 corresponding to the resonant frequency of the cavity. When mixed with the frequency $f_0 \pm f_1$ from the frequency-modulated klystron, the difference frequency varies from 0 to f_1. This signal is introduced into a high-Q low-frequency circuit which is tuned to a frequency equal to one-half the cavity bandwidth. The detected signal from the resonant circuit produces a "pip" which may be used to mark the transmission curve by introducing it into the Z axis of the oscilloscope (or to the vertical plates through an electronic switch). A consideration of typical numbers makes the example more meaningful. Suppose the cavity with $Q_0 = 10^4$ is resonant at 3,000 Mc; the half-power points occur at ± 0.15 Mc. To display the transmission curve, the frequency swing f_1 may typically be ± 0.5 Mc. The low-frequency resonant circuit

---

[1] A similar system is described by H. LeCaine, The Q of a Microwave Cavity by Comparison with a Calibrated High-frequency Circuit, *Proc. IRE*, vol. 40, no. 2, p. 155, February, 1952.

is then tuned to 150 kc. If its Q_0 is 100, the detected marker signal has a bandwidth of 1.5 kc, providing a means to mark the resonance curve to an accuracy of about 1 per cent. In practice, the marker circuit is tuned until the marker signals appear at the half-power points, as shown in Fig. 9.22a. From the calibration of the low-frequency circuit, the half-power frequencies are found. A practical difficulty encountered in this arrangement is the necessity of sweeping the frequency slowly enough to allow the voltages in the resonant circuit to build up to steady state.

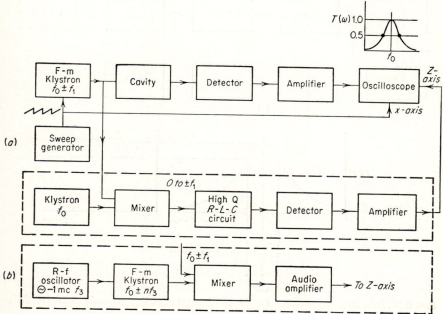

FIG. 9.25. Dynamic measurement of cavity Q. (a) The half-power frequency markers are generated with a low-frequency circuit; (b) the markers are generated by beating the signal against a series of frequencies derived from a frequency-modulated klystron.

The markers in the above system can also be provided by the alternate method shown in Fig. 9.25b. The local oscillator klystron is frequency-modulated with r-f frequency f_3 which is intended to correspond to the frequencies at half-power points. This produces several frequencies spaced f_3 cycles apart. As the frequency of the main klystron is swept by one of the frequencies produced by the local oscillator, an audio beat signal is produced. This, therefore, produces markers at the carrier and at frequencies f_3 from the carrier. These audio markers can be amplified and introduced into the oscilloscope as described above. The frequency f_3 is adjusted until the observed markers appear at the half-power points.

The third example of dynamic Q measurement is shown in Fig. 9.26.

The transmission method is again used, but the bandwidth is determined differently. The klystron signal source is modulated with some convenient sinusoidal voltage, such as 1 Mc. By reference to Fig. 9.26b, it can be seen that if the carrier is adjusted to the resonant frequency of the cavity, the modulation envelope of the transmitted signal contains only the second harmonic of the modulation frequency. Upon rectification, the signal can be passed through a 2-Mc-tuned amplifier and

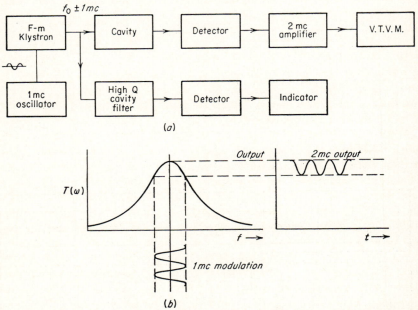

FIG. 9.26. Microwave Q meter. (a) Block diagram showing the main elements of the equipment; (b) second-harmonic output from the detector.

measured by a voltmeter. The magnitude of the second-harmonic frequency is proportional to the frequency swing and the cavity Q.

The degree of frequency modulation, i.e., the frequency swing, can be determined in several ways. For example, the modulated signal can be passed through a high-Q filter cavity in order to reject the sidebands. According to the theory of frequency modulation, the magnitude of the carrier is proportional to $J_0(\Delta f/F)$, where Δf is the frequency swing and F is the modulation frequency. If the modulation index $\Delta f/F = 2.405$, the magnitude of the carrier is equal to zero. This condition can be detected experimentally by adjusting the magnitude of the modulation voltage until the detected output from the high-Q filter becomes zero. The known modulation frequency determines the frequency swing; if $F = 1$ Mc, the frequency swing is 2.405 Mc.

CHAPTER 10

RESONANT-CAVITY CHARACTERISTICS: MEASUREMENT OF R_0/Q_0

10.1. Introduction. The shunt resistance of a cavity or its impedance at resonance, together with ω_0 and Q_0, is required for a complete description of a cavity resonator. It is also an important quantity in various practical applications, especially in those which involve the interaction of r-f fields with charged particles.

According to the definition given in Eq. (9.3), the calculation of the shunt resistance requires the knowledge of the electric field along a prescribed path. Therefore, an experimental technique for the measurement of R_0 necessitates the measurement of the electric field in the cavity over the region of interest. Some reflection on the subject will show that the impedance measurements described in Chap. 5 cannot be applied directly to this problem even in idealized cases. Furthermore, in most typical arrangements, the cavity in question is separated from uniform transmission lines by regions of geometrical discontinuities such as coupling loops, irises, etc., which introduce, as a minimum, an ideal transformer with an unknown turn ratio between the points in question and the region where standing-wave phenomena can be observed. For these reasons, special techniques must be used to derive sufficient information for computation of R_0.

Although several techniques can be conceived which would permit the direct measurement of the shunt resistance, it is usually more convenient to use an indirect method. As in the low-frequency case, the shunt resistance R_0 and Q_0 are proportional to each other and depend upon the power dissipation in the cavity, as can be verified by comparing the defining Eqs. (7.4) and (9.3). The ratio R_0/Q_0 is, therefore, independent of losses and governed only by the geometrical factors. For instance, for the low-frequency resonance circuit this ratio, determined from Eq. (9.2), is

$$\frac{R_0}{Q_0} = \sqrt{\frac{L}{C}} \qquad (10.1)$$

The ratio L/C is determined by the dimensions and geometrical configurations of the circuit. Therefore, in determining the shunt resistance R_0

435

the problem may be divided into two parts: the measurement of the geometrical factor R_0/Q_0 and the measurement of Q_0. Since Q_0 can be measured easily, this procedure provides an indirect method of determining R_0.

This approach has some special merit. The fact that R_0/Q_0 is independent of losses makes it possible to conduct laboratory measurements without regard to their presence. Test cavities can be built with demountable parts because the losses in the joints do not affect appreciably the distribution of the fields. Also, since R_0/Q_0 is proportional to

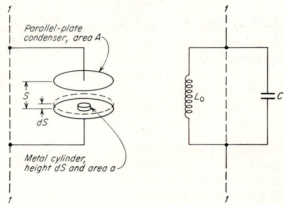

FIG. 10.1. Definition of symbols used in the explanation of the frequency-variation method of R_0/Q_0 measurement.

the frequency, measurements can be made on scaled models at any convenient wavelength provided that all dimensions of the model cavity are linearly scaled. The value of Q_0 needed to compute R_0 is found by measuring its value under real environmental conditions, such as the presence of the electron beam, dielectrics, etc.

The following sections show that the geometrical factor R_0/Q_0 can be found by perturbation techniques which involve the measurement of the resonant frequency of the cavity as a function of position of certain perturbing objects. Since the resonant frequency can be measured accurately, this procedure provides a simple powerful way to determine R_0/Q_0. The frequency-perturbation method also makes it possible to find the relative magnitude and direction of the fields throughout the cavity.

In addition to the perturbation techniques, there are also several other methods to measure R_0, applicable to particular problems; these are mentioned briefly in Sec. 10.9.

10.2. The Perturbation Method: Low-frequency Analogue. To understand the perturbation method of measuring R_0/Q_0, first consider its application to a low-frequency resonant circuit shown in Fig. 10.1. The angular resonant frequency of the circuit shown at right is

$$\omega_0 = \frac{1}{\sqrt{L_0 C_0}} \tag{10.2}$$

where the subscripts denote the values of the quantities at resonance. Consider the change in the resonant frequency caused by small changes in the capacity C. The change in the resonant frequency can be obtained by differentiating Eq. (10.2) with respect to C. Thus,

$$\frac{d\omega}{dC} = -\frac{1}{2} \frac{L_0}{(L_0 C)^{3/2}} \tag{10.3}$$

If the changes in C are small, $C = C_0$, $\omega = \omega_0$. Combining Eqs. (10.2) and (10.3),

$$d\omega = -\frac{1}{2} \omega_0 \frac{dC}{C} \tag{10.4}$$

or

$$d\omega = -\frac{1}{2} \omega_0{}^3 L_0 \, dC \tag{10.5}$$

Equation (10.5) relates changes in capacity to the resultant changes in frequency. Using the relation $R_0 = \omega_0 L_0 Q_0$ and combining it with Eq. (10.5) gives

$$\frac{R_0}{Q_0} = -\frac{2}{\omega_0{}^2} \frac{d\omega}{dC} \tag{10.6}$$

Equation (10.6) shows that R_0/Q_0 can be determined by measuring the rate of change of frequency with changes in capacity. If, in addition, Q_0 is measured, it is possible to determine the impedance *without any direct measurement of impedance*. Because of the procedure used, this is termed the *capacity* (or *susceptance*) *variation* method; it is not well known at the low radio frequencies because the circuit constants can be measured directly. It should be noted that the derivative $d\omega/dC$ can be determined as the slope of the curve of ω vs. C at the point $C = C_0$. Thus, the value of the derivative is determined by the variational procedure for the *unperturbed* condition, a feature especially useful in the microwave analogue.[1]

[1] It is interesting to consider the following experiment. Referring to Fig. 10.1, suppose a metallic cylinder of height dS and area a is placed into the electric field of the condenser C. The capacity of the condenser in esu units is

$$C = \frac{A}{4\pi S} \tag{10.7}$$

where A is the area of the condenser plate. If the condenser plate is displaced by

The corresponding experiment can be performed with the cavity resonator. If some object is introduced into a cavity in a region where the magnetic field is essentially zero, the resonant frequency will change because the altered fields correspond to a change in capacity in the low-frequency case. This is illustrated for a special case in Fig. 10.2 where a metallic button is introduced into the electric field region of a klystron cavity. The presence of the perturbing button increases the capacity and lowers the frequency. This experiment is closely analogous to the low-frequency case just discussed and R_0/Q_0 for the cavity can be determined in the same way. The desired relations are derived in Sec. 10.4.

10.3. Slater Perturbation Theorem. In the derivation of the R_0/Q_0 formula in the general case, it is necessary to relate the change in frequency of a microwave cavity to the volume, shape, material, and position

---

distance dS, the capacity C changes by

$$dC = -\frac{A}{4\pi S^2} dS \qquad (10.8)$$

Since the area of the cylindrical button is smaller than A, the change in the capacity due to the presence of the button is

$$dC = -\frac{A}{4\pi S^2} dS \frac{a}{A} = -\frac{a\,dS}{4\pi S^2} \qquad (10.9)$$

Let the volume of the cylinder $a\,ds = d\tau$. Hence,

$$dC = \frac{d\tau}{4\pi S^2} \qquad \text{esu}$$
$$= \frac{1}{c^2}\frac{d\tau}{4\pi S^2} \qquad \text{emu} \qquad (10.10)$$

Since $df/f = -d\lambda/\lambda$, Eq. (10.6) becomes

$$\frac{R_0}{Q_0} = -\frac{2}{\omega_0}\frac{d\omega}{\omega}\frac{1}{dC}$$
$$\frac{R_0}{Q_0} = \frac{1}{\pi f_0}\frac{d\lambda}{\lambda}\frac{1}{dC} = \frac{1}{\pi c}\frac{d\lambda}{dC} \qquad (10.11)$$

Combining with Eq. (10.10),

$$\frac{R_0}{Q_0} = 4cS^2 \frac{d\lambda}{d\tau}$$

Converting emu to practical units ($c = 30$ ohms—see Sec. B.4),

$$\frac{R_0}{Q_0} = 120S^2 \frac{d\lambda}{d\tau} \qquad (10.12)$$

Thus, R_0/Q_0 can be found by measuring the wavelength change $d\lambda$ caused by the metallic button of volume $d\tau$. It is of interest to compare this relation to the more general microwave result based on the field equations.

of the perturbing object. The desired result is obtained from the Slater perturbation theorem, which can be written as follows:[1]

$$\omega^2 = \omega_0{}^2 \left[1 + k \frac{\displaystyle\int_{\Delta\tau} (\mu \mathbf{H}^2 - \epsilon \mathbf{E}^2)d\tau}{\displaystyle\int_V (\mu \mathbf{H}^2 + \epsilon \mathbf{E}^2)dv} \right] \tag{10.13}$$

where $d\tau$ is an element of the volume of the perturbing object and dv an element of volume in the cavity. The numerator represents integration over the volume of the perturbing object; the denominator is equal to twice the *average* energy stored in the cavity U. Thus,

$$\omega^2 = \omega_0{}^2 \left[1 + \frac{k\int (\mu \mathbf{H}^2 - \epsilon \mathbf{E}^2)d\tau}{2U} \right] \tag{10.14}$$

If perturbation is small, $\omega = \omega_0$, $\delta = (\omega - \omega_0)/\omega_0$, and

$$\delta = \frac{k\int (\mu \mathbf{H}^2 - \epsilon \mathbf{E}^2)d\tau}{4U} \tag{10.15}$$

This important relation states that the perturbed frequency ω is changed from the natural resonant frequency ω_0 by an amount which depends upon the integral $\int_{\Delta\tau} (\mu \mathbf{H}^2 - \epsilon \mathbf{E}^2)d\tau$ over the volume removed by the perturbing object $\Delta\tau$. The con-
stant k in Eqs. (10.13) and (10.14) depends upon the shape of the perturbing volume and is equal to unity for those shapes for which the fields in the cavity approach the natural fields as the volume of the object approaches zero.[2] For example, referring to Fig. 10.2, Eq. (10.13) would apply with $k = 1$, if the height of the cylindrical button is considered to be the variable; for, if the height is made zero, the fields return to the undisturbed condi-

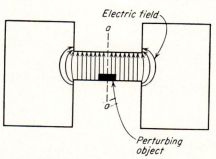

Fig. 10.2. Application of the frequency-variation method to the measurement of R_0/Q_0 of a reentrant cavity with constant electric field.

tion. If, however, the radius of the perturbing object is the variable, in the limit of vanishing volume, a sharp spike is produced, causing the field

[1] J. C. Slater, "Microwave Electronics," pp. 81–83, D. Van Nostrand Company, Inc., Princeton, N.J., 1950.

[2] W. W. Hansen and R. F. Post, On the Measurement of Cavity Impedance, *J. Appl. Phys.*, vol. 19, no. 11, pp. 1059–1061, November, 1948. The constant k should, in fact, appear inside the integral multiplying $\mathbf{E}$ and $\mathbf{H}$ terms separately and can have different values in the two terms.

distribution to be radically changed. The constant k in this case is infinite. Further discussion relevant to this question is given in Sec. 10.6.

10.4. Application to Cavity with Constant Electric Field. The capacity variation method of measuring R_0/Q_0 described in Sec. 10.2 can be extended to the microwave problems by using the Slater perturbation theorem. First, consider the simple case shown in Fig. 10.2, which represents a resonant cavity suitable for a klystron. To determine the shunt resistance along a-a, assume the electric field to have only an axial component, constant over the region of the gap; the magnetic field is assumed to be zero in this region. These methods are applied to a more general case where the fields may vary along the path of integration in Sec. 10.5.

For convenience, the general definitions of Q_0 and R_0 are repeated:

$$Q_0 = 2\pi \frac{\text{energy stored}}{\text{energy lost per cycle}} \tag{10.16}$$

$$= \omega \frac{\text{energy stored}}{\text{energy lost per second}} \tag{10.17}$$

$$= \frac{\omega U}{W} \tag{10.18}$$

where W is the power loss (the energy lost per second).

$$R_0 = \frac{(\text{effective voltage})^2}{\text{power loss}}$$

$$= \frac{(\int \mathbf{E}\, dS)^2}{2W} \tag{10.19}$$

Combining Eqs. (10.18) and (10.19),

$$\frac{R_0}{Q_0} = \frac{(\int \mathbf{E}\, dS)^2}{2\omega U} \tag{10.20}$$

If the electric field $\mathbf{E}$ is constant, $\int \mathbf{E}\, dS = \mathbf{E}S$,

$$\frac{R_0}{Q_0} = \frac{S^2}{2\omega} \frac{\mathbf{E}^2}{U} \tag{10.21}$$

The quantity $\mathbf{E}^2/U$ can be determined experimentally by placing a perturbing object of volume $\Delta\tau$ into the cavity and measuring the resultant change in frequency. For the case under discussion, $\mathbf{H} = 0$, and the desired relation is obtained from Eq. (10.15). It is

$$\delta = -\frac{k\epsilon \mathbf{E}^2 \Delta\tau}{4U} \tag{10.22}$$

where $\Delta\tau$ is the volume of the perturbing object. Combining Eq. (10.22) with (10.21) gives

$$\frac{R_0}{Q_0} = - \frac{2S^2}{k\omega\epsilon f}\frac{\Delta f}{\Delta \tau} \qquad (10.23)$$

$$= - \frac{2S^2}{k\omega\epsilon\lambda}\frac{\Delta\lambda}{\lambda} \qquad (10.24)$$

In mks units, $1/\omega\epsilon\lambda = 60$.   Hence,

$$\frac{R_0}{Q_0} = \frac{120}{k} S^2 \frac{\Delta\lambda}{\Delta \tau} \qquad (10.25)$$

Thus, the ratio R_0/Q_0 can be determined by finding the change in the resonant wavelength $\Delta\lambda$ caused by the perturbing object of volume $\Delta\tau$.

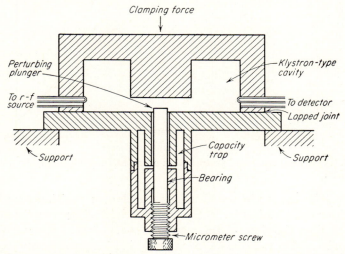

FIG. 10.3. Principal details of the plunger construction used in the R_0/Q_0 experiment. The plunger enters the cavity through a hole only slightly larger than the diameter of the plunger, making the positive and negative volume displacements nearly equal.

The constant k in the denominator of Eq. (10.25) has been retained to emphasize the importance of the shape of the perturbing object. As stated in Sec. 10.3, the value of k depends upon the manner in which $\Delta\tau$ approaches zero. In order to apply the perturbation method correctly, it is necessary to determine the appropriate factor k in Eq. (10.25) in one of several ways. For some simple shapes, such as a metallic sphere, the constant k can be determined theoretically; or, it can be found experimentally by inserting the perturbing object into a cavity with known fields and measuring the resultant frequency change; a cavity resonant in the TM_{010} mode can be used for this purpose.[1]   The necessity

[1] The ratio R_0/Q_0 for the cylindrical cavity operating in the TM_{010} mode is $371 L/D$, where L and D are length and diameter, respectively.

of calibrating the perturbing object can be avoided by choosing the geometry of the perturbing object which causes negligible distortion of the cavity fields.   This can be done by using a movable metallic plunger, as indicated in Fig. 10.3, to provide positive and negative changes in

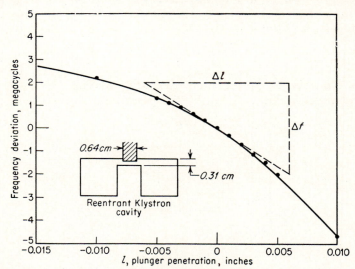

Fig. 10.4. Typical experimental perturbation data obtained with a klystron resonator at 2,800 Mc.

volume.   The change in wavelength with plunger position for a typical case is shown plotted in Fig. 10.4.   This procedure increases the accuracy and determines the slope of the resultant curve at zero plunger displacement.   The resultant value $\Delta\lambda/\Delta\tau$ is derived at the position of the plunger at which the fields are unperturbed, leading automatically to $k = 1$.*

An experiment to determine R_0/Q_0 can be carried out as follows: A

---

* Hansen and Post, *op. cit.*   This reference also shows that an error results if the perturbing object is too large in diameter or in height.   The electric and magnetic fields in a cavity with axial symmetry can be written in the form $J_1(k_1 r) \cos k_3 z$, where $k_1 a = 2.405$; r and z are radial and axial coordinates, respectively; a is the radius of the cavity; and $k_3 = 2\pi/\lambda_t$.   In this case, integration of Eq. (10.15) leads to

$$\delta = -\frac{\epsilon E^2 \Delta\tau}{4U} [1 - (\tfrac{3}{8}k_1{}^2 - \tfrac{1}{4}k_3{}^2)R^2]$$

from which the constant k has the value [by comparison with Eq. (10.22)]

$$k = 1 - (\tfrac{3}{8}k_1{}^2 - \tfrac{1}{4}k_3{}^2)R^2$$

where R is the radius of the perturbing object.   If the electric field is constant in the z direction, $k = 1 - \tfrac{3}{8}(k_1 R)^2 = 1 - 2.17(R/a)^2$.   For a TM$_{010}$ cavity resonant at 10 cm, plungers 0.75, 0.5, and 0.25 in. in diameter cause k to have the values 0.885, 0.948, and 0.987, respectively.

cavity is constructed with the desired proportions, with the dimensions chosen to resonate at some convenient frequency.   If possible, the structure should be demountable so that an end plate with a movable metallic plunger can be attached as indicated in Fig. 10.3.   The cavity is connected by coupling loops or probes to a system which allows the measurement of the resonant frequency.   One convenient arrangement uses the

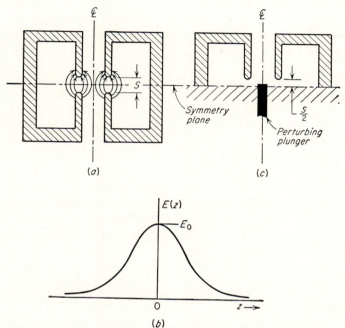

FIG. 10.5. Determination of the maximum value of the axial electric field in a gridless klystron resonator by the perturbation experiment.   (a) Typical gridless cavity with the approximate distribution of the electric field; (b) the approximate variation of the electric field along the axis of the cavity; (c) perturbation of the electric field in the half-cavity resonator.

cavity under test as a reaction wavemeter in parallel with a calibrated wavemeter.   The plunger is moved through a series of positions at which the resonant frequencies are measured; these are plotted, as in Fig. 10.4, and the slope determined graphically or analytically.   To insure that the plunger is sufficiently small in diameter, it may be necessary to repeat the experiment with a plunger of a different diameter.   Low residual losses in the cavity are important, as they determine Q_0 and, consequently, the accuracy with which the resonant frequency can be measured.

10.5. Application to Cavities with Variable Fields.   The perturbation method described in Sec. 10.4 can be extended easily to the more general case in which the fields may vary along the path of integration.   Consider, for example, the gridless cavity illustrated in Fig. 10.5a which may be useful in a klystron. The approximate field distribution along the axis is shown in Fig. 10.5b. Suppose E_0 represents the field on the axis at the plane of symmetry (or at any other arbitrarily chosen point). The general definition of R_0/Q_0 given by Eq. (10.20) can be rewritten as

$$\frac{R_0}{Q_0} = \frac{(E_0 S)^2}{2\omega U}\left(\frac{\int E\ dS}{E_0 S}\right)^2 \quad (10.26)$$

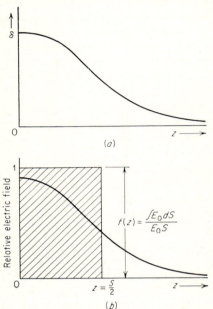

(a)

(b)

FIG. 10.6. Determination of the relative field distribution in the gridless cavity shown in Fig. 10.5 by the bead experiment. (a) Variation of resonant frequency with bead position along the axis. (b) The variation of the electric field along the axis computed by taking the square root of the curve in (a); the area of the rectangle with the base $z = S/2$ is equal to the area under the curve. The height of the rectangle determines the magnitude of the correction term in Eq. (10.26).

where S is the equivalent gap spacing chosen in some meaningful manner as indicated in Fig. 10.5a. The first term in Eq. (10.26) corresponds to the value R_0/Q_0 would have if the field over the distance S were constant, which can be measured by the perturbation experiment described in Sec. 10.4. For the situation shown in Fig. 10.5, a plane of symmetry can be found as indicated in Fig. 10.5c. The introduction of a metallic plunger at this plane permits E_0 to be measured. With the aid of Eq. (10.24), the first term in Eq. (10.26) is determined. (This procedure is based on the assumption that the electric field E is constant in the vicinity of the perturbing plunger. This assumption can be made valid by using a sufficiently small plunger, or by correcting the result for the variation of the field due to finite plunger size.)

In the figure, the curve is labeled $f(z) = \dfrac{\int E_0\ dS}{E_0 S}$ and marked at $z = \dfrac{S}{2}$.

To evaluate the second term in Eq. (10.26), it is necessary to determine the functional dependence of E_z upon z. The variation of the electric field along the axis of the cavity can be found by performing an additional perturbation experiment. If a small perturbing object is moved along the axis of the cavity, the changes in frequency will be a measure of the fields at the axis. The Slater perturbation formula, given by Eq. (10.15), can be used to relate the observed changes in frequency to the fields at the point in question. Since the second term of Eq.

(10.26) involves only the measurement of relative fields, the constant k in Eq. (10.15) is not needed.   The perturbing object can be a small cylindrical button, either metallic or dielectric, suspended in the cavity by a thin thread.   A plot of the frequency change δ vs. z can be converted into the plot of relative values of $\mathbf{E}$ vs. z which results in a curve similar to that shown in Fig. 10.6b.   The value of the second term in Eq. (10.26) can be found from the height of the rectangle whose area is made equal to the area under the curve of Fig. 10.6b; the width of the rectangle corresponds to one-half the gap lengths, $S/2$.

The choice between various possible perturbing objects for the exploration of the axial field requires special consideration.   Unless the radial electric field at the axis is negligibly small, the changes in frequency will be due in part to the variation of the radial component rather than to the perturbation of the desired axial field.   For this reason, it may be preferable to use a small sharp needle oriented in the axial direction which strongly affects the axial field with only a negligible distortion of the radial component.   The use of needles is discussed more fully in Sec. 10.6.

10.6. Determination of Field Components in Cavity Resonators.

Techniques for measuring R_0/Q_0, described in the preceding section, can be extended to provide information from which the field strength in a cavity resonator of an arbitrary shape can be determined.   Whereas, some idea of field components in the cavity can be obtained on the basis of symmetry arguments, or by exploring the fields near the walls of the cavity by loops or probes, these methods do not provide any detailed knowledge of the field components throughout the volume of the cavity. It is possible to determine these with the aid of the perturbation techniques.

For a qualitative explanation of the method, suppose a small metallic needle-shaped object is suspended in a cavity.   If the needle happens to be perpendicular to the electric field, its presence will perturb the fields but slightly, and the resonant frequency of the cavity will be practically undisturbed.   The frequency will change as the needle orientation is changed, and the maximum perturbation will occur when the needle is parallel to the electric field.   Thus, the direction of the field is established by finding the orientation of the needle which corresponds to the maximum change in frequency.   The magnitude of the field is determined with the aid of the Slater perturbation theorem as in the R_0/Q_0 studies. The shape constant k in Eq. (10.14) is evaluated by a calibration experiment by observing the frequency change in a cavity in which the fields are accurately known.   Theoretically derived formulas, for needles of idealized shape, which can be used as a guide in selecting a needle of the proper proportions are given below.

The needle-shaped objects are useful in determining the direction and magnitude of the electric fields, but they do not perturb the magnetic field. However, another convenient perturbing object, a thin metallic disk, can be used for this purpose. Its usefulness can be demonstrated by considering the following example: Referring to Fig. 10.7, suppose a cylindrical cavity is excited in the TM_{010} mode. The resonant frequency of the cavity is unperturbed if the disk is placed in position A where it is perpendicular to the electric field E_z. If the disk is placed in the position B with its face perpendicular to the radius R, the field E_z is perturbed, but not the magnetic field H_ϕ. If the disk is oriented in the r-z plane as shown by position C, the circumferential magnetic flux lines become perpendicular to the face of the disk, and the frequency change is due to the perturbation of E_z and H_ϕ. More careful consideration shows that, in the general case, a disk can be oriented to measure E_z only, E_r only, or a combination of H_ϕ and E_r. The perturbation constant k for the disk can be determined either by calibration experiment or theoretical calculation.

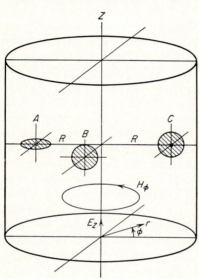

FIG. 10.7. Determination of field components in a resonant cavity by a metallic disk. In the TM_{010} mode, the disk at (A) is perpendicular to the **E** lines and parallel to the **H** lines where it does not perturb the fields; at (B), the disk perturbs E_z and, at (C), both E_z and H_ϕ.

The field components in the cavity of an arbitrary shape can be studied in the following manner: In general, there may be six components of the fields in a resonant cavity; the determination of these requires the simultaneous solution of six equations. The simplest procedure for obtaining the required six sets of relations involves the use of the needle and the disk, each being oriented along the three coordinate axes. The three orientations of the needle immediately determine the three components in the electric field. The use of the disk produces perturbations which depend upon the combination of electric and magnetic fields mentioned above, and described more fully below. In the general case, this procedure must be repeated at each point in question. Although it appears to be tedious, the procedure is used when no other information pertaining to distribution of the fields in the cavity is available. Any knowledge of symmetry conditions, mode type, and other general facts can simplify the procedure and reduce the required number of experiments.

It is sometimes convenient to make a preliminary exploration of the fields by using a small metallic sphere instead of the needles or disks. Because its perturbation is completely nondirectional, it indicates the general distribution of the fields throughout the volume of the cavity.

In practice, the perturbing objects are supported by thin threads running through the appropriate parts of the cavity, or by rigid dielectric rods. If the supporting structures are thin enough not to perturb the fields, the distribution and orientation of the electric fields can be explored by moving the needle to maximize the frequency change at each point in question.

This procedure for measuring field components can be modified to measure the total fields. In high-Q cavities with orthogonal electric and magnetic fields, the direction of the electric field is first determined by a needle in the manner described. Then the direction and magnitude of the electric and magnetic fields can be determined with the aid of a thin disk. It is placed with its face parallel to the known direction of $\mathbf{E}$; if it is rotated about the axis corresponding to the direction of $\mathbf{E}$, the resonant frequency of the cavity changes. The frequency is minimum when the disk lies in a plane defined by the $\mathbf{E}$ and $\mathbf{H}$ vectors. Equation (10.14) can be used to determine the magnitude of the electric field; the theoretical value of k can be found from Eq. (10.36) because the magnetic field is not perturbed. If the disk is rotated (about the E lines as the axis) through an angle of 90°, it will lie with its face perpendicular to the magnetic field. The change in frequency caused by the perturbation of the magnetic field can be used to compute the magnitude of $\mathbf{H}$. However, since $\mathbf{E}$ and $\mathbf{H}$ are assumed to be perpendicular to each other, the disk placed perpendicularly to $\mathbf{H}$ is parallel to $\mathbf{E}$. Therefore, the perturbation of $\mathbf{H}$ is always accompanied by a perturbation of $\mathbf{E}$.

Thus, while the use of needles permits independent determination of either the component values or the total electric field, the use of disks to evaluate the magnetic fields simultaneously perturbs the electric fields; the calculation of the magnetic field from the disk experiment requires the knowledge of the electric field. This complication is not serious in practice. Equations (10.14) and (10.15) show that changes in frequency due to the perturbation of the electric and magnetic fields (for small changes in frequency) can be obtained by superposition. That is, in the experimental procedure described, the change in frequency, as the disk is rotated from the parallel to the perpendicular positions with respect to the magnetic field, can be used to evaluate the magnetic field; the constant perturbation of the electric field is of no concern, assuming that the disk remains parallel to the electric field, and that the **E** field is sufficiently constant over the volume swept out by the rotation of the disk.

Theoretical formulas that predict the perturbation effect due to metallic objects of various shapes of importance have been obtained by Maier.[1] These have been obtained for idealized objects being figures of revolution of an ellipse around either the minor or major axes that resemble either needles or disks. Maier's results verify the qualitative arguments given above that predict the effect of perturbation due to needles and disks. The following formulas are valuable for the qualitative understanding of the degree of perturbation caused by needles and disks of various proportions. If the real objects are constructed with sufficient care to resemble the ellipsoidal shapes, these formulas can be used to calculate the magnitude of the fields in terms of the measured frequency shifts.

For convenience, the notation used in Sec. 10.3 is altered:

$$\mathbf{E}_0^2 = \frac{\epsilon \mathbf{E}^2}{2U}$$
$$\mathbf{H}_0^2 = \frac{\mu \mathbf{H}^2}{2U} \tag{10.27}$$

In terms of these normalized qualities, Eq. (10.13) can be written as

$$\frac{\omega^2 - \omega_0^2}{\omega_0^2} = k \int_{\Delta\tau} (\mathbf{H}_0^2 - \mathbf{E}_0^2) dv \tag{10.28}$$

The constant k for the various shapes of metallic buttons obtained by Maier and Slater is given below.

a. Perturbation by Metallic Spheres. If a sphere of radius a is introduced into a region where only the electric field exists, the frequency change is given by

$$\frac{\omega_0^2 - \omega^2}{\omega_0^2} = 3\mathbf{E}_0^2 \frac{4\pi a^3}{3} \tag{10.29}$$

In the presence of the magnetic field only, the change in frequency is given by

$$\frac{\omega_0^2 - \omega^2}{\omega_0^2} = -\frac{3}{2} \mathbf{H}_0^2 \frac{4\pi a^3}{3} \tag{10.30}$$

By superposition, if both types of fields are present, the frequency change is

$$\frac{\omega_0^2 - \omega^2}{\omega_0^2} = 3 \left(\mathbf{E}_0^2 - \frac{1}{2} \mathbf{H}_0^2 \right) \frac{4\pi a^3}{3} \tag{10.31}$$

[1] L. C. Maier, Jr., Field Strength Measurements in Resonant Cavities, *Massachusetts Institute of Technology Research Laboratory of Electronics Tech. Rept.* 143, Nov. 2, 1949; also L. C. Maier, Jr., and J. C. Slater, Field Strength Measurements in Resonant Cavities, *J. Appl. Phys.*, vol. 23, no. 1, pp. 68–77, January, 1952.

b. Perturbation by Metallic Needles. The following expressions are obtained by considering a needle as a figure of revolution of an ellipse about its major axis. The ratio of major to minor axes of the ellipsoid is called β. A slender needle is characterized by small β. The length of the needle is $2a$.

The needle can be either parallel or perpendicular to either the electric or magnetic field. It is necessary to consider these four cases separately; the changes in frequency for these are:

Needle parallel to **E**:

$$\frac{\omega_0^2 - \omega^2}{\omega_0^2} = \frac{E_0^2(1 - \beta^2)^{3/2}\dfrac{4\pi a^3}{3}}{\frac{1}{2}\ln\dfrac{1 + (1 - \beta^2)^{1/2}}{1 - (1 - \beta^2)^{1/2}} - (1 - \beta^2)^{1/2}} \tag{10.32}$$

Needle perpendicular to **E**:

$$\frac{\omega_0^2 - \omega^2}{\omega_0^2} = \frac{2E_0^2(1 - \beta^2)^{3/2}\dfrac{4\pi a^3}{3}}{\dfrac{(1 - \beta^2)^{1/2}}{\beta^2} - \frac{1}{2}\ln\dfrac{1 + (1 - \beta^2)^{1/2}}{1 - (1 - \beta^2)^{1/2}}} \tag{10.33}$$

Needle parallel to **H**:

$$\frac{\omega_0^2 - \omega^2}{\omega_0^2} = -\frac{H_0^2(1 - \beta^2)^{3/2}\dfrac{4\pi a^3}{3}}{\dfrac{(1 - \beta^2)^{1/2}}{\beta^2} - \frac{1}{2}\ln\dfrac{1 + (1 - \beta^2)^{1/2}}{1 - (1 - \beta^2)^{1/2}}} \tag{10.34}$$

Needle perpendicular to **H**:

$$\frac{\omega_0^2 - \omega^2}{\omega_0^2} = -\frac{2H_0^2(1 - \beta^2)^{3/2}\dfrac{4\pi a^3}{3}}{\dfrac{(1 - 2\beta^2)}{\beta^2}(1 - \beta^2)^{1/2} + \frac{1}{2}\ln\dfrac{1 + (1 - \beta^2)^{1/2}}{1 - (1 - \beta^2)^{1/2}}} \tag{10.35}$$

The frequency changes for each of the four cases are shown plotted in Fig. 10.8. The ordinate represents the changes in frequency normalized with respect to changes caused by a sphere whose diameter is equal to the length of the needle. The function $F(\beta)$ represents the ratio of frequency changes given by Eqs. (10.32) through (10.35) to the frequency changes for a sphere as obtained from Eqs. (10.29) and (10.30) as appropriate. The abscissa in Fig. 10.8 is the slenderness ratio β defined above. For small values of β the needle perturbs the fields significantly only if it is parallel to the electric field and, by comparison, the perturbation of other fields is negligible. This effect permits the use of needles to determine both the direction and magnitude of the electric field. For values of β approaching unity, the ellipsoid approaches a sphere, and the perturbation effects become nondirectional.

c. Perturbation by Metallic Disks. A circular metallic disk can be approximated analytically by a figure of revolution of an ellipse about its minor axis. The quantity β represents the ratio of the semiminor to the semimajor axes. As in the case of the needle, it is necessary to con-

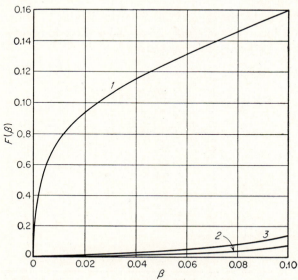

FIG. 10.8. Frequency perturbation by metallic needles as a function of the slenderness ratio β. The ordinate $F(\beta)$ represents the ratio of frequency change due to the needle to the frequency change produced by a sphere whose diameter is equal to the length of the needle. Curve 1 is for the case of the needle being parallel to the electric field; curve 2 corresponds to the two cases of the needle being perpendicular to the electric and the magnetic fields; curve 3 corresponds to the needle being parallel to the magnetic field. (*Adopted by permission from L. C. Maier, Jr., and J. C. Slater, Field Strength Measurements in Resonant Cavities, J. Appl. Phys., vol. 23, no. 1, January, 1952.*)

sider four separate cases. If $2a$ represents the diameter of the disk, the frequency changes for each case are:

E parallel to disk:

$$\frac{\omega_0^2 - \omega^2}{\omega_0^2} = \frac{2\mathbf{E}_0^2(1 - \beta^2)^{3/2}\dfrac{4\pi a^3}{3}}{\dfrac{\pi}{2} - \tan^{-1}\dfrac{\beta}{(1 - \beta^2)^{1/2}} - \beta(1 - \beta^2)^{1/2}} \qquad (10.36)$$

E normal to disk:

$$\frac{\omega_0^2 - \omega^2}{\omega_0^2} = \frac{\mathbf{E}_0^2(1 - \beta^2)^{3/2}\dfrac{4\pi a^3}{3}}{\dfrac{(1 - \beta^2)^{1/2}}{\beta} + \tan^{-1}\dfrac{\beta}{(1 - \beta^2)^{1/2}} - \dfrac{\pi}{2}} \qquad (10.37)$$

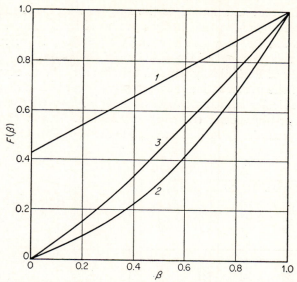

Fig. 10.9. Frequency-perturbation parameter for metallic disks as a function of the slenderness ratio β. The ordinate $F(\beta)$ corresponds to the ratio of the frequency change due to the disk to the frequency changes produced by a sphere whose diameter is equal to the diameter of the disk. Curve 1 corresponds to the disk being parallel to the electric field and also to the magnetic field being perpendicular to the disk; curve 2, to the electric field being perpendicular to the disk; and curve 3, to the magnetic field being parallel to the disk. (*Adopted by permission from L. C. Maier, Jr., and J. C. Slater, Field Strength Measurements in Resonant Cavities, J. Appl. Phys., vol. 23, no. 1, January, 1952.*)

H normal to disk:

$$\frac{\omega_0^2 - \omega^2}{\omega_0^2} = - \frac{\mathbf{H}_0^2 (1 - \beta^2)^{3/2} \dfrac{4\pi a^3}{3}}{\dfrac{\pi}{2} - \tan^{-1} \dfrac{\beta}{(1 - \beta^2)^{1/2}} - \beta(1 - \beta^2)^{1/2}} \tag{10.38}$$

H parallel to disk:

$$\frac{\omega_0^2 - \omega^2}{\omega_0^2} = - \frac{2\mathbf{H}_0^2 (1 - \beta^2)^{3/2} \dfrac{4\pi a^3}{3}}{\tan^{-1} \dfrac{\beta}{(1 - \beta^2)^{1/2}} + \dfrac{2 - \beta^2}{\beta} (1 - \beta^2)^{1/2} - \dfrac{\pi}{2}} \tag{10.39}$$

Figure 10.9 shows Eqs. (10.36) through (10.39) plotted in normalized form. The ordinate shows the frequency changes normalized with respect to the changes due to a sphere. The abscissa is the factor β; small values of β correspond to thin disks. As was already discussed, a disk oriented with its face perpendicular to the electric field **E** and parallel to magnetic field **H** produces negligible perturbation of the fields. An examination of the equations predicts that when the disk is parallel to the electric field and normal to the magnetic field, the resultant perturbation corresponds to the changes produced by a sphere. However, the perturbation due to a disk is strongly affected by its orientation and permits the measurement of the direction of the fields.

10.7. Study of Periodically Loaded Structures. As an example of the usefulness of the perturbation measurements described in Sec. 10.6, consider a periodically loaded waveguide, such as may be useful in linear accelerators or high-power traveling-wave tubes. A few compartments of a typical periodically loaded waveguide are shown in Fig. 10.10. For

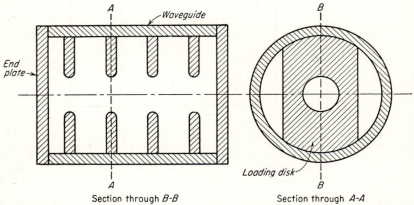

Fig. 10.10. Periodically loaded waveguide suitable for high-power traveling-wave tubes, accelerators, or filter structures.

these applications, it may be important to determine the phase and group velocities and the effective circuit impedance.

A multiple-compartment resonant cavity can be formed from the periodically loaded waveguide by placing short circuits at suitable symmetry planes, such as shown in Fig. 10.10. In such a cavity resonances occur at frequencies at which the length L is some multiple of half-wavelength. The *Brillouin diagram* (i.e., frequency vs. the phase shift per section, corresponding to Fig. 4.3) can be constructed by measuring the phase shift at each of the possible resonant frequencies. The phase shift can be found for each frequency by exploring the axial field with a perturbing object, such as a needle, and counting the number of nodes in the standing-wave pattern in the cavity. The n-compartment cavity will have $n + 1$ resonant frequencies which occur when the phase shift through the structure is $m\pi$ $(m = 0, 1, \ldots, n)$. The experimental study begins with finding the $n + 1$ resonant frequencies, after which the resonances can be identified in the following manner: With the cavity excited at a particular resonant frequency, a perturbing object is moved along the axis; the resonant frequency will vary but will return to its unperturbed value when the object reaches the voltage nodes.   The phase shift per section is determined by counting the number of voltage nodes contained in the total length L, since the number of nodes identifies the number of half-wavelengths in the structure; each half-wavelength corresponds to a phase shift of π radians.   After the phase shift is measured for each of the resonant frequencies, a Brillouin diagram, shown in Fig. 10.11, can be constructed and the phase group and velocities determined as indicated in Fig. 4.3.[1]

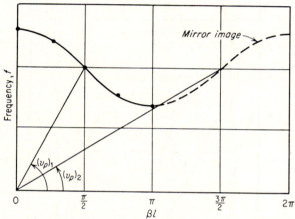

FIG. 10.11. Brillouin diagram for the periodically loaded waveguide obtained with a four-cavity section shown in Fig. 10.10.

The shunt impedance of the periodically loaded cavity must be defined in the manner appropriate to its use.   It can be measured by conducting two additional perturbation experiments to obtain an accurate distribution of the axial electric field.

An example of typical variation of frequency with axial position due to a perturbing object for a two-compartment cavity is illustrated in Fig. 10.12.   The relative field strength can be obtained by computing the square root of the frequency variation δ as discussed in Sec. 10.5 and is shown as the curve labeled E_0.   This field may be decomposed by Fourier analysis into its components; in Fig. 10.12, the fundamental and the second harmonics are sufficient to describe the total field accurately. This procedure determines the amplitude of the various *space* harmonics. A method for determining the absolute value of the electric field at the end of the cavity by the plunger experiment is described in Sec. 10.5. The knowledge of the relative field in the appropriate space harmonic and the absolute field at the wall can be used to compute the effective

[1] Slater, *op. cit.*, pp. 169–177.

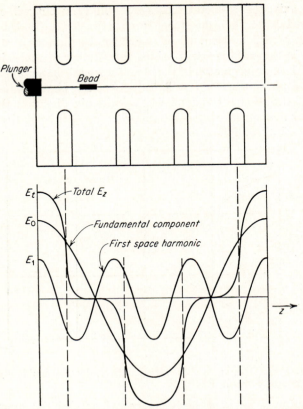

FIG. 10.12. Determination of the axial field distribution of a periodically loaded waveguide by means of the bead perturbation experiment in a four-cavity section.

impedance of the circuit in a manner which is analogous to the case discussed in Sec. 10.5.[1]

10.8. Measurement of Nonresonant Waveguide Impedance. In some applications it is necessary to know the numerical value of the waveguide

[1] For description of the methods of studying the characteristics of periodically loaded waveguides, see M. Chodorow, E. L. Ginzton, W. W. Hansen, R. L. Kyhl, R. B. Neal, W. K. H. Panofsky, and staff of the W. W. Hansen Laboratories of Physics, Stanford High-Energy Linear Electron Accelerator (Mark III), *Rev. Sci. Instr.*, vol. 26, no. 2, pp. 158–164, February, 1955; E. T. Jaynes, The Concept and Measurement of Impedance in Periodically Loaded Waveguides, *J. Appl. Phys.*, vol. 23, no. 10, pp. 1027–1084, October, 1952; R. L. Kyhl, The Use of Non-Euclidean Geometry in Measurements of Periodically Loaded Transmission Lines, *Trans. IRE*, vol. MTT-4, no. 4, pp. 111–115, April, 1956; E. J. Nalos, Measurement of Circuit Impedance of Periodically Loaded Structures by Frequency Perturbation, *Proc. IRE*, vol. 42, no. 10, pp. 1508–1511, October, 1954.

impedance. For transmission lines of simple geometry, such as a rectangular or circular waveguide, the several kinds of impedance can be computed easily. However, if the cross section is more complicated, such as in a ridged waveguide, direct computation is difficult. The desired impedance can be obtained experimentally, using the perturbation technique to determine the field components. This is done by forming a resonant cavity from a section of the waveguide by placing two short circuits some convenient distance apart. The connection between the cavity perturbation experiments and the characteristics of the nonresonant waveguide can be established easily.[1]

A resonant cavity formed from a section of transmission line $\lambda_t/2$ long can be analyzed by considering traveling waves in a nonresonant waveguide. Since the transverse distribution of the fields in the cavity is identical to the fields in the traveling waves, it is possible to use the resonant cavity to obtain the field distribution in the waveguide. The transverse fields in the cavity are determined by perturbing objects, as described in Sec. 10.6.

Elementary considerations show that the total energy of a running wave is equally divided between the electric and the magnetic energy and that the electric and magnetic fields must be in time phase. In the resonant cavity, the electric and magnetic fields are 90° apart in time phase, but the energy stored in the two fields is equal. If the amplitude of the transverse electric field in the waveguide is equal to the amplitude of the transverse electric field at the center of the cavity, the maximum energy stored in the electric fields in the two cases is equal. The total energy stored in the waveguide is twice the maximum energy stored in its electric field; the total energy stored in the cavity is equal to the maximum energy of the electric field. Hence, the energy stored in the electric field of the running wave must be equal to the total energy stored in the cavity of equal length. Let

U_l = average total energy per unit length in running wave
U_T = the total energy stored in $\lambda_t/2$ length of waveguide
U = the energy stored in the electric field in a waveguide $\lambda_t/2$ long;
    also equals total energy stored in the cavity of same length

Therefore,

$$\frac{\lambda_t}{2} U_l = U_T = 2U \tag{10.40}$$

from which

$$U_l = \frac{4}{\lambda_t} U \tag{10.41}$$

---

[1] Private communication to the author by H. J. Shaw and K. Y. Chow; also, K. Y. Chow, A Method of Measuring Waveguide Power Impedance, E.E. thesis, Stanford University, December, 1951.

This relates the energy stored in a cavity to the energy stored in the running wave of a waveguide of an arbitrary cross section.

Suppose it is of interest to determine the impedance of the waveguide on the power-voltage basis. This is given by

$$Z_{w,v} = \frac{V^2}{2W} \tag{10.42}$$

where W represents the power transmitted, and V the integral of the electric field along the desired path. In terms of the electric field, Eq. (10.42) becomes

$$Z_{w,v} = \frac{(\int \mathbf{E} \, dS)^2}{2W} \tag{10.43}$$

Power W can be expressed as the product of the energy stored per unit length U_l and the group velocity v_g:

$$W = U_l v_g \tag{10.44}$$

Combining Eqs. (10.43) and (10.44), the impedance becomes

$$Z_{w,v} = \frac{\lambda_t}{8U v_g} (\int \mathbf{E} \, dS)^2 \tag{10.45}$$

If the perturbation experiment is carried out by using a plunger in the region of the electric field only, the resultant change in frequency can be determined from Eq. (10.22). Combining Eqs. (10.22), (10.45), and (4.37b),

$$Z_{w,v} = Z_0 \frac{L}{\lambda_0} \frac{\Delta\lambda}{\Delta\tau} S^2 \left(\frac{\int \mathbf{E} \, dS}{\mathbf{E}S}\right)^2 \tag{10.46}$$

where Z_0 is the wave impedance of the waveguide given by Eq. (4.45), L is the length of the cavity, and S is the height of the waveguide at the point of interest. The last term in Eq. (10.46) represents the form factor, taking into account the variation of the electric field along the path of integration across the waveguide. To measure the waveguide impedance by this method, it is necessary to perform two separate perturbation experiments in a manner analogous to the study of the shunt impedance in a cavity with variable fields discussed in Sec. 10.5. The first experiment measures the quantity $\Delta\lambda/\Delta\tau$ using the plunger at the wall of the waveguide and determines the absolute value of the electric field. The second experiment is performed by a needle or some suitable perturbing object to determine the relative strength of the field over the path of integration as discussed in Sec. 10.5. Both of these experiments are straightforward and permit the determination of the waveguide impedance with good accuracy.

10.9. Miscellaneous Methods of R_0/Q_0 Measurement. Several other ways of measuring shunt resistance are known in addition to the perturbation method. Several techniques are involved, some applicable in certain cases but not in others. For example, it may be desirable to determine R_0/Q_0 for a cavity of an operating klystron where substantial losses are introduced by the presence of the electron beam; in this case, the perturbation experiment is obviously impossible, but the cavity shunt resistance can be deduced from a study of certain operating characteristics of the klystron. Several methods capable of providing absolute, rather than relative, values of shunt resistance are described below.

a. Resistance-variation Method. A capacity-variation method was described in Sec. 10.2 to measure the shunt resistance of a tuned circuit from the rate of change of frequency with tuning of the circuit. A complementary *resistance-variation* procedure can be developed by placing a known shunting resistor across the circuit and measuring the resultant change in Q. An equivalent procedure can be developed easily for the microwave case.[1]

In this method, a small cylindrical resistance is introduced across the gap of the resonant cavity parallel to the constant electric field. The diameter of the resistor must be small compared to the cavity dimensions so that neither the field configuration nor the resonant frequency of the cavity is appreciably disturbed. The resistor must also be in intimate contact with the opposite poles of the cavity gap. In practice, the resistor can be a rod of lossy dielectric substance or a capillary tube filled with a suitable liquid; in either case, the sample can be inserted into the cavity through small holes in the opposite walls of the gap as shown in Fig. 10.13a, provided that the hole diameters are small compared to the gap width. The effective resistance of the resistor must be known under the exact operating conditions. This means that the characteristics of the substance must be known at the frequency in question and that the method of insertion should leave no doubt in regard to the effective contact between the resistor and the gap poles. In practice, these uncertainties can be avoided by placing the desired resistor into a cavity with known fields, such as TM_{010} cavity, and inverting the following procedure to determine the effective value of the resistor.

Figures 10.13a and 10.13b show the calibrating resistor R_1 inserted into the unknown cavity and into the TM_{010} calibration cavity, respectively. Four Q values are measured before and after the insertion of the resistor into the two cavities. The height of the calibration cavity should be equal to the pole separation of the unknown cavity. Figure

[1] Sproull and Linder, *op. cit.*

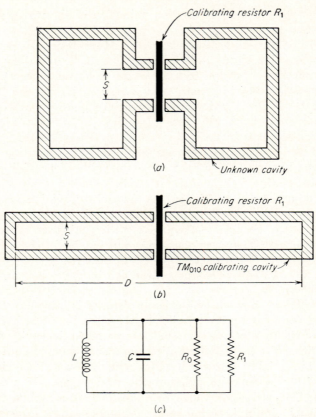

FIG. 10.13. Measurement of R_0/Q_0 by the resistance-variation experiment. This shows (a) a microwave cavity under test with the calibrating resistor R_1 placed across its r-f gap through small holes; (b) the resistor inserted into a calibrating cavity; (c) the equivalent circuit used in the analysis of the experiment.

10.13c shows the equivalent circuit of the unknown cavity with its shunt resistance R_0 in parallel with calibrating resistor R_1. Let

$Q_0 = Q$ of unknown cavity without resistor R_1
$Q_1 = Q$ of unknown cavity with resistor R_1
$Q_2 = Q$ of TM_{010} cavity without resistor R_1
$Q_3 = Q$ of TM_{010} cavity with resistor R_1
$R_0 = $ shunt resistance of unknown cavity
$R_1 = $ resistance of the calibration resistor
$R_2 = $ shunt resistance of TM_{010} cavity

The shunt resistance of the unknown cavity can be determined from the value of the calibration resistor R_1 and the two Q measurements of the unknown cavity.   The result is

$$R_0 = R_1\left(\frac{Q_0}{Q_1} - 1\right) \tag{10.47}$$

The value of the calibrating resistor can be determined from the TM_{010} calibrating cavity from the relation

$$R_2 = R_1\left(\frac{Q_2}{Q_3} - 1\right) \tag{10.48}$$

Since R/Q for the TM_{010} cavity is given by

$$\frac{R_2}{Q_2} = 371\frac{L}{D} = 371\frac{S}{D} \tag{10.49}$$

these relations can be combined to give

$$R_0 = 371\frac{S}{D}\frac{Q_2Q_3}{Q_1}\frac{Q_0 - Q_1}{Q_2 - Q_3} \tag{10.50}$$

Therefore, the measurement of the four Q values is sufficient to determine the shunt impedance of the unknown cavity.   Calibration procedure can be avoided if the values of resistor R_1 can be determined from its known conductivity and dimensions.

A careful examination of Eq. (10.50) shows that for good accuracy it is necessary for the resistor R_1 to be low enough to make Q_3 substantially lower than Q_2.   However, if R_1 is sufficiently low, Q_1 may become too low to be measured accurately.

b. *Electron Velocity-spectrograph Method.*   The shunt resistance of a cavity can be measured directly by a method based upon the observation of the velocity variation produced in an electron beam passing through a cavity when r-f power W is supplied to the cavity.   The velocity distribution in the electron stream can be determined by an electrostatic or magnetic spectrograph.   The simultaneous measurement of the r-f power and peak velocity change permit the shunt resistance to be computed.

c. *Modulation-sensitivity Method.*   The shunt resistance of a cavity of a reflex klystron oscillator can be determined by observing the modulation sensitivity of a reflex klystron as a function of the external loading of the tube.   If the reflex klystron is modulated by applying the modulation voltage to its reflector electrode, the resultant frequency modulation will depend upon the loaded Q of the cavity.   Varying the effective impedance of the cavity by varying the external load permits the shunt resistance to be determined from the dependence of the modulation sensitivity upon the external load.[1]

[1] After the method developed by M. Chodorow.

The analytic relation between the frequency of oscillation Q_L and the reflector voltage V_r can be obtained by differentiating Eq. (1.43). Using conventional approximations, it can be shown that

$$\frac{df}{dV_r} = \frac{f_0}{2Q_0} \frac{d\phi}{dV_r} \left(1 + \frac{G_B}{G_0} + \frac{G_L}{G_0}\right) \tag{10.51}$$

where ϕ is the transit time in the reflection space, V_r the reflector voltage, and G_B, G_L, and G_0 are the cavity conductances corresponding to the components due to the electron beam loading, the external load, and the unloaded cavity conductance, respectively. The left-hand side of this

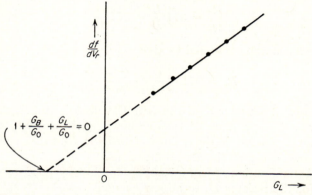

Fig. 10.14. Frequency-modulation sensitivity of a reflex klystron as a function of the load conductance.

equation represents the quantity often referred to as the *modulation sensitivity*. It can be measured by observing the frequency change caused by a given applied reflector voltage change. As the external load is varied, the modulation sensitivity will vary; df/dV_r plotted as a function of the load conductance results in a straight line, as indicated in Fig. 10.14. By extrapolating this line to the point where df/dV_r equals zero, it is possible to find the value of the load conductance corresponding to the condition in which the bracketed term in Eq. (10.51) equals zero. Thus, one can determine the sum of the unloaded cavity conductance and the beam-loading conductance, quantities which are important under operating conditions.

d. Induced Shot-noise Method. The cavity shunt resistance can be deduced by another electronic method which is based upon the fact that temperature-limited current passing through the cavity induces shot noise. The magnitude of the induced shot noise can be determined by connecting the cavity to a calibrated microwave receiver. From the measured magnitude of the induced noise and the value of the d-c current passing through the cavity, the shunt resistance can be determined.

The noise current in a temperature-limited electron beam can be computed from the formula

$$\bar{i}_n{}^2 = 2eI_0\,\Delta f \tag{10.52}$$

where $\bar{i}_n{}^2$ is the RMS fluctuating shot current per cycle of bandwidth, e is the charge of the electron, and I_0 is the d-c beam current.   The shunt resistance of the cavity can then be determined from the formula

$$R_0 = \frac{4W_n}{\beta^2 \bar{i}_n{}^2} \tag{10.53}$$

where W_n = observed noise power in frequency band Δf
β = beam coupling coefficient in the cavity gap
Combining Eqs. (10.52) and (10.53),

$$R_0 = \frac{4W_n}{\beta^2 2eI_0\,\Delta f} \tag{10.54}$$

There are several considerations necessary to apply this method properly.   The electron beam must be strictly temperature-limited to avoid partial space-charge suppression of noise.   The collector must be arranged to collect the entire current passing through the cavity.   If grids are used, the current lost by grid interception must be accounted for, at least approximately.   The receiver measuring the power W_n must be connected to the cavity through an impedance transformer of known characteristics.   If the transformer is adjusted to deliver the maximum noise to the receiver, it can be assumed that the impedances are matched and that the shunt resistance of the cavity is reduced by a factor of 2. The equivalent bandwidth of the receiver and the coupling coefficient in the cavity gap must also be determined.   These factors can be determined with fair accuracy and the method is useful when the available apparatus permits its use.

CHAPTER 11

MEASUREMENT OF ATTENUATION

11.1. Introduction. The dissipation and reflection losses caused by the insertion of a network are important in many transmission-line problems. In transmission components consisting of waveguides, joints, or connectors, the incidental loss of power either due to dissipation or reflections is often of practical importance. In addition, many measurement applications require fixed or variable attenuators with known insertion loss.

a. Definition of Attenuation. In considering the effect of the insertion of a network between a generator and a load it is important to understand clearly the definitions of the terms usually used to describe the reflection and dissipation losses caused by the network.

The *insertion loss* of a network is defined as the ratio of the power delivered by a generator to a load in the absence of the network to the power delivered to the load with the network inserted, as shown in Fig. 11.1a. Expressed in decibels, the insertion loss L is given by

$$L = 10 \log \frac{P_1}{P_2} \tag{11.1}$$

Under these general conditions the insertion loss depends upon the characteristics of the network as well as upon the impedance matching between the load and the generator with the network removed. In the general case, the insertion loss produced by an unsymmetrical network depends upon which side of the network is considered to be the input. If the generator and load impedances are not equal, the insertion loss L can be either positive or negative: dissipation in the network will always produce loss, but the presence of an impedance-matching transformer may increase the power delivered to the load.

To avoid this uncertainty, it is common to modify the definition of the insertion loss as follows: Referring to Fig. 11.1b, P_1 is assumed to be the *maximum available* power from the generator, i.e., the power the generator delivers to a matched load, and P_2 is the power delivered to a

462

matched load with the network inserted. Under these conditions, the
definition of insertion loss given by Eq. (11.1) becomes more specific,
as it measures unambiguously the characteristics of the network, including the dissipation losses in the network and the reflection losses caused
by the mismatch between the network and the generator.

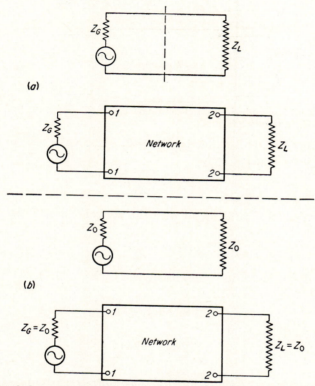

FIG. 11.1. Symbols used in the definition of the insertion loss of a network. (a) The
generator and load impedances are arbitrary; (b) the generator and load impedances
are equal.

It is often necessary to distinguish between dissipative losses and the
reflection losses. Explicit definitions of these terms can be obtained as
follows: Figure 11.2 shows an arbitrary four-terminal network connected
between the generator and the load. The characteristic impedances of
the transmission lines connecting the generator and the load to the network are Z_1 and Z_2, respectively. Referring to the second definition of
L as given above, the load impedance is assumed to be equal to the
characteristic impedance of the transmission line Z_2 and the generator
impedance to be equal to the characteristic impedance of the input trans-

mission line Z_1.* The incident wave propagating from the generator to the network is given by a voltage coefficient, $V_1{}^i$. With the network in place as shown, the magnitude of the reflected wave, $V_1{}^r$, depends upon the impedance mismatch between the network and the transmission line. The generator delivers the maximum available power to the network if

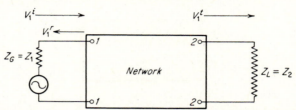

FIG. 11.2. Definitions of incident, reflected, and transmitted signals used in the derivation of the insertion-loss formula.

its impedance equals Z_1, that is, $V_1{}^r = 0$. The value of the maximum available power is given by

$$P_1 = \frac{(V_1{}^i)^2}{Z_1} \tag{11.2}$$

The power delivered to the load with the network inserted is

$$P_2 = \frac{(V_1{}^t)^2}{Z_2} \tag{11.3}$$

Using the definition of insertion loss given by Eq. (11.1),

$$L = 10 \log \left(\frac{V_1{}^i}{V_1{}^t} \right)^2 \frac{Z_2}{Z_1} \tag{11.4}$$

which can be written as[1]

$$L = 10 \log \frac{1}{S_{12}{}^2} \tag{11.5}$$

* To apply the definition of insertion loss given by Eq. (11.1) in the general case, it is necessary first to determine the maximum available power at the load. With dissimilar impedances ($Z_1 \neq Z_2$) it is necessary to assume that the power P_1 is obtained by inserting an ideal transformer which matches the generator to load impedances.

[1] It may appear that the scattering coefficient S_{12} (the voltage-transmission coefficient) is merely a ratio of normalized transmitted to incident voltages. However, since the magnitude of an impedance in microwave systems is always arbitrarily defined, the value of the transmitted voltage for a given power flow is as arbitrary as the definition of the impedance itself. For this reason, the following convention is adopted in defining S_{12}: If an ideal transformer joins two dissimilar lines, a given power flow produces voltages which are different on the two sides of the transformer. The scattering coefficient S_{12} of the ideal transformer is then defined as *unity* by adjusting the characteristic impedances of one of the lines so that the apparent magnitude of the transmitted voltage is equal to the incident voltage. This normalization has been used in going from Eq. (11.4) to (11.5).

Multiplying and dividing Eq. (11.5) by $1 - S_{11}{}^2$,

$$L = -10 \log |S_{12}|^2 \frac{1 - |S_{11}|^2}{1 - |S_{11}|^2} \tag{11.6}$$

$$= -10 \log (1 - |S_{11}|^2) - 10 \log \frac{|S_{12}|^2}{1 - |S_{11}|^2} \tag{11.7}$$

which can be written as

$$L = L_R + L_D \tag{11.8}$$

where

$$L_R = -10 \log (1 - |S_{11}|^2) \tag{11.9}$$

and

$$L_D = -10 \log \frac{|S_{12}|^2}{1 - |S_{11}|^2} \tag{11.10}$$

Equation (11.9) determines the power loss due to reflection at terminals 1-1 and Eq. (11.10) determines the dissipation losses in the network.[1]

The *transmission efficiency* of a network is defined as the ratio of power output to power input. It is equal to L_D expressed as a power ratio; for transmission from terminals 1-1 to 2-2, it is equal to

$$\eta = \frac{|S_{12}|^2}{1 - |S_{11}|^2} \tag{11.11a}$$

and for transmission from terminals 2-2 to 1-1,

$$\eta = \frac{|S_{12}|^2}{1 - |S_{22}|^2} \tag{11.11b}$$

The *essential* or *intrinsic* loss of a network is equal to the attenuation suffered by a wave propagating in one direction. If the network is matched at its input and output terminals (using ideal matching transformers, if necessary), $S_{11} = S_{22} = 0$, the essential loss can be obtained from Eq. (11.10) as

$$L_I = -10 \log |S_{12}|^2 \tag{11.12}$$

This expression also gives the attenuation constant of a network formed from a section of uniform transmission line. If the network is operated between mismatched impedances, the dissipation loss L_D is greater than the intrinsic loss L_I due to the dissipative loss caused by the waves propagating through the network in both directions.

[1] Equation (11.9) represents reflection loss, because

$$1 - |S_{11}|^2 = 1 - \left| \frac{V_1{}^r}{V_1{}^i} \right|^2 = \frac{|V_1{}^i|^2 - |V_1{}^r|^2}{|V_1{}^i|^2}$$

This is a fractional measure of the incident power lost by reflection. Equation (11.10) represents the power lost in the network. The power input and output are $(V_1{}^i)^2/Z_1 - (V_1{}^r)^2/Z_1$ and $(V_1{}^t)^2/Z_2$, respectively. Their ratio, written in terms of the scattering coefficients, leads to Eq. (11.10).

b. Methods of Measurement.[1]   The experimental procedures to measure the insertion loss L of a four-terminal network, based upon the definitions given above, are divided into four groups for convenience:

1. Insertion or power-ratio method
2. Substitution method
3. Cavity-resonance method
4. Scattering-coefficient method

The first is based directly upon the definition of insertion loss.   The insertion loss L can be computed according to the defining equation given by Eq. (11.1) from the power measurements made by a suitable watt-meter before and after the insertion of the network.

The substitution method uses a precision standard attenuator connected at some convenient point between the generator and an indicating detector at the output terminals.   The attenuator is first adjusted to some convenient reference level.   After the insertion of the network, the attenuator setting is changed to restore the detected signal to the original value and the change in the attenuator reading determines the insertion loss.   The attenuator can be placed, as mentioned, anywhere in the system.   In particular, it can be placed after the detector, allowing the use of a low-frequency precision attenuator.

The attenuation in uniform transmission lines, such as waveguides, can be determined from the relationship between the distributed loss in the waveguide and the Q value of a cavity formed from a section of the waveguide.   Measurement of the cavity Q leads to the determination of the attenuation in the waveguide.

Although these three methods have a wide range of applicability, they require physical disarrangement of the system for the purpose of testing which is sometimes inconvenient or impossible.   The characteristics of the network can be determined by an alternate method by finding the scattering coefficients of the network from impedance measurements. The relationships between the quantities of interest, scattering coefficients, and simple experimental procedures are established easily.

[1] For further information, see E. Weber, The Measurement of Attenuation, chap. 13, pp. 804–853, in C. G. Montgomery (ed.), "Technique of Microwave Measurements," vol. 11, Massachusetts Institute of Technology Radiation Laboratory Series, McGraw-Hill Book Company, Inc., New York, 1947; S. A. Rinkel and W. E. Waller, Microwave Attenuation Measurements, Polytechnic Research and Development Company, Inc., *PRD Repts.*, vol. IV, no. 1, April, 1955; B. Steinman, Measurement of Attenuation, in M. Wind and H. Rappaport (eds.), "Handbook of Microwave Measurements," sec. III, Polytechnic Institute of Brooklyn, Microwave Research Institute, New York, 1954; F. E. Terman and J. M. Pettit, "Electronic Measurements," pp. 187–192, McGraw-Hill Book Company, Inc., New York, 1952.

11.2. The Insertion or Power-ratio Method.   The insertion loss L of a four-terminal network can be determined from Eq. (11.1) by measuring the power delivered to a matched load from a matched generator with and without the network under test.   Since microwave wattmeters, capable of measuring power over extremely large range, are available, this is a simple, rapid, and fairly accurate method for most laboratory problems. The intrinsic loss L_I of an arbitrary network cannot be measured so simply because of the reflections at the input and output terminals.   It is possible to determine the magnitude of these reflections by appropriate impedance measurements on both sides of the network; however, the more direct method (described in Sec. 11.5) of measuring L_I is generally more satisfactory.

When the attenuation of the network is large, it is necessary to measure the original and final power values by different power-measuring devices. In this case, absolute power measurements are necessary and the accuracy of each one is important.   Absolute power measurements can be avoided if a detecting device, with accurately known response law, is available to measure the power over the dynamic range of interest.   The use of bolometers and carefully calibrated amplifiers allows rapid measurements with fair accuracy.   The problems of the linearity of response and the limiting noise determine the useful range of this method.   In order to apply it correctly, it is essential that the signal generator and the power-measuring devices be accurately matched.[1]

11.3. Substitution Method.   The insertion loss of a network L can be determined by a substitution process with the aid of a precision standard attenuator.   In this method a signal source, the unknown network, a precision variable attenuator, and a suitable detecting system are connected in series.   The power level at the detector is adjusted to some convenient reference level by the variable-standard attenuator and this initial reading is noted.   The network under test is then removed and the detected output restored to the original level by the adjusting of the standard attenuator.   The difference in the two readings corresponds to the insertion loss of the network.   There are several possible arrangements based upon this principle which differ in the placement of the variable standard; three possible schemes are shown in Fig. 11.3.

In Fig. 11.3a, the substitution attenuator is used directly at microwave frequencies and is followed by some suitable detector system.   In Fig. 11.3b, the signal is detected immediately beyond the unknown network by a superheterodyne detector.   Since superheterodyne receivers are linear over a wide signal range, the standard attenuator can be

[1] R. W. Beatty, Mismatch Errors in the Measurement of Ultra-High Frequency and Microwave Variable Attenuators, *J. Research Natl. Bur. Standards*, vol. 52, January, 1954.

inserted in the i-f channel. The detector and indicator can take a variety of forms, the details of which are not particularly important. It is also possible to insert the attenuator after the second detector in the audio channel. Finally, in Fig. 11.3c, the attenuator is shown placed in the audio channel. If the detector is a bolometer, the problems of response law and linearity are of paramount importance.

The use of either the r-f substitution or the i-f substitution techniques offers the greatest possible accuracy, especially for high-insertion loss.

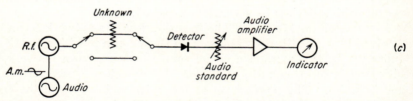

Fig. 11.3. Three variations of the substitution method for measuring insertion loss. The standard attenuator is adjusted to produce the same output indication before and after the insertion of the unknown network. (a) The r-f substitution; (b) the i-f substitution; (c) the audio substitution.

The range of measurements depends upon the power available from the signal generator, the sensitivity of the receiving system, and the range of the variable standard attenuator. The power level of the signal source is limited by the availability of power and the ability of the network to withstand it. The sensitivity of the receiver has a theoretical limit; however, if narrow bandwidths are used, extremely low-level signals can be measured. Using synchrodyne techniques to derive the local-oscillator power, bandwidths of a few cycles per second or less are practical.

The range of attenuation in the variable standard attenuator is practically unlimited. A waveguide below cutoff possesses extremely high accuracy and unlimited range of attenuation and is the most accurate device available for either r-f or i-f purposes. Unfortunately these attenuators possess a substantial initial insertion loss, such as 20 or 30 db. Other types of attenuators employing resistive films can also be constructed with high precision for a limited range of attenuation.

Further details of this technique can be found in the literature.[1]

11.4. Cavity-resonance Method. The attenuation constant of a uniform transmission line can be determined by measuring the Q value of a long resonator formed by shorting a length of the transmission line.[2] It can be shown that Q_0 of a long waveguide resonator is given by

$$Q_0 = \left(\frac{\lambda_t}{\lambda_0}\right)^2 \frac{\pi L}{(\alpha L + 2R/Z_0)\lambda_t} \qquad (11.13)$$

where L = length of transmission line
R = resistance of short-circuiting devices at its ends
λ_t = guided wavelength
λ_0 = free-space wavelength (TEM) in dielectric medium which fills the transmission line
α = attenuation constant, nepers per unit length

Rearranging Eq. (11.13),

$$\frac{1}{Q_0} = \left(\frac{\lambda_0}{\lambda_t}\right)^2 \left(\frac{\alpha\lambda_t}{\pi} + \frac{2}{\pi}\frac{R}{Z_0}\frac{\lambda_t}{L}\right) \qquad (11.14)$$

Thus, plotting $1/Q_0$ vs. $1/L$ for a series of resonance lengths results in a straight line. Extrapolating the straight line to the point $1/L = 0$ produces an intercept on the $1/Q_0$ axis whose value is given by the first term of Eq. (11.14). The knowledge of λ_0 and λ_t, together with the value of the intercept, is sufficient to determine the attenuation constant.

This procedure can be simplified if the waveguide cavity is long enough to make the losses in the shorting plungers negligible. Thus, if R is sufficiently small, Eq. (11.14) reduces to

$$Q_0 = \frac{\pi}{\alpha\lambda_t}\left(\frac{\lambda_t}{\lambda_0}\right)^2 \qquad (11.15)$$

or

$$\alpha = \frac{\pi}{Q_0\lambda_t}\left(\frac{\lambda_t}{\lambda_0}\right)^2 = \frac{\pi}{Q_0\lambda_0}\left(\frac{\lambda_t}{\lambda_0}\right) \qquad (11.16)$$

There are two alternative ways to use the transmission method to measure Q_0. Either the frequency of a signal generator can be varied

[1] G. F. Gainsborough, A Method of Calibrating Standard Signal Generators and Radio-frequency Attenuators, *J. IEE*, pt. III, pp. 203–210, May, 1947; R. E. Grantham and J. J. Freeman, Microwave Attenuation Standard, *Elec. Eng.*, pp. 535–537, June, 1948.

[2] H. M. Barlow and A. L. Cullen, "Microwave Measurements," pp. 239–241, Constable & Co., Ltd., London, 1951.

to find the half-power points in the response curve, or the frequency can be kept constant while the position of the shorting plunger is changed to determine its positions corresponding to the half-power response points. Although the cavity Q can be determined by either means, the resultant formulas are somewhat different. The length of the cavity at resonance is given by

$$L_0 = N \frac{\lambda_t}{2} \tag{11.17}$$

where N is some integer; also,

$$\lambda_t = \frac{\lambda_0}{\sqrt{1 - (\lambda_0/\lambda_c)^2}}$$
$$= \frac{\lambda_0}{\sqrt{1 - (f_c/f_0)^2}} \tag{11.18}$$

Hence,
$$L_0 = \frac{N}{2} \frac{c}{f_0} \frac{1}{\sqrt{1 - (f_c/f_0)^2}} \tag{11.19}$$

The cavity can be tuned by changing either the length or the frequency; the relation between these is obtained by differentiating Eq. (11.19) with respect to frequency,

$$\frac{dL_0}{L_0} = \frac{df}{f_0} \left(\frac{\lambda_t}{\lambda_0}\right)^2 \tag{11.20}$$

Q_0 can be determined by the transmission measurement in terms of the frequency bandwidth between the half-power points,

$$Q_0 = \frac{f_0}{2 \, df} = \frac{f_0}{\Delta f} \tag{11.21}$$

Using Eq. (11.20), Q_0 becomes

$$Q_0 = \frac{L_0}{2 \, dL_0} \left(\frac{\lambda_t}{\lambda_0}\right)^2 = \frac{L_0}{\Delta L_0} \left(\frac{\lambda_t}{\lambda_0}\right)^2 \tag{11.22}$$

Therefore, the attenuation constant determined by the two experiments is given by

$$\alpha = \frac{\pi}{\lambda_t} \left(\frac{\lambda_t}{\lambda_0}\right)^2 \frac{\Delta f}{f} \tag{11.23}$$

$$\alpha = \frac{\pi}{\lambda_t} \frac{\Delta L}{L} \tag{11.24}$$

The resonance-cavity method is especially useful in determining the loss in low-loss structures, such as the ordinary air-filled waveguide. In practice, this experiment can be performed by fitting a length of waveguide with a pair of noncontacting plungers. Their losses may or may not be appreciable depending upon construction details. To insure adequate precision, it is necessary to measure Q_0 at a number of lengths to ascertain whether the losses in the plungers are sufficiently small to be neglected. It is also possible to use the more elaborate procedure described above even for cavities in which the shorting plunger losses cannot be neglected.

11.5. Scattering-coefficient Method. The insertion loss L can be computed from Eq. (11.7) using the scattering coefficients of the network. Referring to Fig. 11.2, the insertion loss of the network from terminals 1-1 to 2-2 is given by

$$L_{1-2} = -10 \log (1 - |S_{11}|^2) - 10 \log \frac{|S_{12}|^2}{1 - |S_{11}|^2} \qquad (11.25)$$

Similarly, the insertion loss from terminals 2-2 to 1-1 is given by

$$L_{2-1} = -10 \log (1 - |S_{22}|^2) - 10 \log \frac{|S_{12}|^2}{1 - |S_{22}|^2} \qquad (11.26)$$

The scattering coefficients can be found by any one of the several methods described in Chap. 6, of which the impedance method given in Sec. 6.5b is the most useful. According to the theory of this method, if a generator is placed at terminals 2-2 and a shorting plunger at 1-1, as indicated in Fig. 11.4a, the measured impedance locus plotted on a Smith chart will result in a circle with a radius R given by

$$R = \frac{|S_{12}|^2}{1 - |S_{11}|^2} \qquad (11.27)$$

Similarly, interchanging the generator and the shorting plunger, as shown in Fig. 11.4b, results in an impedance locus seen from terminals 1-1 with a radius R given by

$$R = \frac{|S_{12}|^2}{1 - |S_{22}|^2} \qquad (11.28)$$

A comparison with Eqs. (11.25) and (11.26) shows that the dissipative loss in the network is given by

$$L_D = 10 \log \frac{1}{R} \qquad (11.29)$$

where R is the radius of the proper impedance locus, as mentioned.

Thus, to measure the dissipative losses in a given network for a desired direction of propagation of power, an experiment is performed by sending a signal into the network in the *opposite* direction and terminating it in a movable short circuit as indicated in Fig. 11.4. The impedance of the network is measured for several positions of the short circuit, permitting the circular locus to be drawn and the radius determined.   Equation (11.29) permits the dissipative loss to be computed.

The reflection losses due to the network can be computed from the first terms of Eqs. (11.25) and (11.26), using the laboratory impedance data to compute the scattering coefficients as discussed in Sec. 6.5b. Alternatively, S_{11} and S_{22} can be determined directly by performing subsidiary experiments by terminating the output and input, respectively,

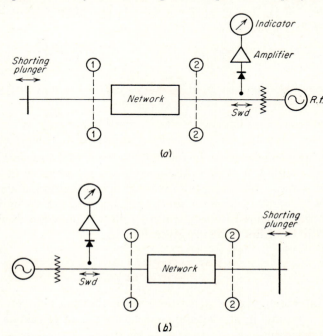

Fig. 11.4. Determination of the insertion loss of a network by impedance measurement.   (a) The arrangement used to measure the insertion loss from terminals 1-1 to 2-2; (b) for measurement from terminals 2-2 to 1-1.

with matched loads and measuring the corresponding input impedances from the opposite side.   This experiment is simple to perform and may serve as an additional check upon the accuracy of the entire procedure.

If only the dissipative losses are of interest, it is possible to omit some of the data that would otherwise be needed to plot the circle diagram. The *location* of the circle on the Smith chart depends upon the reflection at the network terminals; the circle may or may not enclose the origin ($r = 1$, $x = 0$).   The size of the circle can be determined by finding the maximum and minimum values of the VSWR which occur as the shorting plunger is moved.

It can be shown that if the circle encloses the origin, the positions of the voltage minimum for the maximum and minimum VSWR occur $\lambda_t/4$ apart. In this case, the radius of the circle R is given by[1]

$$R = \frac{r_{max}r_{min} - 1}{(r_{max} + 1)(r_{min} + 1)} \qquad (11.30)$$

where r_{max} and r_{min} are the maximum and minimum values of VSWR, respectively. If the circle does not enclose the origin, the positions of the voltage minimum for the maximum and minimum VSWR occur at the same place. In this case, the radius of the circle is given by

$$R = \frac{r_{max} - r_{min}}{(r_{max} + 1)(r_{min} + 1)} \qquad (11.31)$$

The dissipative loss can be determined by measuring the maximum and minimum standing-wave ratios and observing the relative location of the two voltage minima. The dissipation loss is given by

$$L_D = 10 \log R \qquad (11.32)$$

where R is the radius of the impedance locus determined by the simplified procedure through Eqs. (11.30) and (11.31). The precautions stated above regarding the sequence of equipment arrangement, shown in Fig. 11.4, should be observed also. The accuracy of this method can be improved if the VSWR is plotted as a function of the plunger position in the vicinity of the points of maximum and minimum values of VSWR.

The intrinsic (one-way) loss L_I of an arbitrary four-terminal network can be found by measuring the input impedance of the network for a series of positions of a movable short circuit at the output terminals. The necessary equipment is arranged as shown in Fig. 11.4; a set of typical data necessary for this purpose is shown in Fig. 11.5. This data can be used to calculate the intrinsic loss, the value of the impedance at the input if the network were matched, and the value of the impedance looking into the network from the output terminals if the input impedance were matched. It should be emphasized that the determination of the intrinsic loss L_I by this method does not require the network to be matched at either end.

The necessary data can be taken for a series of positions of the movable short circuit, such as nine positions, $\frac{1}{16}\lambda_t$ apart; if the value of the output impedance is not needed, the position of the short circuit need not be

---

[1] R. W. Beatty, Determination of Attenuation from Impedance Measurements, *Proc. IRE*, vol. 38, no. 8, p. 895, August, 1950.

measured. If input impedance locus is plotted on a Smith chart, the intrinsic loss of the network L_I as defined by Eq. (11.12) is given by

$$L_I = 10 \log \frac{\sqrt{(1 + R)^2 - \rho^2} + \sqrt{(1 - R)^2 - \rho^2}}{\sqrt{(1 + R)^2 - \rho^2} - \sqrt{(1 - R)^2 - \rho^2}} \qquad (11.33)$$

where R and ρ are the radii shown in Fig. 11.5, normalized to unity with respect to the radius of the Smith chart.[1]

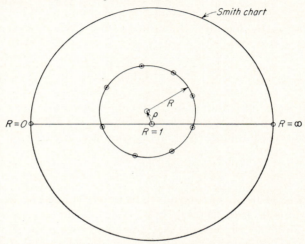

FIG. 11.5. Typical impedance locus obtained with the equipment arranged as in Fig. 11.4 with a 14.3-ft section of RG-5U cable. The radii R and ρ, measured as linear distances using the radius of the Smith chart as unity, permit the determination of the intrinsic loss of the network.

Alternatively, the impedance locus shown in Fig. 11.5 can be rotated about the center of the Smith chart until the center of the locus falls on the resistive axis. Let $\Re_1$ and $\Re_2$ be the two intersections of the impedance locus with the resistive axis (with $Z_0 = 1$ and $\Re_2 \geqq \Re_1$). Then

$$L_I = 10 \log \frac{\sqrt{\Re_2/\Re_1} + 1}{\sqrt{\Re_2/\Re_1} - 1} \qquad (11.34)$$

The VSWR that would be produced at the input terminals of the network if its output were matched is given by

$$r_{\text{input}} = \sqrt{\Re_2 \Re_1} \qquad (11.35)$$

The VSWR that would be produced at the output terminals with the input matched can be found either by repeating the experiment with the

[1] K. Tomiyasu, Intrinsic Insertion Loss of a Mismatched Network, *Trans. IRE*, vol. MTT-3, no. 1, pp. 40–44, January, 1955.

network reversed or by finding the iconocenter of the *transformed* locus as described in the footnote below.[1]

The accuracy of measurement of dissipative losses by the scattering-coefficient method is highest for moderate values of dissipation. If the dissipation is too small, the VSWR are high and too difficult to measure.

---

[1] The above method can be understood and the equations derived as follows: For the purpose of the proof, imagine that two ideal transformers with turn ratios $n_1:1$ and $n_2:1$ are used to match the network to its input and output transmission lines. If the output transmission line is shorted by a moving short circuit, the input impedance locus obtained by moving the shorting plunger through $\lambda_t/2$ will result in a circle symmetrically located about the center of the Smith chart. Let the geometrical radius of this circle be R_1 (i.e., the reflection coefficient) and its extreme resistance values $1/r$ and r, where r is the VSWR at the input (with the ideal transformers in place, r is independent of the shorting plunger position). Under these conditions $S_{11} = S_{22} = 0$, and, from Eq. (11.12), the intrinsic loss is

$$L_I = 10 \log \frac{1}{S_{12}{}^2}$$
$$= 10 \log \frac{1}{R_1} \tag{11.36}$$

This fictitious circle with the radius R_1 can be called the *transformed* locus; the relation between it and the experimental circle obtained without the use of ideal transformers can be derived easily. Once this relation is established, the intrinsic loss can be found from Eq. (11.36).

Consider first the result of omitting the output impedance transformer. With the transformer in place, for a given position of the shorting plunger the output of the network is terminated with a certain reactance; upon removal of the transformer, it is possible to find another location of the shorting plunger which will result in the initial reactance. Thus, upon removal of the output transformer, a given point on the input impedance locus can be found by merely displacing the shorting plunger. This demonstrates that the input impedance locus is unaltered by the omission of the output transformer except that the distribution of points along it for a series of uniformly spaced shorting plunger positions becomes nonuniform.

Using the methods discussed in Sec. 6.5b, the iconocenter can be found; using Eq. (6.62), the scattering coefficient S_{22} can be computed. The VSWR at the output of the network with the input matched is found from

$$r_{\text{output}} = \frac{1 + |S_{22}|}{1 - |S_{22}|} \tag{11.37}$$

Consider next the omission of the input impedance transformer. Removing the transformer causes each point on the symmetrical impedance (transformed) locus to be multiplied by $n_1{}^2$. The extreme resistance values $1/r$ and r of the symmetrical locus upon transformation become $\mathcal{R}_1$ and $\mathcal{R}_2$, respectively, and are equal to

$$\mathcal{R}_1 = \frac{n_1{}^2}{r} \tag{11.38}$$
$$\mathcal{R}_2 = n_1{}^2 r \tag{11.39}$$

The resistance values $\mathcal{R}_1$ and $\mathcal{R}_2$ correspond to the extreme resistance points found on an experimental impedance locus. Thus, the transformer constant $n_1{}^2$ needed to

In addition, the maximum and minimum VSWR are nearly the same, and the difference between them is difficult to determine accurately. On the other hand, when the dissipation is too great, the VSWR become small and are also too difficult to measure accurately. The method is most useful for values of insertion loss in the range of a few up to perhaps 20 db where an accuracy of about 0.1 db is possible.

---

make the experimental locus symmetrical (i.e., to make $S_{11} = 0$) can be found by multiplying Eq. (11.38) by Eq. (11.39) and solving for n_1^2. This gives

$$n_1^2 = \sqrt{\mathcal{R}_1 \mathcal{R}_2} \qquad (11.40)$$

The point $Z_0 = 1$ corresponds to the impedance that would be seen with the transformer n_1 in place if the output were matched. Removing the transformer causes the point $Z_0 = 1$ to become $Z_0 n_1^2 = \sqrt{\mathcal{R}_1 \mathcal{R}_2}$ and corresponds to the impedance that would be presented by the actual network if its output terminals were matched. This proves Eq. (11.35). The VSWR r that would be observed with the transformer n_1 in place with the output shorted is found by taking the ratio of Eqs. (11.38) and (11.39), giving

$$r = \sqrt{\frac{\mathcal{R}_2}{\mathcal{R}_1}} \qquad (11.41)$$

The radius of the transformed circle R_1, being simply the reflection coefficient corresponding to VSWR r given by Eq. (11.41), is given by

$$R_1 = \frac{\sqrt{\mathcal{R}_2/\mathcal{R}_1} - 1}{\sqrt{\mathcal{R}_2/\mathcal{R}_1} + 1} \qquad (11.42)$$

The intrinsic loss is obtained from Eqs. (11.42) and (11.36).

Equation (11.33) can be obtained as follows: The extremal resistance values of the circle of radius R_1 upon transformation become n_1^2/r and $n_1^2 r$. The corresponding reflection coefficients are $(n_1^2 - r)/(n_1^2 + r)$ and $(n_1^2 r - 1)/(n_1^2 r + 1)$. From these, the center of the displaced circle and its radius are

$$\rho = \frac{\dfrac{n_1^2 r - 1}{n_1^2 r + 1} + \dfrac{n_1^2 - r}{n_1^2 + r}}{2} \qquad (11.43)$$

$$R = \frac{\dfrac{n_1^2 r - 1}{n_1^2 r + 1} - \dfrac{n_1^2 - r}{n_1^2 + r}}{2} \qquad (11.44)$$

Eliminating n_1^2 and using $r = (1 + R_1)/(1 - R_1)$ give

$$R_1 = \frac{\sqrt{(1 + R)^2 - \rho^2} - \sqrt{(1 - R)^2 - \rho^2}}{\sqrt{(1 + R)^2 - \rho^2} + \sqrt{(1 - R)^2 - \rho^2}} \qquad (11.45)$$

Substituting into Eq. (11.36) leads to Eq. (11.33).

FIELD CONFIGURATIONS AND CUTOFF WAVELENGTHS
FOR COMMON WAVEGUIDES

Field configurations for some common transmission lines are shown in Figs. A.1 to A.10. These show the cross-sectional and longitudinal views with the electric-field lines being indicated by the solid lines and magnetic-field lines by dashed lines. The radius of the circular waveguide is a; the radius of the outer and inner conductor of the coaxial lines are b and a, respectively; the width and height of the rectangular waveguides are a and b, respectively. In the case of the rectangular waveguides, the longitudinal section is taken through points l-l shown in Fig. A.7.

Cutoff wavelengths λ_c for the circular waveguides, accurate to four places, and for the rectangular waveguide are also shown in these figures. The cutoff wavelengths for higher-order modes for the coaxial line are shown in Fig. A.11.

The cutoff wavelengths for the first 177 modes in a right circular cylindrical waveguide are shown in Tables A.1 and A.2.

TABLE A.1. VALUES OF λ_c/a FOR CIRCULAR WAVEGUIDES FOR $TE_{m,n}$ MODES

m \ n	1	2	3	4	5	6	7	8
0	1.639788	0.895604	0.617605	0.471580	0.381478	0.320312	0.276062	0.242560
1	3.412586	1.178516	0.736053	0.536749	0.422723	0.348766	0.296875	0.258447
2	2.057201	0.936932	0.630243	0.477069	0.384351	0.322002	0.277139	0.243289
3	1.495573	0.783905	0.553785	0.430774	0.353212	0.299592	0.260228	
4	1.181594	0.676892	0.495445	0.393582	0.327317	0.280487	0.245535	
5	0.979357	0.597267	0.449210	0.362921	0.305372	0.263959		
6	0.837616	0.535427	0.411521	0.337128	0.286489	0.249492		
7	0.732490	0.485848	0.380122	0.315075	0.270034			
8	0.651281	0.445127	0.353504	0.295970	0.255547			
9	0.586589	0.411023	0.330614	0.279235	0.242676			
10	0.533790	0.382005	0.310695	0.264436				
11	0.489860	0.356993	0.293183	0.251242				
12	0.452718	0.335191	0.277657	0.239396				
13	0.420888	0.316005	0.263784					
14	0.393304	0.298980	0.251307					
15	0.369158	0.283765	0.240020					
16	0.347843	0.270078						
17	0.328885	0.257699						
18	0.311912	0.246442						
19	0.296624							
20	0.282783							

TABLE A.2. VALUES OF λ_c/a FOR CIRCULAR WAVEGUIDES FOR $TM_{m,n}$ MODES

m \ n	1	2	3	4	5	6	7	8
0	2.612705	1.138242	0.726067	0.532856	0.420817	0.347693	0.296214	0.258010
1	1.639788	0.895604	0.617605	0.471580	0.381478	0.320312	0.276062	0.242560
2	1.223452	0.746466	0.540729	0.424656	0.349847	0.297542	0.258886	
3	0.984800	0.643702	0.482757	0.387290	0.323718	0.278230	0.244025	
4	0.828005	0.567858	0.437166	0.356676	0.301686	0.261592		
5	0.716320	0.509230	0.400198	0.331040	0.282800	0.247074		
6	0.632359	0.462363	0.369517	0.309200	0.266394			
7	0.566747	0.423930	0.343576	0.290330	0.251984			
8	0.513958	0.391774	0.321317	0.273834				
9	0.470499	0.364429	0.301975	0.259273				
10	0.434057	0.340857	0.284990	0.246309				
11	0.403032	0.320309	0.269944					
12	0.376279	0.302223	0.256510					
13	0.352960	0.286169	0.244433					
14	0.332444	0.271813						
15	0.314247	0.258895						
16	0.297992	0.247204						
17	0.283377							
18	0.270166							
19	0.258161							
20	0.247203							

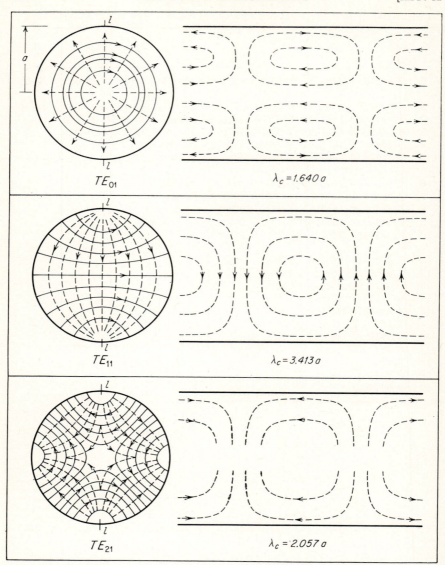

FIG. A.1. Field configurations in a circular waveguide for TE modes.

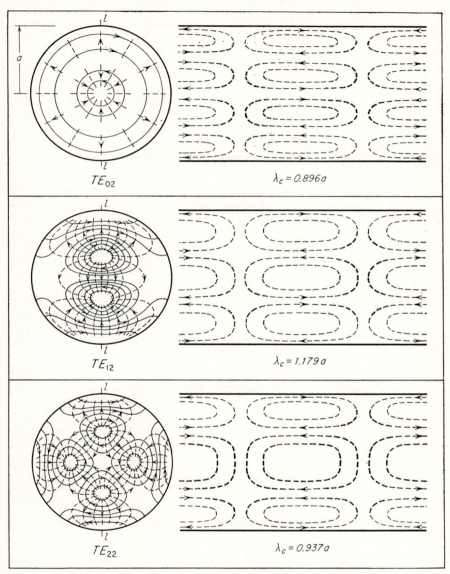

FIG. A.2. Field configurations in a circular waveguide for TE modes.

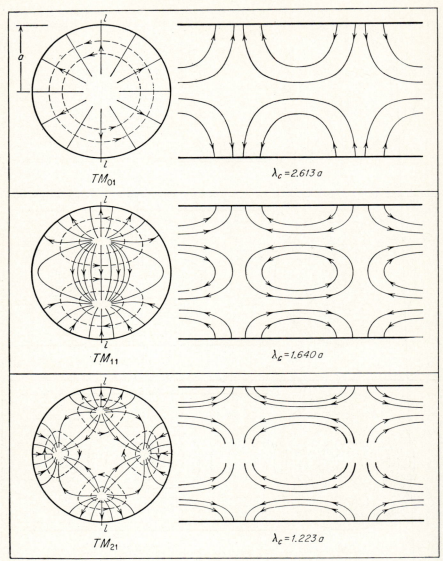

FIG. A.3. Field configuration in a circular waveguide for TM modes.

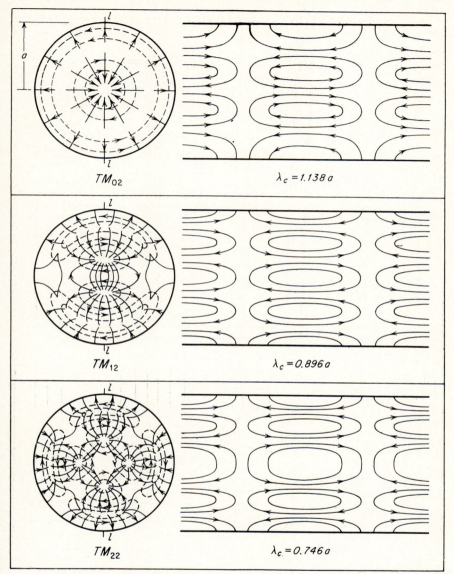

FIG. A.4. Field configuration in a circular waveguide for TM modes.

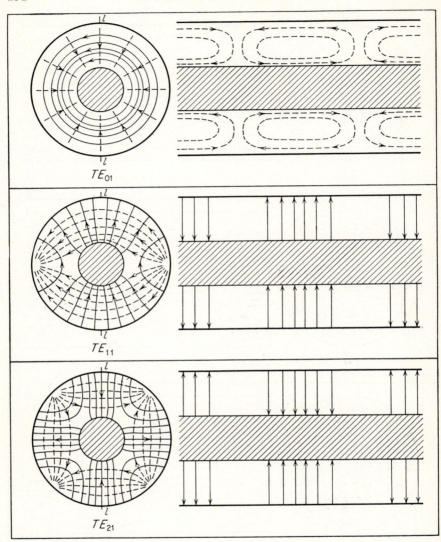

FIG. A.5. Field configurations for TE-type modes in a coaxial line.

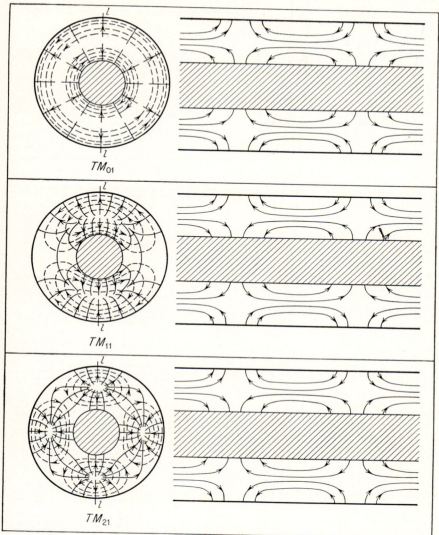

TM_{01}

TM_{11}

TM_{21}

Fig. A.6. Field configurations for TM-type modes in a coaxial line.

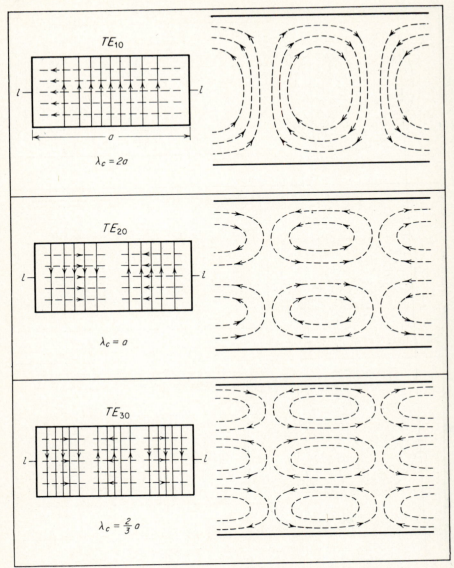

FIG. A.7. Field configurations in a rectangular waveguide for TE modes.

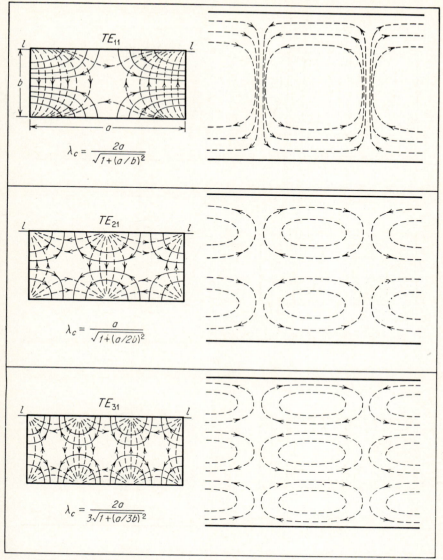

Fig. A.8. Field configurations in a rectangular waveguide for TE modes.

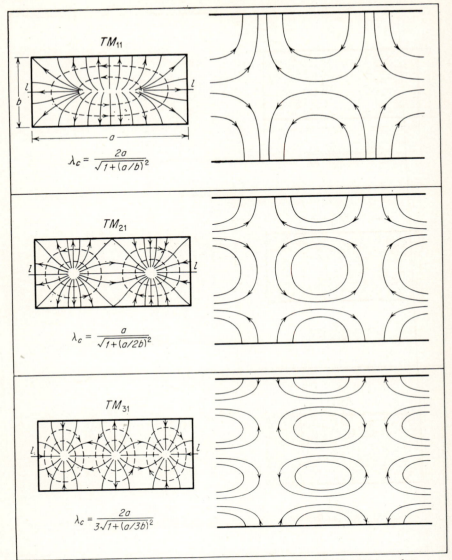

Fig. A.9. Field configurations in a rectangular waveguide for TM modes.

FIG. A.10. Field configurations in a rectangular waveguide for TM modes.

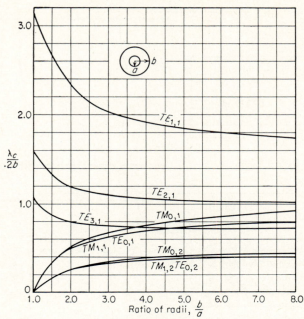

FIG. A.11. Cutoff wavelengths for higher-order modes in a coaxial line. (*From T. Moreno, "Microwave Transmission Design Data," p. 71, McGraw-Hill Book Company, Inc., New York, 1948.*)

FORMULAS AND CONSTANTS

B.1. Some Useful Vector Formulas. If V is a scalar, the *gradient* in the cartesian and cylindrical coordinates is given by

$$\nabla V = \mathbf{k}_x \frac{\partial V}{\partial x} + \mathbf{k}_y \frac{\partial V}{\partial y} + \mathbf{k}_z \frac{\partial V}{\partial z} \tag{B.1}$$

$$\nabla V = \mathbf{k}_r \frac{\partial V}{\partial r} + \mathbf{k}_\phi \frac{1}{r} \frac{\partial V}{\partial \phi} + \mathbf{k}_z \frac{\partial V}{\partial z} \tag{B.2}$$

If $\mathbf{E}$ is a vector, the *divergence* in the cartesian and cylindrical coordinates is given by

$$\nabla \cdot \mathbf{E} = \frac{\partial E_x}{\partial x} + \frac{\partial E_y}{\partial y} + \frac{\partial E_z}{\partial z} \tag{B.3}$$

$$\nabla \cdot \mathbf{E} = \frac{1}{r} \frac{\partial}{\partial r} (r E_r) + \frac{1}{r} \frac{\partial E_\phi}{\partial \phi} + \frac{\partial E_z}{\partial z} \tag{B.4}$$

If V is a scalar, the *Laplacian* in the cartesian and cylindrical coordinates is given by

$$\nabla^2 V = \frac{\partial^2 V}{\partial x^2} + \frac{\partial^2 V}{\partial y^2} + \frac{\partial^2 V}{\partial z^2} \tag{B.5}$$

$$\nabla^2 V = \frac{1}{r} \frac{\partial}{\partial r} \left(r \frac{\partial V}{\partial r} \right) + \frac{1}{r^2} \frac{\partial^2 V}{\partial \phi^2} + \frac{\partial^2 V}{\partial z^2} \tag{B.6}$$

If $\mathbf{E}$ is a vector, the *curl* in the cartesian and cylindrical coordinates is given by

$$\nabla \times \mathbf{E} = \mathbf{k}_x \left(\frac{\partial E_z}{\partial y} - \frac{\partial E_y}{\partial z} \right) + \mathbf{k}_y \left(\frac{\partial E_x}{\partial z} - \frac{\partial E_z}{\partial x} \right) + \mathbf{k}_z \left(\frac{\partial E_y}{\partial x} - \frac{\partial E_x}{\partial y} \right) \tag{B.7}$$

$$\nabla \times \mathbf{E} = \mathbf{k}_r \left(\frac{1}{r} \frac{\partial E_z}{\partial \phi} - \frac{\partial E_\phi}{\partial z} \right) + \mathbf{k}_\phi \left(\frac{\partial E_r}{\partial z} - \frac{\partial E_z}{\partial r} \right) + \mathbf{k}_z \frac{1}{r} \left[\frac{\partial}{\partial r} (r E_\phi) - \frac{\partial E_r}{\partial \phi} \right] \tag{B.8}$$

B.2. Some Physical Constants

Velocity of light	$c = 299{,}793.0 \pm 0.3$ km/sec
Electronic charge	$e = 1.60206 \times 10^{-19}$ coulomb
	$= 4.80286 \times 10^{-10}$ esu
Mass of electron	$m = 9.1083 \times 10^{-31}$ kg
Ratio of charge to mass of electron	$\dfrac{e}{m} = 1.7578 \times 10^{11}$ coulombs/kg
Planck's constant	$h = 6.62517 \times 10^{-27}$ erg-sec
Boltzmann's constant	$k = 1.38044 \times 10^{-16}$ erg/deg
	$= 1.38044 \times 10^{-23}$ joule/deg
Wien displacement law	$\lambda_{max} T = 0.289782$ cm-deg
Permittivity of free space	$\epsilon_0 = 8.854 \times 10^{-12}$ farad/m

Permeability of free space	$\mu_0 = 4\pi \times 10^{-7}$ h/m
Impedance of free space	$\left(\dfrac{\mu_0}{\epsilon_0}\right)^{1/2} = 377$ ohms
Resistivity of copper	$\rho = 1.724 \times 10^{-8}$ ohm-m

B.3. Conversion Factors

Distance	1 in. $= 2.5400$ cm
Energy	1 erg $= 10^{-7}$ joule
	1 cal $= 4.182$ joules
	1 ft-lb $= 1.356$ joules
	1 Btu $= 1{,}055$ joules
Power	1 joule/sec $= 1$ watt
	1 cal/sec $= 4.182$ watts
	1 Btu/hr $= 0.2930$ watt
Pressure	1 dyne/sq cm $= 10^{-1}$ newton/sq m
Specific heat	1 cal/g/deg $= 4{,}182$ joules/kg/deg
Charge	1 statcoulomb (esu) $= 3.333 \times 10^{-10}$ coulomb
	1 abcoulomb (emu) $= 10$ coulombs
Potential difference	1 statvolt (esu) $= 300$ volts
	1 abvolt (emu) $= 10^{-8}$ volt
Inductance	1 abhenry (emu) $= 10^{-9}$ h
	1 stathenry (esu) $= 9 \times 10^{11}$ h
Current	1 statamp (esu) $= 1/(3 \times 10^9)$ amp
	1 abamp (emu) $= 10$ amp
Electric-flux density	1 esu $= 1/(12\pi \times 10^5)$ coulomb/sq m
	1 emu $= 10^5/4\pi$ coulombs/sq m
Magnetic-flux density	1 gauss (emu) $= 10^{-4}$ weber/sq m
	1 line/sq in. $= 1.550 \times 10^{-5}$ weber/sq m
	1 esu $= 3 \times 10^6$ webers/sq m
Magnetic flux	1 maxwell (emu) $= 10^{-8}$ weber
	1 esu $= 3 \times 10^{12}$ webers
Resistance	1 statohm (esu) $= 8.988 \times 10^{11}$ ohms
	1 abohm (emu) $= 10^{-9}$ ohm
Permittivity	1 esu $= 8.854 \times 10^{-12}$ farad/m
Permeability	1 emu $= 4\pi \times 10^{-7}$ h/m
Capacitance	1 statfarad (esu) $= 1/(9 \times 10^{11})$ farad
	1 abfarad (emu) $= 10^9$ farads
Inductance	1 abhenry (emu) $= 10^{-9}$ h
	1 stathenry (esu) $= 9 \times 10^{11}$ h

B.4. Skin Depth. The skin depth δ is defined as the distance from the surface of a plane conductor at which the electric and magnetic fields have decreased to $1/\epsilon$ of their values at the surface. It is given by

Mks units:

$$\delta = \frac{1}{\sqrt{\pi f \mu \sigma}} \tag{B.9}$$

$$= \frac{1}{2\pi} \sqrt{\frac{4\pi \rho \lambda}{\mu c}} \tag{B.10}$$

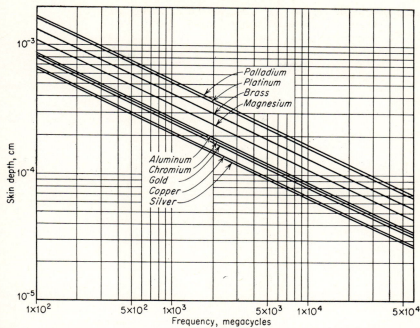

FIG. B.1. Skin depth as a function of frequency for a few common metals. (*From T. Moreno, "Microwave Transmission Design Data," McGraw-Hill Book Company, Inc., New York, 1948.*)

where δ = skin depth, m
ρ = resistivity, ohm-m
μ = permeability, h/m
λ = wavelength, m
c = 3 × 10⁸ m/sec

Gaussian units:

$$\delta = \frac{1}{2\pi} \sqrt{\frac{\rho\lambda}{\mu c}} \tag{B.11}$$

where δ = skin depth, cm
ρ = resistivity, emu
λ = wavelength, cm
μ = relative permeability (μ = 1 for nonmagnetic materials)
c = 3 × 10¹⁰ cm/sec

Hansen (practical) units:

$$\delta = \frac{1}{2\pi} \sqrt{\frac{\rho\lambda}{\mu c}} \tag{B.12}$$

$$= 5.03 \times 10^3 \sqrt{\frac{\rho}{f}} \tag{B.13}$$

where δ = skin depth, cm

      ρ = resistivity, ohm-cm (practical units)

      λ = wavelength, cm

      μ = relative permeability (see above)

      f = frequency, cycles

      c = 30 ohms*

Equation (B.13) is plotted in Fig. B.1 as a function of frequency for a few common metals.

* c = 30 ohms is obtained as a result of the conversion of emu to cgs practical units. Thus, if ρ is in emu,

$$\frac{\rho}{c} = \frac{\rho}{3 \times 10^{10}} = \frac{1}{30}\frac{\rho}{10^9} = \frac{1}{30}\rho'$$

where ρ' is the resistivity in ohm-centimeters. Thus, to convert ρ in emu to ρ in cgs units, use the velocity of light as equal to 30 ohms.

NAME INDEX

SUBJECT INDEX